# Structural and Geotechnical Mechanics

A Volume Honoring
NATHAN M. NEWMARK

*Editor*
W. J. HALL

PRENTICE-HALL, INC., *Englewood Cliffs, New Jersey 07632*

*Library of Congress Cataloging in Publication Data*
Main entry under title:

Structural and geotechnical mechanics.

Proceedings of a symposium held at the University of Illinois, Urbana, Oct. 2–3, 1975.
Includes bibliographical references.
CONTENTS: N. M. Newmark: biography, bibliography, list of doctoral students.—Wright, G. D. T. Education and social issues.—Ang, A. H-S. Risk and reliability analysis in engineering design. [etc.]
1. Structural engineering—Addresses, essays, lectures. 2. Engineering geology—Addresses, essays, lectures. 3. Newmark, Nathan Mortimore, date
I. Hall, William Joel.
TA637.S87 624'.176 76-28735
ISBN 0-13-853804-2





10 9 8 7 6 5 4 3 2 1

Printed in the United States of America

PRENTICE-HALL INTERNATIONAL, INC., *London*
PRENTICE-HALL OF AUSTRALIA PTY. LIMITED, *Sydney*
PRENTICE-HALL OF CANADA, LTD., *Toronto*
PRENTICE-HALL OF INDIA PRIVATE LIMITED, *New Delhi*
PRENTICE-HALL OF JAPAN, INC., *Tokyo*
PRENTICE-HALL OF SOUTHEAST ASIA PTE. LTD., *Singapore*
WHITEHALL BOOKS LIMITED, *Wellington, New Zealand*

# Contents

# Preface

On October 2 and 3, 1975, a symposium on Structural and Geotechnical Mechanics, honoring Professor Nathan M. Newmark, was held at the University of Illinois, Urbana, Illinois. Twenty-one papers, written by some of Professor Newmark's former students and colleagues, were presented. The authors of these papers were asked to review briefly the state-of-the art of the subject area treated in the light of their own and their colleagues' contributions in this area, and to offer observations regarding future research. In keeping with the contributions of the man they honor, the papers push at the forefront of current engineering knowledge and practice, and in this respect should be of lasting interest. The range of topics covered by the papers serves to emphasize the breadth of interest of Professor Newmark, his students and colleagues. The papers cover such broad and diverse fields as earthquake engineering, structural mechanics, strength of materials, risk and reliability analysis, soil and rock mechanics, soil dynamics, development of design specifications, and education and social issues.

The volume begins with a biography and bibliography of Professor Newmark, and a list of his doctoral students to date. The Committee gratefully acknowledges the partial support of the Symposium and this Proceedings volume provided by the National Science Foundation under Grant ENG 75-07841.

It is planned to issue a selected set of his published papers in the near future as a separate volume through the American Society of Civil Engineers.

On behalf of his former students and colleagues, we formally thank Professor Newmark for the education and training he has given us, for the insight he has provided us into techniques for approaching difficult engineering problems, and for his demonstration of the value of sound engineering judgment.

*The Symposium and Proceedings Committee*

W. J. Hall  
J. D. Haltiwanger  
E. Rosenblueth  
A. S. Veletsos

Nathan M. Newmark

# Nathan M. Newmark: Biography

Nathan M. Newmark was born in Plainfield, New Jersey on September 22, 1910, to Abraham S. and Mollie (Nathanson) Newmark; he married Anne May Cohen on August 6, 1932; one son and two daughters, Richard Alan, Linda Beth, and Susan Adele, were born to them.

His grammar school education was obtained in North Carolina and his high school education in New Jersey. He was awarded the B.S. Degree in Civil Engineering from Rutgers University in 1930 and as an undergraduate student received the Phi Lambda Upsilon Prize in Freshman Chemistry, the Bradley Mathematics Prize, the Edward Fuller Brooks Prize in Civil Engineering, and High Honors and Special Honors in Civil Engineering. He received M.S. and Ph.D. degrees in engineering from the University of Illinois, Urbana, in 1932 and 1934, respectively, where he worked with the late Hardy Cross, Harald M. Westergaard, and Frank E. Richart.

Beginning in 1930 as a Research Graduate Assistant in Civil Engineering, University of Illinois, Urbana, Nathan M. Newmark held a succession of positions in the department, becoming Research Professor of Civil Engineering in 1943. In 1956 he was appointed Head of the Department and held that position until 1973. From 1947 to 1957 he was Chairman of the Digital Computer Laboratory of the university. During this period the first large-scale digital computer at the university was constructed. He has served in many other capacities in the university, including the longest appointment to date on the University Research Board. Since 1973 he has been Professor of Civil Engineering and one of the twelve professors in the Center for Advanced Study, at the university.

During World War II Dr. Newmark was a consultant to the National Defense Research Committee and the Office of Field Service of the Office of

Scientific Research and Development; for this service he was awarded the President's Certificate of Merit in 1948.

In 1955 Rutgers University conferred on him the honorary degree of Doctor of Science, in 1967 he was awarded the degree of Doctor Honoris Causa by the University of Liège, Belgium, and in 1969 he received the honorary degree of Doctor of Laws from the University of Notre Dame. In 1972 he received an honorary degree from the National Civil Engineering Laboratory of Lisbon, Portugal.

He was elected a Fellow of the American Academy of Arts and Sciences in 1962, a Founding Member of the National Academy of Engineering in 1964, and a Member of the National Academy of Sciences in 1966. Professor Newmark received the 1968 National Medal of Science from President Lyndon B. Johnson, and in 1969 he received the Washington Award, a joint award given annually by the major engineering societies of the United States.

He has been the recipient of the following awards of the American Society of Civil Engineers: the James R. Croes Medal in 1945, the Mosseiff Award in 1950, the Norman Medal and the Ernest E. Howard Award in 1958, and the Theodore von Kármán Medal in 1962. He also received the Wason Medal of the American Concrete Institute in 1950, an award from the Concrete Reinforcing Steel Institute in 1956, and the Vincent Bendix Award for Engineering Research from the American Society of Engineering Education in 1961. He has received numerous other honors, awards, and citations, including honorary membership in the American Society of Civil Engineers in 1966, the American Concrete Institute in 1967, the American Society of Mechanical Engineers in 1971, and the International Association for Earthquake Engineering in 1969.

Professor Newmark's publications include over 200 papers, books, and chapters in books. He is the coauthor of the following books on earthquake engineering: *Design of Multi-Story Reinforced Concrete Buildings for Earthquake Motion* with John A. Blume and Leo Corning, published by the Portland Cement Association, Chicago, in 1961, and *Fundamentals of Earthquake Engineering* with Emilio Rosenblueth, published by Prentice-Hall, Inc., Englewood Cliffs, N.J., in 1971.

Professor Newmark has developed simple yet powerful and widely used methods for analyzing complex structural components and assemblies under a variety of conditions of loading and for calculating the stresses and deformations in soil beneath foundations. He has contributed significantly to a better understanding of the behavior of structural materials under various environments including fatigue and brittle fracture. He has added materially to knowledge of the behavior and design of highway bridge decks and floor slabs in buildings and of structures subjected to impact, periodic excitation, wave action, wind, blast, and earthquakes. He developed techniques for carrying out analysis and design operations on a practical basis by use of both simple numerical procedures and electronic computers.

He has been a consultant to industrial concerns and governmental agencies nationally and internationally on major seismic, structural, and geotechnical projects. The survival without damage during the 1957 Mexico City earthquake of the 43-story Latino Americana Tower, on which he was earthquake design consultant, attests to his insight and ability. Design criteria for the protective construction program within the United States, for nuclear reactor facilities in the United States and abroad, for the Bay Area Rapid Transit system, for the Trans-Alaska Oil Pipeline, and for other major structures and systems have been based largely on his personal studies and on the reports and publications prepared by him and his associates.

Professor Newmark possesses unusual ability to attract young men to the field of civil engineering, to inspire them with the confidence to undertake new and varied tasks, to guide but not direct their thinking, and to ensure that as individuals they receive appropriate recognition. It is no accident that there have grown up around him one of the most active research centers in civil engineering in the country and one of the nation's largest groups of advanced students in civil engineering or that the alumni of this group have assumed broad leadership in education, industry, and government and in the technical work of the armed services. Further evidence of the stature of his department is provided by the fact that fourteen present or former staff members of its faculty have been elected to membership in the National Academy of Engineering.

His unceasing devotion to research, his noteworthy and continuing contributions to the betterment of structural design practices, and his leadership in engineering education, teaching, and professional activities have had a profound influence on civil engineering. His penetrating insight, his keen engineering judgment, and his genuine interest in people have been a constant source of inspiration to all who have had the privilege of working with him.

W. J. HALL*

## Bibliography: Nathan M. Newmark

1. NEWMARK, N. M., "A Study of Patterns of Abutment Movements in an Arch Dam Corresponding to Some Simple Patterns of Abutment Thrusts," Technical Memorandum, U.S. Bureau of Reclamation, Denver, June 1931.
2. WILSON, W. M., and N. M. NEWMARK, "The Strength of Thin Cylindrical Shells as Columns," *Univ. of Ill. Eng. Exp. Stn. Bull. 255*, Urbana, 1933, 45 pp.

*Professor of Civil Engineering, University of Illinois, Urbana, Illinois.

3. NEWMARK, N. M., "Interaction Between Rib and Superstructure in Concrete Arch Bridges," University of Illinois Doctoral Dissertation, Urbana, Printed Abstract, 1934, 12 pp.
4. RICHART, F. E., and N. M. NEWMARK, "The Strength of Monolithic Concrete Walls," *Univ. of Ill. Eng. Exp. Stn. Bull. 277*, Urbana, 1935, 34 pp.
5. NEWMARK, N. M., "Simplified Computation of Vertical Pressures in Elastic Foundations," *Univ. of Ill. Eng. Exp. Stn. Circ. 24*, Urbana, 1935, 19 pp.
6. NEWMARK, N. M., and R. E. COPELAND, "Structural and Economic Studies of Monolithic Concrete Walls for Dwellings," *Proc. ACI*, Vol. 31, 1935, pp. 478–498.
7. NEWMARK, N. M., Discussion of "Analysis of Multiple Arches," by Alexander Hrennikoff, *Proc. ASCE*, Vol. 61, No. 5, 1935, pp. 724–726. Also *Trans. ASCE*, Vol. 101, 1936, pp. 407–410.
8. NEWMARK, N. M., "A Half Century of Progress in Foundation Theory," *Ill. Soc. Eng. Golden Jubilee Souvenir Program*, Jan. 1936, pp. 144–152.
9. NEWMARK, N. M., and R. E. COPELAND, "Review of Strength Tests on Monolithic Concrete Walls for Residences," *Concrete*, Vol. 44, No. 2, Feb. 1936, pp. 13–14.
10. NEWMARK, N. M., Discussion of "Distribution of Stresses Under a Foundation," by A. E. CUMMINGS, *Proc. ASCE*, Vol. 62, No. 4, 1936, pp. 536–541. Also *Trans. ASCE*, Vol. 101, 1936, pp. 1115–1117.
11. NEWMARK, N. M., Discussion of "The Relation of Analysis to Structural Design," by Hardy Cross, *Proc. ASCE*, Vol. 62, No. 4, 1936, pp. 536–541, Also *Trans. ASCE*, Vol. 101, 1936, pp. 1395–1400.
12. NEWMARK, N. M., "Interaction Between Rib and Superstructure in Concrete Arch Bridges," *Proc. ASCE*, Vol. 62, No. 7, 1936, pp. 1043–1061. Author's Closure to Discussion, Vol. 64, No. 2, 1938, pp. 341–343. Also *Trans. ASCE*, Vol. 103, 1938, pp. 62–88 (with discussions).
13. NEWMARK, N. M., Discussion of "Graphical Distribution of Vertical Pressure Beneath Foundations," by Donald M. Burmister, *Proc. ASCE*, Vol. 63, No. 6, 1937, pp. 1098–1101. Also *Trans. ASCE*, Vol. 103, 1938, pp. 321–324.
14. NEWMARK, N. M., "Estimating Earth Pressures," *Eng. News-Record*, Vol. 120, No. 1, 1938, pp. 23–24.
15. NEWMARK, N. M., Discussion of "A Simple Method for the Computation of Temperatures in Concrete Structures," by Roy W. Carlson, *Proc. ACI*, Vol. 34, 1938, pp. 104–1 to 104–4.
16. NEWMARK, N. M., Discussion of "A Reduction Method for the Analysis of Continuous Beams and Open Frames," by Miklos Hetenyi, *Proc. ACI*, Vol. 34, 1938, pp. 364–4 to 364–5.
17. NEWMARK, N. M., "A Distribution Procedure for the Analysis of Slabs Continuous over Flexible Beams," *Univ. of Ill. Eng. Exp. Stn. Bull. 304*, Urbana, 1938, 118 pp.
18. NEWMARK, N. M., Review of "die Knickfestigkeit von Staben und Stabwerken," by Julius Ratzersdorfer, J. *Appl. Mech., ASME*, Vol. 6, No. 1, March 1939, pp. A-47 to A-48.
19. NEWMARK, N. M., and H. A. LEPPER, Jr., "Tests of Plaster-Model Slabs Sub-

jected to Concentrated Loads," *Univ. of Ill. Eng. Exp. Stan. Bull. 313*, Urbana, 1939, 53 pp.

20. Newmark, N. M., "Stress Distribution in Soils," in *Proceedings, Conference on Soil Mechanics and Its Applications, Purdue University*, West Lafayette, Ind., September 1940, pp. 295–303.
21. Newmark, N. M., "What Do We Know About Concrete Slabs," *Civil Eng.*, Vol. 10, No. 9, 1940, pp. 559–562.
22. Newmark, N. M., "Note on Calculation of Influence Surfaces in Plates by Use of Difference Equations," J. *Appl. Mech., ASME*, Vol. 8, No. 2, June 1941, p. A-92.
23. Newmark, N. M., and C. P. Siess, "Moments in I-Beam Bridges," *Univ. of Ill. Eng. Exp. Stn. Bull. 336*, Urbana, 1942, 150 pp.
24. Newmark, N. M., "Influence Charts for Computation of Stresses in Elastic Foundations," *Univ. of Ill. Eng. Exp. Stn. Bull. 338*, Urbana, 1942, 28 pp.
25. Richart, F. E., and N. M. Newmark, "Impact Tests of Reinforced Concrete Beams," *NDRC Report No. A-125*, 1942, 41 pp.
26. Newmark, N. M., "Numerical Procedures for Computing Deflections, Moments, and Buckling Loads," *Proc. ASCE*, Vol. 68, No. 5, May 1942, pp. 691–718. Also Reprint No. 23, *Univ. of Ill. Eng. Exp. Stn.*, Urbana, 1942, 28 pp. Also *Trans. ASCE*, Vol. 108, 1943, pp. 1161–1234.
27. Newmark, N. M., and C. P. Siess, "Design of Slab and Stringer Highway Bridges," *Public Roads*, Vol. 23, No. 7, Jan., Feb., March 1943, pp. 157–164.
28. Newmark, N. M., and F. E. Richart, "Impact Tests of Reinforced Concrete Beams, II," *NDRC Report No. A-213*, 1943, 77 pp.
29. Newmark, N. M., Discussion of "Effects of Radiant Heat on Reinforced Concrete Rigid Frames," by Milan A. Johnston, *Proc. ASCE*, Vol. 71, No. 9, 1945, pp. 1431–1433.
30. Newmark, N. M., C. P. Siess, and R. R. Penman, "Studies of Slab and Beam Highway Bridges, Part I, Tests of Simple-Span Right I-Beam Bridges," *Univ. of Ill. Eng. Exp. Stn. Bull. 363*, Urbana, 1946, 132 pp.
31. Newmark, N. M., "Aerodynamics and Aircraft Design; Part III, Aircraft Materials and Structures," Report of AAF Scientific Advisory Group, by HQ Air Materiel Command, Wright Field, Dayton, Ohio, May 1946, pp. 101–116.
32. Newmark, N. M., "Explosives and Terminal Ballistics; Part III, Terminal Ballistics and Destructive Effects," Report of AAF Scientific Advisory Group, published by HQ Air Materiel Command, Wright Field, Dayton, Ohio, May 1946, pp. 61–78.
33. Newmark, N. M., "Influence Charts for Computation of Vertical Displacements in Elastic Foundations," *Univ. of Ill. Eng. Exp. Stn. Bull. 367*, Urbana 1947, 11 pp.
34. Siess, C. P., and N. M. Newmark, Discussion of "Reinforced Concrete Columns Under Combined Compression and Bending," by H. E. Wessman, *Proc. ACI*, Vol. 43, 1947, pp. 8–1 to 8–3.
35. Colin, E. C., Jr., and N. M. Newmark, "A Numerical Solution for the Torsion of Hollow Sections," *J. Appl. Mech.*, ASME, Vol. 14, No. 4, Dec. 1947, pp. A313–315.

36. NEWMARK, N. M., C. P. SIESS, and W. M. PECKHAM, "Studies of Slab and Beam Highway Bridges, Part II, Tests of Simple-Span Skew I-Beam Bridges," *Univ. of Ill. Eng. Exp. Stn. Bull. 375*, Urbana, 1948, 60 pp.
37. NEWMARK, N. M., "Design of I-Beam Bridges, Highway Bridge Floors, A Symposium," *Proc. ASCE*, Vol. 74, No. 3, March 1948, pp. 305–330.
38. SIESS, C. P., and N. M. NEWMARK, "Rational Analysis and Design of Two-Way Concrete Slabs," *J., ACI*, Vol. 20, No. 4, Dec. 1948, pp. 273–315.
39. RICHART, F. E., JR., and N. M. NEWMARK, "An Hypothesis for the Determination of Cumulative Damage in Fatigue," *Proc. ASTM*, Vol. 48, 1948, pp. 767–798.
40. NEWMARK, N. M., Review of "Buckling of Curved Sheet in Compression and Its Relation to the Secant Modulus," by E. H. Schuette, *J. Aeronaut. Sci.*, Vol. 15, No. 5, May 1948, p. 262.
41. NEWMARK, N. M., "Numerical Methods of Analysis of Bars, Plates, and Elastic Bodies," Chapter 9 in *Numerical Methods of Analysis in Engineering*, L. E. Grinter, ed. Macmillan, New York, 1949, pp. 138–168.
42. NEWMARK, N. M., "A Simple Approximate Formula for Effective End-Fixity of Columns," *J. Aeronaut. Sci.*, Vol. 16, No. 2, Feb. 1949, p. 116.
43. NEWMARK, N. M., Review of "Soil Mechanics in Engineering Practice," by K. TERZAGHI and R. B. PECK, *J. Appl. Mech.*, ASME, Vol. 16, No. 1, March 1949, p. 107.
44. BRUCKNER, W. H., and N. M. NEWMARK, "Axial Tension Impact Tests of Structural Steels," *Welding J.*, AWS, Vol. 28, No. 2, Feb. 1949, pp. 67s–88s.
45. RICHART, F. E., N. M. NEWMARK, and C. P. SIESS, "Design of I-Beam Bridges, Highway Bridge Floors, A Symposium," *Trans. ASCE*, Vol. 114, 1949, pp. 979–1072.
46. SIESS, C. P., and N. M. NEWMARK, Closing discussion of paper on "Rational Analysis and Design of Two-Way Concrete Slabs," *J., ACI*, Vol. 21, No. 4, Dec. 1949, pp. 316–4 and 316–5. Also *Proc. ACI*, Vol. 45, 1949, pp. 273–315.
47. BRUCKNER, W. H., and N. M. NEWMARK, "Axial Tension Impact Tests of Structural Steels," *Welding J.*, AWS, Vol. 29, No. 4, April 1950, pp. 212s–216s.
48. SIESS, C. P., and N. M. NEWMARK, "Moments in Two-Way Concrete Floor Slabs," *Univ. of Ill. Eng. Exp. Stn. Bull. 385*, Urbana, Feb. 1950, 124 pp.
49. GOSSARD, M. L., C. P. SIESS, N. M. NEWMARK, and L. E. GOODMAN, "Studies of Highway Skew Slab-Bridges with Curbs, Part II: Laboratory Tests," *Univ. of Ill. Eng. Exp. Stn. Bull. 386*, Urbana, Feb. 1950, 80 pp.
50. NEWMARK, N. M., and C. P. SIESS, "Proposed Design Specifications for Two-Way Floor Slabs," *J., ACI*, Vol. 21, No. 8, April 1950, pp. 597–607. Also *Proc. ACI*, Vol. 46, 1950, pp. 597–607.
51. NEWMARK, N. M., and C. P. SIESS, Authors closing discussion to paper on "Proposed Design Specifications for Two-Way Floor Slabs," *J. Proc. Am. Concrete Inst.*, Dec. 1950, pp. 608–5 to 608–8.
52. NEWMARK, N. M., "Methods of Analysis for Structures Subjected to Dynamic Loading," Directorate of Intelligence, U.S. Air Force, Washington D.C., Dec. 18, 1950, 95 pp.
53. NEWMARK, N. M., C. P. SIESS, and I. M. VIEST, "Tests and Analyses of Com-

posite Beams with Incomplete Interaction," *Proc. Soc. Exp. Stress Anal.*, Vol. 9, No. 1, Oct. 1951, pp. 75–92.

54. NEWMARK, N. M., "La Investigacion sobre Estructuras en la Universidad de Illinois," *Informes de la Construccion*, Instituto Tecnico de la Construction y del Cemento, Madrid, Vol. 4, 1951, 4 pp.
55. NEWMARK, N. M., R. J. MOSBORG, W. H. MUNSE, and R. E. ELLING, "Fatigue Tests in Axial Compression," *Proc.*, ASTM, Vol. 51, 1951, pp. 792–810.
56. SIESS, C. P., I. M. VIEST, and N. M. NEWMARK, "Studies of Slab and Beam Highway Bridges: Part III—Small-Scale Tests of Shear Connectors and Composite T-Beams," *Univ. of Ill. Eng. Exp. Stn. Bull. 396*, Urbana, Feb. 1952, 133 pp.
57. NEWMARK, N. M., "Analysis and Design of Structures Subjected to Dynamic Loading," *Proceedings, Conference on Building in the Atomic Age*, M.I.T. Press, Cambridge, Mass., 1952, pp. 34–47.
58. NEWMARK, N. M., "Computation of Dynamic Structural Response in the Range Approaching Failure," *Proceedings, Symposium on Earthquake and Blast Effects on Structures*, UCLA, Los Angeles, 1952, pp. 114–129.
59. VIEST, I. M., C. P. SIESS, J. H. APPLETON, and N. M. NEWMARK, "Studies of Slab and Beam Highway Bridges: Part IV—Full-Scale Tests of Channel Shear Connectors and Composite T-Beams," *Univ. of Ill. Eng. Exp. Stn. Bull. 405*, Urbana, 1952, 155 pp.
60. NEWMARK, N. M., "The Institute's Research Program—Part III (Riveted and Bolted Structural Joints)," *Proceedings, American Institute of Steel Construction National Engineering Conference*, New York, 1952, pp. 24–32.
61. HOELTJE, W. C., and N. M. NEWMARK, "Brittle Strength and Transition Temperature of Structural Steel," *Welding J.*, AWS, Vol. 31, No. 11, 1952, pp. 515s–521s.
62. NEWMARK, N. M., and A. S. VELETSOS, "A Simple Approximation for the Natural Frequencies of Partly Restrained Bars," *J. Appl. Mech.*, ASME, Vol. 19, 1952, p. 563.
63. NEWMARK, N. M., "Bounds and Convergence of Relaxation and Iteration Procedures," *Proceedings, First National Congress of Applied Mechanics*, ASME, 1952. pp. 9–14.
64. NEWMARK, N. M., and E. D'APPOLONIA, "A Method for the Solution of the Restrained Cylinder Under Compression," *Proceedings, First National Congress of Applied Mechanics*, ASME, 1952, pp. 217–226.
65. AUSTIN, W. J., and N. M. NEWMARK, "A Numerical Method for the Solution of Plate Buckling Problems," *Proceedings, First National Congress of Applied Mechanics*, ASME, 1952, pp. 363–371.
66. NEWMARK, N. M., "A Review of Cumulative Damage in Fatigue," Chapter 10 in *Fatigue and Fracture of Metals*, M.I.T. Press and Wiley, New York, 1952, pp. 197–228.
67. NEWMARK, N. M., "What Do We Need To Know About Prestressed Concrete," *J., ACI*, Vol. 24, No. 5, 1953, pp. 445–456.
68. NEWMARK, N. M., "What Do We Need To Know About Prestressed Concrete," *Civil Eng.*, Vol. 23, No. 1, 1953, pp. 59–63.

69. Newmark, N. M., "An Engineering Approach to Blast Resistant Design," *Proceedings, 22nd Annual Convention Structural Engineers Association of California*, San Francisco, 1953, pp. 5–1 to 5–18.
70. Goodman, L. E., E. Rosenblueth, and N. M. Newmark, "Aseismic Design of Elastic Structures Founded on Firm Ground," *Proc. Separate No. 349, ASCE*, Vol. 79, 1953, 27 pp. Also *Trans. ASCE*, Vol. 120, 1955, pp. 782–802.
71. Matthiesen, R. B., L. A. Harris, and N. M. Newmark, "Fatigue Properties of Weld Metal," *Welding J.*, AWS, Vol. 32, No. 9, 1953, pp. 441s–453s.
72. Harris, L. A., R. B. Matthiesen, and N. M. Newmark, "Low-Temperature Bend Test Properties of Bead-on-Plate Welds," *Welding J.*, AWS, Vol. 32, No. 12, 1953, pp. 585s–599s.
73. Munse, W. H., D. T. Wright, and N. M. Newmark, "Laboratory Tests of High Tensile Bolted Structural Joints," *Proc. ASCE*, Vol. 80, Separate No. 441, 1954, 38 pp. Also *Trans. ASCE*, Vol. 120, 1955, pp. 1299–1321.
74. Newmark, N. M., and C. P. Siess, "Research on Highway Bridge Floors at the University of Illinois; 1936–1954," *Proc. Highway Res. Board*, Vol. 33, 1954, pp. 30–53. Also *Univ. of Ill. Eng. Exp. Stn. Reprint Ser.*, No. 52, Urbana, 1954.
75. Hoeltje, W. C., and N. M. Newmark, Closing discussion of "Brittle Strength and Transition Temperature of Structural Steel," *Welding J.*, AWS, Vol. 33, No. 3, 1954, p. 133s.
76. Newmark, N. M., "Review of Brittle Fracture Research at University of Illinois," *Ship Structure Committee Serial No. SSC-69*, NRC, Washington, D.C., 1954, pp. 185–200.
77. Harris, L. A., G. E. Nordmark, and N. M. Newmark, "Fatigue Strength of Butt Welds in Structural Steels," *Welding Res.*, Suppl., AWS., Vol. 20, 1954, pp. 83–96.
78. Veletsos, A. S., and N. M. Newmark, "A Simple Approximation for the Fundamental Frequencies of Two-Span and Three-Span Continuous Beams," *Proceedings, 2nd U.S. National Congress of Applied Mechanics*, ASME, 1954, pp. 143–146.
79. Veletsos, A. S., and N. M. Newmark, "Determination of the Natural Frequencies of Continuous Beams on Flexible Supports," *Proceedings, 2nd U.S. National Congress of Applied Mechanics*, ASME, 1954, pp. 147–155.
80. Laupa, A., C. P. Siess, and N. M. Newmark, "Strength in Shear of Reinforced Concrete Beams," *Univ. of Ill. Eng. Exp. Stn. Bull. 428*, Urbana, 1955.
81. Newmark, N. M., Closing discussion, "An Engineering Approach to Blast Resistant Design," *Proc. ASCE*, Vol. 81, Separate No. 701, 1955, 2 pp.
82. Hall, W. J., and N. M. Newmark, "Shear Deflection of Wide Flange Steel Beams in the Plastic Range," *Proc. ASCE*, Vol. 81, Separate No. 814, 1955, 30 pp. Also *Trans. ASCE*, Vol. 122, 1957, pp. 666–687.
83. Tung, T. P., and N. M. Newmark, "Numerical Analysis of Earthquake Response of a Tall Building," *Bull. Seismological Soc. Am.*, Vol. 45, 1955, pp. 269–278.
84. Veletsos, A. S., and N. M. Newmark, "Natural Frequencies of Continuous Flexural Members," *Proc. ASCE*, Vol. 81, Separate No. 735, 1955, 37 pp. Also *Trans. ASCE*, Vol. 122, 1957, pp. 249–285.
85. Weil, N. A., and N. M. Newmark, "Large Plastic Deformations of Circular Membranes," *J. Appl. Mech.*, ASME, Vol. 22, 1955, pp. 533–538.

86. Harris, L. A., G. E. Nordmark, and N. M. Newmark, "Fatigue Strength of Butt Welds in Structural Steels," *Welding Res. Suppl.*, AWS, Vol. 20, 1955, pp. 83s–90s.
87. Laupa, A., C. P. Siess, and N. M. Newmark, "Strength in Shear of Reinforced Concrete Beams," *Univ. of Ill. Eng. Exp. Stn. Bull. 428*, Urbana, 1955, 73 pp.
88. Newmark, N. M., "A Philosophy for Anti-Blast Structural Design," *Proceedings, Conference on "The A-Bomb and Industry,"* Armour Research Foundation Chicago, 1955, pp. 49–62.
89. Newmark, N. M., "An Engineering Approach to Blast Resistant Design," *Proc. Separate No. 306, ASCE*, Vol. 79, 1953, 16 pp. Also *Trans. ASCE*, Vol. 121, 1956, pp. 45–64. Also *Univ. of Ill. Eng. Exp. Stn.*, Urbana, *Reprint Ser.*, No. 56, 1956.
90. Newmark, N. M., "Analysis and Design of Structures to Resist Atomic Blast," *Bull. Virginia Polytechnic Inst., Eng. Exp. Stn.* Ser. No. 106, Part 2, Jan. 1956, pp. 49–77.
91. Stallmeyer, J. E., G. E. Nordmark, W. H. Munse, and N. M. Newmark, "Fatigue Strength of Welds in Low Alloy Structural Steels," *Welding J.*, AWS, Vol. 35, No. 6, June 1956, pp. 298s–307s.
92. Tung, T. P., and N. M. Newmark, "Shears in a Tall Building Subjected to Strong Motion Earthquakes," *Proceedings of the World Conference on Earthquake Engineerings*, Earthquake Engineering Research Institute, Berkeley, Calif., 1956, pp. 10–1 to 10–11.
93. Tung, T. P., T. Y. Chen, L. E. Goodman, and N. M. Newmark, "Highway-Bridge Impact Problems," *Highway Res. Board Bull. 124*, Vibration and Stresses in Girder Bridges, 1956, pp. 111–134.
94. Veletsos, A. S., and N. M. Newmark, "Natural Frequencies of Continuous Plates," *J. Appl. Mech.*, ASME, Vol. 23, 1956, pp. 97–102.
95. Veletsos, A. S., and N. M. Newmark, Closing discussion of "Natural Frequencies of Continuous Flexural Members," *Proc. ASCE*, Vol. 82, No. ST-5, 1956, pp. 1067–3 to 1067–6.
96. Weil, N. A., and N. M. Newmark, "Large Deflections of Elliptical Plates," *J. Appl. Mech.*, ASME, Vol. 23, 1956, pp. 21–26.
97. Zeevaert, L., and N. M. Newmark, "Aseismic Design of Latino Americana Tower in Mexico City," *Proceedings of the World Conference on Earthquake Engineering*, Earthquake Engineering Research Institute, Berkeley, Calif., 1956, pp. 35–1 to 35–11.
98. Newmark, N. M., "Designing for Atomic Blast Protection," *Proceedings, Structural Engineers Association of California*, San Francisco, 25th Annual Convention, 1956, pp. 48–56.
99. Newmark, N. M., "The Effect of Dynamic Loads on Offshore Structures," *Proceedings, Eighth Texas Conference on Soil Mechanics and Foundation Engineering*, Univ. Texas Bu. Eng. Res., *Special Publ. No. 29*, 1956, 30 pp.
100. Newmark, N. M., "Reinforced Concrete," *Encyclopedia Britannica*, Vol. 19, 1957, pp. 79–80.
101. Newmark, N. M., "Designing for Atomic Blast Protection," *BuDocks Tech. Digest*, Navy Dept., No. 75, March–April 1957, pp. 21–30.
102. Harris, L. A., and N. M. Newmark, "The Effect of Fabricated Edge Con-

ditions on Brittle Fracture of Structural Steels," *Bull. Am. Railway Eng. Assoc.*, Vol. 59, 1957, pp. 245–290.

103. CHEN, T. Y., C. P. SIESS, and N. M. NEWMARK, "Studies of Slab and Beam Highway Bridges: Part VI—Moments in Simply Supported Skew I-Beam Bridges," *Univ. of Ill. Eng. Exp. Stn. Bull. 439*, Urbana, 1957, 72 pp.
104. HARRIS, L. A., and N. M. NEWMARK, "Effect of Fabricated Edge Conditions on Brittle Fracture of Structural Steels," *Welding Res. Suppl.*, AWS, Vol. 37, p. 137s, 1958.
105. BROWN, C. H., H. O. BANKS, F. B. FARQUHARSON, N. M. NEWMARK, K. SMITH, J. B. WILBUR, and A. ACKERMAN, "Report of Task Committee on Professional Education," *Civil Eng.*, Vol. 28, 1958, pp. 111–123.
106. NEWMARK, N. M., "Recommended FCDA Specifications for Blast Resistant Structural Design (Method A)," *Federal Civil Defense Administration Technical Report TR-5-1*, 1958, 6 pp.
107. NEWMARK, N. M., "A Revolution in Design Practice," *Civil Eng.*, Vol. 28, 1958, p. 315.
108. HANSEN, R. J., B. G. JOHNSTON, N. M. NEWMARK, and M. P. WHITE, Discussion of paper, "Destructive Impulse Loading of Reinforced Concrete Beams," by F. T. MAVIS and M. J. GREAVES, *Proc. ACI*, Vol. 54, 1958, pp. 815–816.
109. NEWMARK, N. M., "Welcome Address," *Proceedings, Conference on Electronic Computation, ASCE*, Nov. 1958, pp. 1–2.
110. ROLFE, S. T., W. J. HALL, and N. M. NEWMARK, "Brittle-Fracture Tests of Steel Plates Containing Residual Compressive Strain," *Welding J.*, AWS, Vol. 38, No. 4, April 1959, pp. 169s–175s.
111. NEWMARK, N. M., "The Place of the University in the Education of Civil Engineers," (a) "Undergraduate Study and the Curriculum," pp. N10–11; (b) "Postgraduate Education," pp. N18–19; (c) "The Place of Engineering Research in Universities," pp. N24–25; (d) "Concluding Remarks," p. N24; *Proc. Inst. Civil Eng., Great Britain*, Vol. 12, April 1959.
112. NEWMARK, N. M., "Remarks on Analytical Methods for Protective Structural Design," *Proceedings of the Second Protective Construction Symposium* (*Deep Underground Construction*), The Rand Corporation, Santa Monica, Calif., Report R-341, Vol. 1, March 1959, pp. 367–386.
113. NEWMARK, N. M., Discussion of "Solving Structural Mechanics' Problems on Digital Computers," Ed. by H. J. Greenberg, *Structural Mechanics, Proceedings of the 1st Symposium on Naval Structural Mechanics*, Pergamon Press, Elmsford, N.Y., 1960, pp. 554–556.
114. NEWMARK, N. M., Closing discussion of "A Method of Computation for Structural Dynamics," *J. Struct. Div., Proc. Am. Soc. Civil Engr.*, Vol. 86, ST 8, 1960, p. 89.
115. ANG, A. H.-S., and N. M. NEWMARK, "A Numerical Procedure for the Analysis of Continuous Plates," *American Society of Civil Engineers, Second Conference on Electronic Computation*, Pittsburgh, 1960, pp. 379–413.
116. JENNINGS, R. L., and N. M. NEWMARK, "Elastic Response of Multi-Story Shear Beam Type Structures Subjected to Strong Ground Motion," *Proceedings of the 2nd World Conference on Earthquake Engineering*, Tokyo, Vol. 11, 1960, pp. 699–717.
117. VELETSOS, A. S., and N. M. NEWMARK, "Effects of Inelastic Behavior on the Response of Simple Systems to Earthquake Motions," *Proceedings of the 2nd*

*World Conference on Earthquake Engineering*, Tokyo, Vol. 11, 1960, pp. 895–912.

118. Newmark, N. M., "Keynote Address—The Future of Civil Engineering Education," *Civil Eng. Educ. ASCE*, 1961, pp. 21–27.
119. Newmark, N. M., "Failure Hypotheses for Soils," Opening address, *Research Conference on Shear Strength of Cohesive Soils*, ASCE, 1961, pp. 17–32.
120. Anderson, F. E., Jr., R. J. Hansen, H. L. Murphy, N. M. Newmark, and M. P. White, "Design of Structures to Resist Nuclear Weapons Effects," *ASCE Manual of Engineering Practice No. 42*, 1961, 150 pp.
121. Newmark, N. M., and R. J. Hansen, "Design of Blast Resistant Structures," Chapter 49 in *Shock and Vibration Handbook*, Vol. III, C. M. Harris and C. E. Crede, eds., McGraw-Hill, New York, 1961, 24 pp.
122. Newmark, N. M., "Research and Civil Engineering Education," *J. Professional Practice Proc. ASCE*, Vol. 87, No. PP2, Oct. 1961, 14 pp. Also *Trans. ASCE*, Vol. 128, Part V, 1963, pp. 1–16.
123. Lycan, D. L., and N. M. Newmark, "Effect of Structure and Foundation Interaction," *J. Eng. Mech. Div. Proc. ASCE*, Vol. 87, No. EM5, Oct. 1961, 32 pp. Also *Trans. ASCE*, Vol. 131, 1966, p. 726.
124. Blume, J. A., N. M. Newmark, and Leo Corning, *Design of Multi-Story Reinforced Concrete Building for Earthquake Motions*, Portland Cement Association, Chicago, 1961, 350 pp.
125. Sanders, W. W., Jr., W. H. Munse, and N. M. Newmark, "The Lateral and Longitudinal Distribution of Loading in Steel Railway Bridges," *Bull. Am. Railway Eng. Assoc.*, Vol. 63, No. 566, Sept.–Oct. 1961, pp. 13–16.
126. Newmark, N. M., "Remarks on Analytical Methods for Protective Structural Design," Chapter 20 in *Protective Construction in a Nuclear Age*, Vol. 1, J. J. O'Sullivan, ed., Macmillan, New York, 1961, pp. 329–347.
127. Hall, W. J., S. T. Rolfe, F. W. Barton, and N. M. Newmark, "Brittle-Fracture Propagation in Wide Steel Plates," *Ship Structure Committee Report No. SSC-131*, National Academy of Sciences, National Research Council, NRC, Washington, D.C., Oct. 1961, 30 pp.
128. Newmark, N. M., "A Method of Computation for Structural Dynamics," *J. Eng. Mech. Div. ASCE*, Vol. 85, July 1959, pp. 67–94. Also *Trans. ASCE*, Vol. 127, Part 1, 1962, pp. 1406–1435 (with discussion).
129. Sinnamon, G. K., and N. M. Newmark, "Facilites for Dynamic Testing of Soils," *Symp. Soil Dynamics, ASTM Tech. Publ. No. 305*, 1962, pp. 38–44.
130. Newmark, N. M., et al., "Engineering Conference Report Based on Meeting Held at Boulder, Colorado, August 9–15, 1961," *J. Eng. Educ.*, Vol. 52, No. 9, May 1962, pp. 624–641.
131. Newmark, N. M., "Education en Ingenieria," Ingenieria, National University of Mexico, Mexico, D.F., Vol. 32, No. 4, Oct. 1962, pp. 73–78.
132. Newmark, N. M., and J. D. Haltiwanger, "Air Force Design Manual—Principles and Practices for Design of Hardened Structures," *Report SWC-TDR-62-138*, Research Directorate, Air Force Special Weapons Center, Albuquerque, 1962, 615 pp.
133. Newmark, N. M., W. D. Alexander, R. E. Fadum, E. Hognestad, W. E. Smith, and D. C. Taylor, "1962 ASCE Research Conference, Report by the Committee on Research, ASCE," *J. Professional Practice Proc. ASCE*, Vol. 89, No. PP1, Jan. 1963, pp. 37–91.

134. NEWMARK, N. M., Author's closure, "Research and Civil Engineering Education," *J. Professional Practice Proc. ASCE*, Vol. 89, No. PP1, Jan. 1963, pp. 101–104.
135. NEWMARK, N. M., Introduction to *Arches, Continuous Frames, Columns, and Conduits*, Selected papers of Hardy Cross, University of Illinois Press, Urbana, 1963, pp. vii–x.
136. LYCAN, D. L., and N. M. NEWMARK, Author's closure, "Effect of Structure and Foundation Interaction," *J. Eng. Mech. Div. ASCE*, Vol. 89, No. EM4, Aug. 1963, p. 69–70.
137. NEWMARK, N. M., "Design of Structures for Dynamic Loads Including the Effects of Vibration and Ground Shock," *Symposium on Scientific Problems of Protective Construction*, Swiss Federal Institute of Technology, Zurich, July 1963, pp. 148–248.
138. NEWMARK, N. M., and W. J. HALL, "Design Criteria for Reactor Cells, Building 315, Argonne National Laboratory," Appendices I and J, Safety Analysis Report Argonne Fast Critical Facility (ZPR-VI), *Argonne National Laboratory Report 6271*, Argonne, Ill., Dec. 1963, pp. 171–198.
139. NEWMARK, N. M., C. P. SIESS, and M. A. SOZEN, "Moment-Rotation Characteristics of Reinforced Concrete and Ductility Requirements for Earthquake Resistance," *Proceedings, 30th Annual Convention, Structural Engineers Association of California*, San Francisco, Oct. 3–5, 1963, pp. 54–66.
140. NEWMARK, N. M., "The Basis of Current Criteria for the Design of Underground Protective Construction," *Proceedings, Symposium on Soil-Structure Interaction*, University of Arizona, Tucson, Sept. 1964, pp. 1–24.
141. VELETSOS, A. S., and N. M. NEWMARK, "Design Procedures for Shock Isolation Systems of Underground Protective Structures," Vol. 3, "Response Spectrum of Single-Degree-of-Freedom Elastic and Inelastic Systems," *Report RTD TDR 63–3096*, Vol. III, Air Force Weapons Laboratory, Albuquerque, June 1964, 316 pp.
142. NEWMARK, N. M., "Structural Engineering," Chapter 6 in *Listen to Leaders in Engineering*, ALBERT LOVE and JAMES SAXON CHILDERS, eds., Tupper and Love, Atlanta, Jan. 1965, pp. 73–84.
143. NEWMARK, N. M., "Effects of Earthquakes on Dams and Embankments," Fifth Rankine Lecture, The Institution of Civil Engineers, London, *Geotechnique*, Vol. XV, No. 2, June 1965, pp. 139–159.
144. NEWMARK, N. M., W. J. WALKER, A. S. VELETSOS, and R. J. MOSBORG, "Design Procedures for Shock Isolation Systems of Underground Protective Structures," Vol. IV, "Response of Two-Degree-of-Freedom Elastic and Inelastic Systems," *Report RTD TDR 63–3096*, Vol. IV, Air Force Weapons Laboratory Albuquerque, Dec. 1965, 212 pp.
145. NEWMARK, N. M., W. H. WALKER, and R. J. MOSBORG, "Design Procedures for Shock Isolation Systems of Underground Protective Structures," Vol. V, "Response Spectra of Multi-Degree-of-Freedom Elastic Systems," *Report RTD TDR 63–3096*, Vol. V, Air Force Weapons Laboratory, Albuquerque, Dec. 1965, 126 pp.
146. NEWMARK, N. M., and associates, "Design of Model Test Program for a Buried Field Shelter," *Report No. 1–110*, Waterways Experiment Station, Vicksburg, Miss., May 1965, 108 pp.

147. Newmark, N. M., "Current Trends in the Seismic Analysis and Design of High Rise Structures," *Proceedings, Symposium on Earthquake Engineering*, University of British Columbia, Vancouver, Sept. 1965, pp. VI-1 to VI-55.
148. Newmark, N. M., "State of the Art in Dynamic Analysis and Techniques for the Design of Underground Protective Construction," *Proceedings, Symposium on Protective Structures for Civilian Populations*, National Academy of Sciences, National Research Council, Washington, D.C., April 1965, pp. 166–179.
149. Veletsos, A. S., N. M. Newmark, and C. V. Chelapati, "Deformation Spectra for Elastic and Elasto-plastic Systems Subjected to Ground Shock and Earthquake Motions," *Proceedings, Third World Congress on Earthquake Engineering*, Int. Assoc of Earthquake Engin., New Zealand, Vol. 2, 1965, pp. 11–663 to 11–682.
150. Newmark, N. M., "Notes on Shock Isolation Concepts," in "Vibration in Civil Engineering," *Proceedings, Symposium Organized by the British National Section of the International Association for Earthquake Engineering*, Butterworth's, London, 1966, pp. 71–82.
151. Newmark, N. M., "Prize Bridges of 1967," *Modern Steel Construction*, Vol. 8, No. 4, American Institute of Steel Construction, New York, 4th Quarter 1967, pp. 17–20.
152. Newmark, N. M., "Problems in Wave Propagation in Soil and Rock," *Proceedings, International Symposium on Wave Propagation and Dynamic Properties of Earth Materials, Aug. 23–25, 1967*, University of New Mexico Press, Albuquerque, 1968, pp. 7–26.
153. Newmark, N. M., and W. J. Hall, "Dynamic Behavior of Reinforced and Prestressed Concrete Buildings Under Horizontal Forces and the Design of Joints (Including Wind, Earthquake, Blast Effects), Preliminary Publication 8th Congress, International Association Bridge and Structural Engineering, New York, Sept. 9–14, 1968, pp. 585–613 (French translation pp. 614–638, German translation, pp. 639–661).
154. Newmark, N. M., "Section 3, Earthquake-Resistant Building Design," in *Structural Engineering Handbook*, E. H. and C. N. Gaylord, eds., McGraw-Hill, New York, 1968, pp. 3–1 to 3–30.
155. Newmark, N. M., G. W. Housner, T. Hisada, and others, "Aseismic Design and Testing of Nuclear Facilities" (Report of Panel, Tokyo June 12–16, 1967), International Atomic Energy Agency Technical Reports, Series No. 88, Monograph, Vienna, 1968, 49 pp.
156. Sozen, M. A., P. C. Jennings, R. B. Matthiesen, G. W. Housner, and N. M. Newmark, "Engineering Report on the Caracas Earthquake of 29 July 1967," Committee on Earthquake Engineering Research, Division of Engineering, National Research Council, National Academy of Engineering, Monograph, published by the National Academy of Sciences, Washington, D.C., 1968, 217 pp.
157. Newmark, N. M., "Civil Engineering," in Section of the Science Year in Review, *1969 Brittanica Yearbook of Science and the Future*, Encyclopedia Brittanica, Inc., Chicago, 1969, pp. 299–300.
158. Newmark, N. M., "Relation Between Wind and Earthquake Response of Tall Buildings," *Proceedings, 1966 Illinois Structural Engineering Conference*, Feb. 1969, pp. 137–156.

159. NEWMARK, N. M., "Earthquake Engineering—Learning from Failures," Washington Award Address, *Midwest Engr.*, Vol. 21, No. 7, March 1969, pp. 10–13.

160. NEWMARK, N. M., "Design Criteria for Nuclear Reactors Subjected to Earthquake Hazards," *Proceedings, IAEA Panel on Aseismic Design and Testing of Nuclear Facilities*, the Japan Earthquake Promotion Society, Tokyo, 1969, pp. 90–113.

161. NEWMARK, N. M., and W. J. HALL, "Special Topics for Consideration in Design of Nuclear Power Plants Subjected to Seismic Motion," *Proceedings, IAEA Panel on Aseismic Design and Testing of Nuclear Facilities*, the Japan Earthquake Engineering Promotion Society, Tokyo, 1969, pp. 114–119.

162. NEWMARK, N. M., "Structural Synthesis and Design," Chapter 6 in *Earthquake Engineering Research*, Report to NSF by the NAE Committee on Earthquake Engineering Research, National Academy of Sciences, Washington, D.C., 1969, pp. 199–232.

163. NEWMARK, N. M., "Torsion in Symmetrical Buildings," *Proceedings, Fourth World Conference on Earthquake Engineering, Santiago, Chile*, Vol. 11, 1969, pp. A3–19 to A3–32.

164. NEWMARK, N. M., and W. J. HALL, "Seismic Design Criteria for Nuclear Reactor Facilities," *Proceedings, Fourth World Conference on Earthquake Engineering*, Int. Assoc. of Earthquake Engin., *Santiago, Chile*, Vol. 11, 1969, pp. B4–37 to B4–50.

165. FENVES, S. J., and N. M. NEWMARK, "Seismic Forces and Overturning Moments in Buildings, Towers and Chimneys," *Proceedings, Fourth World Conference on Earthquake Engineering*, Int. Assoc. of Earthquake Engin., *Santiago, Chile*, Vol. 111, 1969, pp. B5–1 to B5–12.

166. SOZEN, M. A., N. M. NEWMARK, and G. W. HOUSNER, "Implications on Seismic Structural Design of the Evaluation of Damage to the Sheraton-Macuto," *Proceedings, Fourth World Conference on Earthquake Engineering, Santiago, Chile*, Int. Assoc. of Earthquake, Engin., Vol. III, 1969, pp. J2–137 to J2–150.

167. NEWMARK, N. M., "Current Trends in the Seismic Analysis and Design of High Rise Structures," Chapter 16 in *Earthquake Engineering*, ROBERT L. WIEGEL, ed., Prentice-Hall, Englewood Cliffs, N. J., 1970, pp. 403–424.

168. NEWMARK, N. M., "Seismic Response of Reactor Facility Components," in *Symposium on Seismic Analysis of Pressure Vessel and Piping Components*, David H. Pai, ed., ASME, New York, 1971, pp. 1–24.

169. AMIN, M., W. J. HALL, N. M. NEWMARK, and R. P. KASSAWARA, "Earthquake Response of Multiply Connected Light Secondary Systems by Spectrum Methods," in *Symposium on Seismic Analysis of Pressure Vessel and Piping Components*, David H. Pai, ed., ASME, New York, 1971, pp. 103–129.

170. NEWMARK, N. M., and E. ROSENBLUETH, *Fundamentals of Earthquake Engineering*, Prentice-Hall, Englewood Cliffs, N. J., 1971, 640 pp.

171. STEINBRUGGE, K., and N. M. NEWMARK et al., Report of Committee on Earthquake Hazard Reduction, *In the Interest of Earthquake Safety*, Institute of Governmental Studies, University of California, Berkeley, 1971, 22 pp.

172. NEWMARK, N. M., "Design Specifications for Earthquake Resistance," in *Civil Engineering Frontiers in Environmental Technology* (a program of public lectures to commemorate the dedication of Raymond E. Davis Hall), Department of Civil Engineering, University of California, Berkeley, 1971, pp. 101–113.

173. NEWMARK, N. M., "Earthquake Response Analysis of Reactor Structures," *Nuclear Eng. Des.*, Vol. 20, No. 2, 1972, pp. 303–322.

174. NEWMARK, N. M., and W. J. HALL, "Seismic Analysis," Chapter 4 in *Pressure Vessels and Piping: Design and Analysis*, Vol. II, G. J. BOHM, R. L. CLOUD, L. C. HSU, D. H. PAI, and R. F. REEDY, eds., ASME, New York, 1972, pp. 1408–1413.

175. NEWMARK, N. M., and W. J. HALL, "Seismic Design Criteria for Nuclear Reactor Facilities" (reprinted from *Proceedings, Fourth World Conference on Earthquake Engineering*), in *Pressure Vessels and Piping: Design and Analysis*, Vol. 11, G. J. BOHM, R. L. CLOUD, L. C. HSU, D. J. PAI, and R. F. REEDY, eds., ASME, New York, 1972, pp. 1414–1427.

176. NEWMARK, N. M., A. R. ROBINSON, A.H.-S. ANG, L. A. LOPEZ, and W. J. HALL, "Methods of Determing Site Characteristics," *Proc. Int. Conf. Microzonation*, Univ. Washington Seattle, Wash., Vol. 1, 1972, pp. 113–129.

177. NEWMARK, N. M., "External Blast," State of Art Report No. 7, ASCE-IABSE International Conference on Planning and Design of Tall Buildings, Vol. 1b, ASCE, New York, Aug. 1972, pp. 661–676.

178. NEWMARK, N. M. (chairman) et al., "Earthquake Guidelines for Reactor Siting," *Technical Reports Series No. 139*, International Atomic Energy Agency, Vienna, 1972, 26 pp.

179. NEWMARK, N. M., and W. J. HALL, "Procedures and Criteria for Earthquake Resistant Design," *Building Practices for Disaster Mitigation*, National Bureau of Standards, Building Science Series 46, Vol. 1, Feb. 1973, pp. 209–236.

180. NEWMARK, N. M., J. A. BLUME, and K. K. KAPUR, "Seismic Design Spectra for Nuclear Power Plants," *J. Power Division ASCE Proc. ASCE*, Vol. 99, No. PO2, Nov. 1973, pp. 287–303.

181. STEINBRUGGE, K. V., G. V. BERG, N. M. NEWMARK, C. H. SAVITT, H. B. SEED, G. H. SUTTON, M. D. TRIFUNAC, and J. T. WILSON, *Strong-Motion Engineering Seismology—The Key to Understanding and Reducing the Damaging Effects of Earthquakes*, National Academy of Sciences, Washington, D.C., 1973, 19 pp.

182. NEWMARK, N. M., W. J. HALL, and B. MOHRAZ, "A Study of Vertical and Horizontal Earthquake Spectra," *Report WASH-1255*, Directorate of Licensing, U.S. Atomic Energy Commission, Washington, D.C., April 1973, 153 pp.

183. HALL, W. J., N. M. NEWMARK, and B. MOHRAZ, "Comments on Earthquake Transmission from Basement Rock to Surface," *Proceedings, Fifth World Conference on Earthquake Engineering*, Vol. 1, International Association for Earthquake Engineering, Rome, 1974, pp. 737–740.

184. NEWMARK, N. M., and W. J. HALL, "Seismic Design Spectra for Trans-Alaska Pipeline," *Proceedings, Fifth World Conference on Earthquake Engineering*, Vol. 1, International Association for Earthquake Engineering, Rome, 1974, pp. 544–557.

185. NEWMARK, N. M., and W. J. HALL, "A Rational Approach to Seismic Design Standards for Structures, *Proceedings, Fifth World Conference on Earthquake Engineering*, Vol. 2, International Association for Earthquake Engineering, Rome, 1974, pp. 2266–2275.

186. NEWMARK, N. M., "Interpretation of Apparent Upthrow of Objects in Earthquakes," *Proceedings, Fifth World Conference on Earthquake Engineering*, Vol. 2, International Association for Earthquake Engineering, Rome, 1974, pp. 2338–2343.

187. Hall, W. J., N. M. Newmark, and A. J. Hendron, Jr., "Classification, Engineering Properties and Field Exploration of Soils, Intact Rock and In Situ Rock Masses," *Rept. WASH-1301*, Directorate of Regulatory Standards, U.S. Atomic Energy Commission, Washington, D.C., May 1974, 262 pp.
188. Haltiwanger, J. D., W. J. Hall, and N. M. Newmark, "Civil Engineering Graduate Education in Evolution," *Civil Eng. Educ.*, ASCE, Vol. 1, Part 1, 1974, pp. 149–156.
189. Newmark, N. M., "Report of Working Subgroup, Analytical and Numerical Techniques," *Proceedings, 3rd National Meeting of the Universities Council for Earthquake Engineering Research, UCEER*, Calif. Institute of Technology, Pasadena, Ca., May 1974, pp. 233–235.
190. Newmark, N. M., "Panel on Special Structures," *Final Report and Proceedings of a Workshop on Simulation of Earthquake Effects on Structures*, National Academy of Engineering, Washington, D.C., 1974, pp. 245–255.
191. Newmark, N. M., "Overview of Seismic Design Margins," Program Report, Workshop on Reactor Licensing and Safety, Vol. 2, No. 1, Atomic Industrial Forum, New York, May 1975, pp. 63–84.
192. Newmark, N. M., "Seismic Design Criteria for Structures and Facilities, Trans-Alaska Pipeline System," *Proceedings, U.S. National Conference on Earthquake Engineering, Ann Arbor, Mich.*, Earthquake Engineering Research Institute, Oakland, Ca., June 1975, pp. 94–103.
193. Sharpe, R. L., N. M. Newmark, A. Goldberg, B. Bresler, N. S. Remmer, and N. C. Donovan, "Nationally-Applicable Seismic Design Recommendations—A Progress Report," *Proceedings, U.S. National Conference on Earthquake Engineering, Ann Arbor, Mich.*, Earthquake Engineering Research Institute, Oakland, Ca., June 1975, pp. 77–86.
194. Newmark, N. M., and W. J. Hall, "Pipeline Design to Resist Large Fault Displacement," *Proceedings, U.S. National Conference on Earthquake Engineering, Ann Arbor, Mich.*, Earthquake Engineering Research Institute, Oakland, Ca., June 1975, pp. 416–425.
195. Hall, W. J., V. J. McDonald, D. J. Nyman, and N. M. Newmark, "Observations on the Process of Equipment Qualification," *Proceedings, U.S. National Conference on Earthquake Engineering, Ann Arbor, Mich.*, Earthquake Engineering Research Institute, Oakland, Ca., June 1975, pp. 495–501.
196. Newmark, N. M., "Design of Structures to Resist Seismic Motions," *Proceedings of the Earthquake Engineering Conference*, Univ. of South Carolina College of Engineering, Columbia, Jan. 23–24, 1975, pp. 235–275.
197. Newmark, N. M., "A Response Spectrum Approach for Inelastic Seismic Design of Nuclear Reactor Facilities," Paper K 5/1, *Transactions, Third International Conference on Structural Mechanics in Reactor Technology*, BAM, Berlin, Vol. 4, Part K, Sept. 1975, 14 pp.
198. Hall, W. J., B. Mohraz, and N. M. Newmark, "Statistical Analyses of Earthquake Response Spectra," Paper K 1/6, *Transactions, Third International Conference on Structural Mechanics in Reactor Technology*, BAM, Berlin, Vol. 4, Part K, Sept. 1975, 11 pp.
199. Newmark, N. M., "Effects of Earthquakes on Dams and Embankments," *Milestones in Soil Mechanics, The First Ten Rankine Lectures*, Institution of Civil Engineers, London, 1975, pp. 109–129.

## Doctoral Students of N. M. Newmark

Professor Newmark has been the advisor or coadvisor of the following students who completed their Ph.D. in Civil Engineering, Graduate College, University of Illinois at Urbana-Champaign:

|  |  |
|---|---|
| Appleton, J. H. | (1959) |
| Au, T. | (1951) |
| Auld, H. E. | (1967) |
| Austin, W. J. | (1949) |
| Badir, M. | (1948) |
| Brooks, J. A. | (1955) |
| Bultmann, E. H., Jr. | (1968) |
| Bustamante, J. I. | (1964) |
| Chan, S. P. | (1953) |
| Chen, T. Y. | (1954) |
| Collins, R. A. | (1958) |
| Cowan, B. M. | (1968) |
| Cox, H. L. | (1953) |
| Daigh, J. D. | (1957) |
| D'Appolonia, E. | (1948) |
| Dorris, A. F. | (1965) |
| Duberg, J. E. | (1948) |
| Egger, W., Jr. | (1960) |
| Eppink, R. T. | (1960) |
| Fisher, W. E. | (1962) |
| Francy, W. J. | (1954) |
| Friedericy, J. A. | (1960) |
| Fuller, J. R. | (1955) |
| Fulton, R. E. | (1960) |
| Gaus, M. P. | (1959) |
| Gossard, M. L. | (1949) |
| Gurfinkel, G. R. | (1966) |
| Hall, W. J. | (1954) |
| Haltiwanger, J. D. | (1957) |
| Hammer, J. G. | (1954) |
| Hanley, J. T. | (1963) |
| Harper, G. N. | (1963) |
| Harris, L. A. | (1954) |
| Heer, J. E., Jr. | (1965) |
| Howland, F. L. | (1955) |
| Iten, R. M. | (1968) |
| Jennings, R. L. | (1964) |
| Jester, G. E. | (1968) |
| Johnson, S. W. | (1964) |
| Laupa, A. | (1953) |
| Lee, D. H. | (1951) |
| Lee, Z. K. | (1950) |
| Lemcoe, M. M. | (1957) |
| Lycan, D. L. | (1960) |
| Massard, J. M. | (1955) |
| Mayerjak, R. J. | (1955) |
| McDonough, G. F., Jr. | (1959) |
| Melin, J. W. | (1961) |
| Merritt, J. L., Jr. | (1958) |
| Murtha, J. P. | (1961) |
| Nakhata, T. | (1973) |
| Pan, S. L. | (1951) |
| Patterson, G. J. | (1969) |
| Paul, S. L. | (1963) |
| Pinckert, R. E. | (1966) |
| Radler, C. M. | (1963) |
| Randall, P. N. | (1948) |
| Richart, F. E., Jr. | (1948) |
| Robinson, A. R. | (1956) |
| Rosenblueth, E. | (1951) |
| Schmidt, R. | (1956) |
| Schnobrich, W. C. | (1962) |
| Schutz, F. W., Jr. | (1952) |
| Shaw, W. A. | (1962) |
| Siess, C. P. | (1948) |
| Smith, R. H. | (1958) |
| Stallmeyer, J. E. | (1953) |
| Stephens, H. E. | (1954) |
| Stockdale, W. K. | (1959) |
| Sutcliffe, S. | (1960) |
| Thibodeaux, M. H. | (1958) |
| Townsley, E. S. | (1959) |
| Tung, C. P. C. | (1951) |
| Untrauer, R. E. | (1961) |
| Vaughan, R. G. | (1966) |
| Veletsos, A. S. | (1953) |
| Wah, T. | (1953) |
| Walls, W. A. | (1960) |
| Wang, C. K. | (1945) |
| Weggel, J. R. | (1968) |
| Wei, C. F. | (1951) |
| Weil, N. A. | (1952) |
| Whipple, C. R. | (1961) |
| Wu, G. S. | (1954) |
| Wu, T. S. | (1952) |
| Yao, W. M. | (1957) |
| Yegian, S. | (1956) |
| Yoshihara, T. | (1963) |
| Yuan, H. K. | (1951) |
| Zwoyer, E. M. | (1953) |

# Education and Social Issues

DOUGLAS T. WRIGHT*

It is a great pleasure, to join in this tribute to Nathan Newmark. And it is a particular honor and privilege for me to participate in the special program, this evening.**

It is certainly fitting that the main themes of this symposium correspond to the subject areas which Dr. Newmark has so powerfully addressed in the course of his long and distinguished work at the University of Illinois. Important as his technical contributions have been, I would, however, argue that they have been eclipsed by his social contributions, as a teacher and as a servant to many public causes. Civil engineering has always been close to public service, and properly so.

As you have heard, I now work in government, primarily concerned with social policy. It may seem strange to have a civil engineer concerned with hospitals and doctors, senior citizens and Indians. But, as Mark Twain said, "just because a man is an engineer doesn't mean he knows much about engineering; it just means he doesn't know much about anything else." In retrospect at least, the route from structural engineering to my present work has really been quite straightforward, via university administration and an initial period in public service concerned with higher educational policy and finance.

In preparing this address it seemed to me best to try to speak to some issues in public policy which affect education and which relate generally to engineering. While I am sure that at all times in human history people have felt uniquely challenged in either intellectual or emotional terms by the current issues that confronted them, we may be excused in thinking that some of the great issues facing the world today are unique. What is certainly true is

*Deputy Provincial Secretary, Secretariat for Social Development, Province of Ontario, Toronto Ontario, CANADA M7A 1A2.

**Presented at the banquet honoring Dr. Newmark. Champaign, Illinois, Oct. 2, 1975.

that engineers play a most significant if not always self-conscious role in world issues today.

One does not need to spend very long looking at any newspaper these days to realize that the so-called rich western countries are facing unprecedented economic and social problems. It used to be thought that unemployment was a cure for inflation, but record levels of inflation and unemployment coexist, in what the magazine *The Economist* has come to call slumpflation. For a while it seemed that much of the difficulty could be attributed to perturbations in international oil prices. It is now evident that more fundamental problems exist in the western economies. But our problems would be seen as the realization of the happiest dreams of most of the world's population. Looking forward just half the time that Nathan Newmark has worked in Urbana, the world's population is going to double from $3\frac{1}{2}$ billion to about 7 billion.

The social history of the world is inseparable from the history of technology. Fernand Braudel, the great French historian, has written "technology is explained by history, and in its turn explains history"[1]. Social and technical issues have always been intertwined, but today they are politicized as well.

The role and scope of government has increased greatly in the past couple of decades. It is not only that government spending and programs have expanded enormously, but governments have come to be thought of as both omniscient and omnipotent. In all the western democratic countries public expectations now seem to require governments to intervene in any significant issue of public concern, even when such interventions are not likely to be effective or may possibly be counterproductive. Engineers, particularly civil engineers, have long experience of governments as agents of change and development. But we perhaps have not fully appreciated how much greater government involvement has become in recent years and how fully this has politicized all major public and social concerns.

A part of this changed process is the way in which public issues are now defined by the media. We are drowned in current events, and because of this, we tend to lose the capacity to distinguish the relative importance of various issues. To the extent that public opinion is a determining power in political affairs, what public opinion does not recognize as fact has no political existence.

The results of these processes do not seem to be particularly beneficial to governments. It is politically hazardous to be expected to solve insoluble problems. If we look at the inflation problem in these terms, we see the politicization of the labor market and the great difficulty democratically elected governments have in trying to resist demands, to distinguish wants from needs.

From the dawn of civilization man has been able to cope with needs in the context of the domestic household. Distribution within the household is not based on economics but reflects finite needs. The market economy is a distributive mechanism in which money is the unit of exchange. In the market economy decisions are made by individuals, and the total system is naturally limited. As a result of the growth in government activity and influence, the public sector now determines the allocation of a very large part of all goods and services. Daniel Bell has written perceptively about the public sector as the "public household"[2]. And he argues that instead of dealing with community *needs* it has come to have to cope with private *wants*, for shares in economic growth, for this or that social service or subsidy. In the public household allocations reflect political rather than economic power. Our recent political history indicates how easily governments can be embarrassed by the demands of public sector employees and the beneficiaries of public programs.

Additional dilemmas are evident in specific policy areas. In education, for instance, there has been an enormous commitment of public monies to qualitative and quantitative improvement in the past two decades. The notion of investment in human capital and the idea of education as a sort of social escalator became very popular in the 1950s and 1960s. By the early 1970s it had become evident that a mass system of higher education could not provide the benefits of elite status to all its graduates. In the face of this, it is really not very surprising that we should have, on the one hand, people talking of a depression in higher education and, on the other, evidence of a special kind of inflation through which the credentials required for various kinds of employment are increased beyond realistic performance requirements.

Turning to the health field, one can identify a number of interesting parallels. In the kind of semipublic health system that operates in Canada, and in the mixed system that operates in the United States, we seem to have a similar kind of inflation in which increased inputs of doctors, hospital beds, radiology, and pharmaceuticals are *not* associated with any positive trends in health outcomes. Life expectancy is much more influenced by life-style factors than by medical inputs [3].

Although evidence of effectiveness is still more difficult to obtain in the fields of social assistance and the direct social services, there is indication here also of similar kinds of inflation, that is, of increased inputs without corresponding improvements in outcomes [4].

Examination of the social services in health, education, and welfare indicates a number of common features. They are all labor intensive, and notions of improved quality are associated with declining labor productivity. Real outputs are elusive; inputs come to be accepted as a proxy for outputs. Strong incentives for institutionalization exist, and institutionalized services tend to have a monopoly on legitimacy and public finance. Artificial shortages are thereby induced and pressures increase for still more government activity—while the individual becomes less competent in providing for his own healthiness, learning, shelter, and mobility.

We may talk of "civil systems," embracing social, economic, and technical elements. For some 200 years in North America, technological progress has largely determined the course of our history and development and was largely taken for granted as it was absorbed into the economy and the society. Now, technological developments are not necessarily identified as progress, and the public has a love-hate relationship with science and technology. People still believe in technological fixes for problems, but there is apprehension about the side effects that may result. As we look at problems in our cities, in our transportation systems, with energy, food production, and so forth, it is evident that the engineering elements in new civil systems will present altogether new challenges. Never before have the interactions of the social and technical elements been so complete or so difficult and demanding.

Over the past several years there have been a number of efforts, sometimes highly touted, to apply engineering systems analysis to civil systems. I think it can be said categorically that the utility of such efforts has been much less than expected—for the obvious reason that civil systems are not deterministic [5].

No one really needs to be very surprised at this experience. Much more attention must be given to the study of sociotechnical, that is, civil, systems. I do not believe that it will be sufficient to imagine a set of social boundary conditions for our technological fix. Much more complex interactions must be acknowledged if adequate levels of understanding are to be achieved. And the work should not be left solely to the social scientists. Engineers are capable of making major contributions to this work, though not with simplistic models.

It is perhaps unfortunate that engineering education and research in the past couple of decades have been so preoccupied with the newly discovered capacity to construct mathematical models of deterministic physical systems. There are, however, a number of people investigating sociotechnical systems in original and even provocative ways. Of those that have come to my attention, I have been struck by the fact that a significant proportion are not university-based. Let me cite some examples.

The Club of Rome has justifiably won great public attention because of its efforts to address the largest problems facing mankind. Aurelio Peccei and Alexander King have successfully defined what they call the "problematique humaine" [6]. Notwithstanding all the methodological criticisms heaped on the computer models that have been developed, the work has great importance and has stimulated many other efforts. It is of particular interest that Eduard Pestel, the coauthor of the second report of the Club of Rome, is the same Pestel whose name we know on the book *Matrix Methods in Elastomechanics.*

E. F. Schumacher has attracted wide attention with his book *Small is Beautiful* [7]. Schumacher offers some fascinating perceptions: "the amount of real leisure a society enjoys tends to be in inverse proportion to the amount of labour-saving machinery it employs." He argues compellingly that capital-intensive labor-saving technology is not appropriate to the third world. He says that the greatest social and economic problem in the world today arises from the massive growth of population in the third world. He goes on to argue that "appropriate technology," that is, technology that is designed to be part of a self-sufficient, viable social and economic system, must be used in providing employment for these people. Schumacher's notions of appropriate technology may have as much relevance to some of our problems as to the problems of the third world.

Ivan Illich continues his critical studies of institutional systems. He has already written provocatively on education, energy, housing, and transportation [8,9], and a major book on health systems is shortly to be published [10].

In Paris, Jean-Pierre Dupuy heads CÉRÈBE, le Centre de recherche sur le bien-être (the Centre for research on well-being). Dupuy is an engineer who has become concerned with social-technical systems. He has completed some remarkably insightful investigations of health, transportation, and the utility of time [11,12,13].

All the efforts I have noted present stimulating challenges to the implicit assumptions most engineers continue to make in addressing what have to be acknowledged as sociotechnical problems. Such new insights cannot be overlooked. Taken positively, they may assist us in inaugurating new kinds of competency.

Nathan Newmark has provided distinguished leadership as engineering has moved from empiricism to rigor. It seems to me that if we are to try to follow his example, we shall turn our efforts to the intellectual challenges of civil systems, in which technical and social issues are joined.

## References

1. Braudel, F., *Capitalism and Material Life 1400–1800*, Harper & Row, New York, 1973.
2. Bell, D., "The Public Household—on Fiscal Sociology and the Liberal Society," *The Public Interest*, No. 37, Fall 1974, pp. 29–68.
3. Department of National Health and Welfare, *A New Perspective on the Health of Canadians*, Ottawa, 1974.
4. Cochrane, A. L., *Effectiveness and Efficiency; Random Reflections on Health Services*, The Nuffield Hospitals Trust, London, 1972.
5. Hoos, I. R., *Systems Analysis in Public Policy: A Critique*, University of California Press, Berkeley, 1972.
6. Peccei, A., and A. King, *Commentary*, as an appendix to M. Mesarovic and E. Pestel, *Mankind at the Turning Point; The Second Report to the Club of Rome*, Dutton, New York, 1974.
7. Schumacher, E. F., *Small is Beautiful; A Study of Economics as if People Mattered*, Blond & Briggs, London, 1973.

8. ILLICH, I., *Tools for Conviviality*, Harper & Row, New York, 1973.
9. ILLICH, I., *Energy and Equity*, Calder & Boyars, London, 1974.
10. ILLICH, I., *Medical Nemesis*, Pantheon, New York, publication expected 1976.
11. DUPUY, J.-P., and S. KARSENTY, *L'invasion pharmaceutique*, Editions du Seuil, Paris, 1974.
12. DEBOUVERIE, Y., and J.-P. DUPUY, *Le lievre ou la tortue ?: sur la vitesse generalisée de l'automobile*, CÉRÈBE, Paris, 1974.
13. DUPUY, J.-P., *Encombrement et valeur sociale du temps*, CÉRÈBE, Paris, 1973.

# Risk, Reliability, and Safety Analyses in Engineering Design

A. H-S. Ang*

## I. Introduction

The assurance of structural safety and reliability is an important objective in engineering design. Indeed, the evaluation of safety and reliability of a given or proposed system is one of the purposes of structural analysis and is necessary in the development of proper criteria for design.

Engineering designs, however, are normally formulated under conditions of uncertainty—the loading processes and structural properties are usually random, or the information and relationships used in the development of the design are imperfect and thus are potentially subject to errors; in either case, there could be significant uncertainty underlying the formulation of the design. In the face of such uncertainties, absolute assurance of safety and reliability would ordinarily be difficult to achieve; realistically, safety and reliability may be assured only with a tolerable risk or probability of failure.

The presence of uncertainty and the need to consider its effects in the analysis of safety and the determination of design are well recognized. In spite of this recognition, however, uncertainty has traditionally been treated implicitly; that is, the significance of uncertainty is presumed to be covered or allowed for through a factor of safety—what constitutes an appropriate safety factor (or load and resistance factors), however, is a matter left entirely to engineering judgment.

The systematic analysis of uncertainty and assessment of its effects on safety and design are the province of the probabilistic theory of structural reliability. In essence, structural reliability is the theoretical basis for dealing

*Professor of Civil Engineering, University of Illinois at Urbana-Champaign, Urbana, Illinois.

explicitly with uncertainty—specifically it provides the systematic framework for the analysis of different sources of uncertainty and the evaluation of their combined effects on safety and design. Equally important is that reliability also provides (1) the consistent basis for considering all potential modes of failure in a structure—including specifically the safety under the lifetime maximum load and reliability under operational loading conditions, and (2) the formal basis for evaluating the reliability (or safety) of a system as a function of the reliabilities of its components.

The essential elements of the theory of structural reliability are summarized with emphasis on those elements of the theory that have direct practical implications.

## II. General Principles of Structural Reliability

### 2.1. Basic Model of Reliability

The performance of an engineering system will, obviously, depend on the characteristics of the system as well as on the environmental condition to which it is subjected. A system and the relevant environment are usually characterized or defined by certain variables (including parameters) that may be called the *design variables;* accordingly, the safety and reliability of a given system would be a function of these design variables. If the design variables are $X_1, X_2, \ldots, X_n$, we may define a *performance function*

$$Z = g(X_1, X_2, \ldots, X_n). \tag{1}$$

Invariably, one or more of the design variables will contain uncertainty and thus should be considered as random variables. It follows, therefore, that $Z$ is also a random variable whose values $z$ represent specific levels of performance.

If the required minimum level of performance is $z_0$, then satisfactory performance would mean $Z \geq z_0$, whereas failure to perform would be $Z < z_0$. Accordingly, we obtain the *probability of successful performance*, which is the measure of safety or reliability, as

$$p_S = P(Z \geq z_0). \tag{2}$$

Conversely, the measure of unreliability is the probability of *failure to perform:*

$$p_F = P(Z < z_0) = 1 - p_S. \tag{3}$$

Equation (2) or (3) may be evaluated readily if the probability distribution of $Z$ is given; that is,

$$p_S = \int_{z_0}^{\infty} f_Z(z)\, dz = 1 - F_Z(z_0), \tag{4}$$

and thus

$$p_F = F_Z(z_0). \tag{5}$$

As expected, $f_Z(z)$ or $F_Z(z)$ is related [through Eq. (1)] to the distributions of the design variables. Conceivably, therefore, if the distributions of the basic design variables $X_1, X_2, \ldots, X_n$ are given or assumed, the distribution of $Z$ may (theoretically) be derived from those of $X_1, X_2, \ldots, X_n$; i.e., given the density functions $f_{X_1}, f_{X_2}, \ldots f_{X_n}$, we would have (for uncorrelated $X_1, X_2, \ldots, X_n$)

$$F_Z(z_0) = \underset{\{g(x_1, x_2, \ldots, x_n) \leq z_0\}}{\iint \cdots \int} f_{X_1} f_{X_2} \cdots f_{X_n} \, dx_1 dx_2 \cdots dx_n. \tag{6}$$

The evaluation of the multiple integral in Eq. (6), however, is a formidable task; except for very specialized and simple cases, direct integration of Eq. (6) would be quite impractical to implement. In general, therefore, efforts to derive the exact distribution of $Z$ would not be warranted—often the distributions $f_{X_1}, \ldots, f_{X_n}$ of the basic variables are not well defined; the information for these variables may be limited only to the respective means and variances.

A practical alternative, therefore, is to prescribe the required distribution of $Z$ and evaluate the necessary reliability measure on the basis of this distribution and the estimated means and variances of the design variables. The required distribution, however, should be judiciously chosen, taking into account all relevant physical conditions that are pertinent to the problem and that may have bearing on the form of the distribution function. In this regard, it is important to point out that when the failure probability $p_F$ is not too small, say $p_F > 10^{-3}$, the choice of the form of $F_Z(z)$ is not too critical—meaning that the calculated $p_F$ will not be very sensitive to the form of the distribution [5]; in such cases, therefore, a mathematically convenient form of $F_Z(z)$ may be prescribed for practical purposes. However, for very small failure probabilities, e.g., $p_F < 10^{-5}$, the correct choice of the form of $F_Z(z)$ becomes more critical—the calculated $p_F$ could be vastly different for different forms of $F_Z(z)$, and thus a much more careful and accurate determination of the pertinent distribution would be required [5]. Even in the latter cases, however, there are occasions when a relative measure of reliability is largely all that is necessary; for this comparative purpose, a convenient distribution form for $Z$ may also suffice.

Once the form of $F_Z(z)$ is prescribed, the remaining problem is the determination of the mean and variance of $Z$. By first-order approximations [7,9], these are

$$\mu_Z \simeq g(\mu_{X_1}, \ldots, \mu_{X_n}) \tag{7}$$

and (for uncorrelated $X_1, \ldots, X_n$)

$$\sigma_Z^2 \simeq \sum_{i=1}^{n} c_i^2 \sigma_{X_i}^2 \tag{8}$$

in which the constant $c_i = \partial g / \partial X_i$ evaluated at $(\mu_{X_1}, \ldots, \mu_{X_n})$.

Therefore, for a prescribed distribution $F_Z(z)$, the failure probability can be evaluated as

$$p_F = F_Z(z_0, \mu_Z, \sigma_Z), \tag{9}$$

where $\mu_Z$ and $\sigma_Z$ are given by Eqs. (7) and (8).

It is quite common to consider structural safety from the standpoint of a resistance $R$ relative to a load $S$ [14]; in these terms, if the respective probability density functions are $f_R(r)$ and $f_S(s)$, the probability of failure can be expressed as [16]

$$p_F = P(R \leq S) = \int_0^\infty F_R(s) f_S(s)\, ds \tag{10}$$

or

$$p_F = \int_0^\infty [1 - F_S(r)] f_R(r)\, dr. \tag{11}$$

Equation (10) or (11) would be useful when numerical evaluation of $p_F$ becomes necessary (see Sec. IV).

In terms of $R$ and $S$, the performance function may be defined as

$$Z = \ln \frac{R}{S}, \qquad \text{with } z_0 = 0.$$

Then, if a probability distribution is prescribed for $Z$, the failure probability may be expressed as [2]

$$p_F = F_Z(0) = F_\zeta\left(\frac{-\ln \bar{\theta}}{\Omega}\right), \tag{12}$$

where $\zeta = (Z - \ln \bar{\theta})/\Omega$, which has the same distribution form as $Z$ but with zero mean and unit variance,

$\bar{\theta} = \mu_R/\mu_S$, the central safety factor,

$\Omega = \sqrt{\Omega_R^2 + \Omega_S^2}$, the total design uncertainty (evaluation of $\Omega$ is discussed in Sec. 2.2).

*The Safety Index.* The probability of failure $p_F$, of course, is a function of the prescribed model distribution $F_\zeta$. Because of the practical difficulty of determining the correct distribution, nonparametric reliability methods have been proposed [12,18,23]. With such methods, explicit reference to the probability of failure is circumvented; in its place, a *safety index* is adopted as the sole measure of reliability [12]. In terms of $R$ and $S$, the safety index $\beta$ may be given as [23]

$$\beta = \frac{\ln \theta}{\Omega}. \tag{13}$$

For multiple variables, the safety index may also be defined accordingly [19].

With the safety index, explicit reference to the probability of failure can be avoided. However, there is still an underlying failure probability for a given $\beta$; indeed this probability is

$$p_F = F_\zeta(-\beta), \tag{14}$$

where $F_\zeta$ is the underlying comulative distribution function (CDF) of $\zeta$. For the purpose of formulating consistent code provisions for design, where the required level of safety of structural components can be calibrated [18] with existing codes, the safety index would be sufficient to provide the necessary consistency in the code format. However, if probabilistic analysis of reliability based on the mathematical theory of probability is required, such as in the evaluation of the reliability of a system as a function of the reliabilities of its components (see Sec. 2.3), then it will be necessary to convert the safety index into explicit failure probability; in these cases, reference to the probability of failure would be unavoidable.

### 2.2. Practical Analysis of Design Uncertainty

From Eqs. (7)–(9), we see that the failure probability is a function of $\mu_{X_i}$ and $\sigma^2_{X_i}$, which are the mean values and variances of the design variables. These must be estimated or determined on the basis of available information for the respective variables. Such estimates may have systematic biases (for the means) as well as random errors. Any error in the estimated mean, however, should be combined with the estimated variability of the corresponding design variable, thus obtaining the total uncertainty of the variable.

Similarly, the assumed performance function may contain imperfections and, therefore, would add further uncertainties.

A formal framework [2,3] for analyzing all such uncertainties is the following: For a specific design variable, write

$$X_i = N_{X_i}\hat{X}_i \tag{15}$$

in which $\hat{X}_i$ = the model of $X_i$, which is also a random variable whose mean $\bar{x}_i$ and standard deviation $\sigma_{\hat{X}_i}$ are the values estimated from available information; the estimated variability is thus given by the coefficient of variation $\delta_{X_i} = \sigma_{\hat{X}_i}/\bar{x}_i$;

$N_{X_i}$ = a factor used to correct any imperfection in $\hat{X}_i$; it is also a random variable with mean $\bar{\nu}_i$ representing the bias in $\bar{x}_i$ and coefficient of variation (c.o.v.) $\Delta_{X_i}$ representing the random error in $\bar{x}_i$.

Then, assuming that $\hat{X}_i$ and $N_{X_i}$ are uncorrelated, the mean value of $X_i$ becomes

$$\mu_{X_i} = \bar{\nu}_i\bar{x}_i, \tag{16}$$

and on the basis of Eq. (8), the total uncertainty associated with $X_i$ becomes

$$\Omega_{X_i} \simeq \sqrt{\delta^2_{X_i} + \Delta^2_{X_i}} \tag{17}$$

from which $\sigma_{X_i} = \Omega_{X_i}\mu_{X_i}$.

Furthermore, the functional relation of Eq. (1) can be written as

$$g = N_g\hat{g} \tag{18}$$

in which $\hat{g}$ = a model function, with average variability $\delta_g$ about $\hat{g}$,
$N_g$ = a factor that corrects the imperfection in $\hat{g}$; its mean value is $\bar{\nu}_g$, representing the systematic bias, and c.o.v. $\Delta_g$ represents the random error in $\hat{g}$.

The uncertainty associated with the function $g(\ldots)$, therefore, becomes

$$\Omega_g = \sqrt{\delta_g^2 + \Delta_g^2}. \tag{19}$$

Applying the above results, Eq. (7) becomes

$$\mu_Z \simeq \bar{\nu}_g \hat{g}(\mu_{X_1}, \ldots, \mu_{X_n}) \tag{20}$$

in which $\mu_{X_i} = \bar{\nu}_i \bar{x}_i$ according to Eq. (16), whereas the total uncertainty in $Z$ would be

$$\Omega_Z^2 \simeq \Omega_g^2 + \frac{1}{\mu_Z^2} \sum_{i=1}^{n} \sum_{j=1}^{n} \rho_{ij} c_i c_j \sigma_{X_i} \sigma_{X_j}, \tag{21}$$

where $c_i = \partial \hat{g} / \partial X_i$ a constant, $\sigma_{X_i} = \Omega_{X_i} \mu_{X_i}$, and $\rho_{ij}$ = correlation coefficient ($\rho_{ii} = 1.0$).

In short, the systematic biases in the estimated values of the design variables, as well as in any equation used in the design process, are adjusted as shown in Eqs. (16) and (20), and all sources of uncertainty (associated with the inherent variability of a design variable as well as with the error of its estimated value) are systematically assessed and combined as indicated in Eqs. (17), (19), and (21).

Implicit in this formulation is the Bayesian philosophy [7,9] in which uncertainties associated with inherent randomness and those arising from imperfect estimation or prediction are combined (irrespective of their sources) as in Eq. (21). This will then permit the systematic evaluation of the significance of all uncertainties on the performance and design of a system.

### *2.3. Analysis of System Reliability*

For a system composed of a number of elements or components, the reliability of the system would clearly depend on the reliabilities of the components. Depending on the system configuration, the failure of certain components may or may not be of serious consequence to the reliability or safety of the system. In this regard, it is important to distinguish between *damage* and *collapse* of a system.

*System Damage.* Damage to a system may be defined as the failure of its constituent components. In accordance with Eq. (3), the failure of component $i$ then is

$$E_i = (Z_i \leq z_{0i}).$$

Then the probability of no damage of the system is

$$p_{SS} = P(\bar{E}_1 \bar{E}_2 \ldots \bar{E}_k) = P\left[\bigcap_{i=1}^{k} (Z_i > z_{0i})\right], \tag{22}$$

and the probability of system damage is

$$p_{SD} = P(\overline{\bar{E}_1 \ldots \bar{E}_k}) = P(E_1 \cup E_2 \cup \ldots \cup E_k). \tag{23}$$

Observe the following for a system:

1. Under an external load $S = s$, the forces or load effects in component $i$ are $c_i(s)$, which must satisfy certain laws of structural mechanics and therefore are perfectly positively correlated.
2. The structural resistances of the different components may be partially correlated; such correlations are, in general, positive.
3. The external load $S$ is generally independent of the component resistances.

Hence, the no-damage probability to load $S$ is

$$p_{SS} = \int_0^\infty \left[ \int_{c_1(s)}^\infty \cdots \int_{c_m(s)}^\infty f_{R_1,\ldots,R_m}\, dr_1 dr_2 \ldots dr_m \right] f_S(s)\, ds, \tag{24}$$

where $R_i$ = resistance of component $i$, and $f_{R_1,\ldots,R_m}$ = joint PDF of $R_1, \ldots, R_m$.

Evaluation of Eq. (24) is obviously out of the question; for practical purposes, several approximations are feasible as follows:

Assuming perfectly correlated $R_1, \ldots, R_m$,

$$p'_{SS} = \min_i p_{S_i}, \qquad i = 1, 2, \ldots, m, \tag{25}$$

where, $\min_i p_{S_i}$ = the probability of nonfailure of the weakest component and can be determined as in Eq. (9) or (12).

Assuming independent $R_1, \ldots, R_m$, Eq. (24) becomes

$$p''_{SS} = \int_0^\infty \left[ \prod_{i=1}^m \int_{c_i(s)}^\infty f_{R_i}\, dr_i \right] f_S(s)\, ds. \tag{26}$$

Finally, assuming independent component failures,

$$p^*_{SS} = \prod_{i=1}^m p_{Si} = \prod_{i=1}^m (1 - p_{Fi}). \tag{27}$$

Because the load effects $c_i(s)$ in the different components are correlated, failures of the components cannot be independent, and thus the last assumption is not physically possible. Nevertheless, the result [Eq. (27)] is useful because of its simplicity; moreover, this is a conservative estimate of the underlying system reliability, as shown in the following [4]:

$$p^*_{SS} \le p''_{SS} \le p_{SS} \le p'_{SS}. \tag{28}$$

The corresponding system damage probability, therefore, is

$$p'_{DS} \le p_{DS} \le p''_{DS} \le p^*_{DS}. \tag{29}$$

Equation (28), therefore, shows that $p_{SS}^*$ and $p'_{SS}$ are, respectively, the lower and upper bounds of the no-damage probability of a system; the corresponding bounds for the system damage probability are, according to Eq. (29),

$$p'_{DS} = \max_i p_{Fi}, \qquad i = 1, 2, \ldots, m, \tag{30}$$

and

$$p_{DS}^* = 1 - \prod_{i=1}^{m} (1 - p_{Fi}) \simeq \sum_{i=1}^{m} p_{Fi}. \tag{31}$$

We observe that depending on the degree of uncertainty in the various component resistances relative to that of the applied load the no-damage probability of a system may tend to $p'_{SS}$ or $p_{SS}^*$. Examination of the assumptions underlying $p'_{SS}$ and $p_{SS}^*$, the following may be inferred [21]:

1. If the uncertainties in $R_1, \ldots, R_m$ are small relative to the uncertainty in $S$, then

$$p_{SS} \longrightarrow p'_{SS}.$$

Indeed, if the $R_i$'s are all deterministic,

$$p_{SS} = p'_{SS}.$$

2. On the other hand, if $R_1, \ldots, R_m$ are statistically independent and the respective uncertainties are large relative to that in $S$, then

$$p_{SS} \longrightarrow p_{SS}^*.$$

In particular, if $S$ is deterministic,

$$p_{SS} = p_{SS}^*.$$

*Determinate vs. Indeterminate Systems.* It may be recognized from the above discussions that insofar as the damage to a system is concerned there is no difference in the determination of the associated probability whether the system is statically determinate or redundant (indeterminate) except, of course, in the structural analysis of the load effects. However, in determining the probability of collapse, there is considerable difference between determinate and redundant systems—in the case of a determinate system, failure of a single component would constitute a serious deterioration of the system, which for all practical purposes may be tantamount to collapse of the system; hence, the probability of system damage is also the probability of system collapse. In the case of a redundant system, however, the failure of one or more components may or may not seriously weaken the original system, depending on the degree of redundancy and the criticality of the failed members to the reliability of the system. Moreover, the collapse of an indeterminate system will be caused by the sequential failures of the components [30]; this failure sequence may or may not be of significance to the determination of the collapse probability depending on whether the component failures are *brittle* or *ductile**—in short, the analysis of collapse of a redundant system may involve many potential *failure paths* of the system and, therefore, is much more involved than that of a determinate system. We present below a conceptual model for its exact formulation and certain approximations that are possible.

*Collapse Probability of Redundant Systems.* Basically, the collapse of a structural system will occur when the capacity of the system is less than the applied load. The basic problem, therefore, lies in the determination of the distribution of the system resistance as a function of the component resistance distributions; with this information, the probability of collapse of the system can then be obtained through Eq. (10) or (11). A conceptual model for formulating the CDF of the system resistance is the following:

Let **R** be a random vector with components $R_1, R_2, \ldots, R_m$ representing the random resistances of the $m$ components of a system, and define $G_i =$ the subdomain of the $m$-dimensional space of $r_1, r_2, \ldots, r_m$ such that if **R** is in $G_i$ failure will occur through the *failure path i*.

Observe that if a system fails, only a single path can be realized; hence, if there are $k$ paths, $G_1, G_2, \ldots, G_k$ are disjoint sets and

$$G_1 \cup G_2 \cup \ldots \cup G_k = S,$$

where $S$ is the $m$-dimensional space of **R**.

Then the system resistance $R$ is

$$R \leq r = \bigcup_{i=1}^{k} (V_i \leq r \cap \mathbf{R} \in G_i)$$

in which $V_i =$ the capacity of the system in the $i$th failure path, and thus its distribution function is

$$F_R(r) = \sum_{i=1}^{k} P(V_i \leq r \cap \mathbf{R} \in G_i). \tag{32}$$

For illustration, consider the three-parallel-bar system shown in Fig. 1. Assume that failure of each bar will be by fracture and thus is of the brittle mode—a bar will carry zero load after failure. It may be clear that the capacity of the system will depend on the sequence in which the different bars fail; in this case, a sequence of bar failures then constitutes a failure path.

Cable 1 will fail first if $r_2/c_2 > r_1/c_1$ and $r_3/c_3 > r_1/c_1$, and cable 2 will fail next if in addition $r_3/c_3 > r_2/c_3$, where $c_1$, $c_2$, and $c_3$ are the respective bar forces under a unit load. In other words, the failure sequence $(1 \longrightarrow 2 \longrightarrow 3)$ will occur if $\mathbf{R} = \{R_1, R_2, R_3\} \supset G_1 = \{r_1/c_1 < r_2/c_2 < r_3/c_3\}$.

*A failure is *brittle* if a failed component is incapable of sustaining any force, whereas a failure is *ductile* if a failed component continues to carry a force equal to its original capacity.

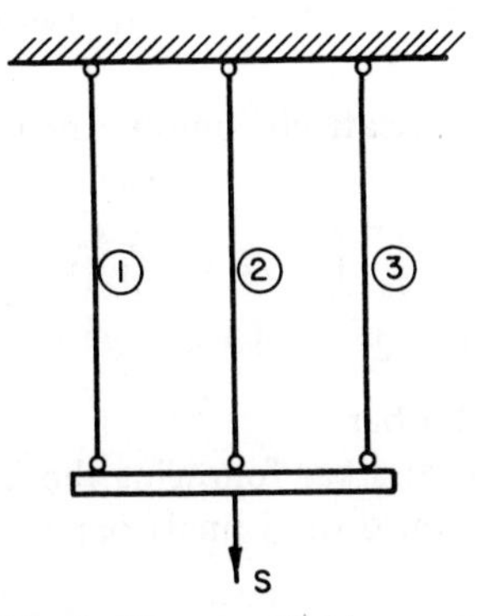


**Fig. 1.** Three-parallel-bar system

If the members fail in another sequence, the ultimate capacity of the system may be different. In the present problem, therefore, there are $3! = 6$ different failure paths, where $G_6 = \{r_1/c_1 > r_2/r_2 > r_3/r_3\}$. Thus,

$$F_R(r) = \sum_{i=1}^{6} P(V_i \leq r \cap \mathbf{R} \in G_i).$$

For example, for failure path 1,

$$P(V_1 \leq r \cap \mathbf{R} \in G_1) = \iiint_{D_1} f_{R_1R_2R_3}\, dr_1\, dr_2\, dr_3,$$

where $D_1 = \{0 < r_1 \leq c_1 r; (c_2/c_1)r_1 < r_2 \leq [c_2/(c_2 + c_3)]r; (c_3/c_2) < r_3 \leq r\}$.

If the bar resistances are independent and identically distributed with CDF $F(r)$ and $c_1 = c_2 = c_3 = \frac{1}{3}$, the above result would yield

$$F_R(r) = F^3\left(\frac{r}{3}\right) - 3F^2\left(\frac{r}{2}\right)F\left(\frac{r}{3}\right) - 3F(r)F^2\left(\frac{r}{3}\right) + 6F(r)F\left(\frac{r}{2}\right)F\left(\frac{r}{3}\right).$$

This result has previously been obtained by Shinozuka and Itagaki [24] using a different formulation. The failure probability of the system to a load $S$ may then be obtained with Eq. (10).

The conceptual model described above is clearly not practical for general indeterminate systems. Nevertheless, it serves as a basis for evaluating approximate formulations as well as for establishing bounds of the system collapse probability. For instance, by assuming that the failures of the bars in a given failure path are statistically independent, we obtain (for the case with identically distributed bar resistances, and where $c_1 = c_2 = c_3 = \frac{1}{3}$) the system collapse probability

$$p''_{FS} = 6 \int_0^{\infty} \left[ \int_0^{s/3} f_{R_1}\, dr_1 \int_{r_1}^{s/2} f_{R_2}\, dr_2 \int_{r_2}^{s} f_{R_3}\, dr_3 \right] f_S(s)\, ds.$$

Clearly,

$$p''_{FS} < 6 \int_0^{\infty} \left[ \int_0^{s/3} f_{R_1}\, dr_1 \int_0^{s/2} f_{R_2}\, dr_2 \int_0^{s} f_{R_3}\, dr_3 \right] f_S(s)\, ds. \tag{33}$$

An assumption that would give relatively simple calculations is the following:

$$p_{FS}^* = 6\int_0^\infty \int_0^{s/3} f_{R_1}\, dr_1 f_S\, ds \cdot \int_0^\infty \int_0^{s/2} f_{R_2}\, dr_2 f_S\, ds \cdot \int_0^\infty \int_0^{s} f_{R_3}\, dr_3 f_S\, ds$$
$$= 6p_F(1)\cdot p_F(2\,|\,1)\cdot p_F(3\,|\,1, 2)$$

in which $p_F(1)$ = first failure of a bar,
$p_F(2\,|\,1)$ = failure of a second bar following the first bar failure,
$p_F(3\,|\,1, 2)$ = failure of the third (and final) bar following the first and second failures.

Similar to the proof of the last inequality of Eq. (29), it can be shown [4] that $p_{FS}^*$ is greater than the right-hand side of Eq. (33). Hence, $p_{FS}'' < p_{FS}^*$, and thus $p_{FS}^*$ is a conservative estimate of the correct collapse probability of the system.

*Collapse Probability of Plastic Frameworks.* A plastic framework may be defined as a structure whose collapse will be through the formation of a plastic hinge mechanism. Analysis of the collapse probability, therefore, is based on the limit or plastic theory of structural analysis; implicitly, therefore, failures of the components (the plastic hinges) are ductile.

In this case, collapse may occur through any one of the possible plastic mechanisms; the order in which plastic hinges are formed in a mechanism, however, is of no consequence. Hence, the possible mechanisms constitute the potential failure paths. In general, the performance function in a given mechanism, say the $i$th, can be given as [25]

$$Z_i = \sum_{j=1}^{n_i} a_{ij}M_j + \sum_{k=1}^{m_i} b_{ik}S_k \tag{34}$$

in which $a_{ij}$ and $b_{ik}$ are coefficients, $M_j$ is the plastic moment capacity at potential hinge location $j$, $S_k$ is an external load, $n_i$ = the number of plastic hinges in mechanism $i$, and $m_i$ = the number of external loads actively involved in mechanism $i$. The structure will collapse through mechanism $i$ if $Z_i \leq 0$; hence, the corresponding probability of collapse is

$$p_{Fi} = P(Z_i \leq 0). \tag{35}$$

Collapse of the system will be realized through the occurrence of any one (or more) of the potential mechanisms; hence, the system collapse probability is

$$p_{FS} = P(Z_1 \leq 0 \cup Z_2 \leq 0 \cup \ldots \cup Z_k \leq 0). \tag{36}$$

Observe that this is equivalent to Eq. (23). Hence, similar to Eq. (29), it can be shown that this is bounded as follows:

$$\max_i p_{Fi} \leq p_{FS} \leq 1 - \prod_{i=1}^{k} (1 - p_{Fi}) \simeq \sum_{i=1}^{k} p_{Fi}. \tag{37}$$

The different hinge mechanisms may contain common plastic hinges; for this reason the various possible mechanisms are generally partially correlated. Although the evaluations of such correlations are straightforward, the exact evaluation of the system collapse probability through Eq. (36) is a formidable task. For this reason, and the fact that the forces in all the potential hinge locations are the result of the same external loads, it may be reasonable to use the lower bound of Eq. (37) (the collapse probability of the weakest mechanism) as representing the collapse probability of systems [10] of the same material; this approximation would be especially suitable when there is a dominant plastic mechanism (i.e., its failure probability is much larger than any of the other potential mechanisms).

### 2.4. Lifetime Reliability

For a proposed structure, it is the reliability over its useful life that is of engineering concern. In this regard, two things are paramount: the safety to the maximum load (or environmental force) that the structure may be subjected to over its life, and its reliability to the permanent and/or cyclic operational loads that the structure must sustain over its useful life.

The lifetime maximum load is the extreme of the underlying loading process; its determination, therefore, would naturally require the consideration of the probability distributions of extreme values. For this purpose, we observe that if the maximum load per *unit time* (e.g., 1 year) is $S_1$, a random variable with CDF $F_{S_1}(s)$, the maximum load $S$ over a life of $T$ time units will have distribution function [assuming statistical independence and invariance of $F_{S_1}(s)$ with time]

$$F_S(s) = [F_{S_1}(s)]^T. \tag{38}$$

Denoting $q_s = P(S_1 > s) = 1 - F_{S_1}(s)$ as the probability of the maximum load exceeding $s$ per unit time, we obtain

$$F_S(s) = (1 - q_s)^T = 1 - Tq_s + \frac{T(T-1)}{2!} q_s^2 \ldots.$$

For small $q_s$ (or large $s$),

$$F_S(s) \simeq 1 - Tq_s. \tag{39}$$

Hence, according to Eq. (11), the probability of failure to the lifetime maximum load is

$$p_F \simeq T \int_0^\infty q_s f_R(r)\, dr = T \int_0^\infty [1 - F_{S_1}(r)] f_R(r)\, dr. \tag{40}$$

Under operational conditions, failure within the life of a structure will be the result of cumulative damage. In this case, the time until failure is unpredictable and appropriately may be described with a random variable $T_f$, with CDF $F_{T_f}(t) = \int_0^t f_{T_f}(t)\, dt$, where $f_{T_f}(t)$ is the corresponding probability density function. The probability of no failure in $t$, therefore, is $L(t) = 1 - F_{T_f}(t)$.

For a structure to perform through $t + dt$ without failure, there must be no failure in $(0, t)$ as well as in $(t, t + dt)$; thus,

$$L(t + dt) = L(t)[1 - h(t)], \tag{41}$$

where $h(t)$ is the *hazard function* such that $h(t)\,dt$ is the conditional probability of failure in $(t, t + dt)$ on the assumption of no failure in $(0, t)$. Specifically [16],

$$h(t) = -\frac{d}{dt} \ln L(t) \tag{42}$$

from which we obtain the fundamental relation

$$L(t) = \exp\left[-\int_0^t h(\tau)\, d\tau\right]. \tag{43}$$

When repeated loadings are involved, the operational life may be more appropriately expressed in terms of the number of load cycles to failure, $n$. In such cases, $t$ would be replaced by $n$ in the above equations.

## III. Structural Evaluation and Criteria Development

Over the life of a structure, one or more potential modes of failure may be critical to its safety and reliability. Accordingly, within the useful life of a proposed design, all such failure modes should be examined. In this regard, the lifetime maximum load would be of special concern in the consideration of structural safety against major damage or collapse, whereas the operational loads would be of importance in considering cumulative damage, such as fatigue, within the anticipated design life.

Under each type of loading, the various potential modes of failure or damage may include the following:

1. Under lifetime maximum load:
   (a) Yielding of material at regions of high stresses.
   (b) Local instability of critical panels or members.
   (c) General instability of major structural elements.
   (d) Brittle fracture at critical regions (such as welded regions of metal structures).
2. Under operational load:
   (a) Excessive fatigue damage in regions of high stress reversals.
   (b) Stress corrosion damage.
   (c) Fracture under lifetime maximum load in regions where fatigue cracks have grown to critical size under repeated or sustained operational loads.

In the following, the evaluations of reliability and formulations of associated design criteria for various modes of failure are developed and illustrated.

### 3.1. Safety under Lifetime Maximum Load

*Evaluation of a Design.* The level of reliability may be evaluated for a specific structure or for structures designed in accordance with a specified set of code provisions. To illustrate the evaluation of the reliability implicit in a design procedure, consider a specific mode of failure—namely, the yielding of the material in a critical region of a plate structure subjected to a biaxial state of stress. Assume that the design procedure requires a factor of safety of 1.5 against localized yielding as defined by the Mises-Hencky criterion [17].

In the present case, under a plane-stress condition, initiation of yielding will occur when

$$\sigma_0 \geq k,$$

where

$$\sigma_0 = \sqrt{\tfrac{1}{3}(\sigma_x^2 - \sigma_x\sigma_y + \sigma_y^2) + \tau_{xy}^2}$$

is the applied deviatoric stress; $\sigma_x$, $\sigma_y$, and $\tau_{xy}$ are the stress components; and

$$k = \frac{\sigma_Y}{\sqrt{3}},$$

where $\sigma_Y$ is the uniaxial yield strength. Accordingly, we define the performance function,

$$Z = \ln \frac{k}{\sigma_0}$$

and $z_0 = 0$. Thence, prescribing the normal distribution for $Z$, the probability of failure becomes

$$p_F = 1 - \Phi\left(\frac{\ln \bar{\theta}}{\sigma_Z}\right)$$

in which $\bar{\theta} = \mu_k/\mu_{\sigma_0}$ is the central factor of safety, where

$$\mu_{\sigma_0} \simeq \sqrt{\tfrac{1}{3}(\bar{\sigma}_x^2 - \bar{\sigma}_x\bar{\sigma}_y + \bar{\sigma}_y^2) + \bar{\tau}_{xy}^2}$$

and

$$\sigma_Z \simeq \sqrt{\Omega_k^2 + \Omega_{\sigma_0}^2},$$

where $\Omega_k$ = uncertainty in $k$,
$\Omega_{\sigma_0}$ = uncertainty in $\sigma_0$.

In conventional design, the designated design resistance and design load are usually different from the respective mean values such that

$$\mu_k = \nu_k k_D$$

and

$$\mu_s = \nu_s s_D,$$

where $\nu_k > 1.0$ and $\nu_s \leq 1.0$, and $k_D$ and $s_D$ are the specified design values. Then the conventional safety factor is

$$\theta = \frac{k_D}{s_D},$$

which is, therefore, related to $\bar{\theta}$ as follows:

$$\bar{\theta} = \frac{\nu_k}{\nu_s} \cdot \theta.$$

Thus, in terms of the conventional safety factor $\theta$, the failure probability becomes

$$p_F = 1 - \Phi\left[\frac{\ln (\nu_k/\nu_s)\theta}{\sqrt{\Omega_k^2 + \Omega_{\sigma_0}^2}}\right]. \tag{44}$$

*Determination of Design Safety Factor.* The purpose of a reliability analysis is also to provide a logical basis for the formulation of proper and consistent design criteria, such as the determination of the proper factor(s) of safety for each of the potential failure modes. The application of reliability concepts, however, need not (and should not) complicate the design procedure; indeed, an existing design procedure can remain unchanged except that the necessary safety factors (or safety margins) are reevaluated to achieve specified reliability levels, as follows.

Considering the design against yielding, we obtain [from the inversion of Eq. (44)] the required safety factor corresponding to a prescribed permissible failure probability $p_F$,

$$\theta = \frac{\nu_s}{\nu_k} \exp(\beta\sqrt{\Omega_k^2 + \Omega_{\sigma_0}^2}) \tag{45}$$

where $\beta = \Phi^{-1}(1 - p_F)$.

*Numerical Example.* To illustrate the above formulations numerically, suppose that the variabilities in the yield strength and applied load are, respectively,

$$\delta_{\sigma_Y} = 0.10 \quad \text{and} \quad \delta_s = 0.20.$$

Assuming $\Omega_{\sigma_Y} = \delta_{\sigma_Y}$, it can be shown, through Eq. (8) or (21), that $\Omega_k = \Omega_{\sigma_Y}$ and

$$\Omega_{\sigma_0} \simeq \sqrt{\delta_s^2 + \Delta_A^2},$$

where $\Delta_A$ = uncertainty in the analysis of stresses. Assuming $\Delta_A = 0.15$, we obtain $\Omega_{\sigma_0} = \sqrt{(0.20)^2 + (0.15)^2} = 0.25$. If the yield strength $k_D$ used in the design is the $A$-value of MIL-HDBK-5B [20], which is the 1-percentile value, and if the specified design load $s_D$ is one standard deviation above the mean load, then

$$\nu_k = \frac{1}{1 - 2.33\delta_k} = \frac{1}{1 - 2.33(0.10)} = 1.30$$

and

$$\nu_s = \frac{1}{1+\delta_s} = \frac{1}{1+0.20} = 0.83.$$

If the safety factor used in the design is $\theta = 1.5$, then, according to Eq. (44), the underlying probability of failure is

$$p_F = 1 - \Phi\left(\frac{\ln[(1.30/0.83) \times 1.5]}{\sqrt{(0.10)^2 + (.25)^2}}\right)$$
$$= 1 - \Phi(3.17) = \underline{7.62 \times 10^{-4}}.$$

Conversely, the safety factor required to achieve a desired level of reliability is, in the present case,

$$\theta = \frac{0.83}{1.30}\exp[\beta\sqrt{(0.10) + (0.25)^2}]$$
$$= 0.64e^{0.27\beta}.$$

The specific values of $\theta$ for design with a permissible risk $p_F$, therefore, are as given in Table 1. The corresponding required safety margin would be

$$SM = \theta - 1.$$

**Table 1**
**Required θ for Prescribed $p_F$**

| $p_F$ | $\theta$ |
|---|---|
| $10^{-1}$ | 0.90 |
| $10^{-2}$ | 1.20 |
| $10^{-3}$ | 1.47 |
| $10^{-4}$ | 1.75 |
| $10^{-5}$ | 2.02 |
| $10^{-6}$ | 2.31 |

In a practical design situation, the dimensions of a structure would be assumed and the stress analysis performed, obtaining therefore the states of stress, i.e., $\sigma_0$, at all critical regions of the structure. At a critical region, the available safety factor against yielding, therefore, is

$$\theta = \frac{\sigma_Y/\sqrt{3}}{\sigma_0}.$$

Comparing this with the required safety factors of Table 1, the assumed design may then be appraised relative to the specified permissible risk, and if necessary, the assumed design would be revised accordingly.

### 3.2. Reliability under Operational Loads

*Evaluation of Fatigue Reliability.* Under repeated loading and unloading, the cumulative fatigue damage, as measured in terms of the maximum crack size, over the life of a structure is often of concern. The fatigue life of material (e.g., in number of loading cycles until the occurrence of a large fatigue crack) is generally recognized to be a random variable, even when subjected to constant-amplitude stress range. Among the probability distribution functions that have been proposed or used for describing fatigue life of engineering materials, there are good bases and physical arguments [15] to favor the Weibull distribution. On this basis, the probability that the fatigue life $N$ will exceed $n$ cycles of repeated loading can be shown [3] to be

$$L(n) = \exp\left[-\left\{\frac{n}{\bar{n}}\Gamma(1 + \Omega^{1.08})\right\}^{\Omega^{-1.08}}\right] \tag{46}$$

in which $\bar{n}$ = mean fatigue life,
$\Omega$ = total uncertainty in estimated fatigue life $N$.

Observe that the reliability is again a function of the mean value $\bar{n}$ and the design uncertainty $\Omega$.

Under a constant-amplitude stress range, the mean life $\bar{n}$ may be determined from the $SN$ relation appropriate for the given material and structural configuration, or

$$\bar{n} = \frac{c}{s^m}, \tag{47}$$

where $s$ is the applied stress range and $c$ and $m$ are, respectively, the intercept and slope of the regression of log $N$ on log $S$.

If the applied stress range $S$ is random, the corresponding mean life $\bar{n}$ may be determined on the basis of Miner's damage rule using available constant stress $SN$ relations, obtaining [3]

$$\bar{n} = \frac{c}{E(S^m)}, \tag{48}$$

where $E(S^m) = \int_0^\infty s^m f_S(s)\, ds$ is the expected value of $S^m$ or the $m$th moment of the stress-range distribution $f_S(s)$.

If $S$ has a beta distribution between 0 and $s_{\max}$, and with shape parameters $q$ and $r$, it can be shown [3,6] that

$$E(S^m) = s_{\max} \cdot \frac{B(m+q, r)}{B(q, r)} = s_{\max}^m \left[\frac{\Gamma(m+q)\Gamma(q+r)}{\Gamma(q)\Gamma(m+q+r)}\right], \tag{49}$$

where $B(-)$ and $\Gamma(-)$ are, respectively, the beta and gamma functions. If $m$, $q$, and $r$ are all integers, each of the gamma functions, of course, is a factorial; e.g., $\Gamma(q) = (q-1)!$

If $S$ has a Rayleigh distribution with root-mean-square (rms) value $s_r$, $E(S^m)$ is, for integer values of $m$,

$$E(S^m) = \begin{cases} \dfrac{m!}{2^{(m-1)/2}\{[(m-1)/2]!\}}\sqrt{\dfrac{\pi}{2}}\, s_r^m & \text{if } m \text{ is odd.} \quad (50a) \\ 2^{m/2}\left(\dfrac{m}{2}!\right) s_r^m & \text{if } m \text{ is even.} \quad (50b) \end{cases}$$

For noninteger $m$, numerical integration will be necessary to evaluate $E(S^m)$.

The uncertainty $\Omega$ should include all sources of uncertainty underlying the fatigue life $N$. In particular, these should include the uncertainties associated with the inherent variability of the observed fatigue life, inaccuracy of the life prediction model, error in the stress-range determination or specification, and the effects of fabrication and workmanship. The effects of each of these different sources of uncertainty can be reflected properly in evaluating $\Omega$ through the $SN$ relation; on this basis, we obtain, by first-order approximation,

$$\Omega^2 = \Omega_f^2 + \bar{m}^2\Omega_s^2 + \Omega_c^2, \tag{51}$$

where $\Omega_f$, $\Omega_s$, and $\Omega_c$ may be assessed individually [3,6].

*Effect of Endurance Limit on Fatigue Reliability.* There may be a stress range below which there is no fatigue damage; this level of stress range is known as the *fatigue limit* or *endurance limit*. For this reason, the $SN$ relation is (strictly speaking) valid only for stress ranges that are above the fatigue limit; consequently, the fatigue reliability formulated above will be in error on the safe side. The above formulations, however, can be extended to include the effects of the fatigue limit on fatigue reliability as follows.

Suppose the fatigue limit is $s_0$. Then the $SN$ relation, valid for $s \geq s_0$, is

$$\bar{n} = \frac{c}{s^m}, \qquad s \geq s_0.$$

Therefore, under a random stress range $S$, only $S \geq s_0$ will cause damage; hence, following Miner's rule, we obtain

$$r_0\bar{n} = \frac{c}{E'(S^m)}, \tag{52}$$

where

$$E'(S^m) = \int_{s_0}^{\infty} s^m f_S(s)\, ds$$

and $r_0 < 1.0$ is the ratio of the number of load cycles with $s \geq s_0$ to the total number of loading cycles; thus,

$$r_0 = \int_{s_0}^{\infty} f_S(s)\, ds.$$

Observe that if $s_0 = 0$, Eq. (52) reduces to Eq. (48).

If $S$ is beta-distributed between 0 and $s_{\max}$,

$$E'(S^m) = \frac{1}{B(q, r)} \int_{s_0}^{s_{\max}} s^m \cdot \frac{s^{q-1}(s_{\max} - s)^{r-1}}{s_{\max}^{q+r-1}} \, ds.$$

Through a change of variable $y = s/s_{\max}$, it can be shown that

$$E'(S^m) = s_{\max}^m \frac{B(m + q, r)}{B(q, r)} \left[1 - \frac{B_u(m + q, r)}{B(m + q, r)}\right], \tag{53}$$

where $u = s_0/s_{\max}$, and $B_u(m + q, r)$ is the incomplete beta function [22]. Also,

$$r_0 = 1 - \frac{B_u(q, r)}{B(q, r)}. \tag{54}$$

For a Rayleigh-distributed $S$, no general expression for $E'(S^m)$ can be given for all $m$; specific expressions may be derived for specific integer values of $m$. For example, if $m = 3$,

$$E'(S^3) = s_0^3 e^{-(1/2)(s_0/s_{\max})^2} + 3 s_{\text{rms}}^3 \sqrt{2\pi} \left[1 - \Phi\left(\frac{s_0}{s_{\max}}\right)\right]. \tag{55}$$

For a Rayleigh distribution,

$$r_0 = e^{-(1/2)(s_0/s_{\text{rms}})^2} \tag{56}$$

*Determination of Allowable Stress for Fatigue Design.* The objective of a reliability-based design criterion for fatigue resistance is to ensure a useful life (say $n_0$) with a specified reliability $L(n_0)$. To develop such a basis for design, we solve Eq. (46) for $\bar{n}$ with $L(n) = L(n_0)$, obtaining

$$\bar{n} = n_0 \gamma_L, \tag{57}$$

where $\gamma_L$ is known as the *scatter factor* and is given by

$$\gamma_L = \frac{\Gamma(1 + \Omega^{1.08})}{[1 - L(n_0)]^{\Omega^{1.08}}}. \tag{58}$$

The life $\bar{n}$ of Eq. (57) is the mean life necessary to ensure the useful life $n_0$ with reliability $L(n_0)$.

Under constant stress range, the allowable stress for design, then, is obtained from Eq. (47); thus,

$$s_c = \left(\frac{c}{\bar{n}}\right)^{1/m}, \tag{59}$$

where $\bar{n}$ is given by Eq. (57). For random loadings, the corresponding allowable stress range is obtained through Eq. (48); i.e.,

$$E(S^m) = \frac{c}{\bar{n}}. \tag{60}$$

Equation (60), of course, neglects the effects of the fatigue limit $s_0$. If $s_0$ is included, the allowable stress range would be obtained through Eq. (52), or

$$E'(S^m) = \frac{c}{r_0 \bar{n}}. \tag{61}$$

With either Eq. (60) or (61), for random stress range, the allowable design stress range can be given in two parts; namely,

$$s_{\text{all}} = s_c \xi, \tag{62}$$

where $s_c$ = the constant stress component as given by Eq. (59),
$\xi$ = a *random stress factor*, which depends on $m$ and the distribution shape of the applied stress range $S$.

In particular, if $S$ is beta-distributed, Eqs. (49) and (60) yield the random stress factor (neglecting $s_0$)

$$\xi = \left[\frac{B(q, r)}{B(m + q, r)}\right]^{1/m}, \tag{63}$$

whereas if the fatigue limit $s_0$ is included, Eqs. (53) and (61) yield

$$\xi = \left[\frac{B(q, r)}{B(m + q, r)}\right]^{1/m} \left[r_0 \left\{1 - \frac{B_u(m + q, r)}{B(m + q, r)}\right\}\right]^{-1/m}, \tag{64}$$

where $r_0$ is given by Eq. (54).

Similarly, if $S$ has a Rayleigh distribution, the allowable root-mean-square stress range is obtained by using Eq. (50) in Eq. (60), yielding (neglecting $s_0$)

$$\xi = \begin{cases} \left[\dfrac{2^{(m-1)/2}\{[(m-1)/2]!\}}{m!}\sqrt{\dfrac{2}{\pi}}\right]^{1/m} & \text{if } m \text{ is odd,} \quad (65a) \\[2ex] \dfrac{1}{\sqrt{2}\,[(m/2)!]^{1/m}} & \text{if } m \text{ is even.} \quad (65b) \end{cases}$$

If $s_0$ is included, no general expression for $\xi$ can be given.

*Numerical Examples.* For illustration, consider the case of axially loaded butt-welded plates; the *SN* relation for such a configuration may be described with $c = 3.7 \times 10^9$ and $m = 2.88$ [6].

For this case, the AASHTO specification [1] gives an allowable design stress range at 500,000 cycles of 19 ksi.

CASE 1-Beta-distributed $S$:

If the applied stress range has a beta distribution between 0 and $s_{\max}$ with shape parameters $q = 3$ and $r = 4$, which is appropriate for heavy highway truck loadings [6], we obtain the corresponding reliability at 500,000 cycles as follows.

From Eq. (49),

$$\begin{aligned} E(S^{2.88}) &= (19)^{2.88}\frac{\Gamma(5.88)\Gamma(7)}{\Gamma(3)\Gamma(9.88)} \\ &= 19^{2.88}(0.1272) \\ &= 612.64. \end{aligned}$$

Then, according to Eq. (48),

$$\bar{n} = \frac{3.7 \times 10^9}{612.64} = 6{,}039{,}436 \text{ cycles.}$$

The total uncertainty for this configuration has been found [6] to be $\Omega = 0.70$. Then, according to Eq. (46), the reliability in 500,000 cycles is

$$L(500{,}000) = \exp\left\{-\left[\frac{500{,}000}{6{,}039{,}436}\Gamma(1 + 0.70^{1.08})\right]^{0.70^{-1.08}}\right\}$$

$$= \exp\{-[0.0828\Gamma(1.68)]^{1.47}\}.$$

From tables of the gamma function, $\Gamma(1.68) = 0.905$; thus,

$$L(500{,}000) = 0.9781.$$

However, if the effects of $s_0 = 5$ ksi were to be included, the reliability would be revised as follows: In this case, $u = \frac{5}{19} = 0.26$; hence,

$$E'(S^{2.88}) = 19^{2.88}\frac{B(5.88, 4)}{B(3, 4)}\left[1 - \frac{B_{0.26}(5.88, 4)}{B(5.88, 4)}\right].$$

From tables of the incomplete beta function [22], we obtain, after suitable interpolation, $B_{0.26}(5.88, 4)/B(5.88, 4) = 0.0152$. Thus,

$$E'(S^{2.88}) = 19^{2.88}(0.1272)(1 - 0.0152)$$

$$= \underline{603.46.}$$

Also,

$$r_0 = 1 - \frac{B_{0.26}(3, 4)}{B(3, 4)} = \underline{0.8144.}$$

Equation (52) then yields

$$\bar{n} = \frac{1}{0.8144}\left(\frac{3.7 \times 10^9}{603.46}\right) = 7.5246 \times 10^6,$$

and the reliability becomes

$$L(500{,}000) = \underline{0.9841.}$$

CASE 2-Rayleigh-distributed $S$:

If the applied stress range is modeled with a Rayleigh distribution, numerical integration would be required to evaluate $E(S^m)$ with $m = 2.88$. Such numerical integrations may be avoided if we use $m = 3$ in place of 2.88.

Suppose also that the maximum allowable stress is specified to be the 99-percentile value, $s_{0.99}$, of the Rayleigh distribution; the root-mean-square value $s_{\text{rms}}$ of this distribution then is

$$s_{\text{rms}} = 0.33 s_{0.99}.$$

Since the allowable maximum stress is 19 ksi, we have $s_{0.99} = 19$ ksi, which means that the allowable $s_{\text{rms}} = 0.33 \times 19 = 6.27$ ksi. Then, according to Eq. (50),

$$E(S^m) = E(S^3) = 3\sqrt{\frac{\pi}{2}}\, s_{rms}^3$$

$$= 3\sqrt{\frac{\pi}{2}}\,(6.27)^3 = 926.80,$$

and

$$\bar{n} = \frac{3.7 \times 10^9}{926.80} = 3{,}992{,}230 \text{ cycles.}$$

Thus,

$$L(500{,}000) = \exp\left\{-\left[\frac{500{,}000}{3{,}992{,}230}\Gamma(1.68)\right]^{1.47}\right\}$$

$$= \underline{0.9601}.$$

If the effect of $s_0 = 5$ ksi is included, we obtain, with Eq. (55),

$$E'(S^3) = 5^3 e^{-(1/2)(5/6.27)^2} + 3(6.27)^3\sqrt{2\pi}\left[1 - \Phi\left(\frac{5}{6.27}\right)\right]$$

$$= 483.73,$$

and, according to Eq. (56),

$$r_0 = e^{-(1/2)(5/6.27)^2} = 0.728.$$

Therefore,

$$\bar{n} = \frac{1}{0.728}\left(\frac{3.7 \times 10^9}{483.73}\right) = 1.0507 \times 10^7 \text{ cycles,}$$

and

$$L(500{,}000) = \underline{0.9902}.$$

Conversely, if a reliability of 0.99 is desired at 500,000 cycles, the allowable maximum stress can be determined as follows.

We first obtain the constant stress component $s_c$. For 99% reliability, the required mean life according to Eq. (57) would be

$$\bar{n} = 500{,}000\gamma_L,$$

where

$$\gamma_L = \frac{\Gamma(1 + 0.7^{1.08})}{(1 - 0.99)^{0.7^{1.08}}} = \frac{\Gamma(1.68)}{0.0436} = 20.76.$$

Therefore,

$$\bar{n} = 1.0378 \times 10^7 \text{ cycles.}$$

Then, from Eq. (59),

$$s_c = \left(\frac{c}{\bar{n}}\right)^{1/m} = \left(\frac{3.7 \times 10^9}{1.0378 \times 10^7}\right)^{1/2.88} = \underline{7.69 \text{ ksi.}}$$

This would be the allowable design stress range if the cyclic loading is constant. However, if the applied stress range is random with a beta distribution between 0 and $s_{max}$, the allowable $s_{max}$ would be, according to

Eq. (62),

$$s_{\max} = s_c \xi,$$

where $s_c = 7.69$, as obtained above; if $s_0$ is neglected, Eq. (63) yields

$$\xi = \left[\frac{\Gamma(3)\Gamma(9.88)}{\Gamma(5.88)\Gamma(7)}\right]^{1/2.88}$$
$$= 2.05.$$

Hence, the allowable $s_{\max}$ is

$$s_{\max} = 7.69 \times 2.05 = \underline{15.76 \text{ ksi}},$$

If the effect of $s_0 = 5$ ksi is included, trial and error would be necessary to obtain $\xi$ through Eq. (64), as $r_0$ is a function of the allowable maximum stress $s_{\max}$.

If the applied stress range is Rayleigh-distributed, numerical integration would be required to determine $\xi$ for noninteger values of $m$. However, if integer $m$ is used, $\xi$ can be obtained from Eq. (65). Moreover, if the effects of $s_0$ were to be included, trial and error will also be necessary to determine $\xi$.

### 3.3. A Formulation of Brittle Fracture Reliability

In examining the potential for brittle fracture, the operational loads as well as the lifetime extremal loads must be considered. Because brittle fracture is a function of the crack size, which may grow under operational loads, the failure probability of a structure to brittle fracture under occasional extreme loads would increase monotonically throughout its life. A determination of the probability of fracture as a function of life, therefore, is required.

Developed herein is a formulation of the reliability to brittle fracture, based on the existing theory and approximations of fracture mechanics. It is shown that practical reliability analysis of brittle fracture is feasible using the same concepts and methods developed for the other potential modes of structural failure.

The theory of fracture mechanics, e.g., [27], is based on the assumption that brittle fracture can be characterized with a single parameter, the stress-intensity factor $K_I$, which may be given as

$$K_I = C_1 \sigma \sqrt{a}, \tag{66}$$

where $\sigma$ = the nominal tensile stress normal to a crack,

$a$ = crack size, and

$C_1$ = a factor that depends on the crack geometry—e.g., for a through-the-thickness crack in a thick plate such that plane-strain condition applies, $C_1 = \sqrt{\pi}$, whereas for a semielliptical surface crack, $C_1 = 1.1\sqrt{\pi/Q}$, in which $Q$ is a function of the depth-to-length ratio of the crack.

For a given material at a specified temperature and loading rate, the resistance to fracture is the critical value of $K_I$, which may be the plane-strain *fracture toughness*, $K_{Ic}$. For a given crack size $a$, the corresponding critical stress, $\sigma_{cr}$, is then

$$\sigma_{cr} = \frac{K_{Ic}}{C_1\sqrt{a}}. \tag{67}$$

If the nominal applied stress is $\sigma$, the performance function, therefore, may be defined as

$$Z = \ln\frac{\sigma_{cr}}{\sigma},$$

with $z_0 = 0$. Thus,

$$\mu_Z = \ln\frac{\bar{\sigma}_{cr}}{\bar{\sigma}}$$

and

$$\sigma_Z = \sqrt{\Omega^2_{\sigma_{cr}} + \Omega^2_{\sigma}},$$

where, by virtue of Eq. (67),

$$\Omega^2_{\sigma_{cr}} = \Omega^2_{K_{Ic}} + \tfrac{1}{4}\Omega^2_a + \Omega^2_{C_1}.$$

Therefore, for a given crack size $a$, the probability of failure under a nominal stress $\sigma$ is

$$p_F = 1 - \Phi\left(\frac{\ln \bar{\sigma}_{cr}/\bar{\sigma}}{\sqrt{\Omega^2_{\sigma_{cr}} + \Omega^2_{\sigma}}}\right). \tag{68}$$

The crack size, of course, may grow slowly under operational loading. Hence, the probability of failure will increase monotonically with $N$ and may be determined as follows.

The crack size at any life will depend on the crack growth rate, which may be described as (under repeated loads)

$$\frac{da}{dn} = C_2(\Delta K)^m, \tag{69}$$

where $\Delta K$ is the stress-intensity factor range, and $C_2$ and $m$ are material constants. For example, for ferrite-pearlite steels [8], such as A36,

$$C_2 = 3.6 \times 10^{-10}, \qquad m = 3.00,$$

whereas, for martensitic steels [8], such as A517,

$$C_2 = 6.6 \times 10^{-9}, \qquad m = 2.25.$$

$\Delta K$ is a function of the applied stress range $s$ and the existing crack size $a$ as well as the crack geometry; in particular,

$$\Delta K = C_1 s\sqrt{a} \tag{70}$$

in which $C_1$ is as defined earlier in Eq. (66).

Under a constant stress range $s$ (and assuming that the crack size does not significantly affect the nominal stress range $s$ and the crack geometry;

i.e., $C_1$ and $s$ are independent of $a$), the number of cycles $N$ for an initial crack of size $a_i$ to grow to size $a$ can then be obtained from

$$N = \frac{1}{C_2} \int_{a_i}^{a} (\Delta K)^{-m} \, da$$

$$= \frac{1}{C_2} \int_{a_i}^{a} (C_1 s)^{-m} \cdot a^{-m/2} \, da$$

$$= \frac{1}{[1 - (m/2)]C_2(C_1 s)^m}[a^{1-(m/2)} - a_i^{1-(m/2)}]. \tag{71}$$

Conversely, after $N$ cycles of constant $s$, an initial crack $a_i$ will have grown to a final size

$$a = \left[ a_i^{1-(m/2)} + C_2\left(1 - \frac{m}{2}\right)(C_1 s)^m N \right]^{1/[1-(m/2)]}. \tag{72}$$

Equations (71) and (72), of course, are valid for a constant stress range $s$. If the stress range is random with density function $f_S(s)$, the growth rate equation, Eq. (69), becomes

$$\frac{da}{dn} = C_2(C_1\sqrt{a})^m \int_0^\infty s^m f_S(s) \, ds$$

$$= C_2(C_1\sqrt{a})^m \cdot E(S^m). \tag{73}$$

Hence, under a random stress range $S$, the number of cycles for a crack $a_i$ to

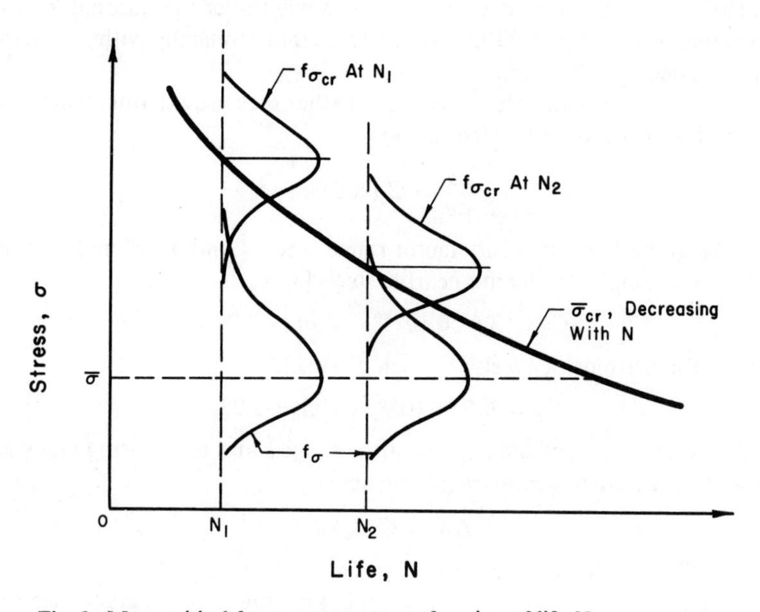


Fig. 2. Mean critical fracture stress $\bar{\sigma}_{cr}$ as function of life $N$

grow to size $a$ is

$$N = \frac{1}{C_1^m C_2[1-(m/2)]E(S^m)}[a^{1-(m/2)} - a_i^{1-(m/2)}], \tag{74}$$

whereas after $N$ cycles of random stress range, the initial $a_i$ will have grown to

$$a = \left[a_i^{1-(m/2)} + C_1^m C_2\left(1-\frac{m}{2}\right)E(S^m)N\right]^{1/[1-(m/2)]}. \tag{75}$$

Using Eq. (75) in Eq. (67), the critical fracture stress $\sigma_{cr}$ can be related to the life $N$; in particular, such a relationship for the mean critical stress $\bar{\sigma}_{cr}$ would be as shown in Fig. 2. At a life $N$, there is a distribution of $\sigma_{cr}$ about the mean value shown in Fig. 2. Then if the distribution of the applied stress $\sigma$ remains invariant with $N$, the overlap between the distributions of $\sigma_{cr}$ and $\sigma$ increases with $N$; this then leads to an increasing probability of fracture failure with $N$, as shown in Fig. 3. More explicitly, this failure probability at any $N$ is given by Eq. (68).

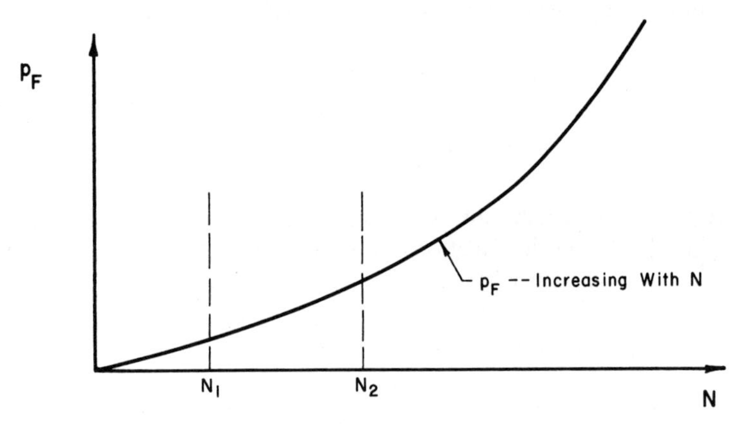


**Fig. 3.** Probability of fracture failure $p_F$ as function of life $N$

## IV. On the Safety Analysis and Design for Extreme Hazards

The safety of a structure against the extreme forces of natural hazards will obviously depend on the maximum force or excitation that can be expected over the life and at the particular location of the structure. In other words, it is the lifetime maximum force that is relevant; such forces are naturally extreme values, and thus extreme distributions would be involved.

The determination of the relevant extremal distribution, therefore, is a necessary step in the evaluation of safety or risk to natural hazards. In certain cases, such as a tornado strike or a high-intensity earthquake motion at a particular site, very localized probabilistic information is required; in these cases, regional statistical data (which are usually the type of data available) would not be sufficient to determine the level of risk needed locally. Supplementary information may be derived through appropriate deductive probabilistic models; certain specific models for this purpose are available—e.g., for assessing the localized risks to tornadoes [29] and strong earthquakes [11,13,28].

In design, it is usual practice to specify a reasonably high level of extreme load (e.g., in terms of a long return period). However, the specification of a high load, by itself, is not sufficient for ensuring a desired level of safety. Because of the uncertainty and randomness in the structural resistance as well as in the load, safety may be assured only in terms of the probability of no failure within the life of the structure. This objective may be accomplished in design if the specified design load is used with an associated factor of safety. In other words, any load can be specified for design as long as an appropriate safety factor is also used. The specification of a design load and its appropriate safety factor may be based on a probabilistic reliability analysis as follows.

According to Eq. (40), the probability of failure over the life $T$ of a structure is

$$p_F = T \int_0^{\infty} [1 - F_S(r)] f_R(r)\, dr, \tag{76}$$

where $F_S(r)$ = the distribution function of the annual maximum load $S$,
$f_R(r)$ = the density function of the structural resistance, assumed to be invariant with time,
$T$ = life in number of years.

Equation (76) may be evaluated numerically as follows:

$$p_F = T \sum_{\text{all } r_i} [1 - F_S(r_i)] f_R(r_i)\, \Delta r. \tag{77}$$

Graphically, Eq. (76) or (77) is the sum of the products of the ordinates $[1 - F_S(r_i)]$ in Fig. 4(a) with the corresponding small areas $f_R(r_i)\, \Delta r$ of Fig. 4(b).

Conceptually, the objective of design is to determine a resistance with mean value $\bar{r}$ [or distribution $f_R(r)$] such that the calculated failure probability $p_F$ of Eq. (76) is less than a prescribed allowable value. Such a design may be obtained, for example, by specifying the 1000-year load $s_{1000}$ and using a safety factor of 1.00 (in the case of Fig. 4). However, the same design would also be obtained had the 100-year load $s_{100}$ been designated as the design load and the corresponding safety factor equal to $s_{1000}/s_{100}$ used, showing, therefore, that a desired level of safety may be achieved through the specification of any design load and its appropriate safety factor.

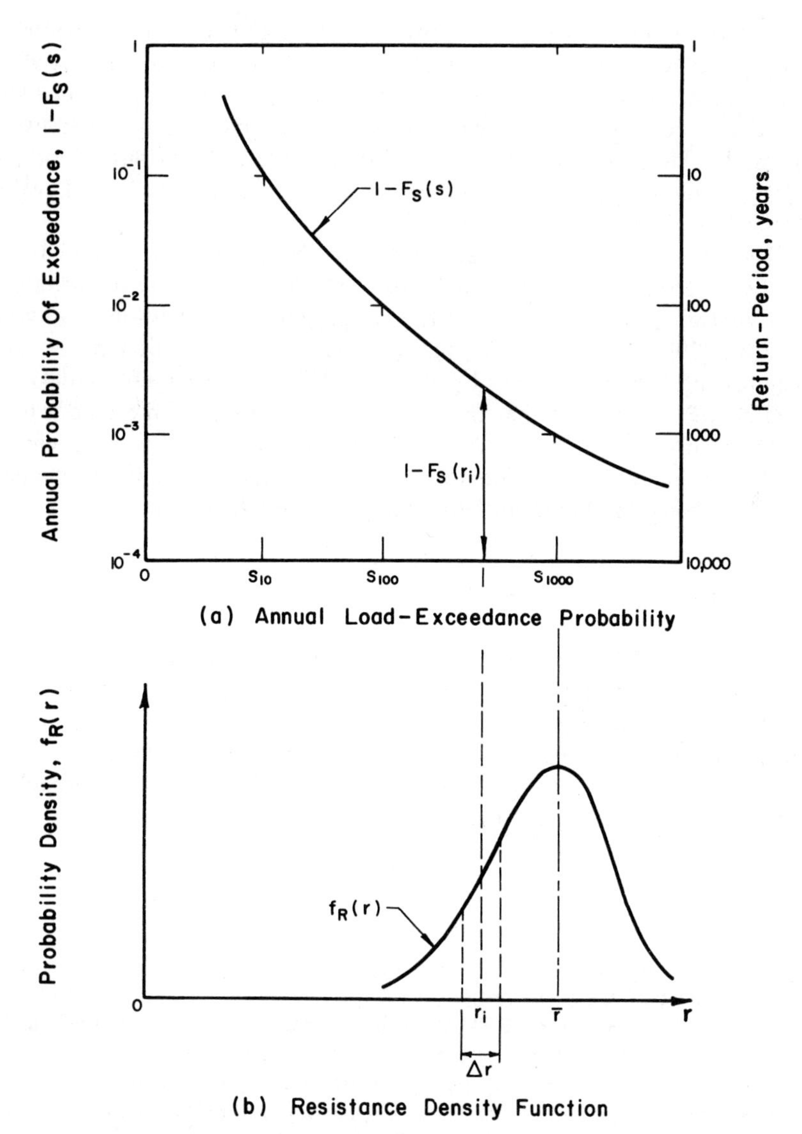


**Fig. 4.** Failure probability to extremal loads

### *4.1. Determination of Extremal Load Distribution*

In certain cases, such as strong winds (without tornadoes) for which extensive extreme-value data over long periods of time are available, the required extremal distribution may be developed on the basis of such data [26]. However, in other cases, such as a tornado strike or high-intensity earthquake motion at a particular site, the extremal load would depend on the local characteristics of the site; in these latter cases, regional statistical data would not be sufficient to derive the relevant distribution. To include the local characteristics of a site, probabilistic analysis may be performed using risk models developed on the basis of reasonable assumptions about the underlying physical process, with the required parameters of a model evaluated from available regional data.

Such risk analyses often lead directly to the probability of exceedance (usually) of the annual extremal force or excitation. In the case of probabilities to tornado strikes, a model for this purpose has been developed by Wen and Chu [29]. For earthquake hazards, seismic risk models have been developed by Cornell [11] and by Vagliente [28]; whereas these models are based on the assumption that the total energy released in an earthquake is effectively concentrated at the focus (a point), a model based on the assumption of line sources in which the total energy is distributed along the slipped planes has been developed by Der-Kiureghian and Ang [13].

## V. Conclusions

Reliability theory, therefore, provides a unified analytical tool for the systematic analysis of risk and safety under conditions of uncertainty. The assurance of adequate safety and reliability (without being overly conservative) is clearly an important objective in the development of design. With the tools of reliability analysis, questions of safety may now be approached in an explicit and systematic manner.

## References

1. American Association of State Highway and Transportation Officials, *Standard Specifications for Highway Bridges*, Washington, D.C., 11th ed., 1973.
2. Ang, A. H-S., "Structural Risk Analysis and Reliability-Based Design," *ASCE J. Struct. Div.*, Vol. 99, No. ST9, Sept. 1973, pp. 1891–1910.
3. Ang, A. H-S., "A Comprehensive Basis for Reliability Analysis and Design," in *Reliability Approach in Structural Engineering*, A. M. Freudenthal et al., eds., Maruzen Co., Ltd., Tokyo, 1975, pp. 29–47.
4. Ang, A. H-S., and M. Amin, "Reliability of Structures and Structural Systems," *ASCE J. Eng. Mech. Div.*, Vol. 94, No. EM2, April 1968, pp. 671–691.
5. Ang, A. H-S, and B. Ellingwood, "Critical Analysis of Reliability Principles Relative to Design," *Proceedings, International Conference on Application of Statistics and Probability to Soil and Structural Engineering*, Hong Kong University Press, Hong Kong, 1971.
6. Ang, A. H-S., and W. H. Munse, "Practical Reliability Basis for Structural

Fatigue," *Preprint 2494*, ASCE National Structural Engineering Conference, April 1975.
7. ANG, A. H-S., and W. H. TANG, *Probability Concepts in Engineering Planning and Design*, Vol. 1—Basic Principles, Wiley, New York, 1975.
8. BARSOM, J. M., "Fatigue-Crack Propagation in Steels of Various Yield Strengths," *Paper No. 71-PVP-12*, 1st National Congress on Pressure Vessel and Piping, ASME, May 1971.
9. BENJAMIN, J. R., and C. A. CORNELL, *Probability Statistics and Decision for Civil Engineers*, McGraw-Hill, New York, 1970.
10. CORNELL, C. A., "Bounds on the Reliability of Structural Systems" *ASCE J. Struct. Div.*, Vol. 93, No. ST1, Feb. 1967, pp. 786–795.
11. CORNELL, C. A., "Engineering Seismic Risk Analysis," *Bull. Seismological Soc. Am.*, Vol. 58, No. 5, Oct. 1968, pp. 1583–1606.
12. CORNELL, C. A., "A Probability-Based Structural Code," *ACI J.*, Vol. 66, 1969, pp. 974–985.
13. DER-KIUREGHIAN, A., and A. H-S. ANG, "A Line-Source Model for Seismic Risk Analysis," *Univ. of Ill. Civil Eng. Studies Structural Research Series 419*, Urbana, Oct. 1975.
14. FREUDENTHAL, A. M., "Safety of Structures," *ASCE Trans.*, Vol. 112, 1947, pp. 125–180.
15. FREUDENTHAL, A. M., "Prediction of Fatigue Failure," *J. Appl. Phys.*, Vol. 31, Dec. 1960, pp. 2196–2198.
16. FREUDENTHAL, A. M., J. M. GARRELTS, and M. SHINOZUKA, "The Analysis of Structural Safety," *ASCE J. Struct. Div.*, Vol. 92, No. ST1, Feb. 1966, pp. 267–325.
17. HILL, R., *The Mathematical Theory of Plasticity*, Oxford University Press, New York, 1950.
18. LIND, N. C., "Consistent Partial Safety Factors," *ASCE J. Struct. Div.*, Vol. 97, No. ST6, June 1971, pp. 1651–1670.
19. LIND, N. C., and A. M. HASOFER, "Exact and Invariant Second-Moment Code Format," *ASCE J. Eng. Mech. Div.*, Vol. 100, No. EM1, Feb. 1974, pp. 111–121.
20. MIL-HDBK-5B, "Metallic Materials and Elements for Aerospace Vehicle Structures," Department of Defense, Washington, D.C., Sept., 1971.
21. MOSES, F., and D. E. KINSER, "Analysis of Structural Reliability," *ASCE J. Struct. Div.*, Vol. 93, No. ST5, Oct. 1967, pp. 147–164.
22. PEARSON, K., *Tables of the Incomplete Beta-Function*, 2nd ed., Cambridge University Press, New York, 1968.
23. ROSENBLUETH, E., and L. ESTEVA, "Reliability Basis for Some Mexico Codes," *Proceedings, ACI Symposium on Probabilistic Design of RC Buildings*, 1971.
24. SHINOZUKA, M., and H. ITAGAKI, "On the Reliability of Redundant Structures," *Ann. Reliability Maintainability AIAA*, Vol. 5, 1966, pp. 605–610.
25. STEVENSON, J., and F. MOSES, "Reliability Analysis of Frame Structures," *ASCE J. Struct. Div.*, Vol. 96, No. ST11, Nov. 1970, pp. 2409–2427.
26. THOM, H. C. S., "New Distributions of Extreme Winds in the United States," *ASCE J. Struct. Div.*, Vol. 94, No. ST7, July 1968, pp. 1787–1801.

27. TIFFANY, C. F., and J. N. MASTERS, "Applied Fracture Mechanics," in *Fracture Toughness Testing and its Applications*, ASTM STP 381, June 1965, pp. 249–277.
28. VAGLIENTE, V. N., "Forecasting the Risk Inherent in Earthquake Resistant Design," *Technical Report No. 174*, Department of Civil Engineering, Stanford University, Stanford, Calif., 1973.
29. WEN, Y. K., and S. L. CHU, "Tornado Risks and Design Wind Speed," *ASCE J. Struct. Div.*, Vol. 99, No. ST12, Dec. 1973, pp. 2409–2421.
30. YAO, J. T-P., and H. Y. YEH, "Formulation of Structural Reliability," *ASCE J. Struct. Div.*, Vol. 95, No. ST12, 1973, pp. 2611–2619.

# Implications of Recent Airblast Studies to Damage of Hardened Structures*

H. L. BRODE AND J. G. LEWIS*

## 1. Introduction

The effects of blast overpressure are a primary problem in the design of structures to withstand a nuclear attack. Newmark, in 1974 [1], studied the effects of height of burst (HOB) on the range to damage for simple structures. He utilized the best airblast predictions then available [2]. More recently, new data [3, 4] have improved our understanding of the effects of HOB on airblast, particularly at high overpressures. In this chapter we shall review the new airblast data and present the results of structural response calculations performed with the revised predictions. In addition, other nuclear phenomena pertinent to survival at high levels of exposure are reviewed.†

## 2. Nuclear Weapons Phenomenology

Blast overpressure represents the main force that a hard structure, buried or at least flush with the ground surface, must be made to withstand. The blast wave can be characterized in terms of the weapon yield, height of burst, distance from the burst, and nearby surface conditions (built-up, hilly, forested, plowed, paved, snow covered, etc.). In general, the overpressure damage to a structure depends on how fast the overpressure rises, how high it goes, and how fast it drops off.

Many reviews of nuclear explosion effects on hardened structures are

*R & D Associates, Marina del Rey, California.

†The authors are indebted to their co-workers at RDA for their substantial assistance in providing early access to research results. In particular, we are grateful to H. J. Carpenter, H. F. Cooper, Jr., and K. Y. Narasimhan.

available [5, 6, 7] and can be most helpful in understanding the design problems faced in constructing a truly survivable facility. The overpressure in the blast wave created by a nuclear explosion is a primary damage mechanism to hard targets, but the nuclear explosion also causes high wind or gust pressures, high air temperatures, thermal radiation, ground shock, blast-driven debris impacts, hot air burns, and dust. In addition, such hazards as nuclear radiations, cratering motions and ejecta, strong electromagnetic transients, and radioactive fallout accompany a nuclear explosion.

After thirty years of testing and research, nuclear blast waves are still not completely understood, and predictions still vary considerably as a consequence of that incomplete knowledge. The most recent peak overpressure predictions [based in large measure on small high-explosive (HE) charge experiments] [3] fall short of the previously accepted standard ideal surface height-of-burst (HOB) curves by less than 10% at 34 atm (500 psi), by no more than 15% at 14 atm (200 psi), but by as much as 20% in range at 7 atm (100 psi). However, these comparisons assume a scaling from an 8-lb PBX-9404 explosive charge to a 1-kT nuclear explosion by factors other than simple yield or blast energy scaling factors. This more complex procedure is adopted in order to accommodate the wave-shape differences which exist between HE and nuclear explosions at high overpressures. This scaling corresponds to a range of scale factors between 46 and 68. The high overpressure Mach reflection region is now understood to be characterized by a double-shock system. The snapshot wave configuration sketched in Fig. 1 represents this phenomenon by the following rationale.

The incident wave (1) from a burst point above the ground is reflected in a regular reflection (2) until the angle it makes with the ground plane becomes large enough to allow the reflected wave to overtake and coalesce with the incident wave, forming a Mach reflection (3). As the Mach stem grows, the

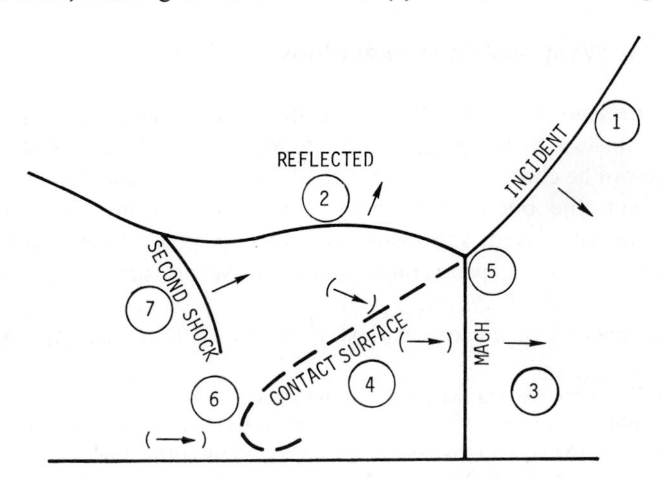


**Fig. 1.** Second-shock phenomenon in strong mach reflections

contact surface (4), separating air that has experienced only the Mach shock from air that has been through both the incident and reflected shocks, trails behind and connects the triple point (5) with the surface. However, air flow above the contact surface has not been completely turned parallel to the surface by the reflected shock and retains some downward momentum. This results in an eventual compression at the surface (6) as the downward-moving double-shocked air above the contact surface is stopped. This compression (7) distorts and chews up the tail of the contact surface streamline (6) and raises the pressure. The Mach shock itself represents a lower pressure than that behind the reflected wave in the regular reflection region, but the second shock quickly builds to appreciably higher values at that transition. The quantitative details of these double-shock phenomena were not well understood prior to the careful experiments and analysis by Carpenter [3].

Figure 2 compares a double-shock overpressure waveform from these recent experiments with the earlier prediction of Ref. 2. The blast waves from chemical explosives have many different characteristics from those expected from a nuclear source, particularly at high overpressures, and these differences make scaling an inexact procedure. Scaling in Fig. 2 was based on the following assumptions: (1) PBX releases 1400 cal/gm on detonation, (2) 1 kT of nuclear yield produces a blast wave equivalent to 0.5 kT of TNT, and (3) TNT releases 1000 cal/gm on detonation ($10^{12}$ cal/kT). Thus, a scale factor for converting 8-lb PBX-9404 to 1-kT nuclear is figured as

$$\left(\frac{0.5 \times 10^{12}\ \text{cal/kT}}{1.4 \times 10^{6}\ \text{cal/kg} \times 0.4536\ \text{kg/lb} \times 8\ \text{lb}}\right)^{1/3} \simeq 46.2. \tag{1}$$

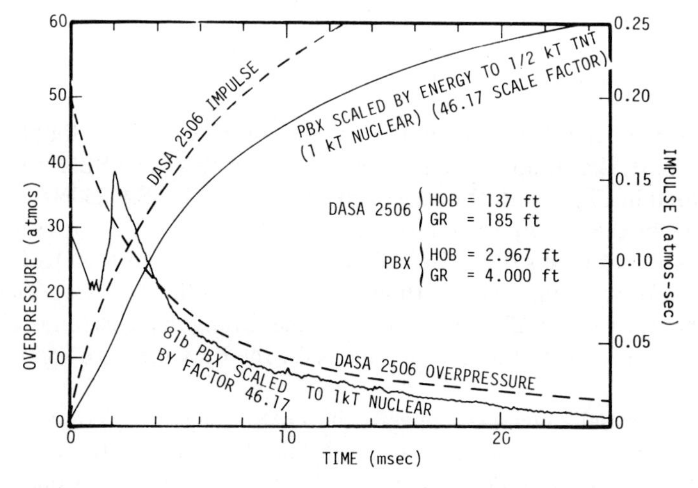


**Fig. 2.** Comparison of recent small charge overpressure and impulse with "ideal" nuclear overpressure and impulse (using energy scale factor on time and range)

Also compared in Fig. 2 are the accumulated impulses for the scaled PBX and the earlier nuclear prediction [2]. The scaled PBX falls below the old "ideal" prediction by almost a factor of 2 in the first 2 sec. This simple energy scaling leads to different peak overpressures: 50 atm from Ref. 2 versus 38 atm from the PBX data. If one compares this PBX new waveform with the DASA 2506 prediction for the same peak overpressure and the same reflection angle but still scales the time by the same energy scale factor (46.2), the impulses match more closely (Fig. 3). However, the scale factor used for the time variable is not critical. If one were to use the same factor as implied by matching peak overpressures (50.6) at the same reflection angle, the comparison would be equally good.

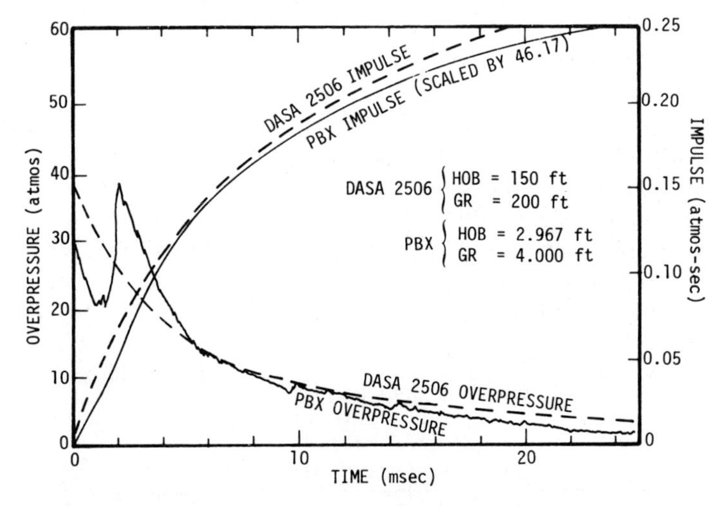


**Fig. 3.** Comparison of PBX wave with DASA 2506 at equal peak overpressure (energy scale factor for time)

In the regular reflection region, where the complexity of the double peaks does not exist, the comparison is more straightforward. The PBX waveform is compared in Fig. 4 with the waveform described in DASA 2506 at a range derived from the energy scaling (scale factor 46.2) and at a corresponding burst height and time scale. Also shown is a comparison of the DASA 2506 prediction for the same peak overpressure (corresponding to a scale factor of 50.2). The relatively small influence on the time scaling that this range of scale factors has is shown by the shaded regions for the PBX pressure and impulse curves.

The principal difference between the DASA 2506 predictions and the scaled PBX results lies in the more rapid initial decay that the PBX result shows. The decay rate immediately behind the shock arrival was derived for the DASA 2506 approximations from the free-field unreflected decay rate as

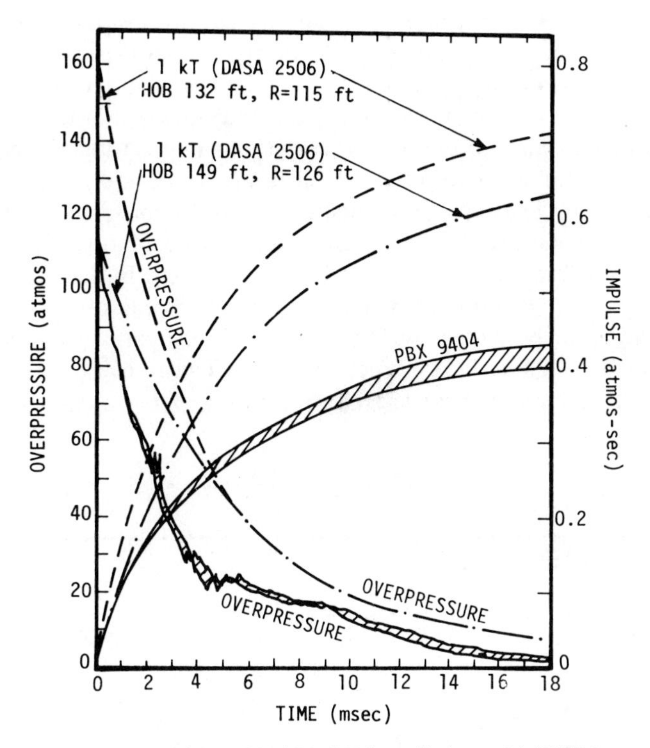


**Fig. 4.** Comparison of DASA 2506 predictions with PBX data scaled to 1 kT in the regular reflection region

defined by detailed calculations. It is plausible that the reflected pressure initial decay rate should be faster than that of the incident wave, since both the incident wave and the reflected wave are divergent, and the latter is expanding into the diminishing pressure field of the former. Just as the free airblast eventually overexpands and creates a negative overpressure phase, these reflected shocks expanding back into the fireball of the airburst can overexpand. The reflected shock can have shorter positive phase durations than the free air shock, but must eventually recover with second shocks or subsequent returns to positive overpressures to provide total impulses comparable to those from a surface burst or an airburst of twice the yield.

The earlier predicted overpressure-time histories of DASA 2506 were predicated on an initial decay similar to the incident wave decay and on a late-time decay approaching that of the free airburst of twice the yield. It now appears more plausible that the initial decay is substantially faster and that the duration of the first pulse (of importance to hard structure response) may be substantially shorter than even the free air positive phase.

While the accuracy of the PBX data is not in question, the applicability to high overpressure phenomena from nuclear explosions is not easily demonstrated. The continuing effort to tie the chemical explosive work to nuclear predictions is through detailed two-dimensional hydrodynamic calculations (done primarily at the Air Force Weapons Laboratory, Kirtland Air Force Base). Calculations of high resolution and precision are required to approach the detail evident in the PBX measurements, and the comparisons are not yet entirely satisfactory. Ultimately, with more precise (larger, longer) calculations, a good match is expected, and then calculations of comparable accuracy can be used to make nuclear blast predictions. In the meantime, the approximate scalings of the PBX data suggest lower peak overpressures and faster decay than predicted by DASA 2506. A comparison of the DASA 2506- and PBX 9404-derived predictions for 1-kT peak overpressure isobars versus height of burst and range are shown in Fig. 5.

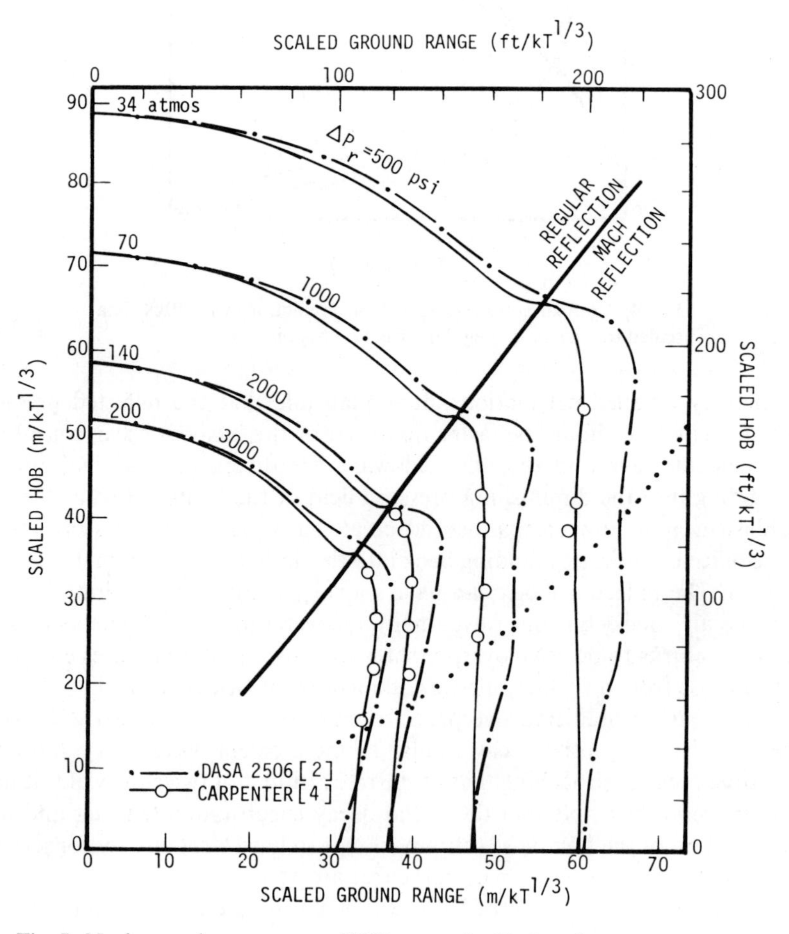


**Fig. 5.** Nuclear peak overpressure HOB curves for ideal surfaces

The airblast predictions [2] tend to maximize the expected range over ideal surfaces for a given overpressure and height of burst. The recent high-explosive small charge work also represents ideal reflecting surfaces and no precursors. Even with ideal conditions, some variation in range for a given peak overpressure must be expected. In reality, over nonideal surfaces and with thermal precursors formed, the ranges to each peak overpressure can be expected to shrink sometimes to values well inside the bands suggested in Fig. 6. The inner and outer limits to the bands correspond to a few percent more

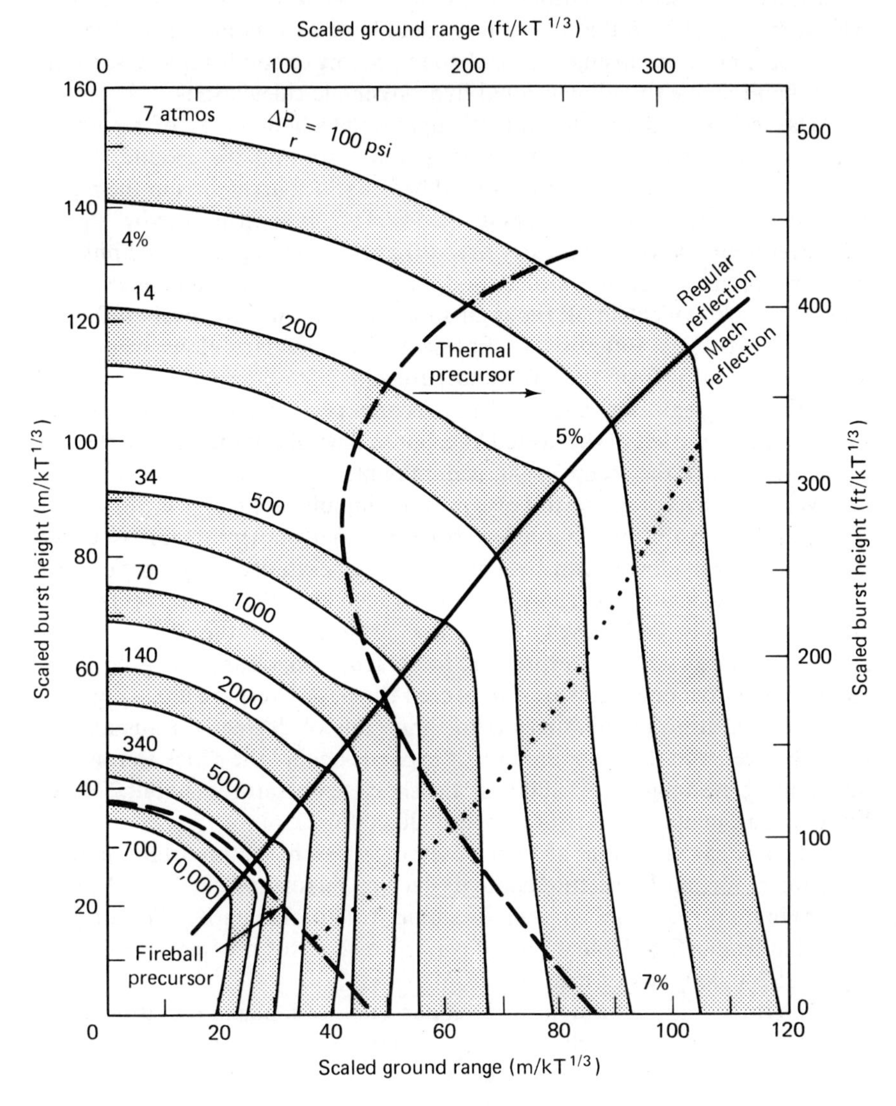


**Fig. 6.** Near-ideal surface peak overpressure isobars

or less than the predictions based on the PBX 8-lb data [3]. The outer limits are frequently less than those of the DASA 2506 predictions. The latter represented maximum credible ranges, while the PBX-derived predictions are aimed at "best values," so that not all the nuclear data lie inside these new outer limits. Furthermore, because of nonideal surfaces, precursors, and inadequate measurements or recording equipment, some of the nuclear data fall inside of the inner bounds. The bands represent the uncertainty in the scaled ranges for a given scaled burst height and peak overpressure due to yield and atmospheric variations and some modest variations in surface slope, with some expectation that the ranges could be less for nonideal surfaces. At present, the most promising approach to improving or confirming these curves is through reliable two-dimensional hydrodynamic calculations.

Dashed lines in Fig. 6 indicate approximate boundaries of regions in which precursors are expected. Thermal precursors on the ground do not form if too little heat has been absorbed before shock arrival, as in the region to the left of the thermal precursor line [4]. The "fireball precursor" occurs whenever a luminous shock (early fireball) intersects the ground. Its physical mechanisms are not clearly understood, but its existence and influence on the blast wave are evident in all the high-speed fireball films for near-surface or surface bursts. The dotted curve represents the boundary along which first and second peaks (from the PBX data) are equal. To the right of the dotted lines, the first peak is greater and the second peak becomes less and less prominent. To the left of the dotted line, but to the right of the Mach reflection onset line (solid), the second peak is dominant.

While the overpressure and overpressure impulse are major factors in the design and survivability of hardened structures, many other factors associated with a nuclear explosion can be a source of vulnerability. Any portion of a structure or associated systems components such as antennas, air vents, door edges, guide rails, and security fences that project above the surface can be subject to drag as well as overpressure forces from a nuclear blast. Above 100 psi, the peak dynamic pressure can exceed the peak overpressure.

Shock heating of the air runs to thousands of degrees Celsius at high overpressures, and the inner fireball air expands behind the shock to raise the temperature even higher. At 1000 psi, the shock temperature is about 2700°C, but the peak temperature rises to nearly 30,000°C [2, 6].

The nuclear radiations at such close ranges can be an important damage mechanism for hard structure contents such as missile systems or personnel but are in no way a problem in maintaining structural integrity. The air dose at 0.8 km from a 1-MT burst ($\sim$200 psi) is like $2 \times 10^6$ roentgens of gamma rays and 200,000 rads of neutrons [2, 6].

The rapid plasma motions and sudden burst of ionizing radiation cause a strong electromagnetic pulse that can disrupt electronics and cause damage from heavy induced currents in conductors within a structure. Even for airbursts, the ground motions induced by the strong shock can be of concern both for structural integrity and for contents survivability.

When surface bursts occur, the threat to structures includes crater-induced ground motions, massive crater ejecta impacts, and debris depths [2, 7].

## 3. Structural Response to Airblast Loading

Newmark [1] has performed calculations of the effects of height of burst on the range to damage for simple horizontal yielding structures. These calculations were performed using the airblast waveform expression developed by Brode [2]. As indicated previously, the PBX-9404 test data and analyses have led to revisions in both the ranges and waveform characteristics [3, 4]. More recent calculations of a similar nature to Newmark's, but using loading functions based on PBX data for input, have led us to somewhat different conclusions concerning the qualitative as well as the quantitative effects of above-ground bursts [8].

Newmark concluded the following:

> There is a substantial bonus that can be obtained with above-ground bursts of nuclear weapons where the height-of-burst is generally less than the range, with a consequent increase in range and often a decrease in overpressure, to produce a specified amount of damage, as measured by ductility factor, in a target having particular characteristics. This increase is greater for targets having a longer natural period, a higher yield strength, or a higher ductility factor, and is greater for small weapon yields than for large ones.

The results to follow indicate that the bonus in range obtained by Newmark and caused by "... increases in both the impulse and effective width of the spike of the pressure-time curve below the so-called 'knee' of the HOB curves ..." [1] exists only for certain selected HOBs, yields, and range combinations.

The reasons for altering this conclusion are threefold. First, the HOB curves utilized by Newmark [2] have been revised and predict shorter ranges for a given peak overpressure at HOBs of interest. Second, in the Mach reflection region, the airblast waveforms may have double peaks and are more complex in both decay and early impulse. Third, nonideal surface effects lead to uncertainties in range predictions.

Calculations reported here use the single-degree-of-freedom (SDOF) load response model described schematically in Fig. 7. The important features of this model are the load resistance ($q_y$), which is reached linearly, the yield deflection ($x_y$), and the ductility factor ($\mu$), which is the ratio of the maximum

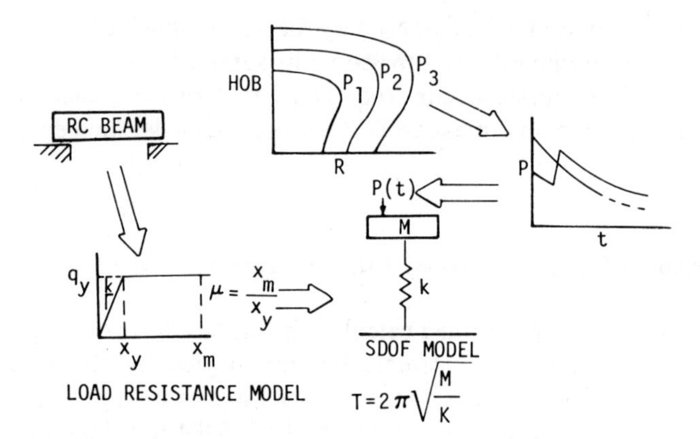


**Fig. 7.** Dynamic structure response analysis

deflection to the deflection at yielding ($x_m/x_y$). The other variable required to define the structure is its natural period ($T$), which can be calculated using methods such as those given in Ref. 7. Thus, $q_y$ can be calculated (or obtained from static test data), $T$ can be calculated or assumed, and $\mu$ is selected as a damage criterion (usually from static test data).

Several sets of calculations were performed; however, only the following representative cases will be reviewed:

| *Yield (MT)* | *HOB (ft)* | *Period (msec)* | *Ductility Factor* | $q_y$ *Range (psi)* |
|---|---|---|---|---|
| 1 | 1400 | 10 | 3.0 | 300–2200 |
| 1 | 1000 | 10 | 3.0 | 300–2200 |
| 1 | 570 | 10 | 3.0 | 1500–3800 |
| 1 | 0 | 10 | 3.0 | 300–3000 |

Figure 8 is a plot of $q_y$ versus range for a 1400-ft HOB and includes examples of the pressure-time waveforms used to load the structural element at different ranges. A structure with a given $q_y$ would be damaged at all ranges shorter than for a given curve and would not be damaged at greater ranges (according to the SDOF model defined above). Note that the damage range is less for the waveforms based on PBX data than for those for Ref. 2. However, when Ref. 2 peak pressures have been adjusted in range only (not in waveform) to agree with the PBX-9404 scaled results, the 1400-ft HOB gives greater ranges for $q_y$ values below about 400 psi. For comparison, $q_y$ values for a zero HOB are also shown. The range reductions (from DASA 2506) caused by the revised HOB range predictions alone are about 8% at $q_y$ equal to 1500 psi and about 9% at $q_y$ equal to 1000 psi. The additional range reductions

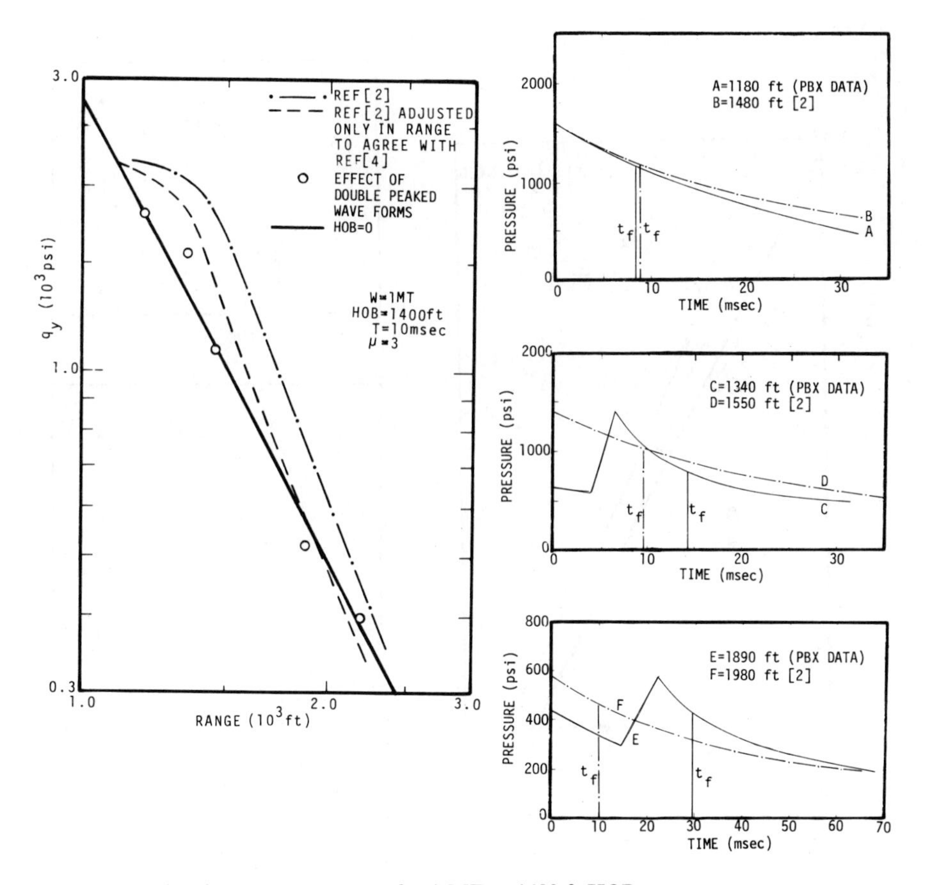


**Fig. 8.** Load resistance versus range for 1 MT at 1400 ft HOB

caused by the double-peaked character of the waveform alone are about 6% at $q_y$ equal to 1500 psi and about 9% at $q_y$ equal to 1000 psi, with total reductions in area coverage of 24% and 28%, respectively. Examination of waveforms A and B (1700 psi) indicates that they are similar but occur at different ranges. Waveforms E and F, having the same peak pressure (at different ranges), give different $q_y$ values because of different rise times to, and decays after, the peak. This is also indicated by the different times of failure $t_f$. Note that E deflects the structure to $\mu = 3$ at 30 msec (or 3 times $T$), whereas F gives a $t_f = 9$ msec (or 0.9 times $T$).

Waveforms for the surface burst are not shown but would be similar in character to those from Ref. 2. Figure 9 gives results from the calculations at a 1000-ft HOB, again compared with the surface burst. At this lower burst height essentially all HOB waveforms produce greater ranges of damage than the surface burst waveforms, although predictions based on double-peaked waveforms again give shorter ranges and area coverage (when range adjusted)

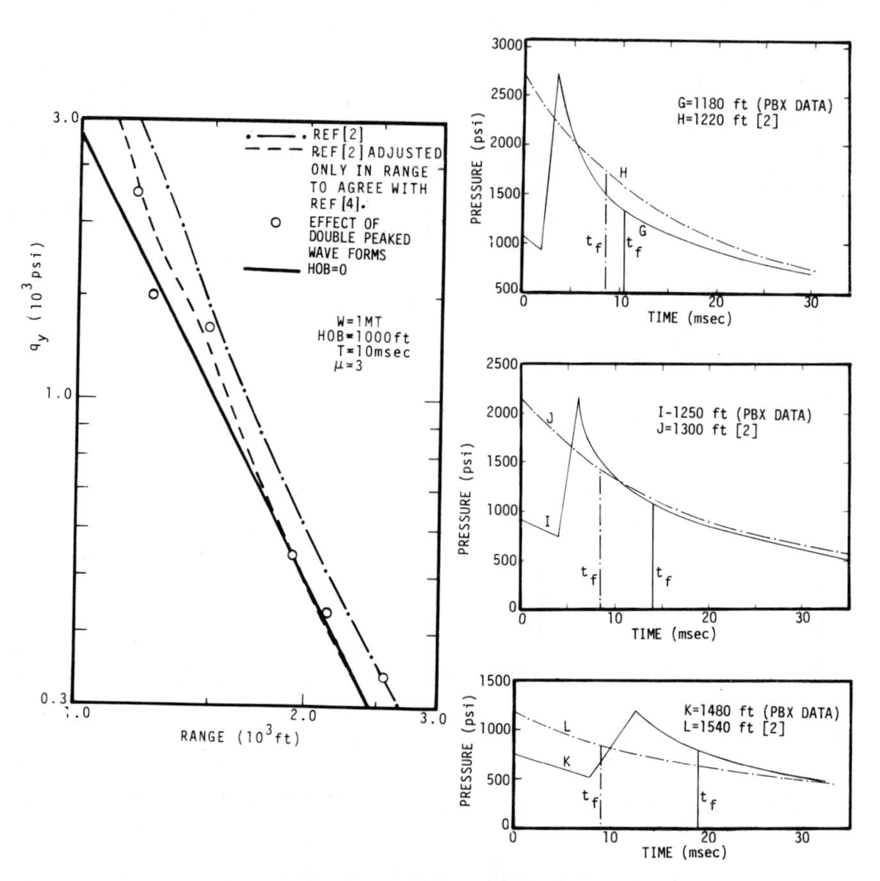


**Fig. 9.** Load resistance versus range for 1 MT at 1000 ft HOB

than Ref. 2 predictions down to $q_y$ values of about 500 psi, at which level the double-peaked waveforms again give increased ranges.

The $q_y$ versus range calculations in Figs. 8 and 9 indicate that, when the HOB lies to the left of and above the dotted line in Fig. 6, range to damage may usually be reduced because the double-peaked waveform will have a higher second peak. To optimize range to damage for structures having $q_y$'s above 1000 psi, it is necessary to lower the HOB such that higher overpressures lie to the right of and below the dotted line where the first peak will be the maximum. Figure 10 gives plots of calculations, similar to those described above, for a 1-MT weapon burst at 570 ft above the surface. Note that the double-peaked waveforms produce damage to only slightly greater ranges than the single peaks of Ref. 2 but give significant increases in range when compared to a surface burst (9% at $q_y = 2100$ psi and 8.5% at $q_y = 1600$ psi). Study of waveforms M through R indicates more impulse in the double-

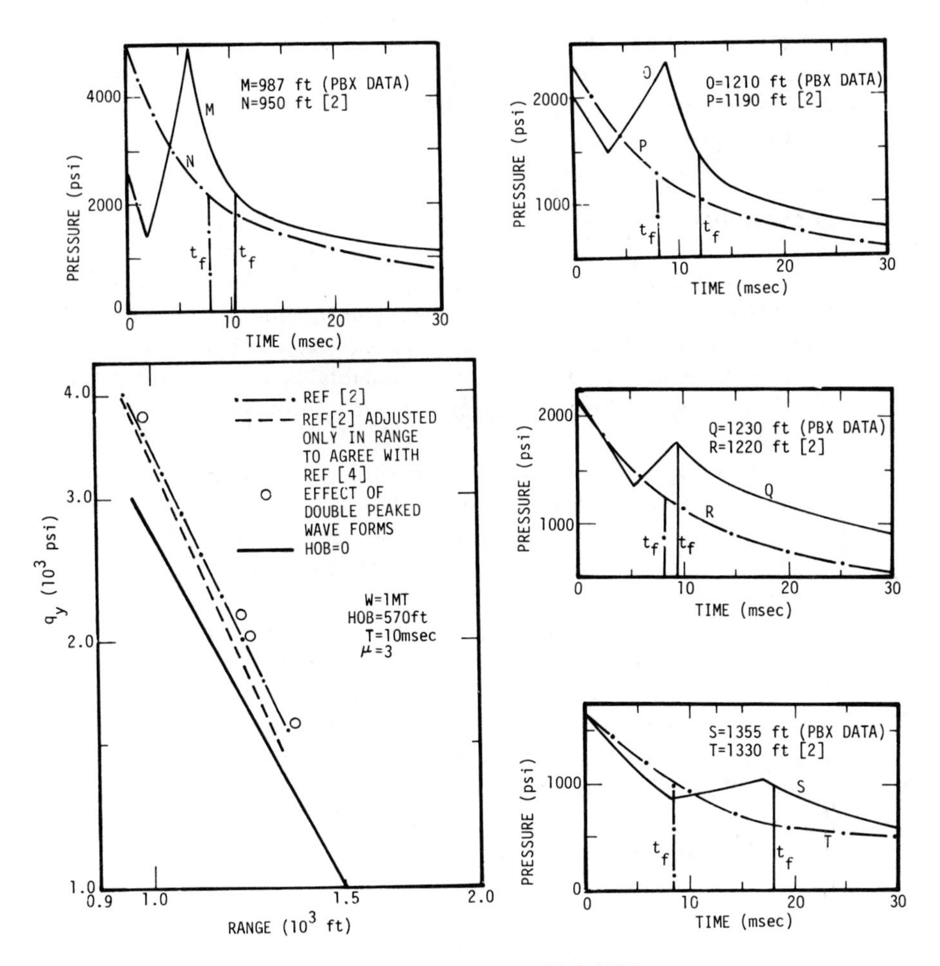


**Fig. 10.** Load resistance versus range for 1 MT at 570 ft HOB

peaked waveforms. Waveform S has comparable impulse to T at the time of the second peak (≈17 msec); consequently, the difference in range to the first peak is probably controlling $q_y$.

The above results are for a single yield, ductility, and natural period. However, results obtained for other yields (10 kT to 25 MT), other natural periods (5 and 20 msec), and ductilities (1, 2, 5, 10), are to be published separately [8] and are in general agreement with the results reported here. Namely, there can be slight increases (or decreases) in range to damage by optimization of the HOB.

These range changes are of the same order as (and often smaller than) the uncertainties in predicting range at which a given peak pressure will occur. In addition, uncertainties in knowledge of the physical characteristics of enemy hard targets can produce a larger variance in range to damage than can be overcome by HOB range enhancement. On the other hand, defensive planners should consider the responses to such complex airblast loads for existing and future planned systems.

## 4. Conclusions

1. For low heights of burst, the airblast waveforms at high overpressures (>500 psi) exhibit double peaks of varying magnitude in the Mach reflection region and complex decay rates and early impulse values. The peak overpressure HOB curves are reasonably well defined (to within $\pm 10\%$ on range) above 100 psi (for all yields) for bursts over near-ideal surfaces.
2. Offensive planners cannot rely on optimizing HOBs to enhance damage ranges for hardened structures. However, if HOBs are desirable for other reasons, no significant degradation in damage effectiveness versus range should be expected for HOBs that are in the vicinity of one-half the height of the knee of the curve.
3. System designers should conduct parametric studies to cover a range of possible airblast waveforms from threat weapons in order to minimize the likelihood that some unexpected loading condition will damage the structure at overpressures lower than design.
4. Range predictions for airblast loading are uncertain because of real surface effects. Prudent offensive planners would tend to consider the shorter predicted ranges, and, conversely, defensive planners should consider the longer predicted ranges.
5. While it is sufficient to consider nuclear blast overpressures in calculating damage to hard structures and designing facilities for reliable survivability, protection must be provided also against a number of other near-simultaneous nuclear burst phenomena.

## Acknowledgment

This work was sponsored by the Defense Nuclear Agency, Washington, D.C., under Contract DNA001-76-C-0001.

## References

1. Newmark, N. M., *Effect of Height-of-Burst on Horizontal Yielding Targets*, Nathan M. Newmark, Consulting Engineering Services, DNA 3252F, Urbana, Ill., March 18, 1974.

2. Brode, H. L., "Height-of-Burst Effects at High Overpressures," *DASA 2506*, The RAND Corporation (RM-6301-DASA), Santa Monica, Calif., July 1970.
3. Carpenter, H. J., and H. L. Brode, "Height-of-Burst Blast at High Overpressure," paper presented at the *Fourth International Symposium on Military Applications of Blast Simulators*, R & D Associates, Marina del Rey, Calif., Sep. 11, 1974.
4. Carpenter, H. J., "On Nuclear Height-of-Burst Airblast at High Overpressure," *RDA-TR-5900-015*, R & D Associates, Marina del Rey, Calif., Jan. 1975.
5. Brode, H. L., "Review of Nuclear Weapons Effects," *The Annual Review of Nuclear Science*, Vol. 18, Annual Reviews Inc., Palo Alto, Calif., 1968, pp. 153–202.
6. Glasstone, S., ed., *The Effects of Nuclear Weapons*, rev. ed., U.S. Atomic Energy Commission, Washington, D.C., 1964.
7. Crawford, R. E., C. J. Higgins, and E. H. Bultmann, *The Air Force Manual for Design and Analysis of Hardened Structures*, Civil Nuclear Systems Corporation, Albuquerque, Oct. 1974.
8. Narasimhan, K. Y., "Effects of Airblast Waveforms on Structure Response," R & D Associates, Marina del Rey, Calif., to be published.

# Fracture Mechanics, Fracture Criteria, and Fracture Control in Structures

S. T. ROLFE* AND W. J. HALL†

## 1. General Problem of Brittle Fracture in Structures

Considerable effort has been devoted to the prevention of brittle fracture‡ in manufactured structures such as aircraft and pressure vessels where large numbers of these structures are fabricated under closely controlled conditions. For example, the emphasis on safety and reliability of nuclear vessels and the ensuing extensive research as well as stringent controls have led to a situation where the probability of a brittle fracture in a nuclear vessel is extremely low. For other types of manufactured structures, the causes of field failures usually can be remedied by changes in design of subsequent units.

In contrast, other certain types of structures such as bridges and buildings are often individually designed for a specific function and location. The service experience of steels in these structures is such that the designer in the past has seldom concerned himself with notch toughness. However, the trend in structural design is such that the following changes are occurring:

1. Structural engineers and architects are designing more complex structures than in the past.

*Chairman and Professor, Department of Civil Engineering, University of Kansas, Lawrence, Kansas.

†Professor of Civil Engineering, University of Illinois, Urbana, Illinois.

‡Brittle fracture is a type of catastrophic failure that usually occurs without prior plastic deformation and at extremely high speeds (as high as 7000 fps or possibly more). The fracture is usually characterized by a flat fracture surface (cleavage) with little or no shear lips and at average stress levels below those of general yielding. Brittle fractures are not so common as fatigue, yielding, or buckling failures but, when they do occur, they may be more costly in terms of human life and/or property damage.

2. There is increased use of high-strength weldable steels as compared with lower-strength steels.
3. The choice of construction practices is becoming increasingly dependent on minimum cost.
4. The magnitude and number of types of loadings considered in design are increasing.

Because of the above-noted changes, the increasing number of structures, the use of more precise methods of analysis, and the explicit recognition of inelastic behavior in the design process, the probability of brittle fracture incidence in structures of many types would appear to be increasing. Thus the designer should become more aware of the situations under which brittle fracture may occur and of the available methods for preventing brittle fractures.

The problem is not one of finding steels with adequate notch toughness to prevent brittle fracture, because steels that are extremely tough at service temperatures are available. The basic problems are whether or not it is necessary to specify notch toughness, and, if necessary, what toughness level should be specified to ensure satisfactory performance at reasonable cost, and what joining techniques and fabrication controls are required. Because the cost of structural steels generally increases with their ability to perform satisfactorily under more severe operating conditions, the designer does not want to specify arbitrarily more toughness than is required. How much toughness is sufficient is a difficult question to answer, and establishing the fracture-toughness requirements and the concomitant quality control and inspection requirements for various structural applications is a major task for materials engineers. It is as much an economic matter as a technical one.

Most large complex structures are designed using structural steels that have yield strengths ranging from 36 to 100 ksi. These steels have inherent levels of notch toughness that usually are adequate for most structural applications. However, it is possible for the notch toughness of these steels to vary depending on manufacturing variables (thermomechanical history), even though the material meets an existing specification. The toughness of structural steels and weldments can be affected significantly also by temperature and loading rate, stress level, and flaw size as well as by plate thickness or constraint, joint geometry, and workmanship. The effect of temperature on toughness is generally well known, but the roles of stress (or strain), flaw size, loading rate, and thickness are less well known.

Over the years many different tests have been used to evaluate the notch toughness of steels. These include the Charpy V-notch (CVN) impact test, the drop-weight nil-ductility transition (NDT) test, the dynamic tear (DT) test, the wideplate test, the Battelle drop-weight tear test (DWTT), and many others [1–7]. Generally, these tests were developed for a specific purpose. The CVN test is widely used as a screening test in alloy steel development as well as a quality-control test. In addition, because of correlations with service experience, the CVN test often is used in specifications for alloy steels for various structural and pressure-vessel applications. The NDT test is used often to establish the minimum service temperature for various Navy and structural applications, whereas the Battelle DWTT was developed to relate the fracture appearance of line-pipe steels to temperature.

All these tests generally have one thing in common, namely to produce fracture in steels under carefully controlled laboratory conditions. Hopefully, the results of the tests can be correlated with service behavior to establish levels of performance for various steels being considered for specific applications. However, even if correlations are developed for a class of materials and structures, they do not necessarily hold for other designs, new operating conditions, or new materials, because the results, which are expressed in terms of energy, fracture appearance, or percentage deformation, cannot be translated into normal structural design and inspection parameters, namely stress and flaw size. Recent advances in the fracture mechanics field have led to techniques and concepts which permit a more rational approach to fracture as a part of the design process than was possible in the past.

It is the purpose of this chapter to review briefly the current state-of-the-art of the concepts employed in fracture mechanics analysis and to describe how these are related to the development of fracture criteria and fracture control plans. The latter are now being recognized increasingly as important parts of the total design effort on large projects. In addition there is presented a summary of the latest findings pertaining to rate-of-loading effects on brittle fracture in low-carbon constructional steels. The chapter concludes with observations of future research needs.

## 2. Fracture Mechanics and Design

As a general rule the designer must properly proportion his structure to prevent failure by tensile overload (yielding or ductile fracture), compressive instability, and stable crack growth (for example, arising from fatigue or stress corrosion) or unstable crack growth (brittle fracture). Design to prevent brittle fracture usually refers to using a relatively low allowable stress as well as to the elimination (as much as possible) of those structural details that act as stress raisers that can be potential fracture initiation sites, e.g., weld joint details, mismatch, holes, intersecting plates, and arc strikes. Unfortunately, large complex structures (welded or bolted) cannot be designed or fabricated without such discontinuities, although good design and fabrication practices can minimize the original size and number of these discontinuities. It is realized that stress concentrations or discontinuities will be present, but the designer assumes that his structural materials will yield locally and redistribute the load in the vicinity of these stress concentrations or discontinuities. The selection of materials and allowable stress levels is based on the appropriate realization of the fact that crack-like discontinuities in large complex structures may be present or may initiate under cyclic loading or stress corrosion and that some level of notch toughness is desirable.

*Fracture mechanics* is a term commonly used to describe a method of characterizing fracture toughness, fatigue crack growth, or stress-corrosion crack growth behavior in terms of structural design parameters familiar to the engineer, namely, stress and flaw size [7]. Fracture mechanics commonly is subdivided into two general categories, namely linear-elastic and elastic-plastic* fracture mechanics. Obviously the engineer wants his materials to exhibit gross structural general-yielding behavior rather than a brittle-type (linear-elastic) behavior. Although linear-elastic fracture mechanics techniques are established reasonably well as compared with elastic-plastic fracture mechanics, most commonly used structural metals do not behave elastically to fracture, and thus linear-elastic fracture analysis techniques are not directly applicable to most structural metals. Elastic-plastic fracture mechanics approaches are not yet well defined and, in fact, no widely accepted simple analysis technique for this type of behavior is available to the engineer. Although considerable research on elastic-plastic fracture mechanics is underway, as discussed later in the section on future needs, the research-based approaches are yet to be simplified to the point where they can be used by engineering designers.

Although research has shown that numerous factors can contribute to brittle fractures in large welded structures, the recent development of fracture mechanics has shown that there are three primary factors (*conceptually*) that control the susceptibility of a structure to brittle fracture. These three primary factors are

1. *Material toughness:* Material toughness can be defined as the resistance to crack propagation in the presence of a notch. For linear-elastic behavior the material toughness is measured in terms of a static critical stress-intensity factor under conditions of plane stress ($K_c$), of plane strain ($K_{Ic}$), or for dynamic loading ($K_{Id}$). For elastic-plastic fracture behavior the material toughness may be measured in terms of ductility-related parameters such as the $J_{Ic}$, R-curve, COD, and equivalent energy approaches as defined next.

*Sometimes referred to as "general yielding" in British literature. The term *elastic-plastic* connotes the situation where a significant zone relative to plate thickness of inelastic straining occurs near the crack tip such that the linear-elastic analyses are not applicable.

(a) *J*-Integral technique: A path-independent integral which is an average measure of the elastic-plastic stress/strain field ahead of a crack. For elastic conditions, $J_{Ic} = K_{Ic}^2/E(1 - \nu^2)$. A test method for this approach is currently in development.

(b) Resistance-curve (R-curve) analysis: A procedure used to characterize the resistance to fracture of materials during incremental slow-stable crack extension, $K_R$. At instability $K_R = K_c$, the plane-stress fracture toughness which is dependent on specimen thickness as well as on temperature and loading rate.

(c) Crack-opening displacement (COD) technique: Toughness evaluation in terms of the prefracture deformation at the tip of a sharp crack.

(d) Equivalent energy approach: An energy approach based on using test results to predict failure, primarily of thick-walled pressure vessels.

2. *Flaw size:* Brittle fractures initiate from flaws or discontinuities of various kinds. These discontinuities can vary from extremely small cracks, as, for example, from within a weld arc strike (as was the case in the brittle fracture of a T-2 tanker during World War II), to much larger weld or fatigue cracks. Even though only small flaws may be present initially, repeated loading (fatigue) or stress corrosion can cause them to enlarge, possibly to a critical size where brittle fracture can occur.
3. *Stress level:* Tensile stresses (applied, residual, or both) are necessary for brittle fractures to occur.

Engineers have known the foregoing facts for many years and have reduced the susceptibility of structures to brittle fractures by applying these concepts to their structures, *qualitatively*. That is, good design (the use of lower stress levels and the minimizing of discontinuities) and sound fabrication practice (decreased flaw size through proper welding control) as well as the use of materials with good notch-toughness levels (e.g., as measured with a Charpy V-notch impact test) have minimized the probability of occurrence of brittle fractures in structures. However, the engineer has not had techniques available to permit evaluation of the relative performance and economic trade-offs among design, fabrication, and materials in a *quantitative* manner.

The fundamental concept of linear-elastic fracture mechanics is that the stress field ahead of a sharp crack can be characterized in terms of a single parameter $K_I$, the stress intensity factor for flat crack propagation (usually referred to as opening mode), having units of ksi$\sqrt{\text{in.}}$. This single parameter, $K_I$, is related to both the stress level ($\sigma$) and the flaw size ($a$). When the particular combination of $\sigma$ and $a$ leads to a critical value of $K_I$, called $K_{Ic}$ or $K_c$, unstable crack growth occurs. The equations that describe the elastic-

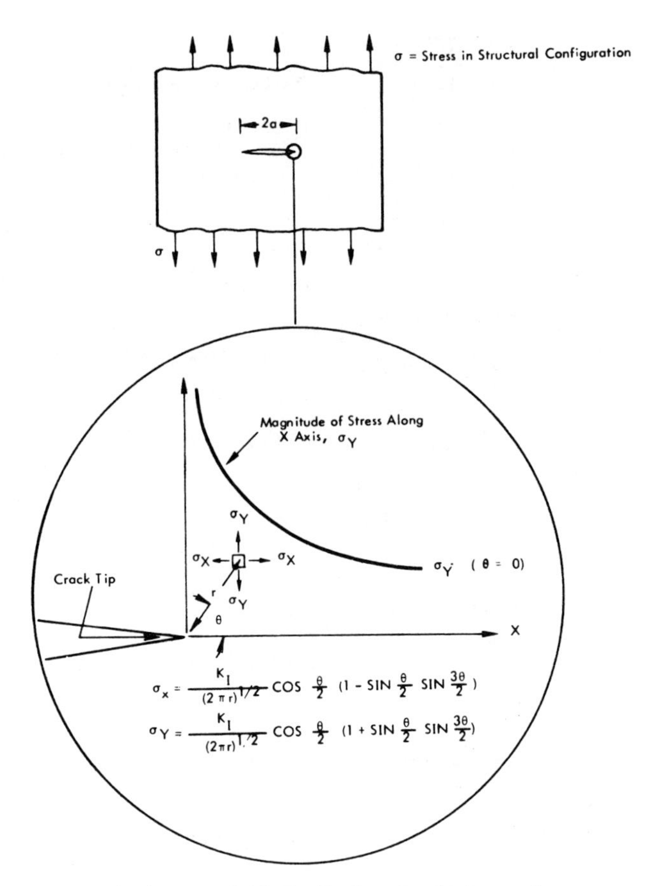


**Fig. 1.** Elastic-stress-field distribution ahead of a crack

stress field in the vicinity of a crack tip in a body subjected to tensile stresses normal to the plane of a simple crack are presented in Fig. 1. These stress-field equations define the distribution of the elastic-stress field in the vicinity of the crack tip and can be used to establish the relation among $K_I$, $\sigma$, and $a$ for different structural configurations, as shown in Fig. 2 [8]. Other crack geometries have been analyzed for different structural configurations and are published elsewhere [9,10].

If the critical value of $K_I$ at failure ($K_c$, $K_{Ic}$, or $K_{Id}$) can be determined for a given metal of a particular thickness and at a specific temperature and loading rate, the designer can determine theoretically the flaw size that can be tolerated in structural members for a given design stress level. Conversely, he can determine the design stress level that can be safely used for a flaw size that may be present in a structure.

This general (conceptual) relationship among material toughness ($K_{Ic}$ or

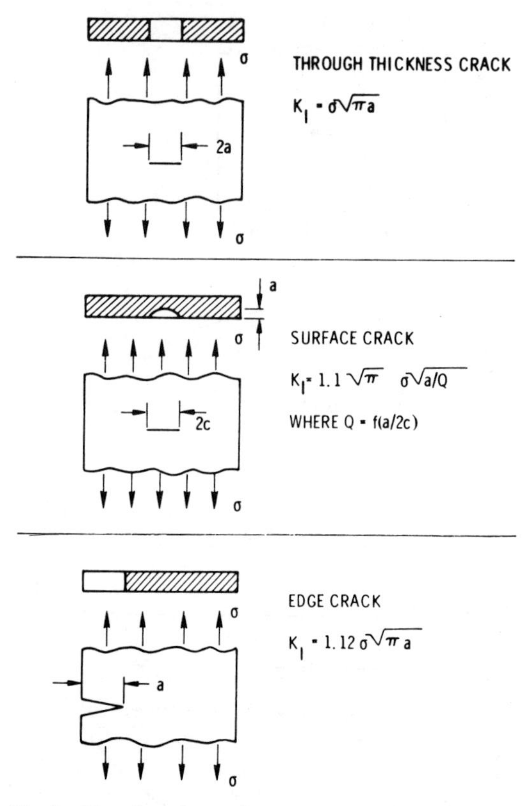


**Fig. 2.** $K_I$ values for various crack geometries

$K_c$), nominal stress ($\sigma$), and flaw size ($a$) is shown schematically in Fig. 3. If a particular combination of stress and flaw size in a structure ($K_I$) reaches the $K_{Ic}$ or $K_c$ level, fracture can occur. Thus there are many combinations of stress and flaw size (e.g., $\sigma_f$ and $a_f$) that may cause fracture in a structure that is fabricated from a steel having a particular value of $K_{Ic}$ or $K_c$ at a particular service temperature, loading rate, and plate thickness. Conversely, there are many combinations of stress and flaw size (e.g., $\sigma$ and $a$) that will not cause failure of a particular steel, i.e., below the $K_{Ic}$ or $K_c$ line.

A useful analogy for the designer is the relation among applied load ($P$), nominal tensile stress ($\sigma$), and yield or limit stress ($\sigma_y$) in an unflawed structural member and among applied load ($P$), stress intensity ($K_I$), and critical stress intensity for fracture ($K_c$, $K_{Ic}$, or $K_{Id}$) in a structural member with a flaw. In an unflawed structural member, as the load is increased, the nominal stress increases until a limit loading (yielding) occurs. As the load is increased in a structural member with a flaw (or as the size of the flaw grows by fatigue or stress corrosion), the stress intensity, $K_I$, increases until a limit condition

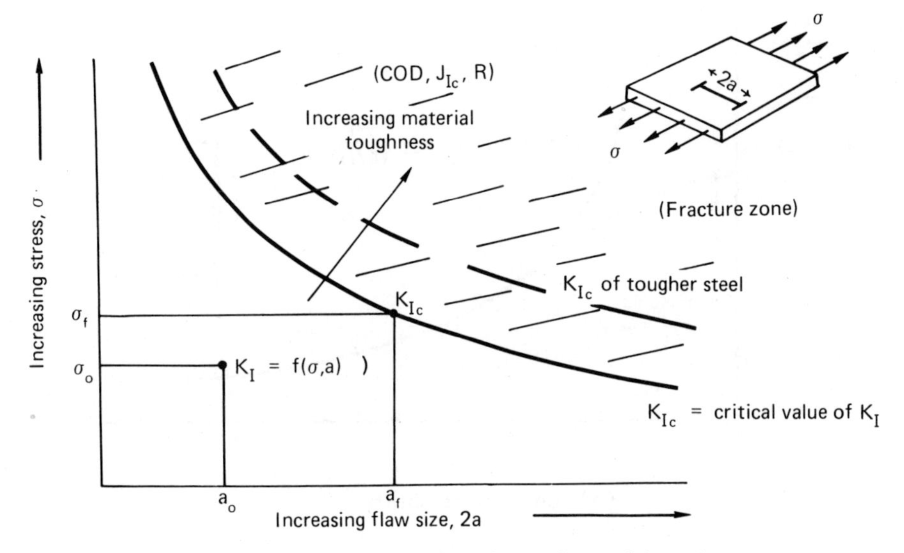


**Fig. 3.** Schematic relation between stress, flaw size, and material toughness

(fracture at $K_c$, $K_{Ic}$, $K_{Id}$) occurs. Thus the $K_I$ level in a structure should always be kept below the appropriate $K_c$ value in the same manner that the nominal design stress is kept below the limit loading.

Another analogy that may be useful in understanding the fundamental aspects of fracture mechanics is the comparison with the Euler column instability (Fig. 4) [11,12]. The stress level required to cause instability in a column (buckling) decreases as the $L/r$ ratio increases. Similarly, the stress level required to cause instability (fracture) in a flawed tension member decreases as the flaw size ($a$) increases. As the stress level in either case approaches the yield strength, both the Euler analysis and the $K_c$ analysis are invalidated because of yielding. To prevent buckling, the actual stress and $L/r$ values must be below the Euler curve. To prevent fracture, the actual stress and flaw size, $a$, must be below the $K_{Ic}$ or $K_c$ level shown in Fig. 4. Obviously, using a material with a high level of notch toughness will increase the possible combinations of design stress and flaw size that a structure can tolerate without fracturing.

At this point, it should be emphasized again that the $K_c$ levels for most common structural steels are so high that they cannot be measured directly using existing ASTM standardized test methods [3]. Thus, although concepts of fracture mechanics can be used to develop fracture control guidelines and desirable toughness levels, the state-of-the-art is such that actual $K_{Ic}$ or $K_c$ values cannot be measured for most commonly used structural metals at service temperatures. Therefore, traditional notch-toughness tests (e.g., CVN, NDT, etc.) are widely used at the present time to specify the notch-

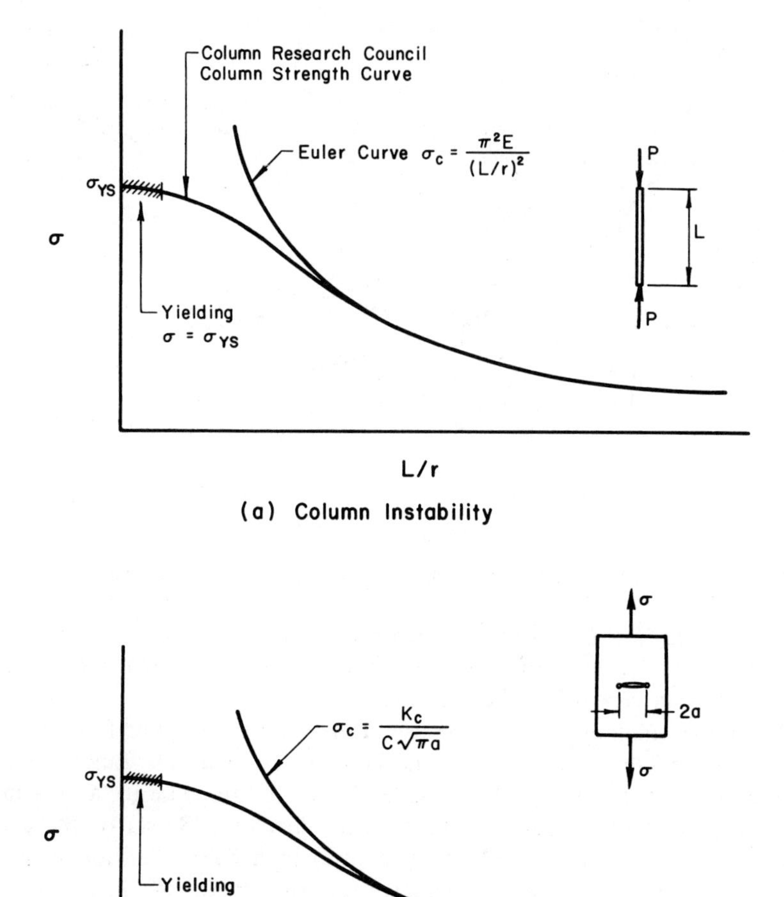


**Fig. 4.** Column instability and crack instability (after Madison (12))

toughness requirements for various structural applications. Examples of the use of such test methods in specifications are the recently developed AASHTO material toughness requirements for bridge steels and the ASME toughness requirements for steels for nuclear vessels. In both these cases, concepts of fracture mechanics were used to develop the desired toughness requirements, but the actual material toughness requirements are in terms of CVN or NDT (values based on empirical correlations) [7].

## 3. Fracture Criteria and Loading Rate Effects

A fracture criterion is a standard against which the expected fracture behavior of a structure can be judged. In general terms, fracture criteria are related to the three levels of fracture performance as shown in Fig. 5, namely macro linear-elastic (often referred to as "plane strain" in the fracture mechanics literature), elastic-plastic, or fully plastic. Although it would appear desirable to specify fully plastic behavior, this is rarely done because it is usually unnecessary as well as being economically undesirable in most cases.

For most structural applications, some moderate level of elastic-plastic behavior at the service temperature and loading rate constitutes a satisfactory performance criterion. While there may be some cases where considerable inelastic behavior is necessary (e.g., dynamically loaded military protective structures) or where low toughness level behavior can be tolerated (e.g., certain short-life aerospace applications where the loading and fabrication can be precisely controlled), for the majority of large complex structures

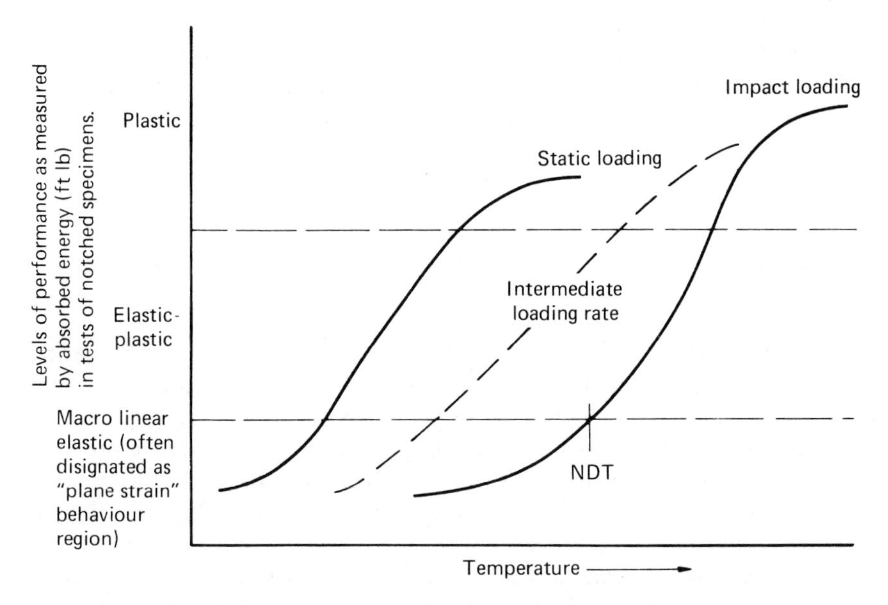


**Fig. 5.** Schematic showing relation between notch-toughness test results and levels of structural performance for various loading rates

(bridges, ships, buildings, pipelines, offshore drilling rigs, etc.) some moderate level of elastic-plastic behavior is satisfactory. The question arises then as to what level of elastic-plastic behavior is required and how this level of performance can be ensured.

Unfortunately the selection of a fracture criterion is often quite arbitrary and based on service experience for other types of structures that may have no relation to the particular structure an engineer may be designing. Also selection of a fracture criterion alone, without considering the other factors involved in fracture control, will not necessarily result in a structure with the desired margin of safety. An example of the use of a fracture toughness criterion developed for one application and yet which is widely used in many other situations is the 15-ft-lb CVN impact criterion at the minimum service temperature, which was established for the World War II ship failures. This criterion has been widely used for various types of structures, even though the material, service conditions, structural redundancy, etc., may be quite different from that of the World War II ships for which the criterion was established.

Criteria selection should be based on a careful study of the particular performance requirements for a given structure. The factors involved in the development of criteria commonly include

1. The service conditions (loadings, temperature, controlling stress and strain levels, loading rate, cyclic loading, etc.), to which the structure will be subjected.
2. The desired level of performance and margin of safety of the structure under both normal service and extreme loading conditions.
3. The possible modes and consequences of failure.

There is no single fracture criterion that can be applied to all structures because optimum design involves economic considerations as well as technical trade-offs.

At the present time it is difficult to establish notch-toughness criteria for the following reasons:

1. Establishment of the specific level of required notch toughness (i.e., the required CVN or $K_{Ic}$ value at a particular test temperature) is costly and time-consuming and is a subject unfamiliar to engineers.
2. There is no well-recognized single "best" approach. Therefore, different experts will have different opinions as to the "best" approach, although the science of fracture mechanics is slowly helping to overcome this difficulty.
3. The cost of structural materials increases with increasing levels of inherent notch toughness. Thus economic considerations must be included when establishing any toughness criterion.

A general fracture criterion defined in terms of the levels of performance (linear-elastic, elastic-plastic, and plastic), as described in Fig. 5, must be translated into some specific fracture test requirement that ensures the desired level of performance. For example, a general requirement that a structural material exhibit elastic-plastic behavior at service temperatures is a general criterion that is useful to the engineer. However, because of ambiguity and differences in opinion, this general criterion must be made specific in terms of a fracture test specimen and some specified index value. An example of a general toughness criterion might be that a low level of elastic-plastic behavior is required under the most severe expected service conditions. The specific toughness criterion for this example might be that "all structural steels used in this assemblege must exhibit 22-ft-lb energy absorption as measured in a standardized longitudinal Charpy V-notch impact test specimen tested at 32°F." Hopefully, this particular criterion would have been based on sufficient laboratory results, service experience, and fracture mechanics analysis to ensure the desired structural behavior. The criterion would then be specified for purchase of materials and quality control.

As a result of several dramatic structural failures in the period 1967–1973 [14–17] as well as a growing concern with the overall reliability and safety of structures, many specifications are now beginning to include specific minimum toughness requirements. This trend is expected to grow as regulatory governmental agencies become increasingly active in the development of mandatory rational fracture prevention criteria. Recent examples are the ASME Nuclear Code [18], AASHTO Material Toughness Requirements [19], and the floating nuclear power plant hull structure toughness requirements imposed by the U.S. Coast Guard and the Atomic Energy Commission (now the Nuclear Regulatory Commission).

There are two general parts to a fracture criterion:

1. *The general test specimens to categorize the material behavior:* Throughout the years various fracture criteria have been specified using notch toughness tests such as CVN impact, NDT, DT, and, more recently, the fracture mechanics test specimens used to measure $K_{Ic}$ and $K_{Id}$. Test specimens currently used as research tools and expected to be used more extensively in the future for metals in the lower-yield-strength category are $J_{Ic}$, COD, and R-curve specimens. The test specimen used for a particular application should be that which most closely models the actual structural behavior. However, commonly the selection of the test specimen is based on past experience as well as on economics of testing.
2. *The specific notch-toughness value or values:* The second and more difficult part of establishing a fracture criterion is the selection of the

specific level of performance in a particular test specimen. The specified values in any criterion should be an optimization of both safe structural performance and cost.

In general, the notch toughness of most structural steels increases with increasing temperature and decreasing loading rate. The effect of temperature is well known and has led to the transition-temperature approach to designing to prevent fracture. However, the effect of loading rate may be equally as important, not only in designing to prevent fracture but in understanding the satisfactory behavior of many existing structures built from structural materials that have low impact toughness values at their service temperatures.

The general effects of temperature and loading rate on $K_{Ic}$ and Charpy V-notch behavior are shown schematically in Figs. 6 and 7. The toughness of most structural steels tested at a constant loading rate undergoes a significant increase with increasing temperature. Thus the general effect of a slow loading rate, compared with rapid loading rates, is to shift the fracture-toughness curve to lower temperatures, regardless of the test specimen used. Examples of this shift in behavior with loading rate are presented in Figs. 8 and 9 for an A36 grade structural steel and an A572 grade 50 structural steel, respectively.

The magnitude of the temperature shift between slow-bend loading and very rapid dynamic loading in steels of various yield strengths has been related to the room-temperature yield strength of the steel and can be approxi-

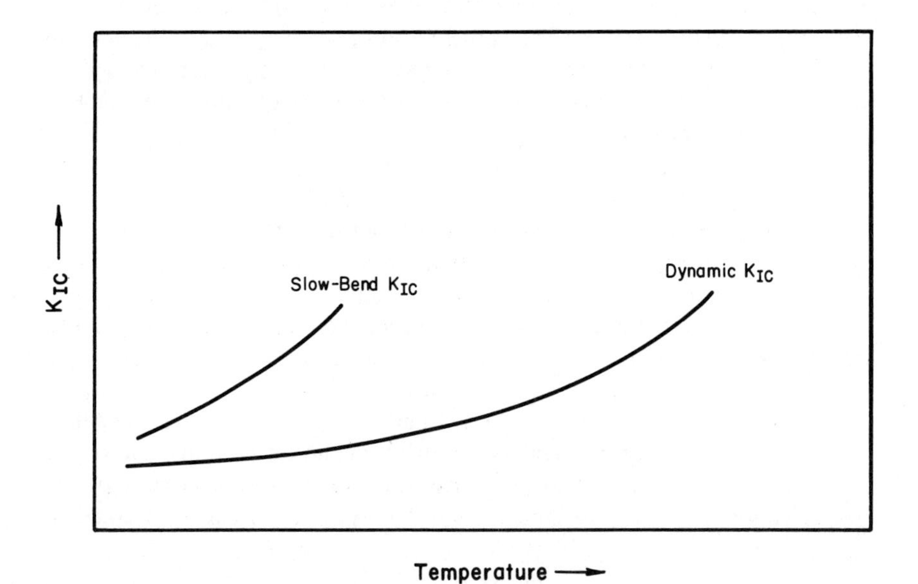


**Fig. 6.** Schematic showing effect of temperature and loading rate on $K_{Ic}$

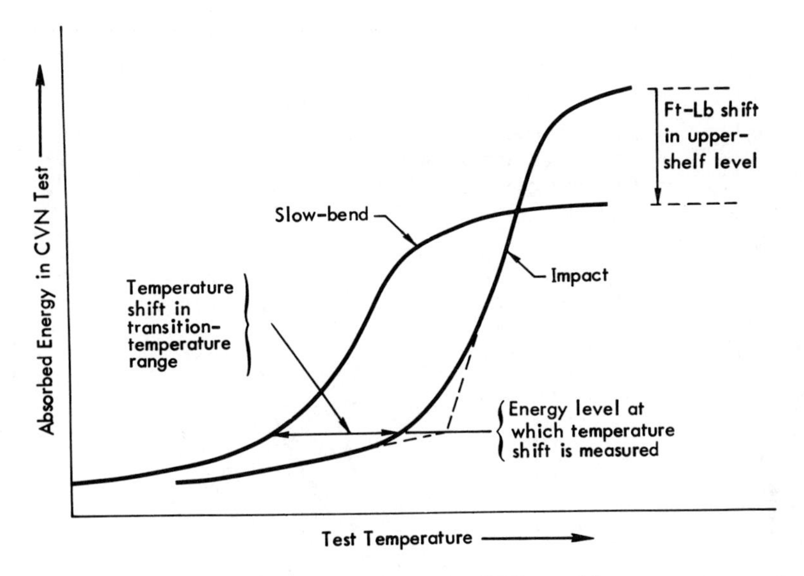


**Fig. 7.** Schematic representation of shift in CVN transition temperature and upper-shelf level due to strain rate

mated by

$$T_{\text{shift}} = 215 - 1.5\sigma_y \qquad \text{for } 36 \text{ ksi} < \sigma_y < 140 \text{ ksi},$$

and

$$T_{\text{shift}} = 0.0 \qquad \text{for } \sigma_y > 140 \text{ ksi},$$

where $T_{\text{shift}}$ = absolute magnitude of the shift in the transition temperature between slow-bend loading and rapid dynamic loading, degrees F,

$\sigma_y$ = room-temperature yield strength, ksi.

Because of this shift, increasing the loading rate can decrease the fracture-toughness value at a particular temperature for steels having yield strengths less than 140 ksi. The change in fracture-toughness values for loading rates varying from slow-bend to dynamic rates is particularly important for those structural applications, such as bridges, that may be loaded slowly.

As a specific example of the use of the loading-rate shift in the development of fracture criteria, assume that a structure is loaded at a slow loading rate of $10^{-5}$ in./in./sec and that the fracture toughness of the material is as shown in Fig. 9. If stress-flaw size calculations show that a $K_{Ic}$ value of about 60 ksi$\sqrt{\text{in.}}$ would ensure satisfactory structural performance, the results presented in Fig. 9 show that this behavior can be obtained at about +40°F dynamically ($\dot{\epsilon} \simeq 10$ in./in./sec), at about −90°F at an intermediate loading rate, and at about −150°F for a slow loading rate.

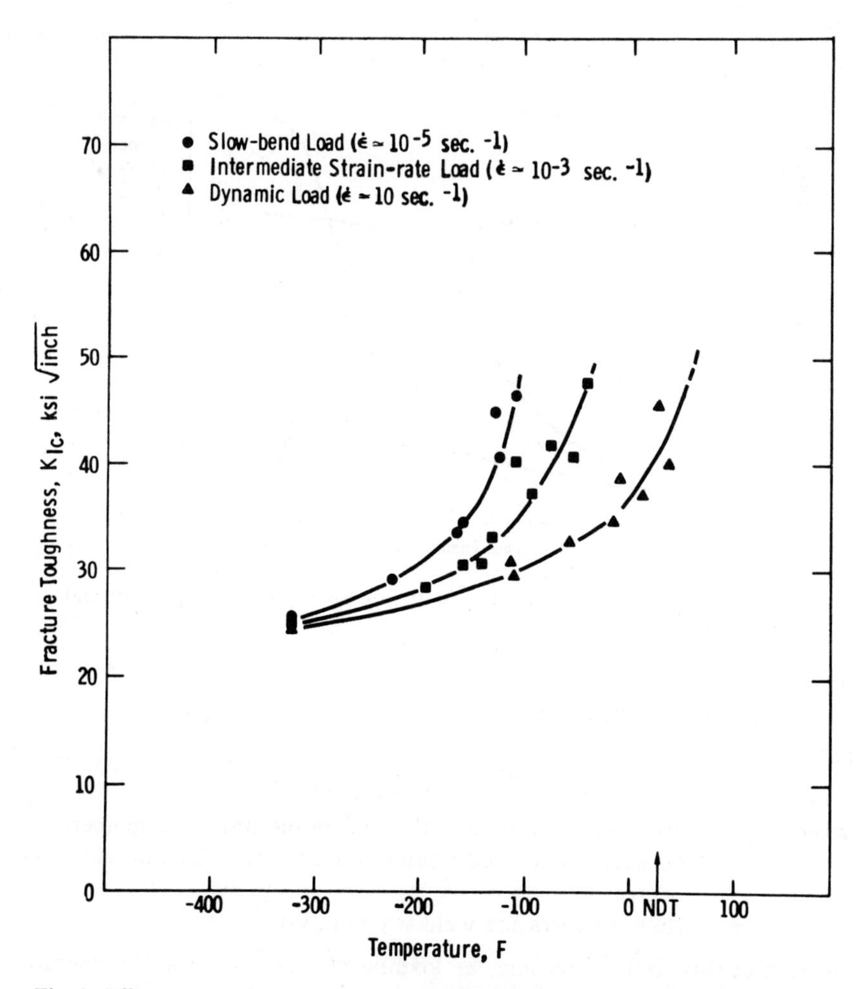


**Fig. 8.** Effect of temperature and strain rate on fracture toughness of A36 steel

Since it is usually much easier and less expensive to conduct impact (dynamic) tests than intermediate loading rate tests, criteria can be established on the basis of one loading rate and the results "shifted" on the basis of a laboratory test conducted at a different loading rate. The recently developed American Association of State Highway and Transportation Officials (AASHTO) material-toughness requirements were based on this reasoning. It should be emphasized that this criterion can be used only with those materials that exhibit a shift in transition behavior with changes in loading rate. The magnitude of this shift can be considerable and helps to explain why many structures have operated successfully at service temperatures well below their "dynamic" transition temperature.

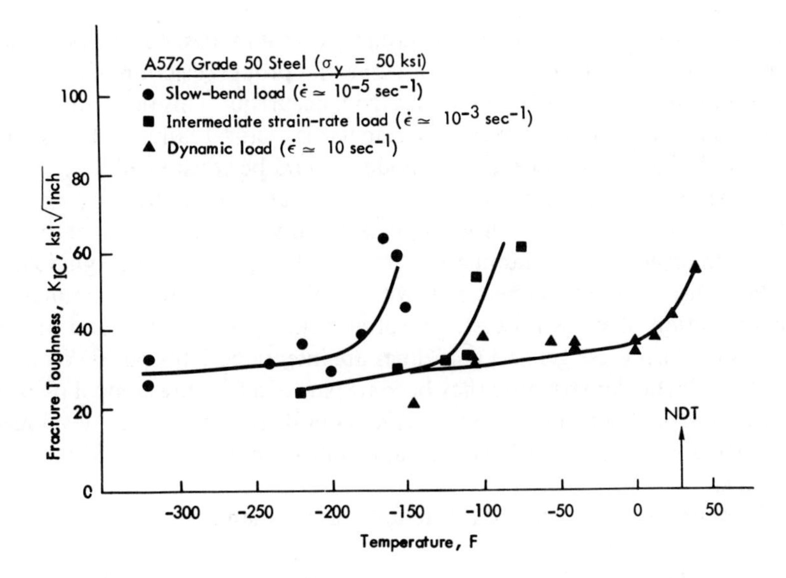


**Fig. 9.** Effect of temperature and strain rate on fracture toughness of A572 grade 50 steel ($\sigma_y = 50$ ksi)

## 4. Fracture Control

The objective in structural design of large complex structures such as bridges, ships, pressure vessels, and aircraft is to optimize the desired performance requirements relative to cost considerations (i.e., the overall cost of materials, design, fabrication, and operation), so that the probability of failure (and its economic consequence) is low. To achieve these objectives, engineers make predictions of service loads and conditions, calculate stresses in various structural members resulting from these loads and service conditions, and compare these stresses with the critical stresses in the particular modes that may lead to failure of the structure. Various criteria are then selected so that failure does not occur by any of the pertinent failure modes.

Possible failure or limit modes usually considered are

1. General yielding or excessive plastic deformation (straining).
2. Buckling or general instability, either elastic or plastic.
3. Subcritical crack growth (through fatigue, stress corrosion, or corrosion fatigue), leading to loss of section or unstable crack growth.
4. Fracture, either ductile or brittle, leading to either partial or complete failure of a member.

Although other failure modes exist, such as general corrosion or creep, the above-mentioned failure modes are the ones that usually receive the greatest attention. Furthermore, of these four failure or limit modes, engineers usually concentrate on only the first two and assume that proper selection of materials will prevent the other two failure modes from occurring. This reasoning is not always true and has led to several spectacular structural failures. For sound structural design all possible failure modes should be considered.

In the case of brittle fracture or fatigue, many of the fracture control guidelines that have been followed to minimize the possibility of brittle fractures in structures are familiar to structural engineers. These guidelines include the use of structural materials with good notch toughness, elimination or minimization of stress raisers, control of welding procedures, and proper inspection. When these general guidelines are integrated into specific requirements for a particular structure they become part of a fracture control plan. A fracture control plan is therefore a specific set of recommendations developed for a particular structure and should not be indiscriminately applied to other structures.

The four basic elements of a fracture control plan are as follows:

1. *Identification* of the factors that may contribute to the brittle fracture of a structural member or to the failure of an entire structure, including a description of service conditions, loadings, and/or deformations.
2. *Establishment* of the relative contribution of each of these factors to a possible brittle fracture in a member or to the failure of the structure.
3. *Determination* of the relative efficiency and trade-offs of various design methods to minimize the possibility of brittle fracture in a member or failure of the structural system.
4. *Recommendation* of specific design considerations to ensure the safety and reliability of the structure against brittle fracture. This would include recommendations for desired levels of material performance as well as material selection, design stress levels, weld performance, design of details (often overlooked), fabrication, inspection, and maintenance.

For those cases where crack growth is a consideration the total useful design life of a structural component can be estimated from the time necessary to initiate a crack and to propagate the crack from subcritical dimensions to the critical size. The life of the component can be prolonged by extending the crack-initiation life and/or the subcritical-crack-propagation life. Consequently, the crack-initiation, subcritical-crack-propagation, and unstable-crack-propagation (fracture) characteristics of structural materials, as well as their fracture behavior, are primary considerations in the formulation of fracture control guidelines for structures. Unstable crack propagation is the final stage in the useful life of a structural component subject to failure by the fracture mode. This stage is governed by the material toughness, the crack size, and the stress level. Consequently unstable crack propagation cannot be attributed only to material toughness, or only to high stress levels, or only to poor fabrication but rather to particular combinations of the above factors. However, if any of these factors are significantly different from that which is normally found in a particular type of structure, experience has shown that for most structures the possibility of failure is generally increased.

To provide a rational basis for designing to prevent fracture it is recommended that a fracture control plan be developed early in the design process. Such a plan represents an attempt to place in proper perspective those items which should be considered in the design process; in many respects it is a design criteria and criteria implementation plan and should include (or reference), for example, such items as (1) loading, deformation, and environmental design criteria; (2) material selection criteria with detailed description of the various types of material evaluation approaches (for strength, ductility, fracture toughness, corrosion, creep, etc.), including appropriate stress analysis procedures; (3) fabrication techniques and their evaluation approaches; (4) subcritical-crack-growth considerations as a function of the life of the structure; (5) consideration, if appropriate, of crack-arrest systems; (6) inspection (at the time of construction and throughout the life of the item, normally by nondestructive inspection methods) and quality control; (7) appropriate consideration of margins of safety, reliability, and redundancy; and (8) maintenance requirements. Occasionally guidance on some of these items is provided by applicable codes; in many cases no code will exist or be applicable.

Accordingly, a fracture control plan is developed only for the specific structure under consideration and can vary from one which must, in essence, provide assurance of no service failures to one which may allow for occasional failures during manufacturing or service. An example of the former situation would be a nuclear power plant structure where the consequences of a structural failure would be such that not even one failure could be tolerated. In the latter case, the consequence of failure might be minimal, and it would be more efficient and economical to periodically maintain and replace parts rather than design them so that no failures occur. An example of the latter might be that of the loading bed of a dump truck where periodic inspection would indicate when plates would need to be repaired or replaced because the consequences of failure would be minor.

## 5. Future Needs

As in any field of design, there are many needs, but in the field of designing to prevent brittle fracture in large structures, there appear to be two pressing needs.

The first need is the translation of existing knowledge (e.g., material behavior, inspection capability, quality control) into practice so that the explainable types of brittle fractures can be eliminated. Almost all the failures in recently constructed structures could have been prevented had existing knowledge possessed by those knowledgeable in the field of brittle fracture been communicated and accepted by designers and fabricators. Thus existing knowledge must be simplified and put into a form useful to practicing engineers.

It is recognized that the use of materials with adequate notch toughness, the proper attention to details and connections, and the use of existing quality-control and inspection techniques increases the cost of the project and complicates the communication problem. However, the consequences of not following proper procedures usually is far more expensive than the initial cost would have been, particularly with the growing tendency toward litigation. During the design stage the lifetime behavior of a structure should be analyzed. The possibility of subcritical crack growth throughout the life of the structure should be considered and nondestructive inspection procedures specified to be sure that crack growth is monitored. In general the basic technology exists for lifetime structural inspection. However, inspection is usually considered to be a maintenance problem rather than a design consideration, and the possible consequences of subcritical crack growth often are not considered in the initial design. In summary the first major need in the field of fracture control in structures is the translation of existing knowledge into a form useful in practice. One aspect of this task is the development of fracture control plans.

The second need arises from the fact that linear-elastic fracture mechanics cannot be used directly in the design of most large structures. Most low- to medium-strength structural steels in the section sizes of interest for large structures are of insufficient thickness to maintain linear-elastic conditions under slow loading and normal service temperatures. For these cases the linear-elastic analysis used to calculate $K_{Ic}$ values is invalidated by yielding and the formation of large inelastic zones near the flaw tip. Under these conditions, which occur in the transition range of elastic-plastic behavior, analyses other than linear-elastic fracture mechanics (LEFM) must be used. However, no simple elastic-plastic yielding fracture mechanics analyses or test methods are yet standardized, as noted earlier herein. It is of interest to note that the toughness requirements for steels used in nuclear vessels are specified in terms of NDT and Charpy V-notch impact values, because the desired behavior is one of nonplane-strain behavior, i.e., elastic-plastic behavior.

At the present time the most promising extensions of LEFM into the elastic-plastic region are the $J$-integral approach, resistance-curve analysis, the crack-opening displacement (COD) method, and the equivalent energy approach. All four techniques are relatively new, and each technique holds promise for specifying material toughness in terms of allowable stress or defect size. Research is needed to prove out these techniques and/or to develop other new promising approaches.

Thus the second general need in the field of fracture control in structures is the development of test methods and analysis techniques to predict rationally the fracture behavior of materials that exhibit elastic-plastic behavior prior to failure. And again, there is a need to translate these procedures into design methods which can be used by engineers in practice.

## References

1. PARKER, E. R., *Brittle Behavior of Engineering Structures*, Wiley, New York, 1957.
2. SHANK, M. E., ed., *Control of Steel Construction To Avoid Brittle Failure*, Welding Research Council, New York, 1957.
3. HALL, W. J., H. KIHARA, W. SOETE, and A. A. WELLS, *Brittle Fracture of Welded Plate*, Prentice-Hall, Englewood Cliffs, N.J., 1967.
4. BOYD, G. M., ed., *Brittle Fracture in Steel Structures*, Butterworth and Co., London, 1970.
5. TIPPER, C. F., *The Brittle Fracture Story*, Cambridge University Press, Cambridge, 1962.
6. LIBOWITZ, H., ed., *Fracture, and Advanced Treatise*, Vols. I–VII, Academic Press, New York, 1968.
7. ROLFE, S. T., and J. M. BARSOM, *Fracture and Fatigue Control in Structures—Applications of Fracture Mechanics*, Prentice-Hall, Englewood Cliffs, N.J., 1976.
8. "Fracture Toughness Testing and Its Applications," *ASTM Special Technical Publication No. 381*, ASTM, Philadelphia, Pa., 1964.
9. SIH, G. C., *Handbook of Stress Intensity Factors*, Lehigh University, Bethlehem, Pa., 1973.
10. HIROSHI, T., *The Stress Analysis of Cracks Handbook*, Del Research Corporation, Bethlehem, Pa., 1973.
11. "Safety and Reliability of Metal Structures," American Society of Civil Engineers Specialty Conference, (Pittsburgh, Pa., Nov. 1972), ASCE 1972.
12. MADISON, R. B., "Application of Fracture Mechanics to Bridges," Ph.D. thesis, Lehigh University, Bethlehem, Pa., 1969, and *Fritz Engineering Laboratory Report No. 335.2*, June 1969.
13. "Standard Method of Test for Plane-Strain Fracture Toughness of Metallic Materials," *ASTM Standard E399*, ASTM, 1972.
14. "Collapse of U.S. 35 Highway Bridge, Point Pleasant, West Virginia, December 15, 1967," *Report No. NTSB-HAR-71-1*, NTSB, Washington, D.C., 1971.
15. BENNETT, J. A., and H. MINDLIN, "Metallurgical Aspects of the Failure of the Pt. Pleasant Bridge," *J. Testing Evaluation*, ASTM, Philadelphia, Pa., March 1973, pp. 152–61.
16. "State Cites Defective Steel in Bryte Bend Failure," *Eng. News Rec.*, Vol. 185, No. 8, Aug. 20, 1970, p. 22.

17. "Joint Redesign on Cracked Box Girder Cuts into Record Tied Arch's Beauty," *Eng. News Rec.*, Vol. 188, No. 13, March 30, 1972, p. 12.
18. *ASME Boiler and Pressure Vessel Code*, Section III, Section G, ASME, New York, 1971.
19. American Association of State Highway and Transportation Officials, *Material Specifications*, AASHTO, Washington, D.C., 1974.

# On Methods of Structural Analysis and Design for Earthquake

JOHN M. BIGGS, ROBERT J. HANSEN, AND MYLE J. HOLLEY, JR.*

## Introduction

Our ability to analyze mathematical models subject to seismic inputs has increased by orders of magnitude over the past two or three decades. Unfortunately, there has not been a corresponding increase in our ability to *design* structures for earthquake. As a partial assessment of the state-of-the-art of seismic design, the authors offer a few comments on the various methods of analysis currently employed and the difficulties encountered in the practical design of structures.

The subject is particularly appropriate for this symposium because of the very significant contributions which Dr. Newmark has made in this field. His early work on numerical methods of analysis [1] paved the way for later exploitation of the computer to give us the very powerful analytical capability we now enjoy. His work on seismic response spectra [2] helped provide a practical means of representing ground motions and analyzing complex structures. The scope of his work has been far-ranging and he has been responsible, perhaps more than any other worker in the field, for the advances made in earthquake engineering.

In fact, Dr. Newmark and others in the analytical field have done their work so well that our ability to analyze has far outstripped our ability to utilize the results for design purposes. Some of us have become so enthralled by the joys of sophisticated analysis that we have lost sight of the real objective, i.e., design for satisfactory performance. This is not meant to imply that Dr. Newmark's work is impractical. To the contrary, those of us who have worked with Dr. Newmark know him to be a most practical engineer,

*Professors of Civil Engineering, M.I.T., and principals, Hansen, Holley & Biggs, Inc., Cambridge, Massachusetts.

and he has made significant contributions in the design area. However, we still have much to learn about the seismic design of multidegree systems, particularly where inelastic behavior is involved.

## Elastic Design

We shall consider first the case of elastic design, i.e,. the design of a structure intended to remain elastic during the design earthquake. Perhaps the outstanding example is the currently used procedure for the design of nuclear reactor containments. Three methods of analysis will be considered: the response spectrum approach utilizing modal analysis, time-history analysis using either real or artificial accelerograms, and random vibration analysis.

The response spectrum approach is the most convenient to use, and the spectrum is probably the easiest and most reliable way to represent the predicted ground motion .The one difficulty in the method lies in the combination of modal components to predict the peak responses. The square root of the sum of the squares (SRSS) of the modal peaks is commonly used, with special consideration given to closely spaced modes, which may be additive.

Time-history analysis may be attractive to some because it provides a completely deterministic result for the particular ground motion. However, any two motions may produce quite different peak responses, even though they have the same intensity and statistical properties. Thus, for design purposes it is necessary to analyze for several motions, and the quantity of computation becomes excessive. The use of artificial motions, generated from a predicted ground motion response spectrum, or a spectral density function, has become popular in recent years. Artificial motions have the advantage over real recorded motions in that a single record can represent the predicted single-degree response over the entire frequency range. However, the difficulty in predicting peak responses is not removed, because two statistically equal artificial motions are still different in detail and produce different results for multidegree systems.

Random vibration analysis is attractive because it recognizes the true probabilistic nature of the seismic design problem. The method easily produces the rms response in a single mode. However, difficulties arise in predicting the ratio of peak to rms response and in combining modal responses. Certain assumptions must be made in these regards to obtain the total peak response. Nevertheless, important progress is currently being made in this area, and it seems probable that random vibration analysis will eventually prove to be the most satisfactory approach.

It may be noted that the difficulties encountered in all three methods really stem from the same problem, namely, that the details of the ground motion time-history have an important effect on the response of a multidegree system and that these details cannot be predicted for a particular site.

The nature of the problem is further illustrated by the results of a recent study at M.I.T. [3]. For this study a group of 39 real earthquake accelerograms were arbitrarily selected and assumed to represent possible motions at a site. A four-degree system was analyzed for all 39 records and comparisons were made among (1) the statistics of the 39 peak responses, (2) the response predicted by the mean response spectrum of the 39 motions, and(3) the response due to 15 artificial motions, all generated from that mean spectrum. The structure considered was a four-story building very simply modeled as a four-degree shear beam with 2% damping. The purpose was not to investigate the modeling of real structures.

Typical results are shown in Table 1, where peak interstory displacements are tabulated. The first column contains the statistics of the responses due to the 39 real earthquakes. All records were normalized to the same peak ground acceleration, although it may be argued that some other basis should have been used. The large coefficients of variation, which are to be expected, indicate that peak ground acceleration is not a sufficient indication of earthquake effect and that use of a real record is not a reasonable design approach. The second column shows the response predicted by a response spectrum analysis using SRSS modal combination. When the mean response spectrum of the 39 earthquakes is used, the result agrees very closely with the mean of the 39 time-history analyses. The same is true for the mean plus one standard deviation or any other probability level. This result confirms

**Table 1**
**Peak Interstory Elastic Displacements of Four-Story Building, Fundamental Period = 1.13 Seconds**

| *Story* | *Time-History Analysis of 39 Earthquakes** | *SRSS Modal Analysis—Mean (or Mean + $\sigma$) Response Spectrum* | *Time-History Analysis of 39 Artificial Motions†* | |
|---|---|---|---|---|
| 1 | 0.122 | 0.126 | 0.133 | Mean |
| 2 | 0.107 | 0.104 | 0.155 | |
| 3 | 0.092 | 0.088 | 0.093 | |
| 4 | 0.063 | 0.059 | 0.064 | |
| 1 | 0.194 | 0.193 | — | Mean + $\sigma$ |
| 2 | 0.169 | 0.166 | — | |
| 3 | 0.137 | 0.131 | — | |
| 4 | 0.089 | 0.083 | — | |
| 1 | 0.58 | — | 0.25 | Coefficient of variation |
| 2 | 0.57 | — | 0.29 | |
| 3 | 0.48 | — | 0.29 | |
| 4 | 0.40 | — | 0.24 | |

*Normalized to 0.3$g$ peak ground accelerations.
†All generated from mean response spectrum.

the belief that the much simpler response spectrum method produces a reliable prediction of the effects of many possible motions at the site and eliminates the need for many time-history analyses.

The third column in Table 1 shows the results obtained from 15 artificial motions, all generated from the mean response spectrum by a widely used method [4]. Again, the means of the 15 responses agree very closely with those obtained by the other methods. However, even though the artificial motions have identical statistical properties, the coefficients of variation are still large. In fact, the ratio of maximum to minimum response for the 15 motions exceeds 2 in all cases. There are two causes for this variation: (1) It is impossible to exactly match the response spectrum, and (2) for different motions the modes combine differently to produce the peak response. This indicates that artificial motions do not solve the problem and that, if used for design, several must be employed to ensure a safe result.

It should be noted that the response to a particular time-history input may be significantly affected by slight changes in the natural periods of the structure. Since for real structures these can never be computed accurately, in time-history analysis it is necessary to assume a range of values, which further complicates the procedure. This need is eliminated in the response spectrum method by using a smooth response spectrum which does not include the valleys found in a real spectrum.

In the seismic design of nuclear power plants the response spectrum approach is used. One exception is the generation of floor response spectra for equipment design. In this case, time-history analysis of the complete structure is normally employed, usually with artificial motions. Frequently, only one such motion is used, and, as indicated above, this may produce an unconservative result. One of the authors has proposed a method [5] which requires only a response spectrum analysis of the structure. It is believed that this, or similar methods proposed by others, is preferable to the time-history procedure.

In summary, it is concluded that, for elastic design, the response spectrum approach is the most reasonable and certainly the most convenient. Time-history analysis requires several inputs and the use of an average or envelope of the results. It is much more convenient to introduce this averaging process in the construction of a smoothed response spectrum. Random vibration analysis is of interest because of its rationality, but further development is required before practicing engineers will be comfortable with this approach.

## Design for Inelastic Behavior

Turning now to inelastic analysis, the situation becomes much more complicated. The design of conventional buildings anticipates inelastic behavior during strong earthquakes even though the design is normally based on elastic analysis. This practice has been followed because of the difficulties of inelastic analysis, with respect to both the effort required and the accuracy that can be achieved. The most urgent need in the structural portion of earthquake engineering is the development of a reliable yet practical design procedure based on inelastic behavior.

At present, only time-history analysis can give a reasonable prediction of the response of multidegree systems in the inelastic range. However, this is not practical for design purposes because of the computational effort required and because of the difficulties in reliable modeling. Also, even more than in the elastic case, the variability in response to different possible motions is great, and design cannot reliably be based on a single motion.

The M.I.T. study previously mentioned also included inelastic responses of the four-degree systems to real and artificial motions. Typical results are shown in Table 2, in the form of interstory ductility ratios [10]. In this case the story resistances were selected so as to be proportional to the first mode elastic story shears. The resistance functions were assumed to be elastoplastic. In contrast to the elastic case (Table 1), the means for the 39 real motions and the 15 artificial motions are considerably different in a particular story, although the averages over the four stories are similar.

The coefficients of variation in Table 2 are generally larger than in the elastic case, and the differences in the maximum and minimum responses for both sets of motions are rather dramatic. This further illustrates the point that any two motions, although presumably similar, can produce radically

**Table 2**
**Peak Interstory Ductility Ratios of Four-Story Building, Fundamental Period = 1.13 Seconds.**

| *Story* | *Analysis of 39 Earthquakes** | *Analysis of 15 Artificial Motions†* | |
|---|---|---|---|
| 1 | 5.7 | 4.4 | Mean |
| 2 | 2.6 | 3.2 | |
| 3 | 4.0 | 5.0 | |
| 4 | 9.7 | 13.8 | |
| 1 | 1.23 | 0.42 | Coefficient of variation |
| 2 | 0.48 | 0.31 | |
| 3 | 0.48 | 0.28 | |
| 4 | 0.49 | 0.39 | |
| 1 | 38.6–0.8 | 10.2–2.6 | Max.-Min. |
| 2 | 5.9–0.8 | 5.6–1.9 | |
| 3 | 8.9–1.0 | 7.6–2.9 | |
| 4 | 27.8–2.2 | 21.1–7.0 | |

*Normalized to 0.3$g$ peak ground acceleration.
†All generated from mean response spectrum.

different inelastic responses, and any particular motion may be unconservative for design.

Table 2 also indicates another inherent difficulty in design for inelastic behavior, namely, that of achieving uniform ductility ratios throughout the structure. In this case, as in most cases, the ratios are much higher in the bottom and top stories. This behavior is not predicted by elastic analysis.

Inspection of the individual responses to the 39 real earthquakes leads to the interesting, though not surprising, observation that a yielding structure has an effective period longer than the elastic period. Little correlation is found between the peak response and the ordinate to the response spectrum at the elastic period. However, there is some correlation at the effective inelastic period, which, unfortunately, is not easily predicted. This suggests that the designer should be cautious in cases where a lengthening period would result in greater elastic response.

The above discussion serves to indicate the difficulties encountered in the design of a structure for a desired level of yielding. The current code procedures, based on equivalent static forces and elastic analysis, are not satisfactory. In another M.I.T. study [6] several typical buildings were designed according to the Uniform Building Code and then analyzed to determine the inelastic response due to a strong ground motion. Five designs were made for each building corresponding to zones 0, 1, 2, and 3 plus a zone 4 with a seismic coefficient of 2. The results are shown in Fig. 1, where the average interstory ductility ratio is plotted against the design zone. With one exception (a shear wall building with relatively short natural period), there is little improvement with increasing design zone. There is even less reduction in peak interstory displacements. The reason for these results, which may not be valid for short period buildings, is that an increase in design forces results in an increase in stiffness and hence an increase in inertia forces greater than the code anticipates. The results also showed a very poor distribution of yielding over the height of the building. Since building damage is primarily related to peak interstory displacements and ductility ratios, increasing the design zone does little to reduce damage in a strong earthquake. The code procedure does not provide the designer with an effective means for improving the building's performance because he has no direct control over the response parameters which cause damage.

An advance over the simple code procedure is provided through the use of the inelastic response spectra proposed by Professors Newmark and Hall [7]. This permits design for specified ductility and drift ratios. However, since it is based on the response of single-degree systems, it does not, by itself, eliminate the difficulty in achieving uniform yielding and displacement over the building height. The seriousness of this problem was demonstrated by an investigation of several possible design applications of the inelastic spectra [8]. Again using simple shear beam models, the systems were designed by

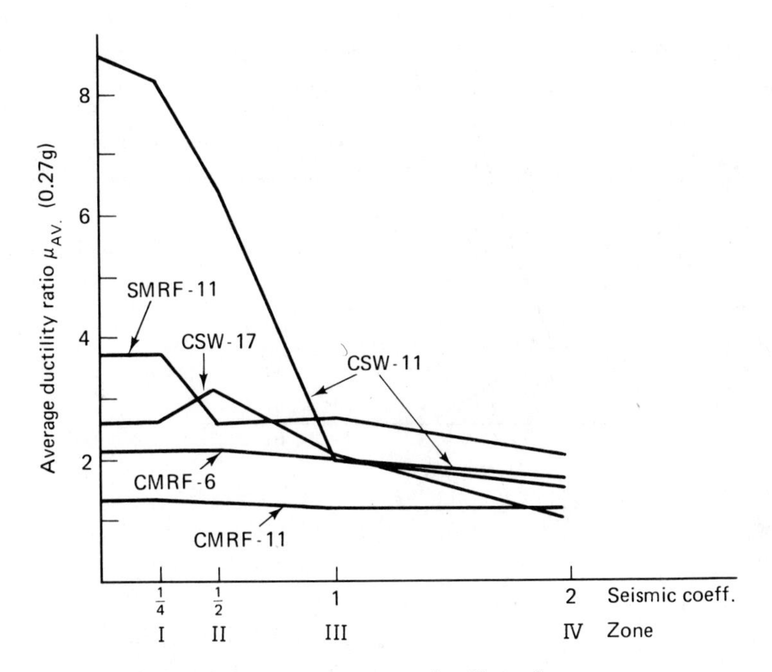


**Fig. 1.** Effect of design zone on average ductility ratio
CSW—Concrete Shear Wall
SMRF—Steel Moment Resisting Frame
CMRF—Concrete Moment Resisting Frame
Numbers indicate stories

the inelastic spectrum and then analyzed to obtain inelastic response to an artificial motion matching the design spectrum. A typical result is shown in Fig. 2. The distribution of stiffness and resistance over the building height was based on elastic analysis, and the resistance function was assumed to be elastoplastic.

As may be seen in Fig. 2, the average inter-story distortions are very close to the design values, but the distribution over the building height is far from uniform. No satisfactory means for controlling this distribution was found. The problem is further complicated by the sensitivity of the results to the assumed resistance function, which cannot be predicted with confidence. When a trilinear function was assumed, the distribution was slightly improved, but when a stiffness-degrading model was employed, excessive distortions were computed in either the top or bottom story.

The design procedure proposed by the ATC Engineering Panel and experimentally applied to several buildings in the ATC-2 project [9] utilizes the inelastic response spectrum and also attempts to control local member ductility ratios and interstory drifts. However, to make the method practical, it is based on elastic modal analysis, and ductility ratios are computed on

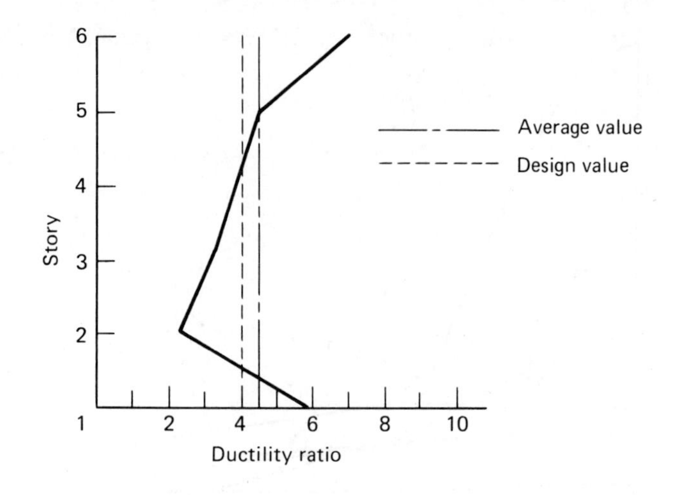


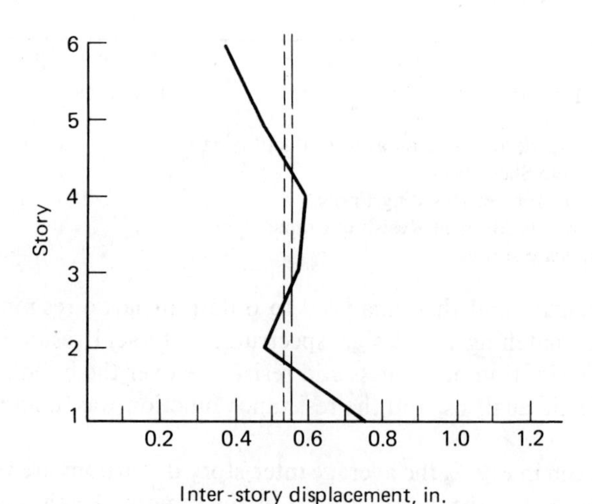


**Fig. 2.** Peak inter-story displacements and ductility ratios for building designed by inelastic response spectrum

the basis of the peak elastic distortion and the yield limit distortion. This procedure is questionable since the local inelastic distortions may be quite different. However, the approach shows considerable promise, and further study based on inelastic analysis may demonstrate its validity.

In summary, we have not yet learned how to design structures so as to ensure satisfactory performance in the inelastic range. Provisions requiring the design of details for adequate ductility may prevent total collapse, but currently known design procedures do not eliminate the possibility of severe damage during a strong earthquake. Use of inelastic response spectra is certainly an improvement over current code procedures, but further research is required on its application to multistoried buildings.

## Seismic Design in Perspective

It is clear that the inadequacies of our methods of predicting the response of building structures to earthquake ground motion derive from

1. Uncertainties in the detail of ground motion input.
2. Inherent sensitivity of the response of the structural systems of interest to the detail of ground motion input.

The inadequacies of our methods of seismic *design* of building structures derive not simply from the uncertainties associated with predictions of response. Rather they reflect an incomplete assessment of the earthquake risk and associated costs.

We engineers have given very little attention to the effectiveness of the total seismic design process, i.e., all the steps from evaluation of the seismic threat and representation of the ground motion, through dynamic analysis, and down to the detailed design of structural components. For a given set of procedures in these steps, what degree of protection against earthquake do we really provide? What protection should be provided? Are we designing to prevent collapse and hence loss of life, or are we also attempting to reduce damage and economic loss? These questions must be answered before we can reasonably select the most appropriate analysis and design procedures.

This is obviously a probabilistic matter. It is possible that use of a relatively crude method of analysis with corresponding uncertainties has little effect on the final probability of failure. On the other hand, there may be considerable economic payoff in the use of more reliable methods, coupled with less conservatism in design. Research is needed in this area. We structural engineers, while continuing to improve our methods, must not become so involved in the details of analysis as to lose sight of the overall objective.

The types of systems commonly used for multistory buildings, and, indeed, for most other constructed facilities, have evolved independently of the earthquake hazard. It is not surprising that research has focused on the response of *these* structural types to ground motion and on modifications solely of those details which may improve their response. If return periods for severe earthquakes were much shorter, say 10 years, it is likely that the evolution of structural systems would have been very different. The costs, real and emotional, as well as the lessons learned from such frequently recurring events would have dictated a different evolution of size, configurations, material combinations, design methods, and criteria. The contrasting real history has witnessed the creation of our complexes of major constructed facilities over a period of time which has been brief when measured in return periods of severe earthquakes. Moreover, much of our present understanding of earthquake phenomena, as well as our present analytical capabilities, has been gained over a still smaller recent time period.

Continuing efforts to improve our methods of predicting response to ground motion surely must be encouraged. However, we may be approaching a time of diminishing returns, in terms of overall design goals, unless such effort is accompanied by accelerated research in other relevant aspects of the total problem of seismic design. This must include better assessment of all costs which may be associated with the occurrence of a severe earthquake in a large urban area. It must also include the development of new structural systems specifically designed to resist severe ground motion with minimum damage and an assessment of the impact of such systems on total cost.

## Summary

The authors have commented on the principal methods of analyzing structural response to ground motion. They have emphasized the difficulties encountered in the application of these methods to structural design, which arise from uncertainties of the detail of ground motion and from the sensitivity of response to such uncertainties, inherent in the structural systems of interest. Finally, they have suggested that further progress in seismic design will require an intensified research effort into aspects of the problem other than response analysis per se. This effort probably should include the development of new structural systems (which may be less sensitive to uncertainties of the detail of ground motion). It must include a better definition of the overall objectives of seismic design and the development of criteria which reflect both the economic impacts of a severe earthquake and the costs of design measures aimed at reduction of those impacts.

## References

1. NEWMARK, N. M., "Computation of Dynamic Structural Response in the Range Approaching Failure," *Proceedings, Symposium on Earthquake and Blast Effects*, EERI, Los Angeles, 1952.
2. NEWMARK, N. M., J. A. BLUME, and K. K. KAPUR, "Seismic Design Spectra for Nuclear Power Plants," *J. Power Div. ASCE*, Vol. 99, Nov. 1973, pp. 287–303.
3. "Comparison of Seismic Analysis Procedures for Elastic Multi-degree Systems," Seismic Safety of Buildings Project (NSF ATA 74-06935), M.I.T. Department of Civil Engineering, Report No. R76-3, Cambridge, Mass., Jan. 1976.
4. VANMARCKE, E. H., and C. A. CORNELL, "Seismic Risk Analysis and Design

Response Spectra," *Proceedings, Conference on Safety and Reliability of Metal Structures*, ASCE, Pittsburgh, 1972.

5. Biggs, J. M., "Seismic Response Spectra for Equipment Design in Nuclear Power Plants," Proceedings of the First International Conference on Structural Mechanics in Reactor Technology, Berlin, Sept. 1972.
6. Biggs, J. M., and P. H. Grace, "Seismic Response of Buildings Designed by Code for Different Earthquake Intensities," *Report R73-7*, M.I.T. Department of Civil Engineering, Cambridge, Mass., Jan. 1973.
7. Newmark, N. M., and W. J. Hall, "A Rational Approach to Seismic Design Standards for Structures," Paper No. 283, Fifth World Conference on Earthquake Engineering, Rome, 1973.
8. Isbell, J. E., and J. M. Biggs, "Inelastic Design of Building Frames to Resist Earthquakes," *Report R74-36*, M.I.T. Department of Civil Engineering, Cambridge, Mass., May 1974.
9. "An Evaluation of a Response Spectrum Approach to Seismic Design of Buildings," Applied Technology Council, San Francisco, Sept. 1974.
10. "Variability of Inelastic Structural Response Due to Real and Artificial Ground Motions," Seismic Safety of Buildings Project (NSF ATA 74–06935), M.I.T. Department of Civil Engineering, Report No. R76-4, Cambridge, Mass., Jan. 1976.

# The Capacity of Extreme Earthquake Motions to Damage Structures

G. W. Housner and P. C. Jennings*

The possible occurrence of an extreme event poses special problems when designing structures to resist the forces of nature, such as floods, winds, and earthquakes. For example, a dam and reservoir system may be designed for the "100-year flood" knowing that a greater flood may occur and cause severe damage, though the probability of its occurrence during the useful life of the structure is very small. When designing a high-rise building in the Midwestern United States for wind forces according to the building code, it is known that greater forces may be encountered which could be expected to cause severe damage to a code-designed building, though again the probability of the building experiencing such extreme wind is very low. In seismic regions a similar question arises as to what consideration should be given to the maximum credible ground shaking when designing a structure. On the one hand, there is the understandable desire to build a structure that can resist the worst possible ground shaking without damage; on the other hand, the extra cost of doing this, combined with the low probability of occurrence, indicates that less severe design criteria should be used. For certain important (costly and/or potentially hazardous) structures the consequences of damage or failure are balanced against the cost of preventing damage and the probability of occurrence, and a decision is made as to the appropriate level of design. Ordinary structures are not sufficiently important to justify the expenditure required to make a careful cost-benefit analysis, and the earthquake design of these structures usually follows the minimum requirements of the building code. In this chapter we shall address the question, What is the capacity of extreme earthquake ground motions to damage modern code-designed

*California Institute of Technology, Pasadena, California.

structures, and how can this capacity be related to quantitative measures of the strength of shaking?

If one had a complete and accurate description of a structure, its structural elements, and the material properties under large as well as small deformations, then, in principle, an analysis could be made which would establish the damage sustained through the action of specified ground shaking and which could determine how the structure would collapse if the severity of ground shaking exceeded the resistive capacity of the structure. Unfortunately, our present knowledge of the dynamic properties of materials and structural elements, although improving rapidly, is not yet adequate to permit such analyses to be made. However, the principles of mechanics can provide some broad understanding of how intense ground motions can progressively damage structures and observations of damage sustained during actual earthquakes whose ground motions were recorded can provide guidelines.

One approach to this problem was that of Newmark and Veletsos [1], who calculated yield spectra for elastoplastic deformation. The use of yield spectra permits estimations to be made of maximum displacements and permanent deformation. Another approach was that of Housner [2], who used the response spectra for linear systems to estimate the energy available to cause damage. Another approach was that of Jennings [3] and Hudson [4], who used "equivalent viscous damping" to represent the energy dissipation of hysteretic systems. All the foregoing are attempts to develop a simple, approximate method of handling a very complex problem. There is great practical value in a simple method that throws light on a complex problem and assists in making correct decisions.

## Available Energy in the Ground Shaking

During an earthquake the motion of the ground puts energy into the structure, both kinetic and potential. In time this is dissipated by damping, i.e., by energy dissipation not associated with observable damage. If the shaking is sufficiently intense energy is dissipated by damage to the elements of the structure. If energy is fed into the structure at a sufficiently slow rate, the dissipation due to damping will prevent the structural members from becoming overstressed, but during a high rate of energy input the dissipation by damping may be inadequate to hold the energy level in the structure below the threshold for damage, and then plastic deformation, cracking, etc., may result. It is possible to draw some general conclusions about energy input in the case of simple linearly elastic oscillators, and these conclusions, it is thought, may also be applied satisfactorily to nonlinear hysteretic systems if the nonlinearity is not too strong. When the base of the structure is shaken by a horizontal acceleration $a$, an equivalent vibration problem is that of the system with fixed base and applied force $ma$, shown in Fig. 1, and we may ask, What is the energy input to the system? The dynamics of the linear system are described by

$$\ddot{x} + 2n\omega\dot{x} + \omega^2 x = a, \tag{1}$$

where $x$ is the relative displacement, $n$ is the fraction of critical damping, and $\omega$ is the circular natural frequency. The total work per unit mass done by the applied force during the excitation is the time integral of the impulse

$$W_1 = \int_0^\infty a(t)\dot{x}\, dt, \tag{2}$$

which is equal to the energy input to the oscillator by the earthquake. We define the "frequency ensemble work," $W_F$, by the integration of $W_1$ with respect to the frequency $\omega$:

$$W_F = \int_0^\infty W_1\, d\omega = \int_0^\infty \int_0^\infty a(t)\dot{x}(t, \omega)\, dt\, d\omega. \tag{3}$$

This is a measure of the capacity of the ground motion to do work on structures of all natural frequencies. Upon interchanging the order of integration,

$$W_F = \int_0^\infty a(t) \left\{ \int_0^\infty \dot{x}\, d\omega \right\} dt. \tag{4}$$

The inner integral can be evaluated by a technique that utilizes the solution of Eq. (1) in the form of a Duhamel integral:

$$x = \frac{1}{\omega_n} \int_0^t a(\tau) e^{-n\omega(t-\tau)} \sin \omega_n(t - \tau)\, d\tau, \tag{5}$$

where $\omega_n = \omega\sqrt{1 - n^2}$. We may, therefore, write, after changing the order of integration and changing variables to $\mu = \omega_n(t - \tau)$,

$$\int_0^\infty x\, d\omega = \int_0^t a(\tau) \left\{ \int_0^\infty e^{-\mu\sqrt{n/(1-n^2)}} (\sin \mu) \frac{d\mu}{\mu} \right\} \frac{d\tau}{\sqrt{1 - n^2}} \tag{6}$$

$$= \int_0^t a(\tau) \frac{\cos^{-1} n}{\sqrt{1 - n^2}}\, d\tau, \tag{7}$$

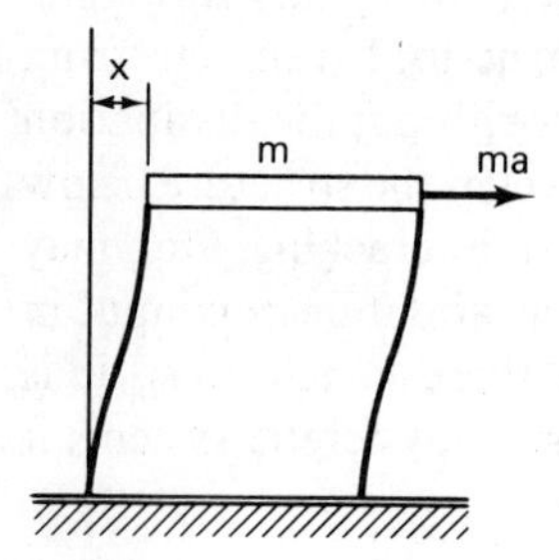


**Fig. 1.** Simple linear structure

from which there is obtained

$$\frac{\sqrt{1-n^2}}{\cos^{-1} n}\int_0^\infty x\,d\omega = v(t), \tag{8}$$

where $v(t)$ is the ground velocity during the earthquake. Differentiating both sides of Eq. (8) with respect to $t$ gives

$$\frac{\sqrt{1-n^2}}{\cos^{-1} n}\int_0^\infty \dot{x}\,d\omega = a(t). \tag{9}$$

Equations (8) and (9) are an integral pair relating the oscillator displacement and velocity to the ground acceleration and velocity in a novel fashion. Making use of Eq. (9), we can write Eq. (4) as

$$W_F = \int_0^\infty W_1\,d\omega = \int_0^\infty a(t)\left\{\int_0^\infty \dot{x}\,d\omega\right\}dt = \frac{\cos^{-1} n}{\sqrt{1-n^2}}\int_0^\infty a^2\,dt. \tag{10}$$

This result was obtained in a different way by Arias and Lange [5] in developing a measure of seismic intensity. The damping function, $\cos^{-1} n/\sqrt{1-n^2}$, decreases as $n$ increases, as shown in Fig. 2. This results from the fact that $\dot{x}$ is smaller for damped oscillations than for undamped, and, consequently, the power input $(m\dot{x})$ is less. However, the decrease with damping is not large for the values of damping applicable to earthquake response: For 5% of critical damping $W_F$ is 3% less than for 0% damping, and for 20% critical damping $W_F$ is only 8% less than for 0% damping.

If the energy input $W_1$ is integrated with respect to period, $T$, instead of

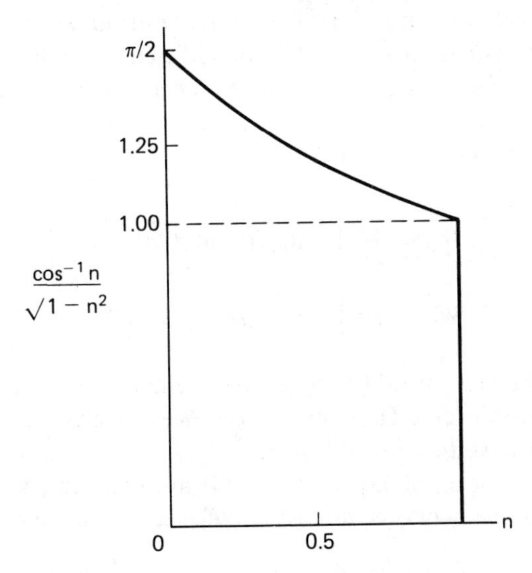


**Fig. 2.** Plot of damping function versus fraction of critical damping

frequency, $\omega$, for an undamped system, there is obtained the "period ensemble work," $W_T$:

$$W_T = \int_{\infty}^{0} W_1\, dT = 2\pi \int_0^{\infty} W_1 \frac{d\omega}{\omega^2} = 2\pi \int_0^{\infty} v\left\{\int_0^{\infty} x\, d\omega\right\} dt = \pi^2 \int_0^{\infty} v^2\, dt, \tag{11}$$

where $v$ is the ground velocity, and integration by parts has been used to evaluate the integral.* $W_T$ is not calculated for $n \neq 0$, because for damped oscillators the factor of $1/\omega^2$ appears to prevent convergence of the integrals at low frequencies.

For an undamped oscillator, therefore, the following set of relations describe the capability of earthquake ground shaking to input energy

$$W_1 = \int_0^{\infty} a\dot{x}\, dt,$$

$$W_F = \int_0^{\infty} W_1\, d\omega = \frac{\pi}{2} \int_0^{\infty} a^2\, dt, \tag{12}$$

$$W_T = \int_{\infty}^{0} W_1\, dT = \pi^2 \int_0^{\infty} v^2\, dt. \tag{13}$$

If the oscillator in Fig. 1 is a nonlinear hysteretic structure, the equation of motion can, in most cases, be written as

$$\ddot{x} + 2n\omega\dot{x} + \omega^2 f(x, t) = a(t) \tag{14}$$

in which $f(x, t)$ denotes the hysteretic force-deflection relation and $n$ is the fraction of critical damping of small, essentially linear vibrations. In writing this equation it has been assumed that for sufficiently small values of $x$ and $t$ that $f(x, t) = x$. Thus, $\omega$ is the natural frequency of the small vibrations at the beginning of the earthquake response. For oscillators described by Eq. (14), the frequency ensemble work and the period ensemble work are again given by

$$W_F = \int_0^{\infty} \int_0^{\infty} a(t)\dot{x}(t, \omega)\, dt\, d\omega, \tag{15}$$

$$W_T = 2\pi \int_0^{\infty} \int_0^{\infty} a(t)\dot{x}(t, \omega)\, dt \frac{d\omega}{\omega^2}, \tag{16}$$

in which the integrals would have to be evaluated numerically using the indicated order of variables, and the convergence of the expressions, especially Eq. (16), would have to be established.

Because the forms of Eq. (15) and (4) are identical, and because the frequency ensemble work is almost unaffected by large changes in the

*The foregoing evaluations of $W_F$ and $W_T$ involve interchanging the order of infinite integrals, and we are indebted to James Beck for deriving a proof of the validity of this procedure.

amount of damping for linear structures, it seems probable that $W_F$ may be relatively insensitive to the mechanism by which energy is dissipated.

The above results indicate that both the integral of the squared ground acceleration and the integral of the squared ground velocity are broadband measures of the energy input capabilities of the ground motions, the former giving more weight to higher frequencies than the latter. It does not follow that they are necessarily good measures of the potential destructiveness of the ground motion without further qualification. For example, $W_F$ and $W_T$ for a strong short-duration ground motion may be the same as for a weaker ground shaking of very long duration. However, if consideration is restricted to strong ground shaking only, $W_F$ and $W_T$ are gross measures of the potential destructiveness of the ground shaking. They are not precise measures, for the damage also depends on the characteristics of the degrading structure as well as on the ground shaking. One structure might be severely damaged by the strong phase of ground shaking and then suffer additional damage to the point of failure from the following less intense ground motion, whereas another structure might be only moderately damaged by the strong phase of ground shaking and not further affected by the weaker following motion. In the latter case, a more meaningful measure would be the squared acceleration, or squared velocity, integrated over the strong phase of shaking only. Some representative values of $W_F$ are given in Table 1, and an example of the

**Table 1**
**Zero Damped Values of $W_F$ (ft$^2$/sec$^3$)**

| | | |
|---|---|---|
| El Centro, 1940 | N-S | 204 |
| | E-W | 140 |
| | U-D | 66 |
| | | 410 |
| Olympia, 1949 | S86W | 128 |
| | S04E | 84 |
| | U-D | 22 |
| | | 234 |
| Taft, 1952 | N69W | 56 |
| | S20W | 56 |
| | U-D | 25 |
| | | 137 |
| El Centro, 1934 | N-S | 58 |
| | E-W | 48 |
| | U-D | 8 |
| | | 114 |
| Millikan Library, 1971 | N-S | 41 |
| | E-W | 37 |
| | U-D | 14 |
| | | 92 |

integral of squared acceleration is shown in Fig. 3 for four different accelerograms from the San Fernando earthquake [11]. The curves in Fig. 3 depict the value of the integral

$$\int_0^\infty (a_x^2 + a_y^2 + a_z^2)\,dt,$$

which is the sum of the $W_F$ for all three components of motion. The figures show clearly that the initial strong phase of shaking was followed by an extended period of weaker, decreasing motion.

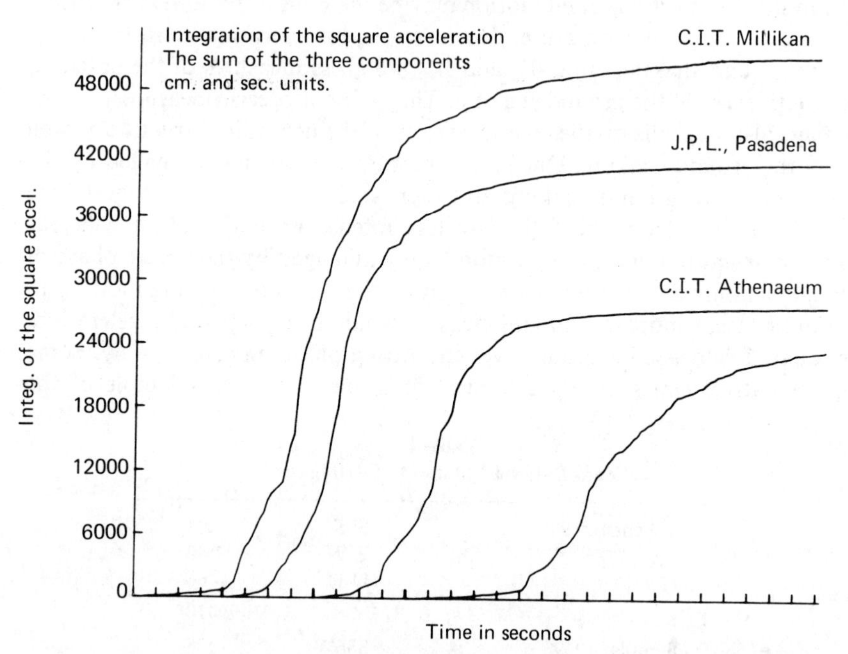


**Fig. 3.** Integration of squared acceleration. Curves represent the sum of the three components of motion in centimeter-second units.

## Available Vibrational Energy

An alternative approach is to look at the maximum total energy of vibration (potential plus kinetic). If the system in Fig. 1 is excited by ground acceleration $a$, the maximum vibrational energy per unit mass attained by the structure can be written

$$E_{\max} = \tfrac{1}{2} S_n^2, \tag{17}$$

where $S_n$ is a velocity response spectrum. The following integral may then be taken as a measure of the energy available for damage:

$$W_n' = \frac{1}{2}\int_0^\infty S_n^2\,d\omega. \tag{18}$$

This expression, which is closely related to the spectrum intensity (6), has an appeal on physical grounds, and its use can also be rationalized by the following argument. It is known from the theory of the Fourier integral that

$$\int_0^\infty a^2 \, dt = \frac{1}{\pi} \int_0^\infty F^2(\omega) \, d\omega, \tag{19}$$

where $F(\omega)$ is the Fourier transform of the acceleration $a(t)$. The expression for evaluating the velocity response spectrum $S_0$ is the same as that for evaluating $F(\omega)$, the only difference being in the limits of integration [7, 8]. The upper limit of the integral for $S_0$ is $t_{\max}$, which gives maximum values of $S_0$, whereas the upper limit for $F(\omega)$ is $t_c$, the time at which the ground motion ceases. $S_0$ is therefore an upper bound for $F(\omega)$ and is, on the average about 15% larger. Hence, we may write

$$W_F = \frac{\pi}{2} \int_0^\infty a^2 \, dt = \int_0^\infty \frac{1}{2} F^2(\omega) \, d\omega = c \int_0^\infty \frac{1}{2} S_0^2(\omega) \, d\omega, \tag{20}$$

where $c$ is approximately equal to $\frac{3}{4}$ for typical accelerograms. In the case of nonzero damping, we define

$$W_n = c \int_0^\infty \frac{1}{2} S_n^2 \, d\omega, \tag{21}$$

where $n$ is the fraction of critical damping. This expression for $W_n$ may be a better estimate of the energy available for damage than $W_F$ as it does not include in the energy input the energy dissipated by damping during the strongest portion of the response. For strong shaking of duration greater than about 5 sec, the relative ordinates of $S_n$ can be represented approximately as shown in Table 2. For example, at 5% damping $S_{0.05}$ is one-half as large as $S_0$ and, therefore, $W_n$ is one-quarter as large as $W_0$. Approximately, then, the energy $0.25W_0$ may be taken as the energy available to do damage to structures that have approximately 5% damping when subjected to strong ground shaking.

Some representative values of $W_n$ are shown in Table 3. These were calculated from the smoothed velocity response spectra (three components)

**Table 2**
**Approximate Relative Ordinates of $S_n$ for Strong Ground Shaking**

| *Damping* | *Ordinates* |
|---|---|
| 0.00 | 1.00 |
| 0.02 | 0.70 |
| 0.05 | 0.50 |
| 0.10 | 0.35 |
| 0.20 | 0.25 |

Table 3

Representative Values of $W_n = \frac{1}{2}\int_0^\infty S_n^2\, d\omega$ (ft²/sec³), Sum of Three Components

| | % Damping | | | | |
|---|---|---|---|---|---|
| *Energy Intensity* | $W_0$ | $W_2$ | $W_5$ | $W_{10}$ | $W_{20}$ |
| 1 | 62 | 31 | 17 | 10 | 5 |
| 2 | 125 | 62 | 35 | 20 | 10 |
| 3 | 280 | 140 | 80 | 45 | 22 |
| 4 | 500 | 250 | 140 | 80 | 40 |
| 5 | 785 | 390 | 220 | 125 | 62 |

of the Millikan Library accelerograms recorded during the San Fernando earthquake (20% $g$ peak acceleration, 10-sec duration of strong shaking), which is listed as energy intensity 2 in Table 3. Energy intensity 1 represents ground motion having amplitudes two-thirds as large, and intensities 3, 4, and 5 correspond to ground motions having amplitudes 1.5, 2.0, and 2.5 times as large, respectively.

## Relation to Observed Earthquake Damage

The relations $W_F$ and $W_n$ are energy inputs integrated over all frequencies and therefore cannot be related directly to damage observed in a single structure. By examining the earthquake response of a large number of structures of different periods, however, and comparing with $W_F$ and $W_n$, it is possible to obtain an estimate of the values of $W_F$ and $W_n$ that are indicative of damage to modern, code-designed structures. The San Fernando earthquake of February 9, 1971 was the first to give enough recorded data to make such a quantitative estimate possible [8, 9, 10, 11]. Figures 4 through 11 show examples of damaged buildings. For example, from a preliminary analysis of the data for $W_n$ it appears that values of $W_0$ from about 100 to 200 ft²/sec³ (sum of all three components of motion) are usually associated with nonstructural damage but no serious structural damage. Values of 200 to 500 are associated with moderate to severe structural damage, as typified by the response illustrated in Figs. 3 and 4. For values of $W_0$ from 500 to 1000 and beyond the structural damage can be very severe, leading in some cases to partial collapse. An example is shown in Fig. 11.

If the relation between $W_F$, or $W_n$, and the capability of structures to dissipate energy without collapse can be established, then the measures may

**Fig. 4.** Nine-story Millikan Library building on Caltech campus. This concrete shear-wall structure was undamaged by the 9/2/71 San Fernando earthquake. ($W_0 = 125\pm$)

**Fig. 5.** Nine-story steel-frame Jet Propulsion Laboratory building No. 180. This structure was not damaged. ($W_0 = 130\pm$)

**Fig. 6.** Twelve-story, concrete frame Bank of California building. Sustained severe structural cracking that was repaired with epoxy. ($W_0 = 120\pm$)

**Fig. 7.** Fourteen-story Union Bank building. Sustained severe structural cracking that was repaired with epoxy. ($W_0 = 130\pm$)

**Fig. 8.** Seven-story Indian Hills Medical Center building. Sustained extensive and severe cracking. Shear walls could not be repaired satisfactorily with epoxy so new shear walls were poured against the old walls. ($W_0$ = 500±)

**Fig. 9.** Seven-story concrete frame Holiday Inn. Sustained considerable cracking of beams and columns that was repaired with epoxy. ($W_0$ = 300±)

**Fig. 10.** Six-story concrete frame Holy Cross Hospital Building. Sustained severe cracking and fracturing of structural members. (The structure was eventually taken down.) ($W_0 = 500\pm$)

**Fig. 11.** Olive View Hospital Building. This concrete structure was severely damaged by cracking, fracturing and large permanent deformations. Repair was deemed not economically possible. ($W_0 = 800\pm$)

provide an improved basis for determining the level of earthquake-resistant design criteria. This seems possible because $W_F$ and $W_n$ are well-defined, quantitative measures of the ground motions, and the capacity of structures to absorb energy without danger of collapse can be determined from the results of laboratory tests of members and joints, from shaking table tests of structures and structural models, and from strong earthquakes.

## Energy-Damage Characteristics

The foregoing analysis has some interesting implications for modern code-designed structures though further ground motion computations and earthquake damage correlations are needed to establish the practical value of the approach proposed in this chapter. The implications do not apply to a specific structure but apply in an average sense to modern structures in the Los Angeles area, excluding structures that have gross weaknesses or that have been designed with significantly greater resistance than required by the building code. The following approximate implications can be drawn. First, we can conclude that if the total energy input per unit mass, $W_F$, for three components of motion does not exceed 200 ft$^2$/sec$^3$, structures will suffer little if any structural damage and, at most, moderate nonstructural damage. If $W_F$ does not exceed 500 ft$^2$/sec$^3$, there may be severe structural damage but small likelihood of collapse. If $W_F$ appreciably exceeds 500 ft$^2$/sec$^3$, there will be very severe structural damage with some likelihood of collapse.

Another conclusion that can be drawn is that moderate amounts of damping are very effective in reducing the energy available for damage. For example, Table 3 shows that 5% of critical damping reduces the energy available for producing damage to about 30% of the total energy input. Even 2% of critical damping reduces the available energy to about 50% of the total input. The available energy, it should be noted, cannot all go into producing damage unless the structure can collapse with a brittle-type failure.

It can be seen in Table 3 that the available energy increases rapidly with intensity of ground shaking. For example, with 5% damping $W_5$ is 35 for class 2 and 140 for class 4; i.e., for an amplitude of motion two times larger the available energy is about four times larger. This implies that severity of damage increases much more rapidly than the increase in amplitude of ground motion.

## References

1. Veletsos, A. S., and N. M. Newmark, "Effect of Inelastic Behavior on the Response of Simple Systems to Earthquake Motions," *Proceedings of the 2nd World Conference on Earthquake Engineering, Tokyo*, 1960.
2. Housner, G. W., "Limit Design of Structures to Resist Earthquakes," *Proceedings of the 1956 World Conference on Earthquake Engineering*, Earthquake Engineering Research Institute, Oakland, Calif., 1956.
3. Jennings, P. C., "Response of Yielding Structures to Statistically Generated

Ground Motion," *Proceedings of the 3rd World Conference on Earthquake Engineering, Auckland, New Zeland,* 1965.

4. Hudson, D. E., "Equivalent Viscous Friction for Hysteretic Systems with Earthquake-Like Excitation," *Proceedings of the 3rd World Conference on Earthquake Engineering, Auckland, New Zealand,* 1965.
5. Lange, J. G., "Una Medida de Intensidad Sismica," Departmento de Obras Civiles, Universidad de Chile, Santiago, 1968.
6. Housner, G. W., "Spectrum Intensities of Strong-Motion Earthquakes," *Proceedings of Symposium on Earthquake and Blast Effects on Structures,* Engineering Research Institute, Los Angeles, 1952.
7. Hudson, D. E., "Some Problems in the Application of Spectrum Techniques to Strong-Motion Earthquake Analysis," *Bull. Seism. Soc. Am.*, Vol. 52, No. 2, April 1961, pp. 417–430.
8. Jennings, P. C., "Calculation of Selected Ordinates of Fourier Spectra," *J. Int. Assoc. Earthquake Eng.*, Vol. 2, No. 3, Jan.–March 1974, pp. 281–293.
9. Jennings, P. C., ed., *Engineering Features of the San Fernando Earthquake,* Earthquake Engineering Research Laboratory, California Institute of Technology, 1971.
10. Murphy, L. M., ed., *San Fernando California Earthquake of February 9, 1971,* National Oceanic and Atmospheric Administration, 1973.
11. Hudson, D. E., ed., *Strong-Motion Instrumental Data on the San Fernando Earthquake of February 9, 1971,* Earthquake Engineering Research Laboratory, California Institute of Technology, 1971.

# On Seismic Behavior of Two R/C Structural Systems for Tall Buildings

E. P. POPOV AND V. V. BERTERO*

## Abstract

*Since publication of the classical book* Design of Multistory Reinforced Concrete Buildings for Earthquake Motions [1] *in 1961, some new advances in the subject area have been made. Two reinforced concrete structural systems of the type discussed in the above book that were investigated experimentally and analytically at Berkeley are discussed in this chapter. In the first, the behavior of moment-resisting frames, with the serious problem of bond degradation due to cyclic loading at the interior joints, is considered. In the second, the behavior of tall structural walls subjected to cycles of high shear stress reversals, together with realistic gravity loads and overturning moments, is discussed. This investigation throws some serious doubts on the current design assumption that moment-resisting frames provide a reliable second bracing system after the structural walls are damaged.*

## Introduction

Among the broad range of engineering problems to which Professor Newmark has so richly contributed, his concern with the seismic safety of structures as it affects lives and property plays, perhaps, a dominant role. It is in this general area where the wealth of his knowledge and unusual abilities combined to provide solutions to some of these problems for society. One of his lasting contributions in this area is his collaborative book *Design of Multistory Reinforced Concrete Buildings for Earthquake Motions* [1]. There are numerous other publications on earthquake engineering by Professor

*Professors of Civil Engineering, University of California, Berkeley, California.

Newmark which could be cited, but the one given, in a sense, is in the precise area where, in recent years, the authors have worked and can, perhaps, add some useful information.

The behavior of half-scale R/C cruciform beam-column subassemblages under simulated severe seismic loading is described first. In these experiments, both the material and the geometric ($P\delta$ effect) nonlinearities were prominent. Bond degradation of the main reinforcement, due to the cycles of load reversals at the interior joint, was clearly brought out. The need for further research in this area is indicated. This presentation is followed by observations of the behavior of tall structural walls that were isolated from a structural system that included moment-resisting frames. These walls, made to one-third scale, were subjected to cycles of severe shearing stress reversals as well as realistic gravity loads and overturning moments. This investigation suggests the need for reexamining the present code design concept for this *dual* bracing system.

## R/C Ductile Frames

In large measure, currrent seismic code provisions are based on experimental results obtained from monotonic loadings modified to some extent by observations in the field [2,3]. Therefore, it is essential to perform and evaluate experimental research done with realistic structural members and systems subjected to simulated earthquake loadings. One of the structural systems studied by the authors at Berkeley was that of reinforced concrete moment-resisting ductile frames. This was done experimentally by studying the behavior of some beam-column subassemblages subjected to repeated and reversed (cyclic) loadings slowly applied. This type of pseudostatic loading appears to be reliable [4], as most of the energy is dissipated through hysteresis, which is not significantly affected by the speed of the test. This approach also permits the use of relatively large specimens. Evaluation of such experimental results and comparisons with analytic solutions should provide useful information.

### *Selection and Design of Specimens*

A 20-story moment-resisting reinforced concrete frame having the dimensions shown in Fig. 1 was selected as the basic prototype in these studies. This building was designed according to the UBC [5] for conventional gravity loads for an office building and lateral wind and earthquake loadings in accordance with the same code. In proportioning the members, the approach of having strong column weak beams was adopted; i.e., significant inelastic deformations were assumed to occur only in the beams.

The subassemblage for the experimental work was chosen from the third

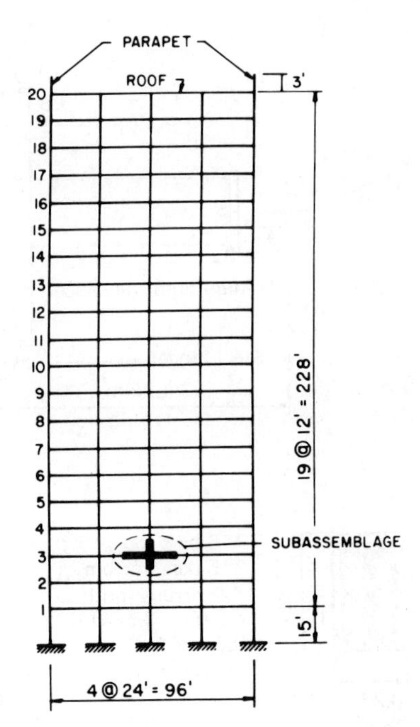


**Fig. 1.** Prototype of 20-story R/C frame

floor framing, as indicated in the figure. Since in the lower stories the gravity loads within the span have little influence on the behavior of the beams, which mainly resist earthquake forces, these beams were terminated at their respective midspans. For lateral loading, these points correspond to the points of inflection in such beams and, therefore, can be taken as hinges in the specimen. The columns were also terminated in hinges at midstory heights. Only in-plane loadings were considered in this investigation.

The details of the beam-column subassemblage used in this investigation are shown in Fig. 2. These specimens were made to half-scale of the prototype. The 9 by 16-in. beams had top longitudinal reinforcement consisting of four #6 bars. The three bottom bars were #5. In this manner, half as much longitudinal steel was provided at the bottom of the beam as at the top, which is the minimal ACI requirement [2]. The stirrups consisted of #2 stirrup ties and #2 hair-pin ties, both at 3.5-in. spacing. The column was reinforced with 12 #6 bars and #2 triple ties at 1.6 in. on center. This spacing of ties was increased to 2 in. on centers within the joint, providing an adequate design in shear according to ACI-71 Code [2]. The deformed reinforcing steel bars used were of Grade 60. The actual yield strength was 65 ksi for the #2 bars and 71 ksi for the #5 and the #6 bars. The concrete strength for the specimens varied approximately between 4500 and 5000 psi.

To simulate gravity loads during an experiment, the column was loaded axially with a force $P = 470$ kips. The beam ends could freely translate only

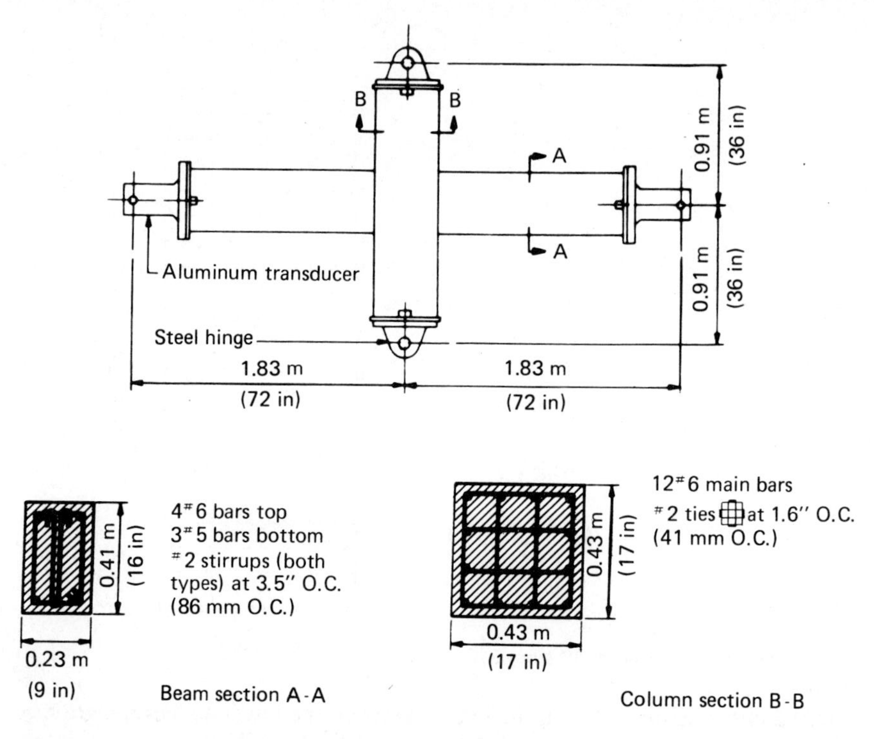


**Fig. 2.** Beam-column subassemblage

horizontally, as a cyclic horizontal force $H$ was applied to the bottom hinge, causing it to displace horizontally an amount $\delta$. The displacement $\delta$, together with the axial force $P$, induced a $P\delta$ effect on the joint. The displacements $\delta$ were varied to suit the experimental requirements.

#### *Analytical and Experimental Hysteretic Loops*

It is the very essence of applied research to be able to analytically predict the actual behavior of a structural system. In this discussion, the behavior of specimen BC4 is singled out for consideration. This specimen was subjected to a relatively simple, although severe, single cycle of load application. The degree of agreement or disagreement of the analytical prediction with the experimental results will give an indication of the current state of knowledge in this area.

Assuming cracked plane sections and progressively changing the strength of steel as it increases with strain, numerous points were computed to define postyield moment-curvature relationships for the two opposite senses of beam bending. This resulted in two slightly irregular bilinear curves in the first and the third quadrants. In each quadrant these curves were idealized as a bilinear moment-curvature relationship [6, 7]. For the purposes of analysis, it was assumed that, for loading in the opposite sense, the maximum moment range between the inelastic regions remains constant.

For the subassemblages studied here a beam on either side of the column acts as a cantilever with only an end load. Therefore, it is possible to make use of the beam rotation $\theta$ at the built-in end as the key parameter. This approach was successfully applied by Otani and Sozen [8] in their studies of moment-resisting frames. Using this procedure, the $M$-$\theta$ diagram for an end moment for a simply supported beam was established (Fig. 3). For simplicity, however, the curved regions $NB$ and $LE$ were replaced by the straight lines. Therefore, the idealized moment-rotation diagram consists of four straight lines $OA$, $AK$, $OD$, and $DM$. It is at this level that a degrading model can be introduced. The Takeda model [9] was used by Otani and Sozen [8]. Here, the Clough degrading model [10] was applied.

According to the Clough model, if the unloading process begins at a point such as $B$ (Fig. 3), the member first exhibits elastic stiffness represented by the line $BC$. However, on loading in the opposite direction, the stiffness of the member degrades following the line $CD$. In a simple manner, this accounts for the Bauschinger effect in steel as well as effects of flexural and shear cracking, crushing, spalling, and bond deterioration. If the loading continues beyond point $D$, the line $DM$ is followed. If unloading occurs at point $E$, the unloading line $EF$ is parallel to $OD$. An application of a positive reloading moment after point $F$ has been reached causes the stiffness of the

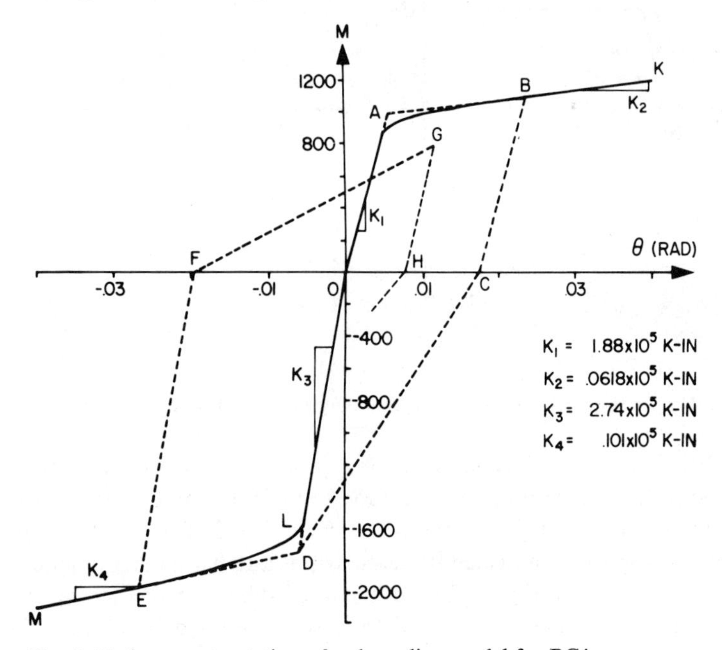


**Fig. 3.** End moment-rotation of a degrading model for BC4

member to become such as to return to point $B$ from which the member was unloaded. In other words, the straight lines representing reloading are directed toward the furthermost points they ever reached, either on the line $AK$ or $DM$. This model attempts to account for the degrading in stiffness of members loaded in an opposite sense to what is normally observed.

By distributing the progressively increasing applied moment to the joint in accordance to the stiffnesses given by the $M$-$\theta$ diagram and using the adopted degrading model for reloading, the $H$-$\delta$ shown in Fig. 4 was constructed. In using this approach, the agreement between the calculated and the experimental loops is seen to be very good. This comparison is far superior to that obtained with use of the elastoplastic idealization. The areas enclosed by the two diagrams, which correspond to the energy of dissipation, are nearly the same. It must be pointed out, however, that the agreement between the two loops was achieved by requiring in the calculations the same displacements of the bottom column hinge as in the experiment. This problem requires further scrutiny, which leads to the following considerations.

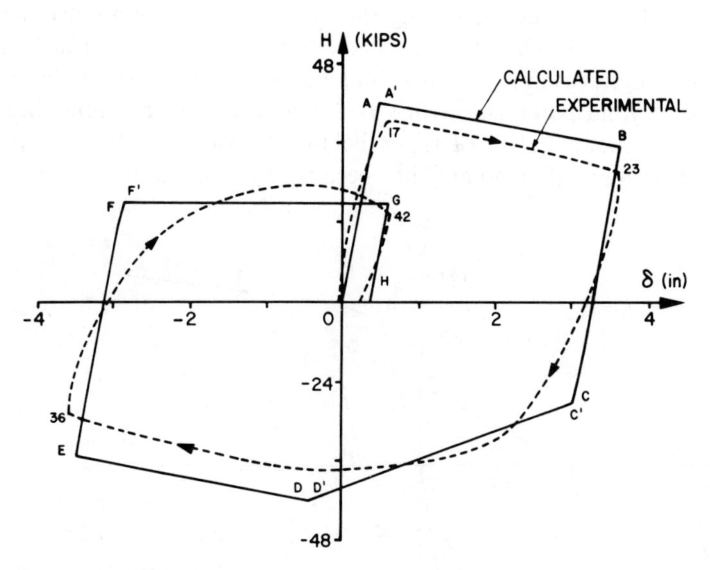


**Fig. 4.** Experimental and calculated $H$-$\delta$ diagrams for BC4

In addition to the $H$-$\delta$ hysteretic loops, it is significant to examine the beam rotations at the column faces as a function of the moments they carry. Such a diagram for one of the beams is shown in Fig. 5. The set of straight dashed lines shown was established by calculations and has a correspondence with the $H$-$\delta$ diagram of Fig. 4. The other lines shown in the figure were found differently. Of these, the dashed loop was obtained by determining

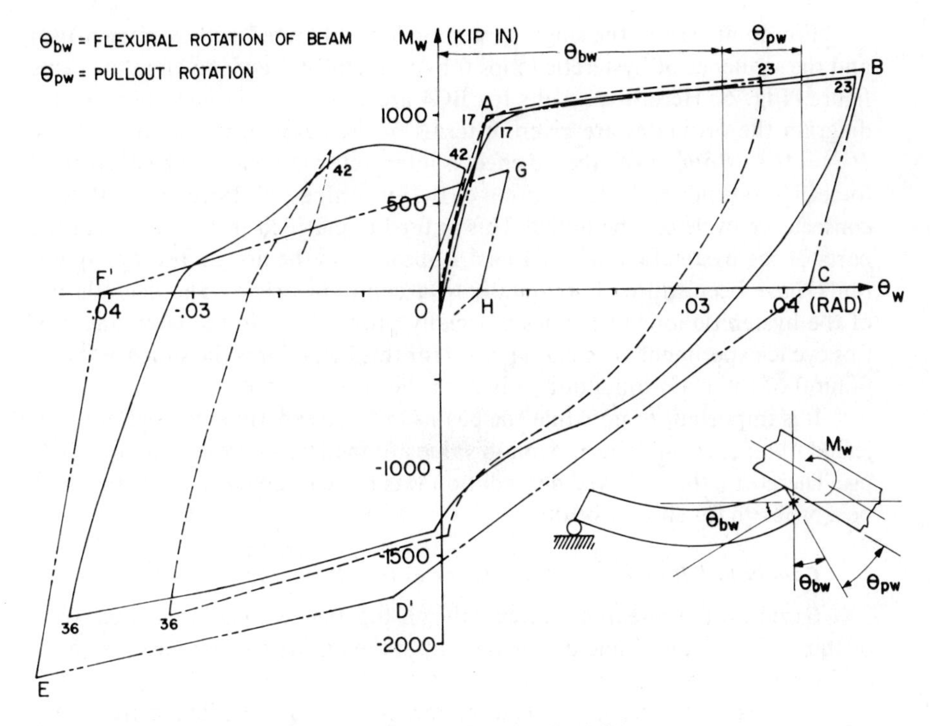


**Fig. 5.** Experimental and calculated beam end rotation for BC4

the flexural rotations of the beam. This was done by measurements in the inelastic portion of the beam, to which calculated rotations for the elastic part were added. These rotations are designated $\theta_{bw}$. This loop by itself falls far short of the computed one, because, in addition to the rotation caused by flexure, a substantial pullout of the longitudinal bars from the joint took place. Bar pullout from the joint permits further column rotation $\theta_{pw}$; this effect can be treated as an additional rotation of the beam's end; i.e., the total rotation $\theta_w = \theta_{bw} + \theta_{pw}$.

In these experiments, the pullout of the bars from the joint was measured and, for the purposes at hand, can be converted into an equivalent rotation of $\theta_{pw}$ of a beam's end. By adding this equivalent angle of rotation to the flexural rotation of the beam, the curve shown by the solid line in Fig. 5 was obtained. This total rotation compares favorably with the calculated one. Therefore, in achieving an agreement between the experimental and the calculated $H$-$\delta$ loops of Fig. 4, it must be clearly understood that the pullout phenomenon has not been isolated. It has simply been made a part of the flexural response. For complex cyclic displacements an even larger discrepancy between the actual and the analytical results would occur.

For comparison, the single hysteretic loop obtained with specimen BC4 and the sequence of hysteretic loops for specimen BC3 are shown in the same figure, Fig. 6. Here, the results for BC4 are shown by dashed lines. In this diagram the ordinates are given in terms of the equivalent horizontal force $H_{eq} = H + P\delta/h_{col}$; i.e., the $P\delta$ effect is interpreted as a part of the horizontal force. The considerable degradation of BC3 in stiffness and strength with each consecutive cycle can be noted. This is further clarified in Fig. 7, where the parts of the hysteretic loops of Fig. 6, appearing in the first and second quadrants, have been shifted horizontally to a common origin. The degradation of the hysteretic loops becomes especially pronounced in the later stages of this cyclic experiment. The main reason for this behavior is the slippage (bond failure) of the main longitudinal bars in the column core.

It is important to note that the beams in these experiments were not subjected to large shear. The maximum value attained was on the order of $3\sqrt{f'_c}$ psi. Therefore, the observed degradation was not caused by shear, which may be a problem for shorter beams.

#### *Concluding Remarks and Needs for Future Research*

Based on the research outlined above, together with some related work of the authors, some conclusions regarding the analysis of moment-resisting R/C ductile frames can be made.

1. Reasonably accurate cyclic moment-curvature relations can be generated analytically using the mechanical properties of materials for R/C flex-

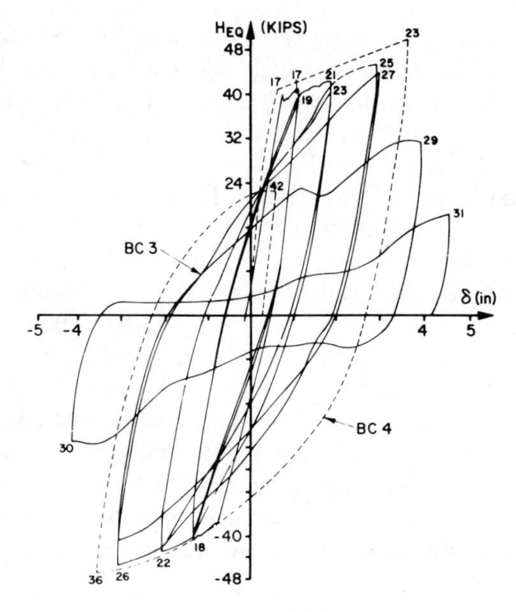


Fig. 6. Hysteretic behavior of BC3 and BC4

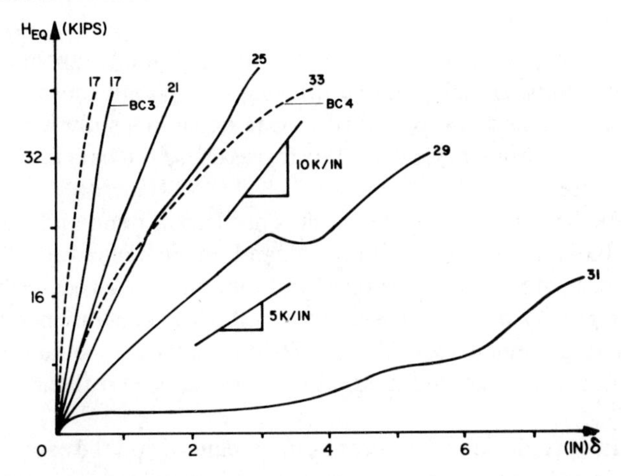


**Fig. 7.** Comparison of $H_{eq}$-$\delta$ curves for BC3 and BC4 at different cycles

ural members subjected to small shear [11]. The state of present knowledge is inadequate, however, to formulate the degradation in stiffness of the whole subassemblage due to bond failure in the joint. Such failures were observed at the interior joints of the R/C subassemblages studied. At large displacements, cyclic slippage of the main bars occurred through the core of very conservatively designed columns. Therefore, one can question the implication of Fig. A-7 of the ACI Commentary [2] as to what it may imply regarding the bond or anchorage of the main longitudinal bars. The ACI concept of joint behavior under seismic loading is reproduced in Fig. 8(a). It is believed that for severe loadings, instead of this single diagram, a whole sequence of different free-body diagrams must be considered. Such a detailed analysis is

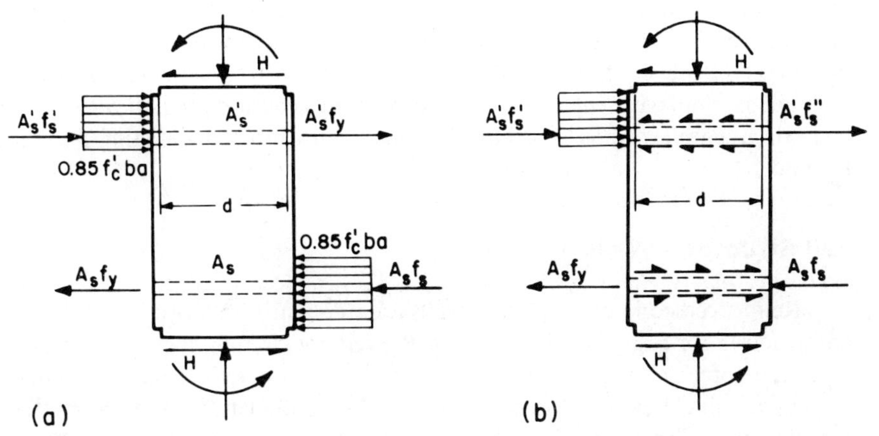


**Fig. 8.** Joint free-bodies for determining (a) connection shearing forces (ACI 318-71) and (b) bond in bottom bars

given in Ref. 12. For examining the condition of bond or anchorage failure in the bottom bars, the diagram shown in Fig. 8(b) is believed to be more appropriate. Such bars may be pulled on one side and simultaneously pushed from the other. As bond degrades, these forces cause the bars to slide through the column core.

Some further fundamental research is needed on bond and anchorage of reinforcing bars under the conditions of random cyclic loading. This should include the case of simultaneous push and pull on the bars described above. This would greatly aid the development of mathematical models for the behavior of R/C members and frames. Such information could then be used in appropriate computer programs for determining a realistic response of structures.

2. Bond degradation of the beam's main bars within the core of a column at interior joints may be delayed or entirely prevented by forcing plastic hinges to occur in the beams away from the column faces. This approach was successfully applied in an experimental study of large short cantilever beams subjected to severe cyclic loadings [13]. For the given moment requirements, the beam can be so designed that the hinge will form some distance away from the column. Either a reduced amount of reinforcement at the plastic hinge or a beam haunch can be used to obtain the desired result. The use of inclined bars at the plastic hinges has also been found to be very effective in resisting the repeated application of shear reversals [13]. This detail is recommended for short beams that must carry large shear.

Further experimental effort to verify the above approach on subassemblages with interior and exterior joints is necessary.

3. As most of the American experimental work on the cyclic behavior of reinforced concrete beams was done with members having rectangular cross sections, additional tests should be performed using T-sections. It has been found that slab reinforcement significantly modifies the behavior of beams [11]. Such work logically should be extended to include experiments with subassemblages, since only then can more accurate predictions of the inelastic dynamic response of R/C buildings with moment-resisting frames be made.

## Tall Structural Walls

Reinforced concrete structural walls are frequently employed in building construction for resisting lateral forces. Present code requirements underestimate the forces acting on such walls, and their hysteretic behavior under earthquake-like conditions is not clearly understood. This is reflected in the significantly different requirements for the design and analysis of structural walls according to the ACI and the UBC code provisions [14]. The present American and Japanese design philosophies for wall systems also have substantial differences [15]. All of this is largely due to lack of reliable data in this area. Until very recently, experimental results were available only from tests on one- or two-story walls. In these experiments for higher walls the correct boundary conditions were not fulfilled, and the applied loadings were not characteristic of the ones occurring on such walls during a strong shake.

In the analysis and design of walls for seismic loading, one must differentiate between short and tall walls, as their behavior is not the same. Short walls are subjected to very low flexural stresses, and they have such large shear capacities that they tend to "elastically" resist even severe ground shaking. Therefore, the forces acting upon this type of wall should be determined from linear-elastic design spectra corresponding to the maximum credible earthquake. These are true *shear* walls, and it is logical to base their design on allowable maximum shearing stresses. Walls which have a height to width ratio of less than 0.5, according to Fintel [16], or, of less than 1.0, according to Paulay [17], belong to this category; i.e., the delineation between these two types of walls based on geometry alone is not precise. The shear span to depth ratio, rather than height to depth ratio, may be a more accurate index for their classification [13]. The higher walls, in addition to having to meet the requirements for shear, strongly depend on their behavior in flexure—more precisely, by the interaction between flexure and shear. Such walls are called *flexural* walls. The behavior of flexural walls, such as occur in tall buildings, is discussed here. Often these walls are used in combination with moment-resisting frames. The interaction, particularly in the inelastic range, between flexural walls and moment-resisting frames complicates even more the analysis and design of these walls. There is a great need for studying the hysteretic behavior of such walls in combination with moment-resisting frames under earthquake-like conditions. Because of this, work was initiated at Berkeley in 1971 on an integrated experimental and analytical study of reinforced concrete flexural (tall) walls. This required the design of a special testing facility, with which experiments with two flexural walls were just completed. Some of the experimental observations on these walls with seismic design implications are described.

### *Testing Facility*

The testing facility was developed for wall component specimens for moderate and high-rise buildings. To determine the size of the required facility, two buildings of 10 and 20 stories in height with structural walls were designed according to the UBC seismic provisions. This study resulted in the selection of a $\frac{1}{3}$ scale for the test models.

The principal feature of the test facility is its ability to simulate, in a pseudostatic manner, the significant effects of the actual dynamic loading conditions induced in a subassemblage of a building during earthquake ground motion. As an example, consider the prototype building for the first

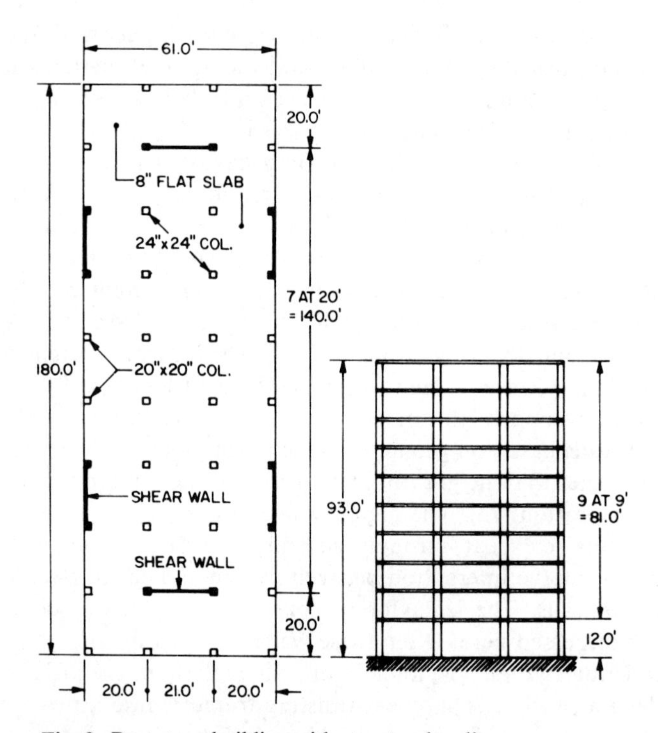


**Fig. 9.** Prototype building with structural walls

experiments shown in Fig. 9. To simulate reasonably well the actual boundary conditions for the lower story, a subassemblage of three stories in height is adopted (Fig. 10). The forces applied to this specimen simulate gravity loads existing in the prototype above the top floor of the subassemblage as well as the cyclic horizontal lateral forces and the vertical forces caused by the overturning moment acting on the columns. The simultaneous application of these forces is necessary for studying inelastic behavior, as, for such behavior, superposition of stresses does not apply. In the experiment the application of gravity, overturning, and shear forces is electronically synchronized.

In the Berkeley facility, the actual experiment is performed with the walls in a horizontal position (Fig. 11). The main part of this installation consists of a series of reinforced concrete blocks and a steel reaction box, all of which is prestressed with rods to the laboratory tie-down slab. Hydraulic actuators provide the application of the necessary forces to the specimen.

The specimens are extensively instrumented to study the hysteretic behavior of the models. Automatic plots of the most significant parameters are obtained during the course of a test using X-Y-Y recorders. In addition

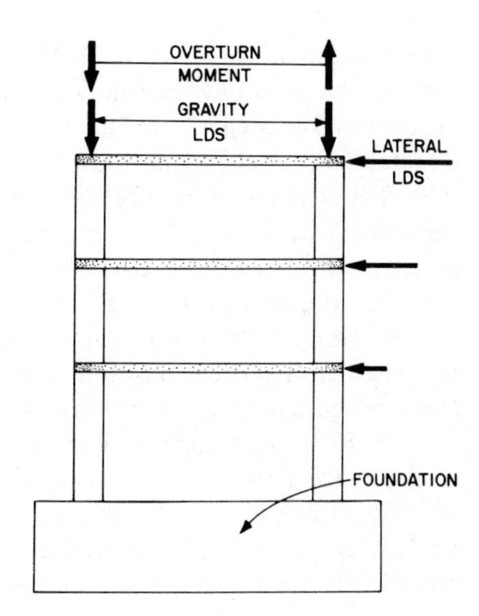


**Fig. 10.** Isolated structural wall component

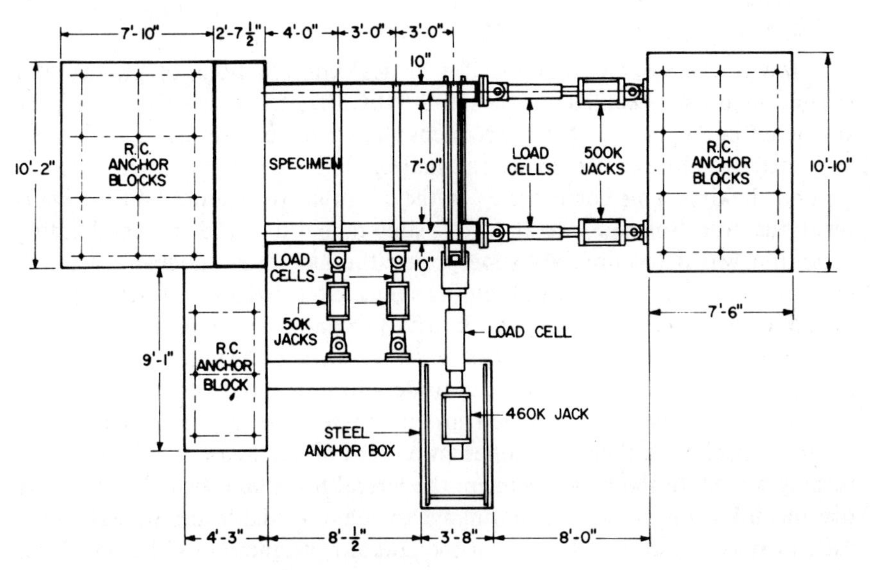


**Fig. 11.** Plan of wall component test arrangement

to visual observations, photogrammetric pictures are taken at critical stages of the experiment. This provides an unique quantitative record on the movement of the cracked mosaic of the wall at various loads.

### *Design of Specimens*

A structural wall component from an area corresponding to the lower 3 stories of a 10-story building designed using present UBC seismic provisions served as the prototype (Fig. 9). The details of the wall specimens, made to $\frac{1}{3}$ scale of the prototype, are shown in Fig. 12. As illustrated in this figure, the specimens consisted of 4-in.-thick walls framed by two 10-in.-square columns. The total width of the specimen was 7 ft, 10 in. and the total height was, 13 ft, 7 in. The walls were reinforced with two layers of horizontal and vertical reinforcement. In each layer #2 bars were spaced 3 in. apart both ways. The spirally reinforced columns had eight #6 main bars; the 8.33-in.-outside-diameter spirals, having a 0.83-in. pitch, were made of 0.21-in. steel wire.

To simulate the usual construction sequence in the field, the specimens were cast in a vertical position one story at a time. At the time of testing, the average concrete compressive strength for each specimen was approximately 5000 psi, compared with a specified strength of 4000 psi. The yield strengths for Grade 60 bars were also higher than specified. Moreover, their ultimate strengths considerably exceeded their yield strengths. For the #2 and the #6 bars, yield occurred at 73 ksi and the ultimate at nearly 106 ksi, whereas for the column wire, these values were 82 and 101 ksi, respectively.

### *Loading Program*

The prototype was designed for critical combinations of gravity and seismic loads as specified by the 1973 UBC. These loads could easily be simulated in the testing of the specimens; however, instead, these walls were subjected to a more critical load combination that could develop with extreme ground shaking. This corresponds to the case that the frames and the walls resist the total seismic lateral forces simultaneously. The critical loading condition was determined by superposing the first three modes of a linear elastic dynamic analysis of this building subjected to an El Centro-type earthquake, with a maximum acceleration of 0.33 $g$ and 5% damping. Of the several cases analyzed, this resulted in the most critical shear force in the first story, giving the smallest shear span to depth ratio.

After applying the simulated gravity forces, the two specimens were tested by subjecting them to a different pattern of lateral and matching overturning forces. In the first specimen, the lateral force and the corresponding overturning moment causing the change in column axial forces were monotically increased until a reduction in the lateral resistance could be observed. Then a closed large hysteretic loop was generated. The second specimen was subjected to a history of lateral shear and corresponding overturning moment that induced gradually increasing cycles of full displacement reversals. Several cycles were applied at each displacement amplitude. The second loading program caused a more rapid degradation in shear resistance.

### *Experimental Results*

The experiment with wall 1 generated a large hysteretic loop and provided some important information on the behavior of a monotonically loaded case [13]. The principal results may be summarized as follows.

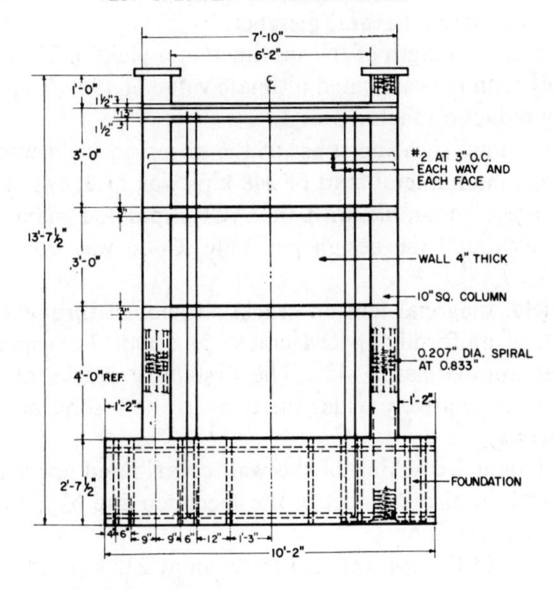


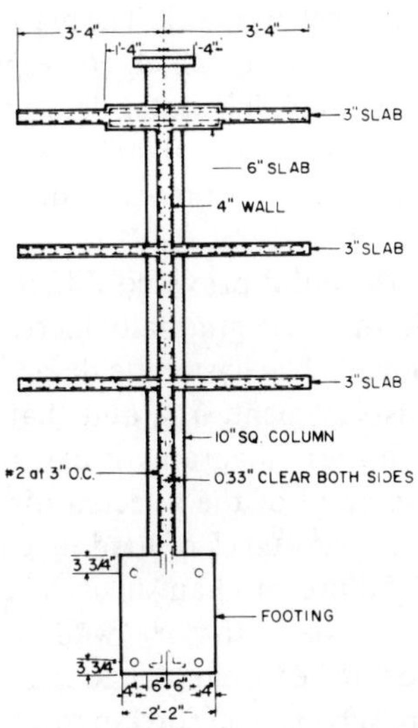


**Fig. 12.** Dimensions and details of wall specimen

1. The overall behavior of the specimen was essentially that of a ductile reinforced concrete flexural member.
2. The lateral strength of the specimen at a yield of 215 kips compared favorably with the calculated ultimate value of 196 kips per ACI with a capacity reduction factor $\phi = 1$.
3. The nominal shearing stress at the observed yield was $9.5\sqrt{f'_c}$ and at the maximum lateral load of 248 kips was $11.3\sqrt{f'_c}$. These shearing stresses are comparable with the ACI stipulated maximum value of $10\sqrt{f'_c}$, although the design per UBC Code was done so as not to exceed $5\sqrt{f'_c}$.
4. At yield, diagonal tension cracks developed throughout the specimen. These uniformly spaced cracks at about 3-in. spacing were inclined at approximately 45°. The first-story cracks at this stage of loading were relatively wide; the ones in the second and third stories were narrow.
5. The diagonal cracking of the wall contributed approximately 34% to the total tip displacement of the specimen and 62% to the displacement of the first floor.
6. Crushing of the concrete cover began at 235 kips at the edge of the column in compression; however, the load-carrying capacity of the wall continued to increase to a value of 248 kips. At this higher load level the concrete on the wall began to spall, causing buckling of the bars in this region, and the lateral load resistance decreased.
7. Insofar as ductility is concerned, the walls with the spirally reinforced end columns behaved well. The maximum displacement ductility factor was on the order of 6, which corresponded to a total maximum tip deflection of over 4 in. The total drift index at working load, yield, and maximum resistance was 0.002, 0.008, and 0.036, respectively. The maximum inelastic rotation was 0.02 rad.

The experiment with wall 2 provided different data from that obtained with the first wall, as in this case gradually increasing cycles of full displacement reversals were applied. The hysteretic diagrams of the total lateral force $P_T$ vs. tip horizontal displacement, $\delta_{3R}$, and that of the first story, $\delta_{1R}$, are shown in Fig. 13. From these diagrams it can be noted that three or four cycles were applied at several of the selected displacement amplitudes. The appearance of the wall at two stages of loading can be seen in Fig. 14(a) and (b). A diagram of the failure mechanism is schematized in Fig. 15. Large shearing deformations of the first-story wall can be noted from Fig. 16, where the characteristic pinched hysteretic loops of the horizontal shear $V$ vs. angular distortion $\gamma_1$ are shown. The corresponding distortions for the second and third stories were only approximately one-third as large. The importance of the shearing distortions to the story drifts can be noted from Fig. 17. The consistently large contribution of the shearing distortions may be seen here.

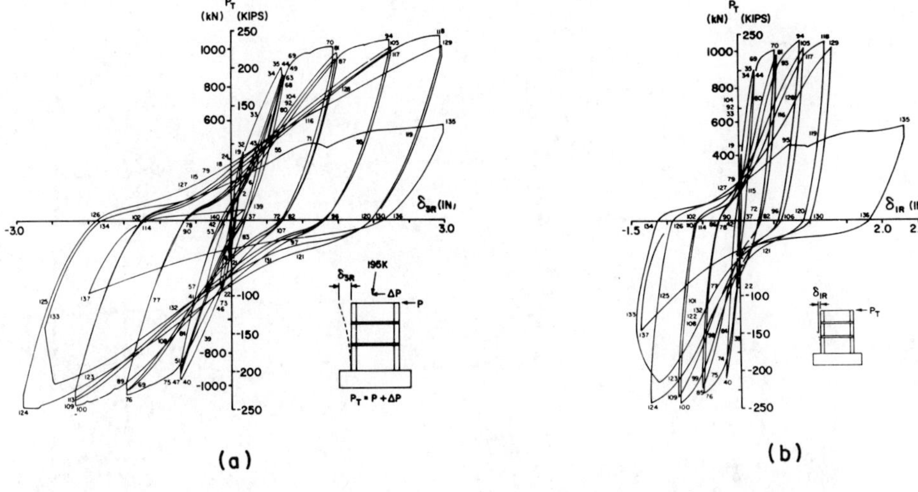


**Fig. 13.** Lateral load versus story displacements of wall 2

By studying the data for wall 2 and comparing them with those of wall 1, some observations of the differences in behavior of monotonically and cyclically loaded walls can be made. Among these are the following:

1. Both the yield strength and the ultimate strength are minimally affected by the type of loading.
2. At and above yield, considerable degradation of the hysteretic loops takes place under repeated cyclic load reversals. This is associated with a continuous degradation in the stiffness of the wall.
3. The contribution of the shear deformation to lateral displacements was increased by the effect of deformation reversals. The displacement ductility factor, however, was reduced by about one-third.
4. Whereas the wall failure mechanism was not significantly affected, the process was accelerated by the repeated cycles of deformation.
5. Several free vibration tests with wall 2 indicated a considerable increase in damping (2.7% to 9.1%) after numerous diagonal cracks developed in the walls along the entire height of the specimen. During the later stages of testing, as damage was concentrated along a band (Fig. 15), the damping coefficient decreased (5.6%). Ambient dynamic tests at small amplitudes gave greater natural frequencies and considerably lower values of critical damping coefficients. A questionable validity of such tests at extremely low-level signals is thus indicated.

### *Conclusions and Design Implications*

Based on the results of these experiments, some tentative conclusions and design implications can be reached.

(a) First story crack pattern after cycle with $\delta_{3R} = \pm 0.7$ in. ($\mu = \pm 1$).

(b) First story after cycle with $\delta_{3R} = \pm 2.94$ ($\mu = \pm 5$).

**Fig. 14.** Illustrations of damaged wall 2

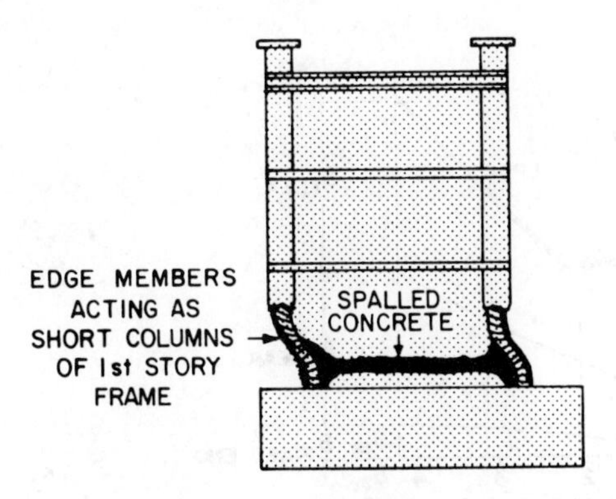


**Fig. 15.** Wall failure mechanism

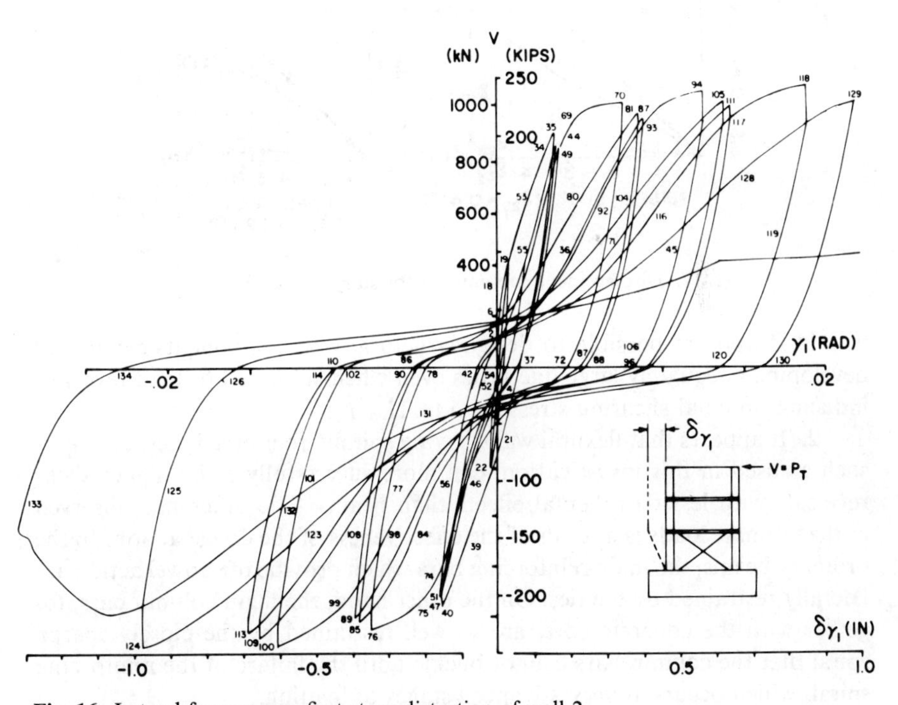


**Fig. 16.** Lateral force versus first story distortion of wall 2

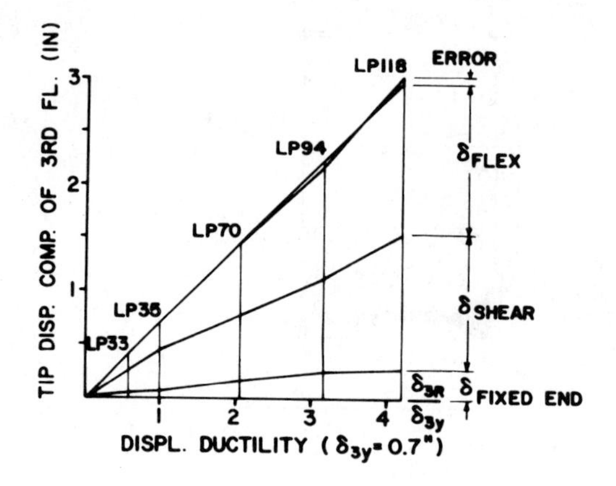


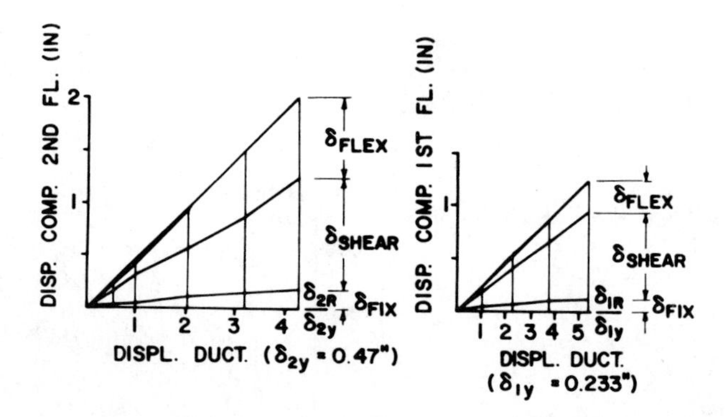


**Fig. 17.** Displacement components for story of wall 2

1. It appears possible to design structural wall components capable of developing adequately large ductilities even when subjected to load reversals inducing nominal shearing stresses up to $11\sqrt{f'_c}$.

2. It appears that flexural walls having spirally reinforced edge columns, such as used in this investigation, can more successfully resist higher shear reversals with less detrimental effects than beams. The difference observed at the ultimate loads is a result of the effectiveness of the dowel action. In the ordinary beams, the main reinforcing bars which provide the dowel action are laterally restrained by the ties. On the other hand, the main column bars, together with the concrete core, are so well restrained by the closely spaced spiral that the column bars cannot buckle until the failure of the reinforcing spiral, which occurs at very advanced stages of loading.

3. The completed experiments gave a strong indication that large horizontal beams at floor levels are unnecessary. The practice of putting such beams at each floor level and thereby containing the wall for each story between such beams and the columns is rather common. These results place

doubts of the necessity of this costly practice. Further research is thus indicated.

4. In the walls tested, most of the severe damage occurred in the first story as the result of flexural and shear interaction after yielding along the critical region. Because of this concentration of deformation, the wall component behaves like a system with a soft first story (Fig. 15). Since the complete frame-wall system is usually controlled by the behavior of such wall components, the frame system will also be forced to behave as a moment-resisting frame with a soft first story (Fig. 18) rather than a ductile moment-resisting frame as assumed by the UBC. This observation throws some serious doubts on the widely accepted design criterion of a dual bracing structural system, as recommended by SEAOC [3].

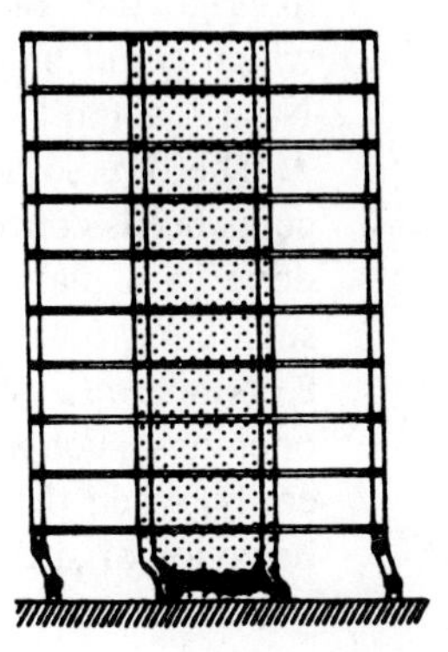

**Fig. 18.** Collapse mechanism of dual wall-frame system

### *Needs for Future Research*

As stated in the introduction to this section on tall structural walls, there are many unsettled problems in this general area. In the opinion of the authors, a number of topics require immediate attention. Some of these are being actively pursued at Berkeley.

1. The next two walls to be investigated at Berkeley will be identical to the walls described above except that the edge columns will have square ties rather than spiral reinforcement.
2. Another important topic for investigation is that of walls with a rectangular cross section without any protruding columns. Such walls are less expensive to build and are very desirable from an architectural point of view. It appears possible to contain structural columns within the wall thickness for resisting not only the gravity forces but also the effects of lateral forces and overturning. Experiments of the type discussed earlier would be most useful in confirming the adequacy of this design.
3. A number of design engineers advocate the use of diagonally placed

reinforcement for flexural walls. This method of reinforcement now looks economically feasible. No information of their behavior, of the type described in this chapter, is now available.

4. In spite of the fact that reinforced masonry infilled walls are widely used, their behavior under cyclic loads is poorly understood, and research information on such walls for moderate-rise construction is needed.

5. Walls consisting of precast units tied together with *in situ* cast-reinforced concrete beams and columns offer a number of economic advantages. This area of research as it applies to their seismic behavior is virtually untouched.

6. Coupled walls appear to offer a number of advantages, being often less rigid than the wider tall walls and having numerous coupling beams, which could be designed as energy dissipators. The work initiated in New Zealand [17] needs to be broadened.

7. The three-dimensional behavior of buildings having structural wall cores needs concentrated study. Essentially all current research if being done with planar structures, and information on spatial behavior of such cores must be developed for designers.

8. Numerous problems await investigations of structural walls with openings, such as commonly occur in elevator shafts, and, more generally, when they are a part of the wall system of a building. Inelastic behavior of such components under cyclic loading is not well understood.

This listing of topics requiring experimental research, particularly on large-sized specimens, could be enlarged. However, in closing it must be strongly emphasized that such research must be in conjunction with analytic studies. Only by developing refined analyses based on accurate knowledge of material behavior under random cyclic loads from which mathematical models of the framing systems can be formulated together with experimental corroboration on large components can real progress in this area be achieved. Dynamic computer analyses in conjunction with this work appear indispensable. It is in this spirit that Professor Newmark has worked and has made lasting contributions.

## Acknowledgments

The work described in this chapter was generously supported by the National Science Foundation over a number of years, the latest grant being AEN73-07732 02, Sub-projects 0-21987 and 0-21997. For this the authors are most grateful. It is also a pleasure to acknowledge the active participation on these projects of the following individuals: Drs. T. Endo, S. M. Ma, H. Krawinkler, and Mr. B. Lotz, as well as graduate students D. Clyde, M. Quint, J. Ragsdale, D. Soleimani, J. Vallenas, S. Viwathanatepa, and T. Y. Wang.

## References

1. Blume, J. A., N. M. Newmark, and L. H. Corning, *Design of Multistory Reinforced Concrete Buildings for Earthquake Motions*, Portland Cement Association, Detroit, 1961.
2. ACI Building Code and Commentary, "Building Code Requirements for R/C (SCI 318-71)," American Concrete Institute, Detroit, 1970.
3. SEAOC, "Recommended Lateral Force Requirements and Commentary," Structural Engineering Association of California, San Francisco, 1973.
4. Gulkan P., and M. Sozen, "Response and Energy-Dissipation of R/C Frames Subjected to Strong Base Motions," CE Studies, *Struc. Res. Ser. No. 377*, University of Illinois, Urbana, Champaign, May 1971.
5. International Conference of Building Officials, *Uniform Building Code*, 1970 ed., Vol. I, Pasadena, 1970.
6. Popov, E. P., V. V. Bertero, and S. Viwathanatepa, "Analytic and Experimental Hysteretic Loops for R/C Subassemblages," Fifth European Conference on Earthquake Engineering, Istanbul, Turkey, Sept. 22–25, 1975.
7. Anderson, J. C., and V. V. Bertero, "Seismic Behavior of Multi-Story Frames Designed by Different Philosophies," *EERC Rpt. No. 69–11*. Univ. of California, Berkeley, 1969.
8. Otani, S., and M. Sozen, "Behavior of Multistory Reinforced Concrete Frames During Earthquakes," *Struct. Res. Series No. 392*, CE Studies, University of Illinois, Urbana, Nov. 1972.
9. Takeda, T., M. Sozen, and N. Nielsen, "R/C Response to Simulated Earthquakes," *J. Struct. Div. ASCE*, Vol. 96, No. ST12, Dec. 1970, pp. 2557–2573.
10. Clough, R. W., "Effect of Stiffness Degradation on Earthquake Ductility Requirements," *Res. Rpt. 66–16*, Dept. of CE, University of California, Berkeley, Oct. 1966.
11. Ma, S. M., "Experimental and Analytical Studies of Hysteretic Behavior of Reinforced Concrete Rectangular and T-Beams," Ph.D. dissertation, University of California, Berkeley, Aug. 1975.
12. Bertero, V. V., and E. P. Popov, "Hysteretic Behavior of Ductile Moment-Resisting Reinforced Concrete Frame Components," *EERC Report 75–16*, Univ. of California, Berkeley, April 1975.
13. Bertero, V. V., E. P. Popov, and T. Y. Wang, "Seismic Design Implications of Hysteretic Behavior of Reinforced Concrete Elements Under High Shear," U.S.-Japan Hawaii Meeting, Aug. 17–19, 1975. (In press.)
14. "Design of Combined Frames and Shear Walls," *Notes of Seminar on Simplified Design of Earthquake-Resistant Concrete Structures*, PCA (Portland Cement Association), San Francisco, June 2, 1973, pp. A.1–A.59.

15. HATAKEYAMA, H., "Comparative Study of Design of Shear Walls in High-Rise Buildings," *CE 299 Report*. Structural Engineering and Structural Mechanics Division, University of California, Berkeley, Fall 1973.
16. FINTEL, M., "Ductile Shear Walls in Multistory Buildings," *Proceedings of the 42nd Annual Convention, Structural Engineer's Association of California, Cororado*, SEAOC, Los Angeles, Oct. 4–6, 1973, pp. 39–58.
17. PAULAY, T., "Design Aspects of Shear Walls for Seismic Areas," *Research Report 74-11*, University of Canterbury, Christchurch, New Zealand, Oct. 1972, 29 pp.

# Influence of Dynamic Soil Properties on Response of Soil Masses

F. E. RICHART, JR. AND E. B. WYLIE*

## Introduction

Soils develop nonlinear inelastic shearing stress-strain relationships when loaded by single or repeated external forces. By appropriate laboratory tests, these stress-strain relationships may be determined for cohesionless and cohesive soils, and some information of this type is now available in the literature. These data permit development of typical stress-strain curves, which may then be approximated by the Ramberg-Osgood analytical curves.

It is the purpose of this study to review the development of dynamic shearing stress-strain relations for soils and to examine the influence of the model used to represent this soil behavior on the response of layered soil systems. In particular, the response spectra and stress patterns obtained from a soil model developing strain-compatible secant modulus and damping are compared with those obtained from a hysteretic soil model utilizing the tangent modulus at each stress level and with those obtained from an elastic-slip soil model.

## Dynamic Soil Properties

The soil properties exerting the greatest influence on dynamic responses of soil masses are those related to the stress-strain curve. For shearing deformations of the soil the shearing stress-strain curve is strain-softening, having an initial slope of $G_0$ at the origin and a slope of zero at the maximum shearing stress, $\tau_m$. A continuous curve connects these limits, as shown in Fig. 1, for loading from the unstressed conditions.

*Professors of Civil Engineering, The University of Michigan, Ann Arbor, Michigan.

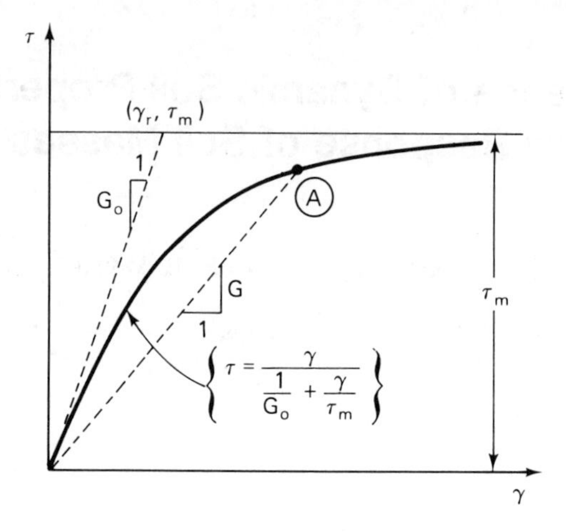


**Fig. 1.** Basic parameters for hyperbolic shearing stress-shearing strain curves

For reversed loadings from a particular shearing stress, $\tau_1$, a hysteresis loop is formed as shown in Fig. 2. The secant modulus ($G$ in Fig. 1) connecting the origin with the point at $A$ $(\tau_1, \gamma_1)$ on the original loading curve and the width of the loop vary with the magnitude of $\tau_1$. The area of the hysteresis loop formed is a measure of the hysteretic damping occurring in the soil. Thus, the initial shear modulus, $G_0$, the maximum shearing stress, $\tau_m$, and the shape of the curve determine the secant modulus, $G$, and the

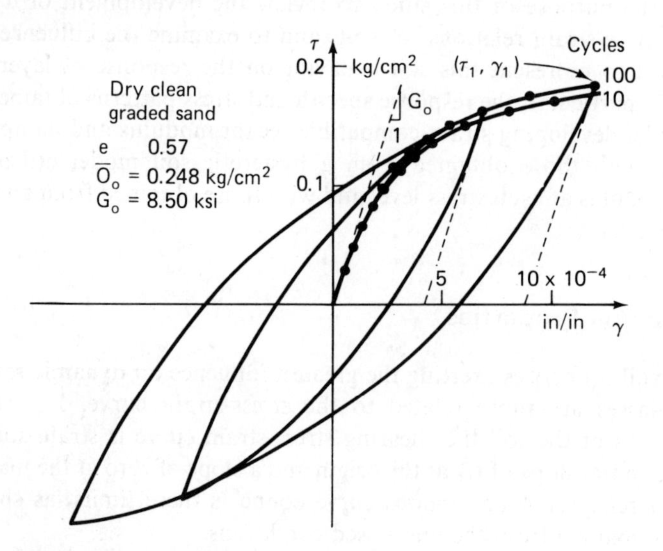


**Fig. 2.** Stress-strain loop end points at 10 and 100 cycles of loading (from Hardin and Drnevich, 1972B)

hysteretic damping associated with any particular shearing stress (or strain) level.

### *Values of the Shear Modulus*

Values of the shear modulus, $G_0$, at low-amplitude shearing strains (initial slope of the $\tau$-$\gamma$ curve), the variation of the secant modulus, $G$, with increased shearing strain amplitude, and the tangent modulus, $G_T$, may be required for different analytical procedures.

*Low-Amplitude Shear Modulus, $G_0$.* The shear modulus, $G_0$, developed at low-amplitude shearing strains can be evaluated for soils *in situ* by the cross-hole method [22] or in the laboratory by the resonant column method [20]. These methods measure the shear wave velocity, $v_s$, under particular test conditions. Then the shear modulus is evaluated from the expression

$$G = \rho v_s^2 \tag{1}$$

in which $\rho$ ($= \gamma_s/g$) is the mass density of the soil.

The cross-hole field method has advantages in that it determines the shear wave velocity in undisturbed soil at chosen depths below the surface and is relatively inexpensive and easy to use. Disadvantages of this method are primarily that $v_s$ is evaluated only for the stress conditions existing at the time of the test, and these conditions may be modified during and after construction.

Resonant column tests have become standard laboratory procedures for evaluating $v_s$ from soil samples. Their principal advantage lies in the flexibility available for test conditions. The testing environment may be modified to evaluate the effects of changes in confining pressures, shearing strain amplitudes, stress histories, and duration of loading. Primary disadvantages include unavoidable disturbances of the soil samples by unloading and reloading, possible disturbances by handling, and problems of reproducing the *in situ* stress conditions.

The shear modulus, $G_0$, has been shown [7,20] to be a function of 11 variables, some of which are related. However the most important of these are the average confining pressure, $\bar{\sigma}_0$; the void ratio, $e$; the time effects; and the shearing strain amplitude, $\gamma$. The low-amplitude shear modulus, $G_0$, may be evaluated using Eq. (1) and

$$\underset{\text{(ft/sec)}}{v_s} = (170 - 78.2e)\underset{\text{(lb/ft}^2\text{)}}{(\bar{\sigma}_0)^{0.25}} \tag{2}$$

for round grained clean sands ($e < 0.80$) or

$$\underset{\text{(ft/sec)}}{v_s} = (159 - 53.5e)\underset{\text{(lb/ft}^2\text{)}}{(\bar{\sigma}_0)^{0.25}} \tag{3}$$

for angular grained clean sands. Equation (3) also gives a first estimate of $v_s$

at 1000-min test duration for normally consolidated clays of low surface activity.

Seed and Idriss [21] have collected data on the variation of $G$ with shearing strain amplitude for clays and sands, and from their curves the low-amplitude values of $G_0$ are approximately

$$G_0 = 2300 S_u \tag{4}$$

for saturated clays and

$$G_0 = 61{,}000(\bar{\sigma}_0)^{0.5} \text{ (lb/ft}^2\text{)} \tag{5}$$

for sands at a relative density of about 75%. In Eq. (4), $S_u$ is the undrained shear strength. Seed and Idriss have shown an increase of about a factor of 2 in $G_0$ when relative density increased from about 30% to about 90%. Hardin and Richart [10] found a smaller variation over a relative density range from about 20% to about 95%, and this variation was attributed primarily to changes in void ratio, as indicated by Eq. (2).

*Effect of Duration of Loading.* In laboratory resonant column tests, the sample is subjected to a confining pressure $\bar{\sigma}_0$ which simulates the *in situ* stress conditions, and vibration measurements are conducted intermittently throughout the duration of the test. The total testing period may include from 1 day to several weeks' time, depending on the type of soil, the parameters to be investigated, and previous information on the type of soil being tested.

Figure 3 illustrates the increase of the low-amplitude $v_s$ with time for a cohesive soil. When the confining pressure, $\bar{\sigma}_0$, was applied to the sample, consolidation occurred, and the shear wave velocity increased rapidly. For the test described in Fig. 3 primary consolidation was apparently completed in about 1000 min, and thereafter a linear increase in $v_s$ with log time occurred, which is considered to be a secondary compression effect. When this effect was included in laboratory evaluations of $v_s$, it was found [2] that good agreement was obtained with values of $v_s$ obtained in the field by cross-hole measurements. Therefore, each pressure increment applied in resonant column tests should be maintained for a time period sufficient for the secondary time effects to be evaluated.

*Effect of Shearing Strain Amplitude.* The upper curve in Fig. 3 represents the increase in shear wave velocity with time after initial pressure application when the sample was excited into torsional vibrations producing a shearing strain of $0.81 \times 10^{-4}$. After the secondary time range was reached (about 1000 min) the amplitude of vibrations was increased long enough to obtain readings at shearing strain amplitudes of $2.0 \times 10^{-4}$, $4.0 \times 10^{-4}$, $10 \times 10^{-4}$, $46 \times 10^{-4}$, and $85 \times 10^{-4}$. These recorded shear wave velocity values are shown in Fig. 3, and it was noted that the rate of secondary time increase of $v_s$ was essentially independent of the strain level. This was for-

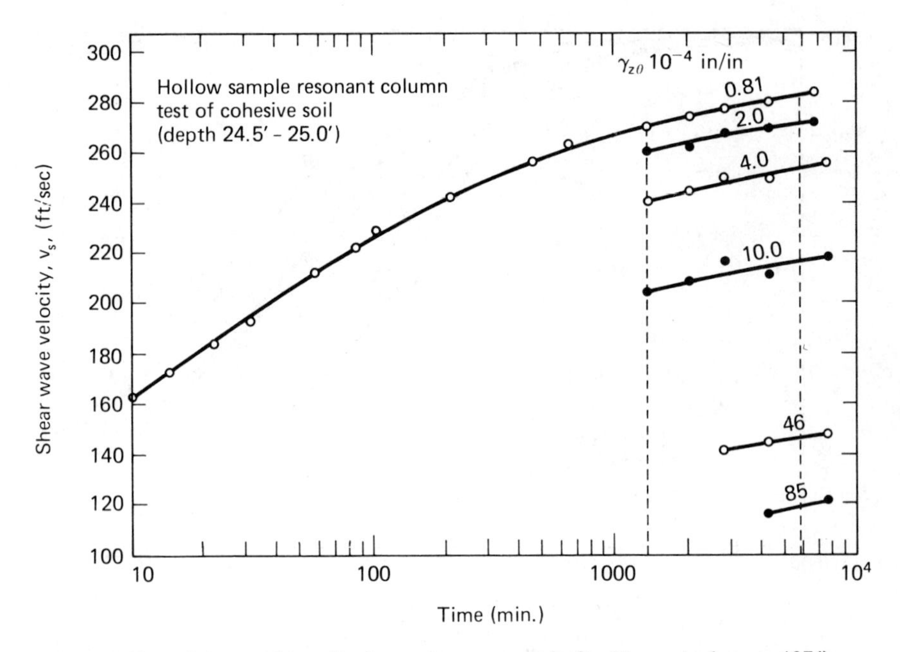


**Fig. 3.** Effect of time and amplitude on shear wave velocity (From Anderson, 1974)

tunate because it permits evaluation of the reduction in $v_s$ with strain amplitude at a chosen time. The two vertical dashed lines in Fig. 3 correspond to times of 1 day (1440 min) and 4 days (5760 min), and values of $v_s$ at each shearing strain level determined the $G$ value [from Eq. (1)], which could be then compared with the low-amplitude value, $G_0$. This information from Fig. 3 produced the two dashed curves shown in Fig. 4. The five other curves shown in Fig. 4 were obtained from tests on one artificial and four natural cohesive soils and correspond to a testing time of 1000 min.

Seed and Idriss [21] presented curves for sands [Fig. 5(a)] and clays [Fig. 5(b)] which illustrated the reduction of the secant shear modulus with increasing shearing strain amplitude. Hardin and Drnevich [9] condensed their numerous test results into a dimensionless form by expressing the abscissa of the diagram in terms of a strain ratio $\gamma/\gamma_r$. The "reference shearing strain, $\gamma_r$," is shown in Fig. 1 and has the magnitude $\tau_m/G_0$. With the introduction of $\gamma/\gamma_r$ as abscissa and $G/G_0$ as ordinate, Hardin and Drnevich found that their test data collapsed essentially to two curves, one for cohesionless soils and one for cohesive soils. Finally, they introduced a term designated the "hyperbolic strain, $\gamma_h$," which included parameters that adjusted the shapes of the two curves to a common curve.

Figure 6 shows the two shearing stress-shearing strain relations for cohesionless (sand) and cohesive (clay) soils from the Hardin and Drnevich tests, expressed on a dimensionless plot. The abscissa is the shearing strain

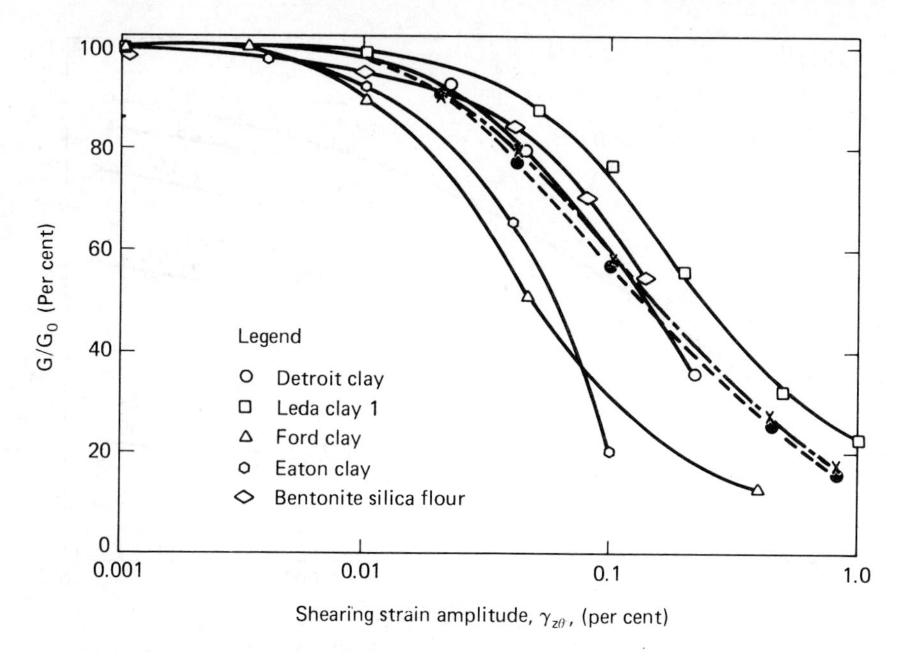


**Fig. 4.** Effect of shearing strain amplitude on shear modulus (From Anderson, 1974)

ratio $\gamma/\gamma_r$, and the ordinate is the shearing stress ratio $\tau/\tau_m$. From these curves the reduction $G/G_0$ may be evaluated from the decreased slope of the secant at increasing strain amplitudes.

*Effect of Stress Repetitions.* Figure 2 shows two curves, one for 10 and one for 100 cycles, which illustrate the influence of repeated stress cycling on sand samples. As the number of repetitions increased, the secant modulus increased slightly. Drnevich and Richart [4] found noticeable increases in the low-amplitude shear modulus, $G_0$, of sands with $10^3$ to $10^6$ cycles of prestrain. Additional test data have confirmed that repeated stressing of sand samples will cause a "stiffening" effect.

On the other hand, for cohesive soils repeated stressing at higher stress levels will cause a slight lowering of the shear modulus, $G$, at a given stress level and also cause a reduction in $G_0$ [1]. Fortunately, these cohesive soil samples regained the original value of $G_0$ after they were allowed to rest under static conditions for a period of time. The time period varied from about a day to a week for the soils tested.

The effects of stiffening of sands or softening of cohesive soils following load repetitions will not be considered in further discussions covered in this chapter, but these effects should be considered when many load repetitions are probable, as, for example, in water wave loading of marine structures and their foundations.

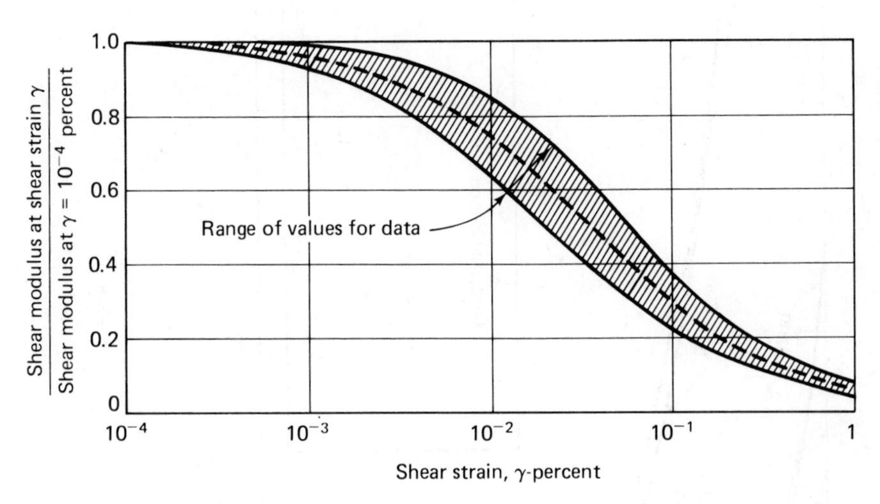


**Fig. 5a.** Variation of shear modulus with shearing strain for sands (From Seed and Idriss, 1970)

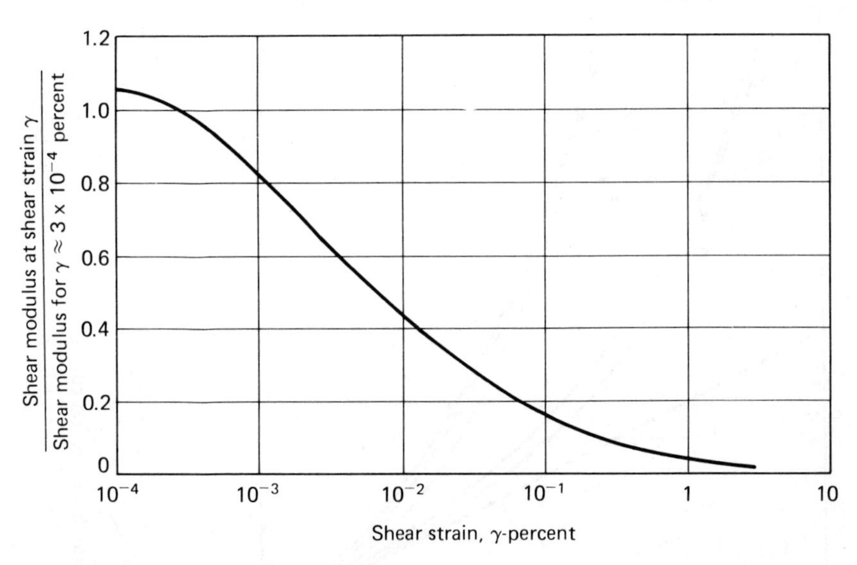


**Fig. 5b.** Typical reduction of shear modulus with shearing strain for saturated clays (From Seed and Idriss, 1970)

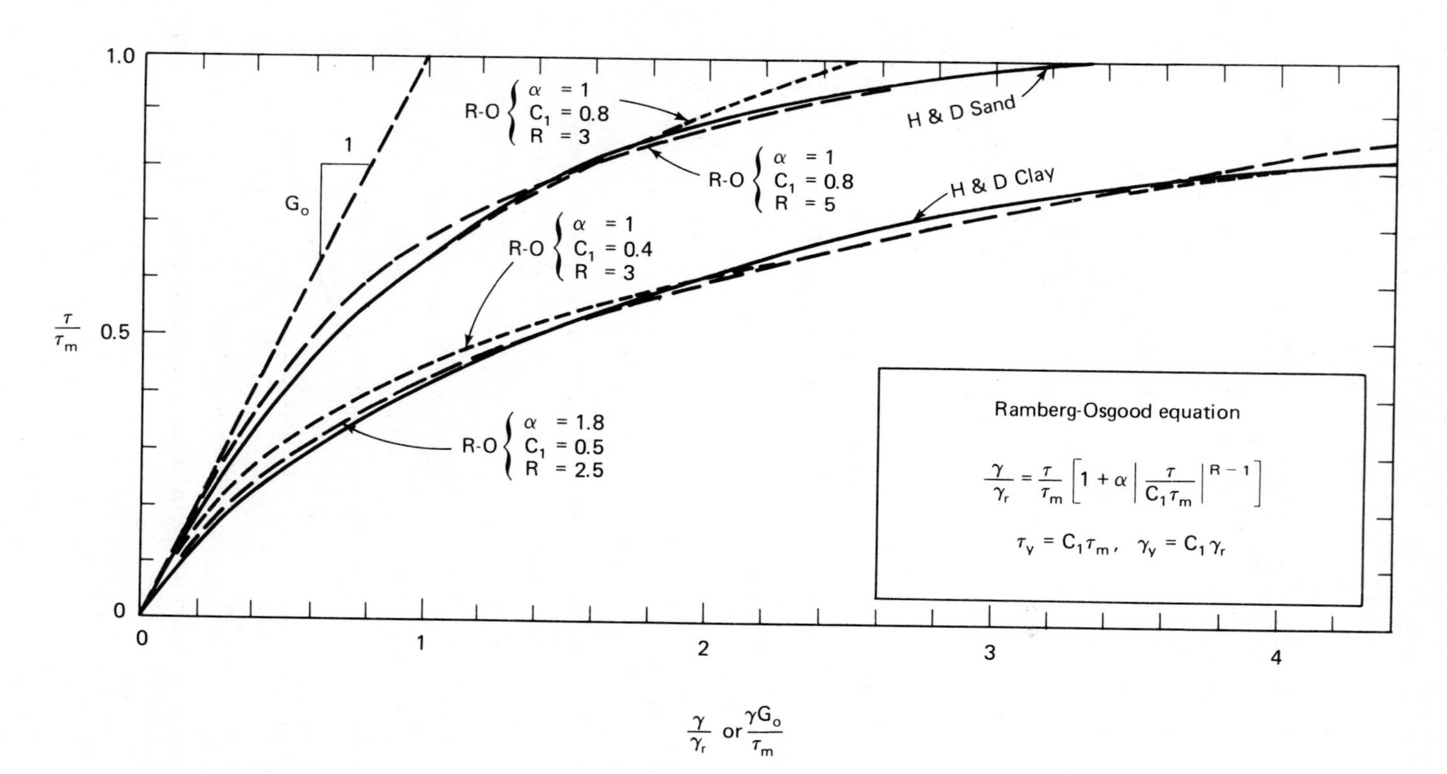


**Fig. 6.** Fit of Ramberg-Osgood curves to soil data

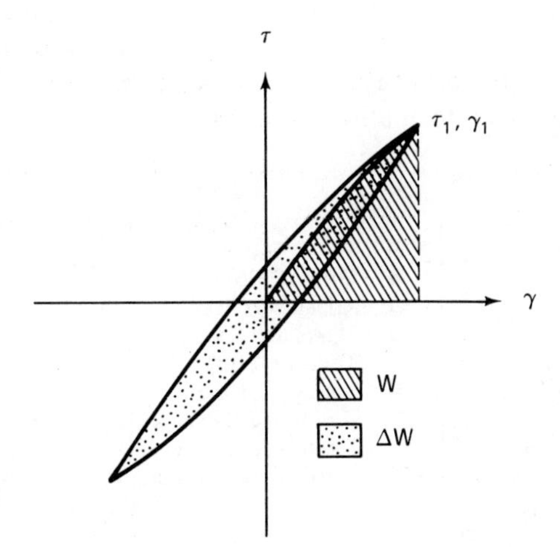


**Fig. 7.** Components of specific damping capacity

*Hysteretic Damping in Soils.* The hysteresis loop shown in Fig. 2 is an indication of the internal energy lost by friction during a reversed loading cycle of a material. Figure 7 shows the area of the hysteresis loop developed upon reversed loading from $\tau_1$, $\gamma_1$, as $\Delta W$, and the area beneath the loading curve from $\tau = 0$ to the point $\tau_1$, $\gamma_1$, as $W$. The ratio $\Delta W/W$ is sometimes called the "specific damping capacity."

The results from resonant column tests of sands [5, 6, 8] have shown that for small shearing strain amplitudes, the damping behavior can be represented by parameters related to a one-degree-of-freedom system with viscous damping (with the viscosity, $\mu$, of the model treated as varying with frequency, $\omega$, to maintain $\mu\omega/G$ constant). For this system the rate of amplitude decay per free vibration cycle (the logarithmic decrement, $\delta$) is related to the damping ratio ($D$) by

$$\delta = \ln \frac{z_1}{z_2} = \frac{2\pi D}{\sqrt{1 - D^2}} \approx 2\pi D. \tag{6}$$

Furthermore, for this system and for small values of $\delta$, the damping ratio ($D$) is related to the specific damping capacity for decaying vibrations by

$$\frac{\Delta W}{W} = 1 - \exp(-2\delta) \approx 4\pi D. \tag{7}$$

For a more complete discussion of these relations, see Richart et al. [20].

Hardin and Drnevich [8] ran numerous resonant column and static torsion tests on hollow samples of cohesive and cohesionless soils. From these tests they were able to determine the increase in damping ratio, $D$ [as established through Eq. (7)], with an increase in hyperbolic shearing strain, $\gamma_h$. Thus, both the decrease in shear modulus and increase in damping were related to an increase in $\gamma_h$, and one curve could represent these effects. However, different parameters were needed to adjust $\gamma_r$ to achieve the $\gamma_h$ used for damping and $\gamma_h$ for modulus reduction.

Seed and Idriss [21] collected test data showing the increases in damping ratio with shearing strain amplitude for both sands and clays. Figure 8 shows this information for clays.

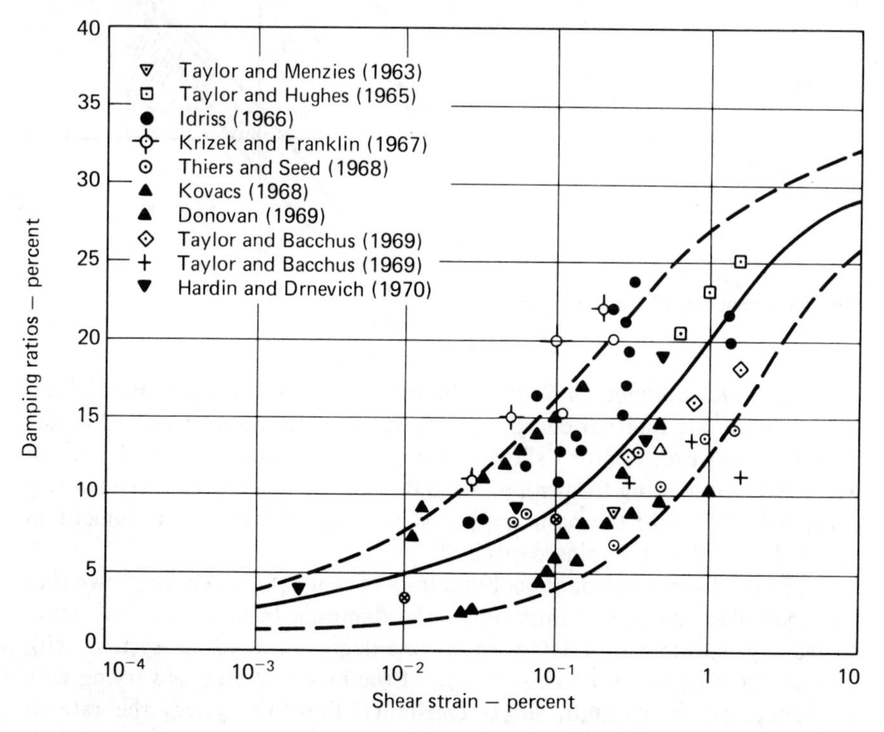


**Fig. 8.** Damping ratios for saturated clays (From Seed and Idriss, 1970)

*Maximum Shearing Stress,* $\tau_m$. The maximum shearing stress at failure, $\tau_m$, is developed for soils in the undrained condition and should be determined for a strain rate compatible with that anticipated in the prototype situation. For water wave or earthquake excitations, the strain rate effect would be negligible for cohesionless soils and would be relatively unimportant for cohesive soils. Therefore, the value of $\tau_m$ determined from simple shear or torsional shear static tests would be satisfactory.

### *Ramberg-Osgood Curves*

Structural engineers [3, 11, 19] have often adopted nonlinear stress-strain curves of the Masing type (see Masing [13]), which will be referred to here as Ramberg-Osgood (R-O) curves. For shearing stresses increasing from zero these curves are described by

$$\gamma = \frac{\tau}{G_0}\left(1 + \alpha\left|\frac{\tau}{C_1\tau_m}\right|^{R-1}\right) \tag{8}$$

and for unloading from point $\tau_1, \gamma_1$ by

$$\gamma - \gamma_1 = \frac{(\tau - \tau_1)}{G_0}\left(1 + \alpha\left|\frac{\tau - \tau_1}{2C_1\tau_m}\right|^{R-1}\right). \tag{9}$$

In Eqs. (8) and (9), $\alpha$ and $R$ are parameters which adjust the position and shape of the curves, and $C_1$ is a factor which relates the "yield" value $\tau_y$ in the original R-O expressions to $\tau_m$, as defined in Fig. 1 (i.e., $\tau_y = C_1\tau_m$).

The shearing stress-strain curves obtained for sand and for clay by Hardin and Drnevich [9] are shown in Fig. 6. Also shown in Fig. 6 are two R-O curves which approximate each curve. For analytical purposes, the R-O curve with $R = 3$, $\alpha = 1$, $C_1 = 0.8$ will be chosen to represent the relations for sand, and the R-O curve with $R = 3$, $\alpha = 1$, and $C_1 = 0.4$ will be chosen to represent clay.

*Shear Modulus.* A special feature of the R-O curve is that upon initial loading the shear modulus has the initial value of $G_0$, and this same value of $G_0$ is again obtained upon unloading from a point $\tau_1, \gamma_1$ [Eq. (9)].

From Eq. (8) the decrease in secant modulus, $G\ (= \tau/\gamma)$, with an increase in shearing stress ratio, $\tau/\tau_m$, is

$$\frac{G}{G_0} = \frac{1}{1 + \alpha|\tau/C_1\tau_m|^{R-1}}, \tag{10}$$

and from differentiation of Eq. (8) the decrease in tangent modulus, $G_T$, is

$$\frac{G_T}{G_0} = \frac{1}{1 + \alpha R|\tau/C_1\tau_m|^{R-1}}. \tag{11}$$

Figure 9 shows the decrease of both tangent and secant shear modulus with strain ratio for the special case of $R = 3$, $\alpha = 1.0$, and $C_1 = 0.4$.

*Damping from the R-O Curves.* The input energy $W$ beneath the loading curve [Eq. (8)] from $\tau = 0$ to $\tau = \tau_1$ and the area of the hysteresis loop $\Delta W$ between $\tau = \tau_1$ and $\tau = -\tau_1$ can be determined by integration. For the special conditions of $R = 3$, $\alpha = 1$, and $C_1 = 0.4$ the specific damping capacity was evaluated as functions of both $\tau_1/\tau_m$ and $\gamma_1/\gamma_r$. These values are given in Table 1.

**Table 1**
**Specific Damping Capicity from R-O Curve ($R = 3$, $\alpha = 1.0$, $C_1 = 0.4$)**

| $\tau_1/\tau_m$ | 0.10 | 0.20 | 0.30 | 0.40 | 0.50 | 0.60 | 0.70 |
|---|---|---|---|---|---|---|---|
| $\gamma_1/\gamma_r$ | 0.11 | 0.25 | 0.47 | 0.80 | 1.28 | 1.95 | 2.84 |
| $\Delta W/W$ | 0.23 | 0.73 | 1.22 | 1.60 | 1.87 | 2.06 | 2.19 |

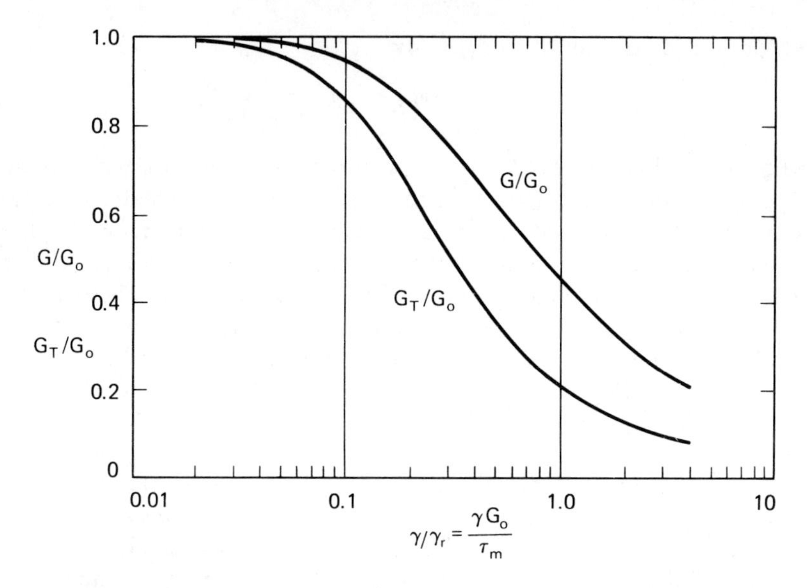


**Fig. 9.** Variation of $G/G_0$ and $G_T/G_0$ with $\gamma/\gamma_r$ for Ramberg-Osgood curve ($R = 3$, $\alpha = 1$, $C_1 = 0.4$)

## Dynamic Response of Layered Soils

In this section the dynamic response of layered soils will be treated as a problem of one-dimensional wave propagation in uniform horizontal or inclined layers of nonlinear materials. Excitation will be provided at the base of the layers and the shearing stress-strain relations, surface motions, permanent displacements, and response spectra will be evaluated. One-dimensional wave transmission through these materials will be treated by the method of characteristics [24].

### *Soil Models*

Three types of soil models will be considered to represent layers of cohesive soils: (1) a Ramberg-Osgood material, (2) a strain-compatible linear viscoelastic material, and (3) an elastic-slip material.

*Ramberg-Osgood Model.* The R-O soil model developed stress-strain relations described by Eqs. (8) and (9) when the parameters were $R = 3$, $\alpha = 1.0$, and $C_1 = 0.4$. In the method of characteristics the tangent modulus was introduced at each stress level, and calculations were developed at each time step by considering the material to be elastic with the instantaneous value of $G_T$ and with the viscosity, $\mu$, equal to zero. By this procedure the calculations develop a hysteresis loop because of variations of $G_T$ during loading and unloading which produces energy losses in each soil layer.

*Strain-Compatible Viscoelastic Model.* An approximation to a nonlinear model was developed by applying successive corrections to a linear viscoelastic model. First the external excitation was applied to the base of a layered system which was considered elastic (values of $G_0$ used) and viscosity was zero. During this loading the maximum shearing strain was evaluated. Then the stress, secant modulus, $G$, and viscosity, $\mu$, were evaluated for a strain equal to 0.7 of the maximum value. This involved use of Eq. (8), Eq. (10), Table 1, Eq. (7), and the expression

$$\mu = \frac{2GD}{\omega}. \tag{12}$$

In Eq. (12) the circular frequency ($\omega = 2\pi f$) was chosen as $4\pi$ (or $f = 2$ cycles/sec) to correspond approximately to the natural frequency of the layer chosen. After five successive corrections, each involving an input earthquake motion of 10-sec duration, the soil properties were compatible with a strain equal to 0.7 times the maximum value developed in each soil layer.

*Elastic-Slip Model.* As a limiting case each soil layer was treated as an elastic material exhibiting a value of shear modulus, $G_0$, until the maximum shearing stress, $\tau_m$, was reached. When this stress was reached, slip was permitted without increasing the stress, but upon reversal of loading the initial value, $G_0$, was again recovered.

#### *Analytical Method*

The analytical method adopted for these studies was the method of characteristics [14, 23, 25]. This method has been applied to one-dimensional wave propagation in nonlinear layered soils [16–18, 24] and has been found to be relatively simple and economical.

Study of one-dimensional shear wave transmission through layered soils involves calculations of particle velocities and shearing stresses in successions throughout the soil depth. Figure 10(a) shows the soil element which deforms only by horizontal displacement, $u$, in the $x$-$z$ plane. Layer and section designations are shown in Fig. 10(b), and the $z$-$t$ diagram for five layers is shown in Fig. 10(c). For elastic conditions, the depth interval, $\Delta z$, and the time interval, $\Delta t$, are chosen such that

$$v_s = \frac{\Delta z}{\Delta t} \tag{13}$$

in each layer. For convenience, the time interval is usually selected as a constant value, and $\Delta z$ is adjusted to satisfy Eq. (13) for each layer. Then the calculations proceed from one time step to the next; for example, the values

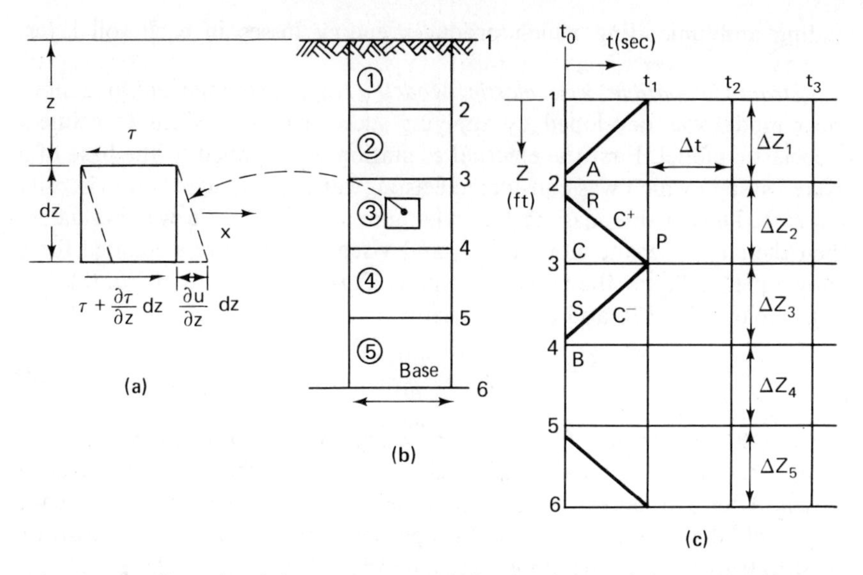


**Fig. 10.** One-dimensional shear wave transmission by characteristics method (a) One-dimensional element (b) Layer and section designation (c) $z - t$ diagram for five soil layers

of shearing stress and particle velocities at point $P$ are established through the characteristics $C^+$ and $C^-$ and the stress and velocity values at points $A$ and $B$. For $G < G_0$ the characteristic lines follow $RP$ and $SP$ and interpolations are required. Details of the calculation procedure were given by Streeter et al. [24].

#### *Response of Horizontal Layered System*

Soil properties influence the transmission of earthquake energy from the underlying rock to the surface. The shearing stress-strain relations developed in each layer, the surface deformations, and the velocity response spectra for the soil surface were compared for a 50-ft-thick layer of cohesive soil resting on rock.

At the surface the soil had $\tau_m = 1080$ lb/ft$^2$ and $G_0 = 1.728 \times 10^6$ lb/ft$^2$, and at a depth of 50 ft (rock surface) these values were $\tau_m = 1615$ lb/ft$^2$ and $G_0 = 2.584 \times 10^6$ lb/ft$^2$. A linear variation of $\tau_m$ and $G_0$ between these limits was assumed and the 50-ft depth was broken up into five layers for calculation purposes. The unit weight of the soil was taken as 120 lb/ft$^3$ in each of the layers.

Excitation occurred at the rock surface (El-50 ft) according to the velocity-time pattern developed by the N-S component of the 1940 El Centro earthquake. Only the first 10 sec of the earthquake motion was applied because this was considered sufficient to demonstrate the differences in response resulting from assumption of the different soil models.

*Shearing Stress-Strain Relations.* Figures 11(a) and 11(b) show the dimensionless shearing stress-strain patterns developed when the soil (1) was considered to behave according to the R-O curve and (2) was a strain-compatible viscoelastic material. These shearing stresses and strains were the average values developed in layer 5 [see Fig. 10(c)] immediately above the

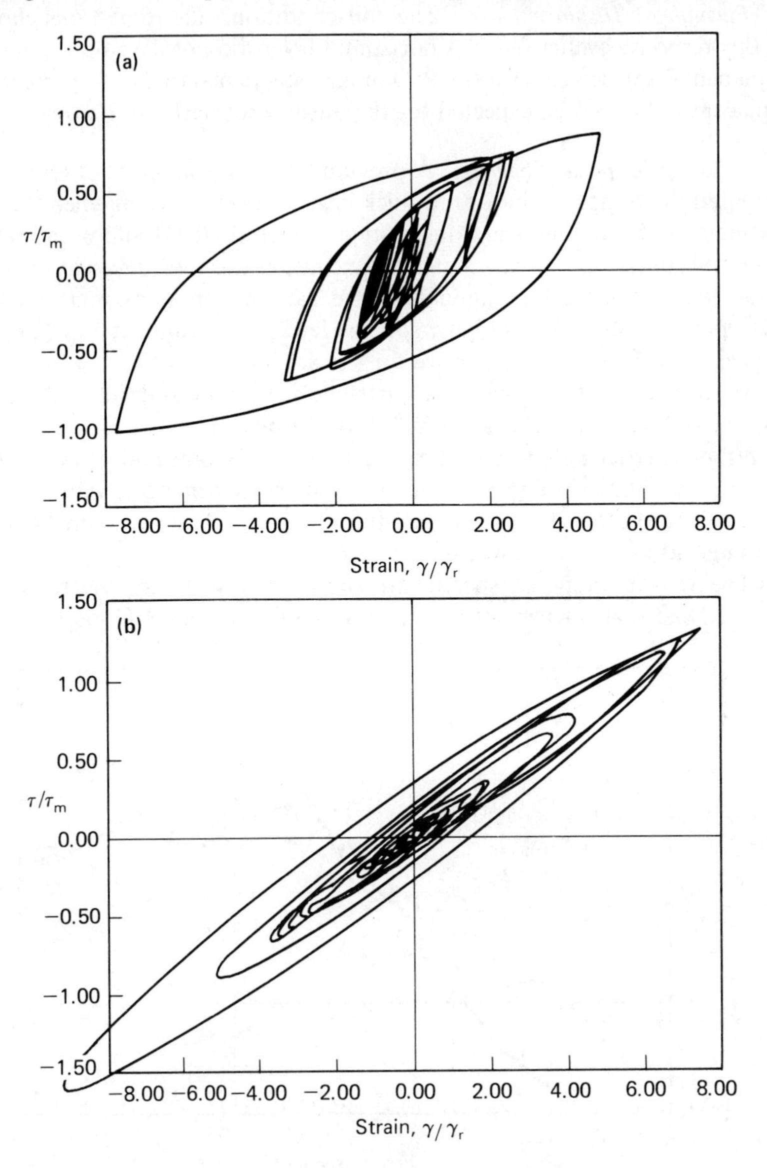


**Fig. 11.** Dimensionless hearing stress-strain relations for horizontal layer No. 5 (a) From R-O soil model (b) From viscoelastic soil model

rock surface. Note the significant changes in the slope and shape of the hysteresis loops in Fig. 11(a) for the R-O material, in contrast to the constant slope and constant shape of the loops for the viscoelastic material in Fig. 11(b).

*Permanent Displacements.* The soil conditions and excitations chosen for this response evaluation of a horizontal layer did not develop significant permanent displacements for the R-O or elastic-slip materials. No permanent displacements would be expected for the linear viscoelastic soil model.

*Velocity Response Spectra.* A previous study by Joyner and Chen [12] compared the response of a 200-m-thick layer of firm alluvium when the soil was modeled as a nonlinear Masing-type material (R-O) and as a strain-compatible linear viscoelastic material. Excitation was introduced at the base of the layer as the N21E component of the Taft accelerogram, multiplied by 4. They found substantially higher spectral levels of response at 5% damping for periods between 0.1 and 0.6 sec for the nonlinear material.

In the present study, the surface particle accelerations developed for the different soil models in the 50-ft-thick layer formed the basis for calculating the response spectra. The program described by Nigam and Jennings [15] permitted evaluation of spectral values of displacement ($S_d$), velocity ($S_v$), and acceleration ($S_a$). Periods ranged from 0.02 to 8.0 sec, and one value of damping ratio ($D$) of 0.02 was introduced.

The velocity response spectra are shown in Fig. 12 for the three soil models. Note that for periods less than about 0.3 sec the R-O model devel-

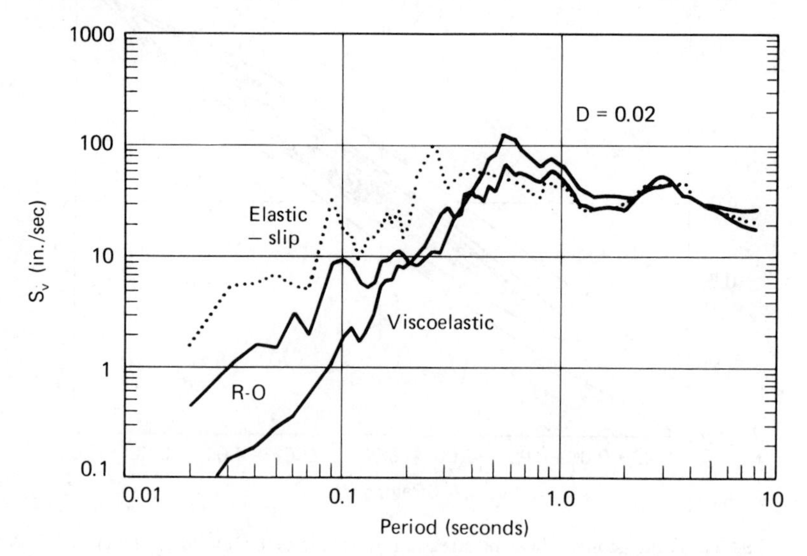


**Fig. 12.** Surface velocity response spectra for 50 ft. thick horizontal soil layer

oped significantly larger values of $S_v$ than did the linear viscoelastic model. The larger value of $G_0$ for the R-O model at small shearing strain changes produced a "stiffer" layer for the low-amplitude excitations that occur at the high frequencies, and hysteretic damping was also reduced at lower strain excursions. Both of these factors tended to increase $S_v$ in this frequency range above that resulting from a constant lower value of $G_0$ and constant shape of the stress-strain loop as produced by the linear viscoelastic material. The elastic-slip material produced a layer which had constant stiffness until the shearing strength was reached; then damping was produced by slip. The lack of damping in the loading-unloading range produced higher values of $S_v$ at high frequencies, and the slip occurring at large energy input depressed the values at periods 0.3 to 1.0 sec. At larger values of the periods, the three curves are quite similar, although small differences may be noted.

### *Response of Inclined Layered System*

To investigate the influence of initial static shearing stresses on the dynamic response of a one-dimensional soil system, the 50-ft-thick layer was considered when it rested upon a rock base inclined at a 4 : 1 slope. For this example, 0.5 times the velocity-time pattern from the N-S component of the 1940 El Centro earthquake was applied at the rock surface, and the response of the soil layer was evaluated when the soil model was of the Ramberg-Osgood type, the strain-compatible viscoelastic type, and the elastic-slip type. The soil layer had $\tau_m = 2160$ lb/ft$^2$ and $G_0 = 1.728 \times 10^6$ lb/ft$^2$ at the surface and $\tau_m = 3230$ lb/ft$^2$ and $G_0 = 2.584 \times 10^6$ lb/ft$^2$ at the rock base, with a linear variation of soil properties between these boundaries.

*Shearing Stress-Strain Relations.* Figure 13 shows the dimensionless shearing stress-shearing strain patterns obtained for layer 5 using the three soil models. In Fig. 13(a) the R-O material shows a permanent strain (downhill) and energy loss through the hysteresis loops. Figure 13(b) shows the typical viscoelastic loops of constant geometry and indicates no residual shearing strains. Figure 13(c) again indicates permanent downhill deformations because of the residual shearing strains. At the end of 10 sec of earthquake excitations the downhill motion of the soil surface (relative to the rock base motion) was about 0.035 ft for the R-O material, 0 ft for the viscoelastic material, and 0.02 ft for the elastic-slip material.

*Surface Velocity-Time Patterns.* Figure 14 shows the variation of surface particle velocities with time for the R-O soil model [Fig. 14(a)], the strain-compatible viscoelastic soil model [Fig. 14(b)], and the elastic-slip soil model Fig. 14(c)]. Note how the viscoelastic model damps out the higher frequency vibrations. The higher frequency vibrations are reduced in amplitude by the R-O model below the values shown for the elastic-slip model

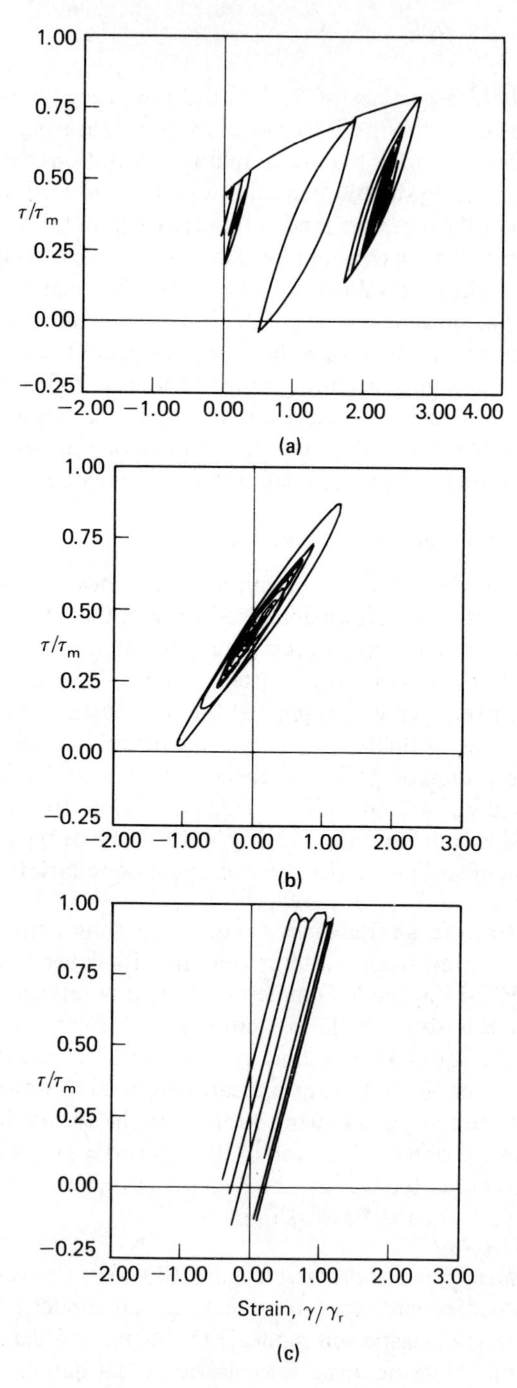


**Fig. 13.** Dimensionless shearing stress-strain relations in No. 5 layer for 4 : 1 slope (a) From R-O model (b) From viscoelastic soil model (c) From elastic-slip model

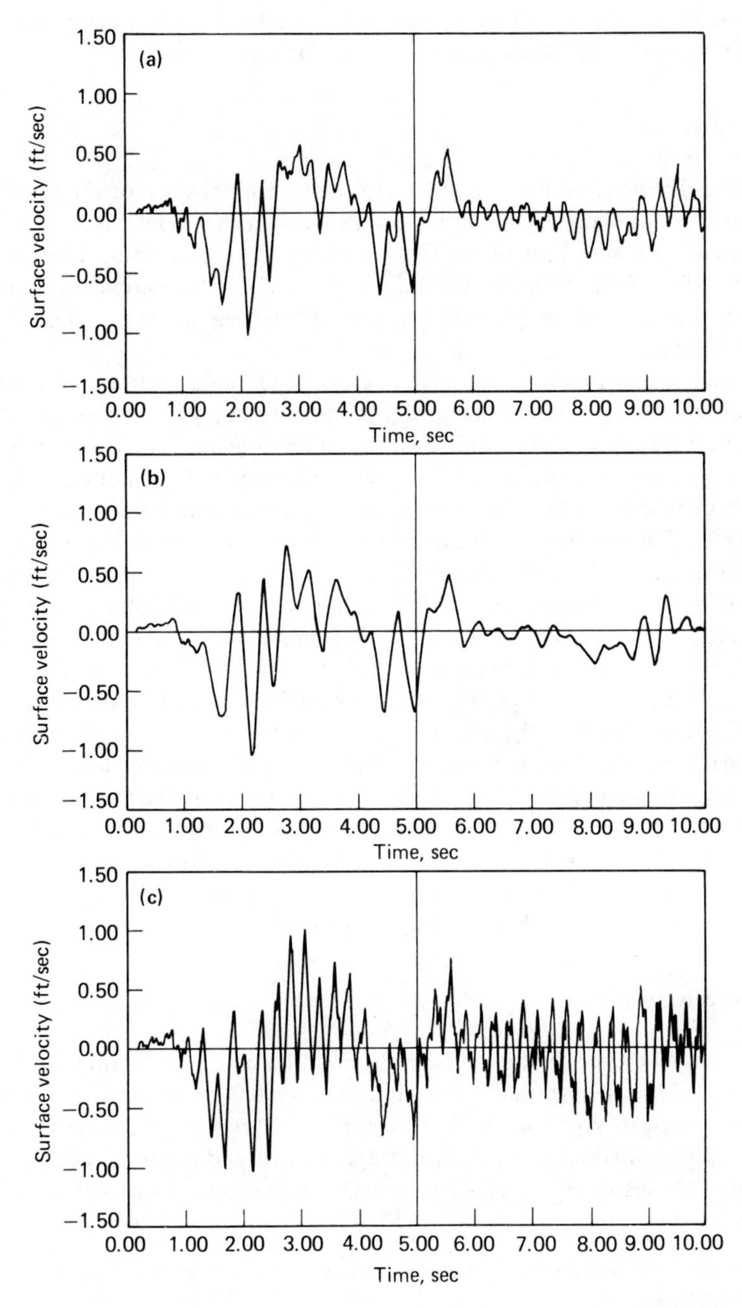


**Fig. 14.** Surface velocity-time records for 4 : 1 slope (a) From R-O soil model (b) From viscoelastic soil model (c) From elastic-slip soil model

because of hysteretic damping at all strain levels. The elastic-slip model is, of course, a limiting case and does not conform to reality.

## Conclusions

The dynamic shearing stress-strain curves for soils are of the nonlinear strain-softening type. A good approximation to this behavior can be obtained analytically by adoption of the Ramberg-Osgood-type curves. Then, introduction of the R-O curve into an analytical procedure for evaluating dynamic responses of soil masses permits study of soil particle motions, stresses, and displacements.

A comparison made by introducing the R-O model, a strain-compatible viscoelastic model, and an elastic-slip model into analyses by the method of characteristics showed the influence of the chosen model on the dynamic behavior of the systems. Use of the viscoelastic model damps out the higher-frequency vibrations and does not permit any permanent deformations of the soil mass. The elastic-slip model retains the high-frequency low-amplitude vibrations and, in fact, accentuates their response due to the lack of hysteretic damping at shearing stresses below the slip stress level. Permanent deformations are possible with this model. The R-O model retains the high-frequency vibrations, introduces hysteretic damping which increases as the strain amplitude increases, and permits evaluation of permanent deformations.

From this study of the one-dimensional dynamic response of soil layers, it appears that the Ramberg-Osgood-type soil model has certain advantages over the strain-compatible linear viscoelastic model. Joyner and Chen [12] found similar results for one-dimensional wave propagations in soils. It is anticipated that the R-O soil model may be introduced into a grid system to simulate two-dimensional wave propagation in soil masses. Initial studies on this problem have been presented by Wylie et al. [26].

## Acknowledgment

Support by the National Science Foundation from Grants GI-34771 and SK-35789 for portions of this study are gratefully acknowledged. Special thanks go to Professor V. L. Streeter for his continual encouragement, advice, and contribution of ideas throughout this and previous studies. The advice of Professor R. D. Hanson on various portions of this study is also appreciated.

## References

1. ANDERSON, D. G., "Dynamic Modulus of Cohesive Soils," Ph.D. dissertation, University of Michigan, Ann Arbor, 1974, 311 pp.

2. Anderson, D. G., and R. D. Woods, "Comparison of Field and Laboratory Shear Moduli," Proc. Conf. on In Situ Measurement of Soil Properties, *Geotechnical Div. Specialty Conf. ASCE*, Vol. 1. North Carolina State University, Raleigh, 1975, pp. 69–92.
3. Berg, G. V., "A Study of the Earthquake Response of Inelastic Systems," *Proc. Struct. Eng. Assoc. Calif.*, Oct. 1965.
4. Drnevich, V. P., and F. E. Richart, Jr., "Dynamic Prestraining of Dry Sand," *J. Soil Mech. Found. Div. Proc. ASCE*, Vol. 96. No. SM2, 1970, pp. 453–469.
5. Hall, J. R., Jr., and F. E. Richart, Jr., "Dissipation of Elastic Wave Energy in Granular Soils." *J. Soil Mech. Found. Div. Proc. ASCE*, Vol. 89, No. SM6, Nov. 1963, pp. 27–56.
6. Hardin, B. O., "The Nature of Damping in Sands," *J. Soil Mech. Found. Div. Proc. ASCE*, Vol. 91, No. SM1, Jan. 1965, pp. 63–97.
7. Hardin, B. O., and W. L. Black, "Vibration Modulus of Normally Consolidated Clay," *J. Soil Mech. Found. Div. Proc. ASCE*, Vol. 94, No. SM2, March 1968, pp. 353–369.
8. Hardin B. O., and V. P. Drnevich, "Shear Modulus and Damping in Soils: Measurement and Parameter Effects," *J. Soil Mech. Found. Div. Proc. ASCE*, Vol. 98, No. SM6, June 1972, pp. 603–624.
9. Hardin, B. O., and V. P. Drnevich, "Shear Modulus and Damping in Soils: Design Equations and Curves," *J. Soil Mech. Found. Div. Proc. ASCE*, Vol. 98, No. SM7, July 1972, pp. 667–692.
10. Hardin, B. O., and F. E. Richart, Jr., "Elastic Wave Velocities in Granular Soils," *J. Soil Mech. Found. Div. Proc. ASCE*, Vol. 89, No. SM1, Feb. 1963, pp. 33–65.
11. Jennings, P. C., "Periodic Response of a General Yielding Structure," *J. Eng. Mech. Div. Proc. ASCE*, Vol. 88, No. EM6, Dec. 1964, pp. 33–63.
12. Joyner, W. B., and A. T. F. Chen, "Calculation of Nonlinear Ground Response in Earthquakes" (presented orally at Am. Seismological Conf., 1974, to be published in *Bull. Seism. Soc. Am.*, Oct. 1975).
13. Masing, G., "Eigenspannungen und Verfestigung beim Messing," Proceedings, Second International Congress on Applied Mechancs, Zurich, 1926.
14. Newmark, N. M., and E. Rosenblueth, *Fundamentals of Earthquake Engineering*, Prentice-Hall, Englewood Cliffs, N.J., 1971, 640 pp.
15. Nigam, N. C., and P. C. Jennings, "Digital Calculations of Response Spectra from Strong Motion Earthquakes," *Bull. Seism. Soc. Am.*, Vol. 59, No. 2, April 1969, p. 909.
16. Papadakis, C. N., and F. E., Richart, Jr., "Earthquake Wave Transmission through Saturated Soil," Proc. Conf. on Analysis and Design in Geotechnical Engineering, *ASCE Geotechnical Div. Specialty Conf.*, Vol. 1, Austin, Texas, 1974, pp. 1–32.
17. Papadakis, C. N., and E. B. Wylie, "Seismic Shear Wave Propagation Through Earth Dams," *Soils Found.* (*J. JSSMFE*), Vol. 15. No. 2, June 1975, pp. 47–61.
18. Papadakis, C. N., V. L. Streeter, and E. B. Wylie, "Bedrock Motions Computed from Surface Seismograms," *J. Geotechnical Eng. Div. Proc. ASCE*, Vol. 100, No. GT10, Oct. 1974, pp. 1091–1106.
19. Ramberg, W., and W. T. Osgood, "Description of Stress-Strain Curves by Three Parameters," *Tech. Note 902*, NACA, 1943.

20. Richart, F. E., Jr., J. R. Hall, Jr., and R. D. Woods, *Vibrations of Soils and Foundations*, Prentice-Hall, Englewood Cliffs, N.J., 1970, 414 pp.
21. Seed, H. B., and I. M. Idriss, "Soil Moduli and Damping Factors for Dynamic Response Analysis," *Rep. No. EERC 70-10*, Earthquake Engineering and Research Center, College of Engineering, University of California, Berkeley, Dec. 1970.
22. Stokoe, K. H., II, and R. D. Woods, "In-Situ Shear Wave Velocity by Cross-Hole Method," *J. Soil Mech. Found. Div. Proc. ASCE*, Vol. 98, No. SM5, May 1972, pp. 443–460.
23. Streeter, V. L., and E. B. Wylie, *Hydraulic Transients*, McGraw-Hill, New York, 1967, 329 pp.
24. Streeter, V. L., E. B. Wylie, and F. E. Richart, Jr., "Soil Motion Computations by Characteristics Method," *J. Geotechnical Div. Proc. ASCE*, Vol. 100, No. GT3, March, 1974, pp. 247–263.
25. Westergaard, H. M., "Earthquake-Shock Transmission in Tall Buildings," *Eng. News-Record*, Vol. 111, 1933, pp. 654–656.
26. Wylie, E. B., V. L. Streeter, and C. N. Papadakis, "Transient Two-Dimensional Analysis of Soils by Latticework," Proceedings, U.S. National Conference on Earthquake Engineering, Ann Arbor, 1975, pp. 166–175. Earthquake Eng. Res. Inst., 424 46th St. Oakland, Ca.

# The Transmitting Boundary—Again

A. R. ROBINSON*

## 1. Introduction

The use of modern, high-speed electronic digital computers has made practical the numerical dynamic analysis of elastic and inelastic continua in cases where analytical solution would not be feasible. Such solutions have made use of finite differences [1], equations obtained with the use of lumped parameter models [2], and finite elements [3]. However, despite the phenomenal increase of speed and storage capacity of computers in the last two decades, restrictions on time and storage still impose severe limits on the direct application of numerical methods to problems of pressing engineering and geophysical interest [1].

In problems of wave propagation in solids, the source of some of the difficulty is readily seen. Consider a mass of soil or rock (Fig. 1) including some buried structure within it and having a limited area of dynamic excitation. If any detail of the structural loading is to be obtained, a fairly small space interval is required. Less obviously, if any rapid loading rate is to be transmitted by a finite model in a reasonably accurate way, a small space interval is likewise required [2,4]. Considerations of convergence of a difference solution to the solution of the governing partial differential equations and considerations of numerical stability of the calculation relate the largest time interval which can be used to the space interval by [5,2]

$$\frac{c_p \, \Delta t}{\Delta x} < r,$$

where $r$ is a number of the rough order of magnitude of unity, and $c_p$ is the

*Department of Civil Engineering, University of Illinois at Urbana-Champaign, Urbana, Illinois.

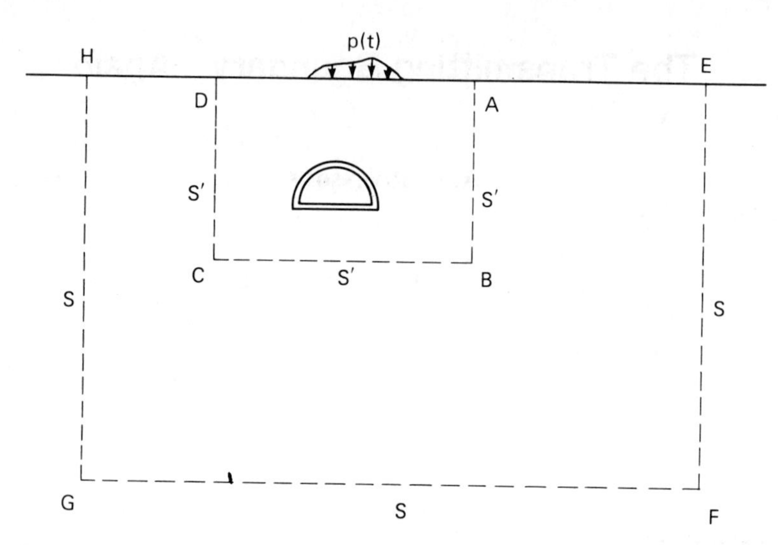


**Fig. 1.** A dynamic problem for a half space

velocity of a $P$ wave in the solid. Now if the time of interest in the problem is long, we can see that a very large region $R$ with boundary $S$ must be used in the calculation in order that spurious reflections from the boundary $S$ not return to the region of direct interest near the structure during the time of calculation. The general conclusion of these simple arguments is that the solution must be carried out over a region with a very large number of discrete variables for a very large number of time intervals.

It is natural to attempt to introduce an artificial boundary $S'$ which allows waves to pass through it without reflection. This "window" or "transmitting boundary" would permit solution of the problem in a much smaller region having many fewer discrete variables per time interval. The computer time and storage can easily be cut by an order of magnitude for a two-dimensional problem of the type indicated in Fig. 1. Such a saving is so obviously attractive that efforts to develop a transmitting boundary for a solid began not long after the first actual numerical experiences with wave propagation problems on computers.

At first sight the problem of arriving at a boundary condition which would provide a transmitting boundary does not appear to be very challenging. Indeed, the one-dimensional elastic case is almost trivial (Fig. 2). In this problem, if we are concerned with the right boundary, we wish to limit the disturbance in the immediate vicinity of that boundary to a wave traveling to the right, that is, to an outward-going wave. If $c$ is the velocity of waves in the (slender) bar, we then have

$$u = f_2(x - ct)$$

near the right boundary.

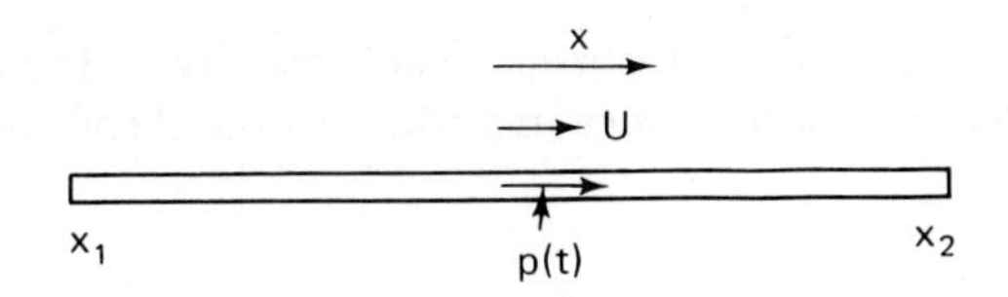


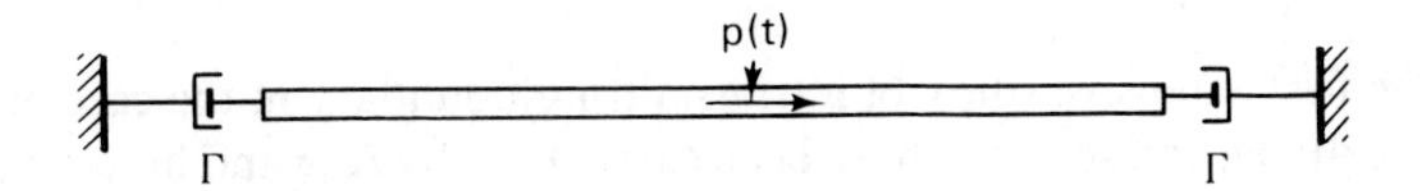


**Fig. 2.** Transmitting boundary for waves in a bar

Then

$$\frac{\partial u}{\partial t} = -cf'_2(x - ct) \quad \text{and} \quad \frac{\partial u}{\partial x} = f'_2(x - ct).$$

Whatever the disturbance, the transmitting boundary at the right end leads to the condition

$$\frac{\partial u}{\partial x} = -\frac{1}{c}\frac{\partial u}{\partial t} \tag{1}$$

at the right boundary $x = x_2$. Similarly, at the left, $x = x_1$, we must have

$$u = f_1(x + ct)$$

and the corresponding condition

$$\frac{\partial u}{\partial x} = +\frac{1}{c}\frac{\partial u}{\partial t} \tag{2}$$

at $x = x_1$.

In both cases the boundary conditions for the elastic case correspond to a dashpot of the appropriate strength attached to the ends of the bar:

$$\Gamma = \frac{EA}{c},$$

where $\Gamma$ is the dashpot strength, $E$ is the Young's modulus of the material, and $A$ is the area of the slender bar.

The simplicity of the result for the case of one dimension is totally misleading for more than one spatial dimension. For an isotropic elastic solid there are two wave speeds for body waves. The variety of wave phenomena which can be observed even in a homogeneous solid having a boundary with given tractions is considerable. In cases where layering is included in the modeling, even more complicated types of disturbances are present. There is, however, one characteristic of problems in two or three dimensions which serves as an advantage over a general one-dimensional problem; namely, the stresses fall off with distance from the center of the disturbance. This means that it is quite possible to consider a transmitting boundary in a region that remains elastic even though sizable inelastic effects may be present closer in to the source of the dynamic disturbance. The elasticity of the material at the transmitting boundary will be very important in the theory to be developed in Sec. 3.

## 2. Previous Work

The first extensive study of a transmitting boundary in the case of more than one dimension seems to have been carried out by Ang and his co-workers [2]. In this work the generalization of the equations for the one-dimensional case, Eq. (1) or (2), was arrived at by considering inertia forces for a single velocity of propagation, either $c_p$ or $c_s$, and then combining the effects differently for normal and shear stresses on the transmitting boundary. In this combination, there is an implication that the boundary orientation and the wave processes are related in some way.

Later work by Lysmer and Kuhlemeyer [6] showed that for an elastic region near the boundary a simple viscous boundary will absorb body waves almost perfectly. However, surface waves required a special treatment with dashpot strength varying with depth from the free surface in a manner which is frequency dependent. The technique works satisfactorily for some problems of harmonic excitation but has not been so satisfactory for general pulse loading. Some of the difficulties which have been noted [7] are attributed to the inability of the model of the transmitting boundary to handle high frequencies.

More recent work by Lysmer and Waas [8] aims at creating finite elements at a boundary which match the impedance of the solid for a given frequency of disturbing force. This procedure seems to consider chiefly the horizontal propagation of waves across a vertical transmitting boundary.

A totally different approach has been proposed by Smith [9]. In this ingenious procedure, reflections from a single plane or corner are eliminated by an extension of the method of images. Two or more elastic problems are solved with different artificial boundary conditions at what is to become the transmitting boundary. The superposition of the fields then eliminates the reflection completely unless a reflected ray hits the same boundary again. These multiple reflections do not cause significant error in most cases. However, the method suffers from the serious limitation that the entire field, not merely the part near the transmitting boundary, must remain elastic if the superposition of fields is to be valid.

It may be remarked that none of the methods outlined can exactly handle the case of a motion consisting of a *P* wave and an *S* wave propagating in general directions with respect to the boundary. In the Ang and Lysmer models, the boundary orientation is somehow tied to the normal to rays from the disturbance. Actually such an arrangement cannot be justified even for the simplest disturbance at the surface of an elastic solid. Figure 3 represents the wave situation some time after the sudden application of the force $q$. In the region $ABC$, the so-called head-wave region, the shear waves are actually traveling normal to the line $AB$. This direction will change when the cylindrical (or spherical) front $CBB'C'$ passes the boundary.

It would seem from these considerations that in order to arrive at a transmitting boundary model which could treat the simplest cases exactly, it is necessary to separate the total field in the vicinity of the transmitting boundary into its $P$ and $S$ constituents. Moreover, the directions of the normals to wave surfaces at the transmitting boundary cannot be assumed *a priori* but must be found as part of the procedure.

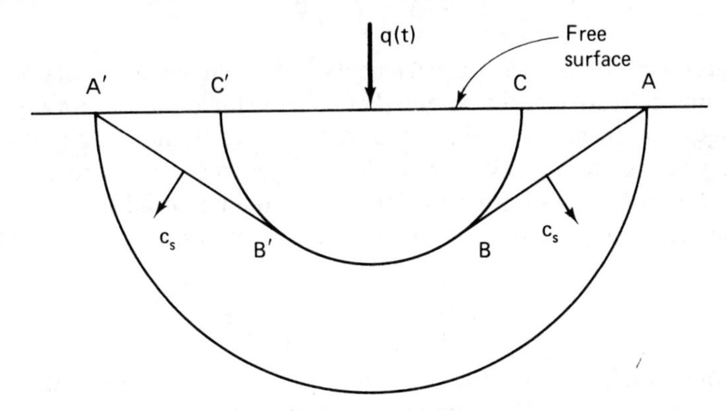


**Fig. 3.** Wave fronts for a suddenly applied load

## 3. The Proposed Theory

A model of a transmitting boundary which attempts to avoid the shortcomings of the available procedures will now be described for two-dimensional (plane-strain) problems. In a sense, the two-dimensional problem is more difficult than the three-dimensional one in that no Huyghens' principle exists exactly for two dimensions. Extensions to three dimensions are likely to be more accurate.

The first step in the development of the new theory consists of performing the split of the total field obtained by finite differences, by a lumped parameter model, or by finite elements into potential for $P$ and $S$ waves in the vicinity of the transmitting boundary. For two dimensions, we have the displacement components

$$u_x = \frac{\partial \phi}{\partial x} - \frac{\partial \psi}{\partial y},$$
$$u_y = \frac{\partial \phi}{\partial y} + \frac{\partial \psi}{\partial x}, \tag{3}$$

where $\phi$ is the potential of the $P$ waves and $\psi$ is the remnant of the vector potential for the $S$ disturbances.

Now the dilatation

$$\Delta = \frac{\partial u_x}{\partial x} + \frac{\partial u_y}{\partial y} \tag{4}$$

can be obtained from the total field quantities. It is also expressible from Eqs. (3) in terms of the potential as

$$\Delta = \nabla^2 \phi. \tag{4a}$$

In addition, the potential $\phi$ must satisfy the wave equation

$$\nabla^2 \phi = \frac{1}{c_p^2} \frac{\partial^2 \phi}{\partial t^2}. \tag{5}$$

From gradients of known displacements it is then possible to obtain the second time derivative of the potential of the $P$ disturbances. Certainly at time zero the displacements are zero at the transmitting boundary, and $\phi$ may be taken as zero there as well without loss of generality. It is then a simple matter of a double quadrature in time to find the potential $\phi$.

The same method, but this time working with essentially the rotation, gives

$$\frac{\partial u_y}{\partial x} - \frac{\partial u_x}{\partial y} = \nabla^2 \psi = \frac{1}{c_s^2} \frac{\partial^2 \psi}{\partial t^2}. \tag{6}$$

The second potential $\psi$ for the $S$ disturbances may then also be determined from the total field quantities in the vicinity of the transmitting boundary.

As mentioned before, the only assumption concerning the elasticity of the medium in what has been done refers to the medium near the transmitting boundary, not further within the region of interest.

### A. The Plane-Wave Approximation

Once the potentials have been found from the total field quantities, it becomes possible to treat the $P$ and $S$ components separately. At fairly large distances from the center of the disturbance, it is reasonable to assume that the wave surfaces are locally plane in a short time. That is, the $P$ and $S$ waves will be approximated as envelopes of plane waves near the boundary. We then have, locally,

$$\phi = f_1(l_1 x + m_1 y - c_p t), \tag{7}$$

$$\psi = f_2(l_2 x + m_2 y - c_s t), \tag{8}$$

where $(l_1, m_1)$ are the direction cosines for the wave surface normal corresponding to the $P$ wave and $(l_2, m_2)$ for the $S$ waves. Since in what follows the two potentials are treated entirely separately and in a completely parallel fashion, for brevity only the equations for the $P$-wave component will be written out explicitly.

It follows from Eq. (7) that

$$\left(\frac{\partial \phi}{\partial x}\right)^2 + \left(\frac{\partial \phi}{\partial y}\right)^2 = \frac{1}{c_p^2}\left(\frac{\partial \phi}{\partial t}\right)^2. \tag{9}$$

This equation turns out to be the required generalization of Eq. (1). If the partial derivative with respect to time,* $\phi_{,t}$, is solved for, the sign of the square root must be chosen so that the wave is an outward-going one. This consideration makes it useful to solve for the normal to the wave surface explicitly in order to compare with the normal to the transmitting boundary at each point. The equations

$$\phi_{,x} = l_1 f_1'(l_1 x + m_1 y - c_p t),$$
$$\phi_{,y} = m_1 f_1'(l_1 x + m_1 y - c_p t),$$

where $f'$ is the derivative of the function of a single variable with respect to its argument, result in the relation

$$\frac{\phi_{,x}}{\phi_{,y}} = \frac{l_1}{m_1}, \tag{10}$$

which determines the normal direction, or rather two opposite directions. The direction pointing out from the boundary is the one chosen, which determines which square root should be taken. In this way different signs are chosen at different points of the boundary just as different signs are present in Eqs. (1) and (2).

What is obtained from the above considerations is a relation at each point of the transmitting boundary between the time and space derivatives of the potential $\phi$. In the same way another relation of the same type involves the potential $\psi$. These two relations are sufficient in the numerical scheme to determine the solution uniquely if applied at the points of the transmitting boundary in conjunction with the more usual boundary conditions at other points.

Some numerical experience with this simple theory will be described in Sec. 4. Even without examining details of the results, several points can be made plausible at this stage. It is seen that Eq. (10) and its counterpart for the other potential determine the normals of the two waves at each point of the transmitting boundary. If these normals diverge significantly from point to point, the waves are highly curved, and the assumption of locally plane waves will be seriously in error unless the space and time intervals are extremely small. Another difficulty is less obvious. On the axis of symmetry of a problem such as that of Figs. 4 and 5, the potential $\psi$ is an odd function of the variable $x$ (in the horizontal direction). This means that the assumption of small change of $\psi$ along the wave front must be seriously in error at this point. All effects of the potential $\psi$ must be due to precisely such tangential variations

*This notation for partial derivatives will often be used in what follows.

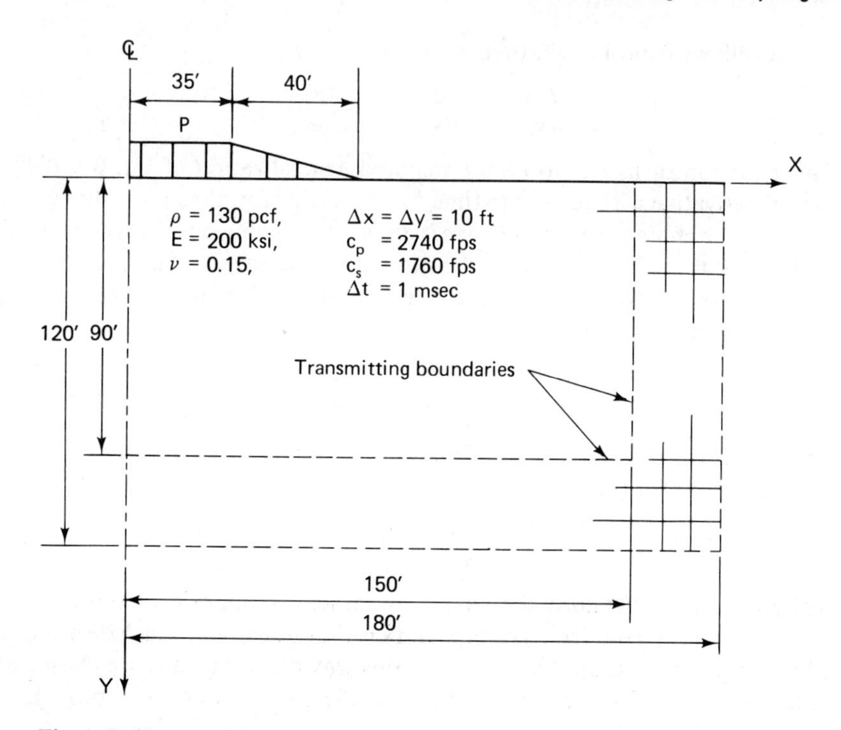


**Fig. 4.** Half space with applied load

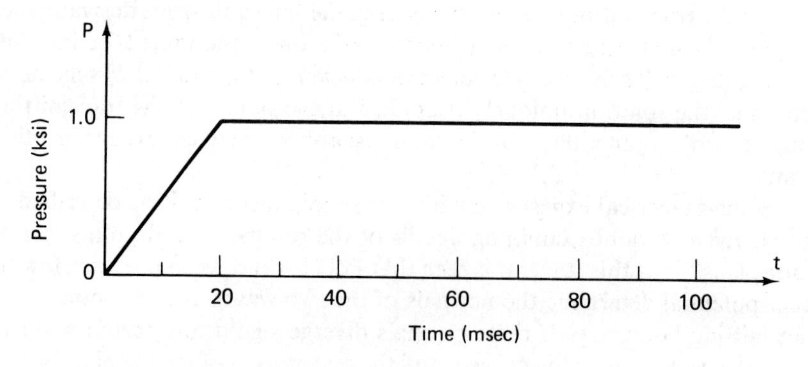


**Fig. 5.** Time variation of applied pressure

of $\psi$. As will be seen, the errors in the plane-wave approximation are most serious at the transmitting boundary near the axis of symmetry, a quite unexpected result. Both of the difficulties just discussed can be eliminated to a large degree by refining the theory so that the waves near the transmitting boundary are taken not as envelopes of plane waves but as envelopes of cylindrical waves.

### B. The Cylindrical-Wave Approximation

To remove the problems which are encountered in the plane-wave approximation and also to provide better results when the boundary is closer to the source of the disturbance, a cylindrical-wave approximation is now developed. It is well known that there is no Huyghens' principle in two dimensions. Therefore, no simple form involving the argument $R - c_p t$ is possible in an exact solution of the wave equation in cylindrical coordinates.

However, for large enough $R$ a simple approximation which is in this form will be accurate enough locally for short time intervals.

The governing partial differential equation for the $\phi$ potential is

$$\nabla^2\phi = \frac{\partial^2\phi}{\partial R^2} + \frac{1}{R}\frac{\partial\phi}{\partial R} + \frac{1}{R^2}\frac{\partial^2\phi}{\partial\theta^2} = \frac{1}{c_p^2}\frac{\partial^2\phi}{\partial t^2}.$$

If we take

$$\phi = \frac{1}{R^{1/2}} g(R - c_p t) f(\theta) \tag{11}$$

where $f$ and $g$ are suitably smooth, but otherwise arbitrary, functions, substitution into the partial differential equation gives a residual

$$\nabla^2\phi - \frac{1}{c_p^2}\frac{\partial^2\phi}{\partial t^2} = \frac{1}{4}R^{-5/2} g(R - c_p t)(f + 4f'') \tag{12}$$

instead of zero. It should be noted that terms in $R^{-1/2}$ and $R^{-3/2}$ cancel exactly. Thus, for fairly large radius of curvature, the solution in Eq. (11) should be quite accurate.

Using the solution in Eq. (11), we have not merely a normal derivative $\phi$, $\phi_{,R}$ but also a tangential derivative $\phi_{,S}$.

These may be expressed in terms of derivatives with respect to rectangular coordinates (Fig. 6) as

$$\begin{aligned} \phi_{,R} &= \phi_{,x}\cos\theta + \phi_{,y}\sin\theta, \\ \phi_{,s} &= -\phi_{,x}\sin\theta + \phi_{,y}\cos\theta, \end{aligned} \tag{13}$$

where the derivatives on the right are known from the field calculations. In distinction to the plane case, one more relation is needed to separate out $\phi_{,R}$ from these relations because the angle $\theta$ is also unknown.

The required extra condition is found from Eq. (11) by differentiating with respect to the angle $\theta$ and noting that

$$\frac{\phi_{,\theta}}{\phi} = \frac{f'(\theta)}{f(\theta)} \tag{14}$$

is independent of $R$ and $t$. That is, if the normal is followed into the body, the ratio on the left-hand side of Eq. (14) cannot change. Now the $s$ and $\theta$ derivatives are related by

$$\phi_{,s} = \frac{1}{R}\phi_{,\theta}.$$

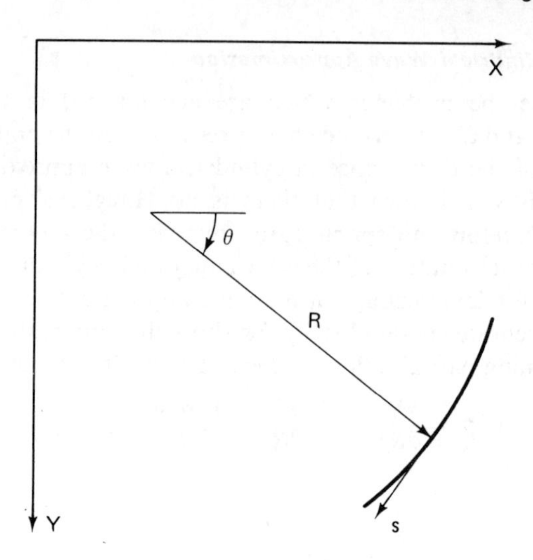


**Fig. 6.** Local cylindrical coordinates

If the normal is known, the value of $\phi_{,s}$ can be inferred from the field by Eqs. (13). There is only one direction of normal which will give values of $\phi_{,s}$ consistent with Eqs. (13) and (14). This normal having been found, we determine $\phi_{,R}$ from Eqs. (13).

The transmitting boundary condition relating time and space derivatives of $\phi$ is easily found from the form of Eq. (11):

$$\frac{\partial\phi}{\partial R} + \frac{\phi}{2R} = -\frac{1}{c_p}\frac{\partial\phi}{\partial t}. \tag{15}$$

In this calculation and the ones to determine the normal, the value of $R$ is found from the convergence of neighboring normals on the bounday. Equation (15) and the corresponding one for the other potential provide the necessary boundary conditions for the transmitting boundary.

## 4. Some Numerical Results and Conclusions

The numerical realization of the two approximate theories described in the last section is far from a trivial matter. Procedures have been worked out by Tseng [10] for applying both the plane-wave model and the cylindrical-wave model in the context of Ang's lumped parameter model [2]. While details will not be studied here, it should be noted that one important result of Tseng's work is the correct mode of application of the conditions developed in the last section to the case of the intersection of a transmitting boundary and a boundary where traction is specified (in particular, a free boundary). Here the transmitting boundary conditions should not be applied to the corner point itself because at this point the waves are not uncoupled but are coupled by the stress boundary condition. Considerations such as this as well as application of the potential scheme to a boundary between two layers are discussed by Tseng in great detail.

Numerical results have been computed for the problem of Figs. 4 and 5, where two sets of boundaries are used. The use of two sets of boundaries permits comparison of results where the discretization error is essentially the same in the two cases.

The results turn out to be worst at the horizontal transmitting boundary near the axis of symmetry. Figure 7 refers to vertical stresses at the point

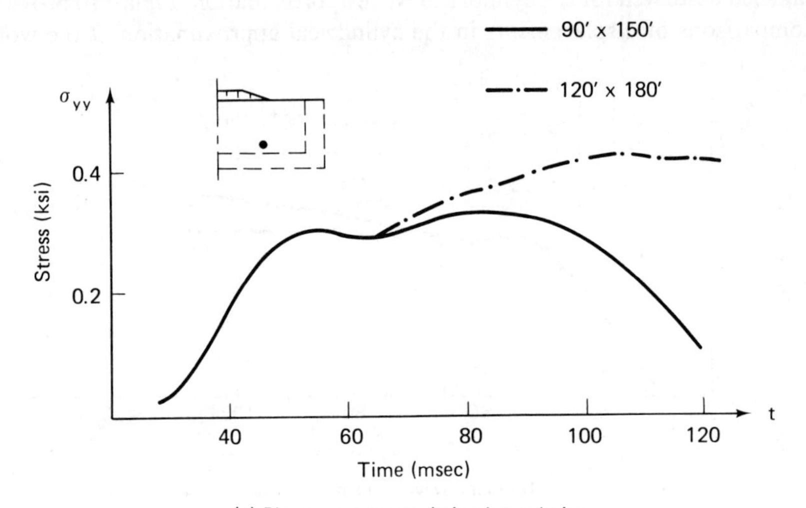


(a) Plane-wave transmitting boundaries

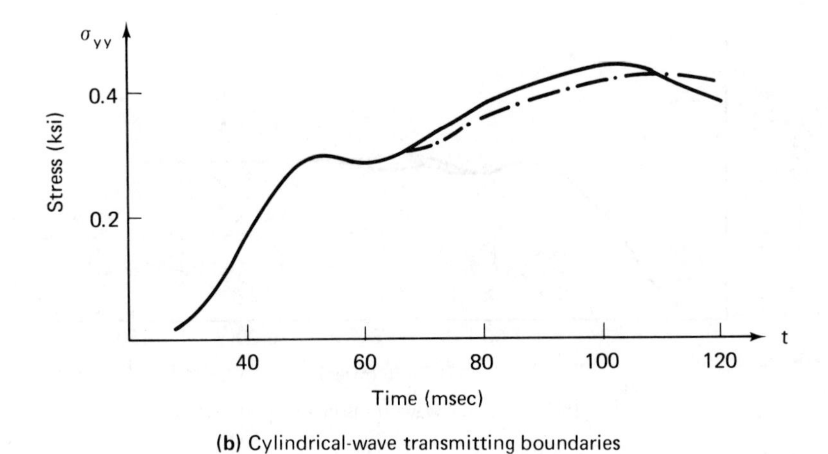


(b) Cylindrical-wave transmitting boundaries

**Fig. 7.** Vertical stresses at $x = 75'$, $y = 75'$

indicated in the insert computed using both plane- and cylindrical-wave approximations. The solid line always refers to results found for the smaller body. It should be noted that the plane and cylindrical approximations for the larger body, the two dotted curves, agree rather well, better than the results using the two regions. That is, well inside the outer transmitting boundary the results of the plane approximation and the cylindrical approximation are fairly close. Since the objective, after all, is to guarantee good answers well within the transmitting boundary, the requirement of good agreement very near the transmitting boundary may be overly stringent. Nevertheless, as shown in Figs. 7, 8, and 9, even this harsh requirement is satisfied quite well for the cylindrical wave approximation. Figure 10 provides comparisons of displacements in the cylindrical approximation at the worst

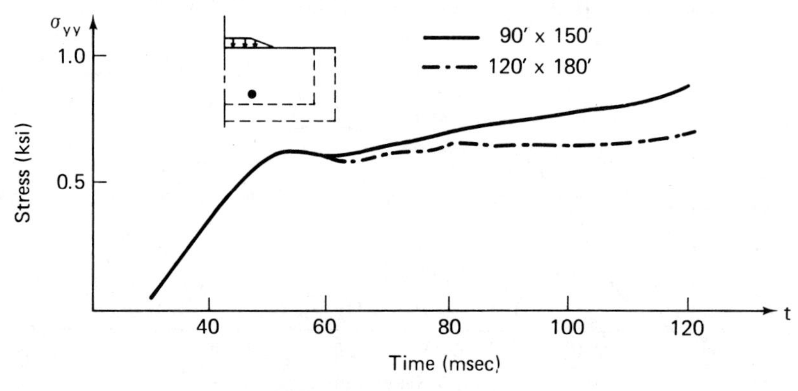


(a) Plane wave transmitting boundaries

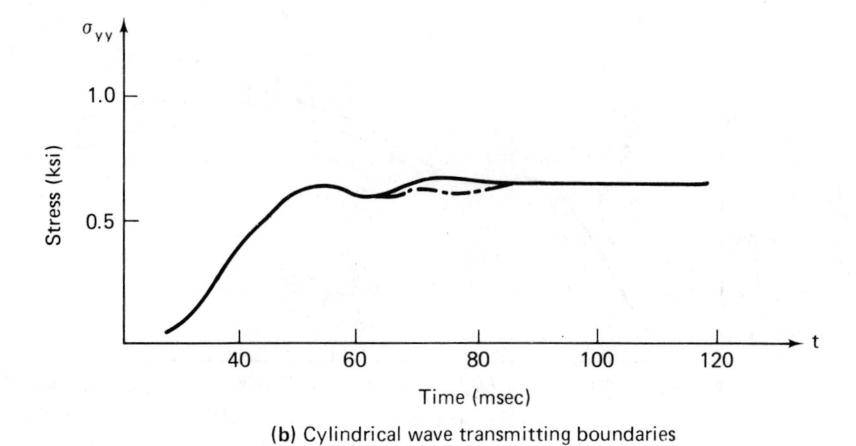


(b) Cylindrical wave transmitting boundaries

**Fig. 8.** Vertical stress at $x = 45'$, $y = 75'$

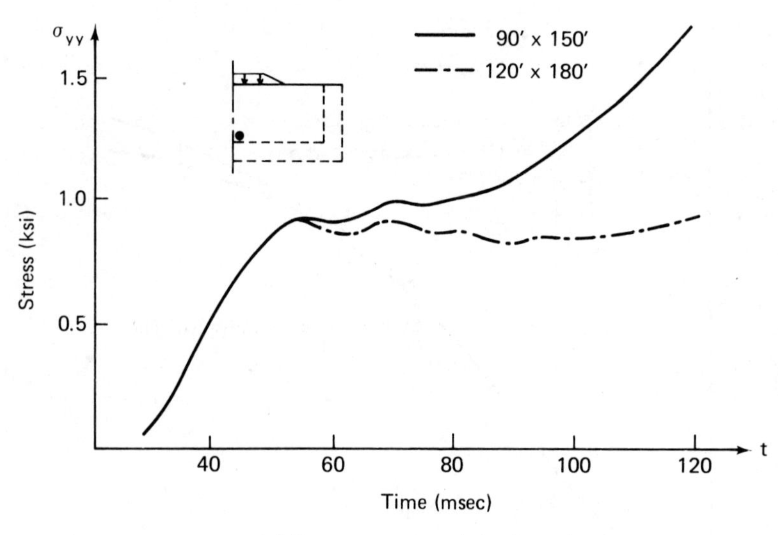


(a) Plane-wave transmitting boundaries

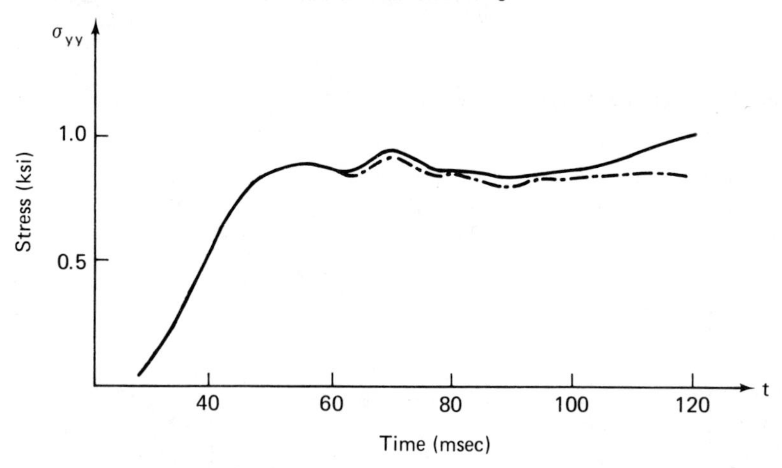


(b) Cylindrical-wave transmitting boundaries

**Fig. 9.** Vertical stresses at $x = 5'$, $y = 75'$

points. It will be noted that in Fig. 9 the comparisons for the plane case near the axis of symmetry and the transmitting boundary are especially poor in view of the absence of the important $\psi_{,s}$ term.

In conclusion, the feasibility of splitting the disturbances into $P$ and $S$ types near the transmitting boundary has been demonstrated. The proposed plane and cylindrical approximations hold considerable promise for practical calculations. The plane-wave approximation appears to give adequate results as long as the points of interest lie at some distance from the transmitting

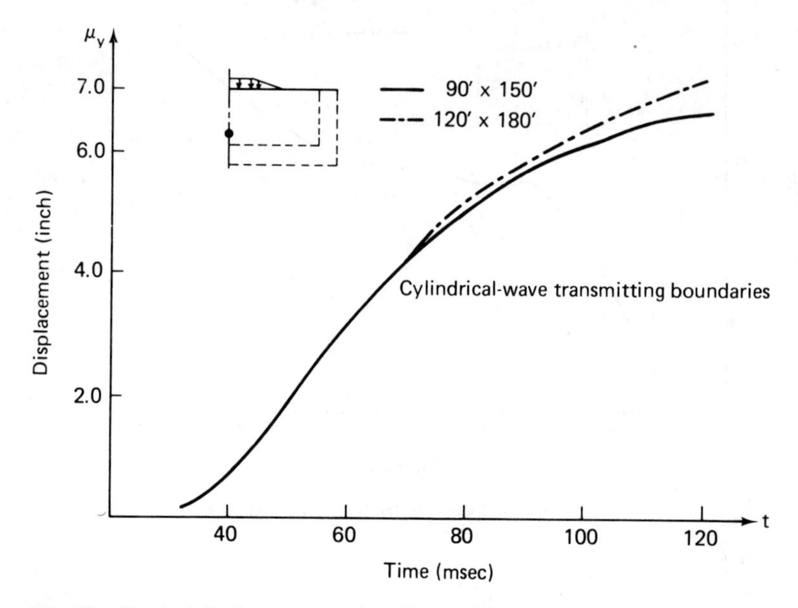


**Fig. 10a.** Vertical displacement at $x = 0'$, $y = 70'$

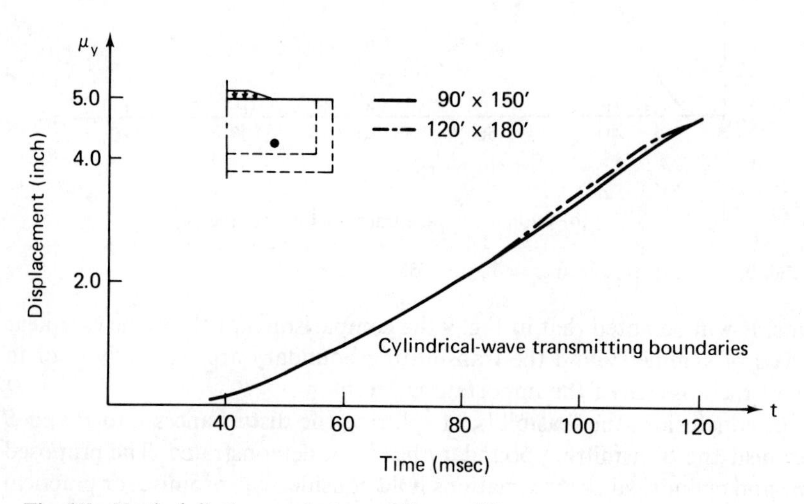


**Fig. 10b.** Vertical displacement at $x = 80'$, $y = 70'$

boundary; the cylindrical approximation is significantly more accurate even near the transmitting boundary itself.

## Acknowledgment

The work reported here was sponsored in part by the National Science Foundation under Contracts GK 24294 (Prediction of Earthquake Motion) and AEN 75–08456 (Design for Protection Against Natural Hazards) and partly by the Office of Naval Research under Contracts N00014-67-A-0305-0010 and N00014-75-C-0164 (Numerical and Approximate Methods of Stress Analysis).

## References

1. BOORE, D. M., "Finite Difference Methods for Seismic Wave Propagation in Heterogeneous Materials" (Sec. 2D), in *Seismology: Surface Waves and Earth Oscillations*, Vol. 11 of *Methods of Computational Physics*, B. A. Bolt, *Ed.* Academic Press, New York, 1972.
2. ANG, A. H.-S., and N. M. NEWMARK, "Development of a Transmitting Boundary for Numerical Wave Motion Calculations," *DASA Report 2631*, Defense Atomic Support Agency (now Defense Nuclear Agency), Washington, D.C., April 1971.
3. LYSMER, J., and L. A. DRAKE, "A Finite Element Method for Seismology," in *Seismology: Surface Waves and Earth Oscillations*, Vol. 11 of *Methods of Computational Physics*, B. A. Bolt, *Ed.* Academic Press, New York, 1972.
4. SMITH, R. H., and N. M. NEWMARK, "Numerical Integration for One-Dimensional Stress Waves," Civil Engineering Studies, *Structural Research Series No. 162*, University of Illinois, Urbana, Aug. 1958.
5. FORSYTHE, G. E., and W. R. WASOW, *Finite-Difference Methods for Partial Differential Equations*, Wiley, New York, 1960, pp. 18–29.
6. LYSMER, J., and R. L. KUHLEMEYER, "Finite Dynamic Model for Infinite Media," *J. Eng. Mech. Div. Proc. ASCE*, Vol. 95, No. EM4, Aug. 1969. pp. 859–877.
7. CASTELLANI, A., "Boundary Conditions to Simulate an Infinite Space," *Meccanica*, Vol. IX, No. 3, 1974. pp. 199–205.
8. LYSMER, J., and G. WAAS, "Shear Waves in Plane Infinite Structures," *J. Eng. Mech. Div. Proc. ASCE*, Vol. 98, No. EM1, Feb. 1972. pp. 85–105
9. SMITH, W. D., "A Nonreflecting Boundary for Wave Propagation Problems," *J. Comput. Phys.*, Vol. 15, No. 4, Aug. 1974. pp. 492–503.
10. TSENG, M. N., and A. R. ROBINSON, "A Transmitting Boundary for Finite-Difference Analysis of Wave Propagation in Solids," Civil Engineering Studies, *Structural Research Series No. 420*, University of Illinois at Urbana-Champaign, Urbana, Nov. 1975.

# Determination of Permeability in Anisotropic Rock Masses from Integral Samples

MANUEL ROCHA* AND FERNANDO FRANCISS†

## Summary

*A method is presented which makes it possible to characterize the permeability of a rock mass as an anisotropic magnitude—i.e., to determine its permeability tensor—from a characterization of its fracturing by means of integral samples.*

*For the purpose, a theory is developed by means of which the permeability tensor can be calculated from the attitudes and openings of the fractures and—if infillings are present—also from their coefficient of permeability. This theory is based on the assumption that the sampled fractures are continuous and plane and have the same characteristics as the section of the fractures present in the samples. Possible deviations with respect to this assumption are taken into account by means of correcting factors derived from the results of pressure tests in situ. The permeability tensor of a rock mass at a point can be determined from a single integral sample, provided this is representative of the fracturing.*

*Results of the application of the method are presented, which show it to look very promising.*

## 1. Introduction

Percolation through rock masses is of great practical importance as regards not only percolation discharges, notably in hydraulic structures, but also the resulting loads on rock masses, which may often seriously endanger their

*President, Council of Civil Engineering Laboratories, and Professor of Rock Mechanics, Technical University, Lisbon, Portugal.

†Professor, Catholic University, and Head, Geotechnology Department, Sondotecnica, Rio de Janeiro, Brazil.

safety. It is thus very important that methods are available by means of which the permeability of rock masses can be adequately characterized.

Owing to the important role of fractures in the permeability of rock masses, this has been characterized by means of *in situ* tests: the well-known pressure tests in boreholes. These tests present, however, a very serious limitation, namely that they characterize the permeability of the rock mass by a scalar: the volume of water absorbed in the unit time by a unit length of borehole, under a unit pressure or a given pressure. Alternatively, the result of the test can be expressed in terms of a coefficient of permeability. Nevertheless, as is well known, permeability is—among the properties of rock masses—the one which may present the most marked anisotropy, differences of several orders of magnitude between extremal permeability values being current. Permeabilities markedly anisotropic may give rise to entirely different behaviors of slopes, foundations of hydraulic structures, etc., according to the orientation of the anisotropy.

It is thus indispensable to have methods by means of which permeability can be characterized as an anisotropic magnitude. Tests along boreholes with different directions can be used for the purpose, and it is even possible to determine the three principal permeabilities from tests in three boreholes, provided these lie along the three principal directions of permeability, which implies that these directions are known beforehand [5,9]. Yet, tests along several directions are expensive and time-consuming, all the more as each point to be characterized requires several (in the most general case, six) boreholes through it.

In this chapter a new method is presented for determining permeability as an anisotropic magnitude from an integral sampling characterization of the rock mass. By means of integral samples it is possible to determine attitudes, openings, and infillings of fractures in a rock mass, from which the principal directions of permeability and the principal coefficients of permeability can be computed by adding up the contribution of each fracture to the permeability tensor. Owing to simplifying assumptions needed for the computation, notably that each fracture is continuous in its plane, correcting factors determined in pressure tests in boreholes must be applied. When the contribution of the percolation discharge through the rock proper is considerable, it can also be taken into account in the determination of permeability of the rock mass.

## 2. Integral Sampling

Although the integral sampling method has been described in several papers [6, 7], its main characteristics are indicated below.

The method consists of obtaining an oriented core sample from the rock mass previously reinforced with a bar, which ensures the integrity of the whole sampled material. A borehole with a diameter $D$ is drilled to the depth where the integral sample is to be obtained [Fig. 1(a)]; then a hole with a diameter $d$, coaxial with the former and with the same length as the sample to be obtained [Fig. 1(b)], is drilled to accommodate a reinforcing bar whose azimuth is defined by positioning rods [Fig. 1(c)], through which, in the following stage, a binder is introduced to bond the bar into the rock mass [Fig. 1(d)]; after the binder has hardened, the drilling of the borehole with the diameter $D$ is resumed, by the conventional techniques, and an integral sample is obtained [Fig. 1(e)].

The method has successfully been applied to formations of widely different natures, from hard to very weathered rocks and even residual soils, yielding complete information on the rock masses, particularly on the attitudes, openings, and infillings of fractures. Integral samples have been obtained in boreholes with diameters $D \geq 76$ mm and lengths $L$ ranging from 1.5 to 3 m.

Indications are given below (Sec. 6) on how attitudes and openings of fractures are determined.

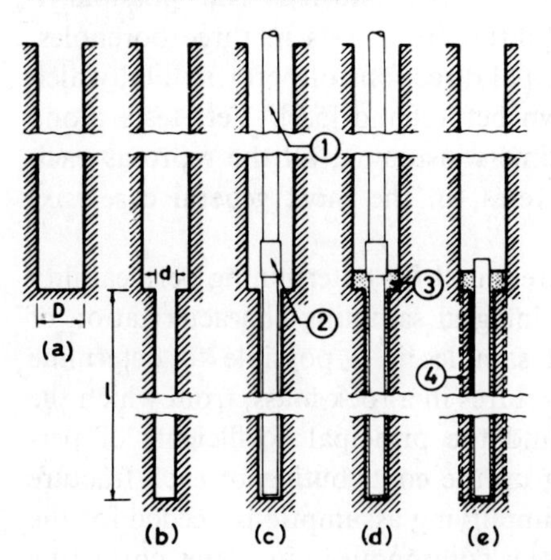


**Fig. 1.** Stages of the integral sampling method: (1) positioning rods, (2) connecting element, (3) binder, (4) integral sample

## 3. Idealization and Sampling of the Rock Mass

With a view to computing the contribution of fractures to the permeability of a rock mass, it is assumed that each fracture intersected by a given borehole is plane and continuous in its plane, that its opening is constant, and that its infilling, if any, has the same characteristics throughout. It is thus that the actual structure of the rock mass [Fig. 2(a)] becomes the idealized structure of Fig. 2(b).

The assumed continuity of each fracture in its plane is the roughest assumption, but it should be noted that the usual presence of fractures with

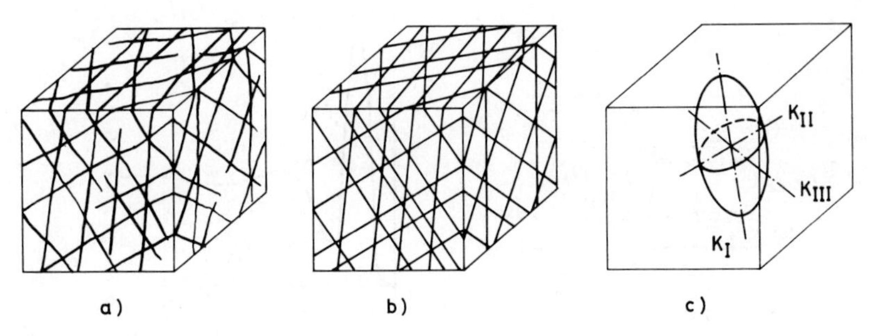


**Fig. 2.** Idealization of the rock mass

different attitudes contributes a certain continuity to percolation through the rock mass. As already mentioned, the method of characterization of permeability described in this chapter includes a factor intended to correct possible deviations due to this assumption.

As a rule the orientation of the fractures—defined by their normal—is variable in space, presenting some concentrations corresponding to families, i.e., sets of near-parallel fractures. In the most general case openings and infillings will also be variable even within the same family.

With a view to treating the rock mass as a continuous medium [Fig. 2(c)], fractures with orientations, openings, and infillings considered important for the permeability of the rock mass must be sufficiently numerous inside volumes which can be deemed small with respect to the geometry of the problem concerned. The fractured rock mass can thus be replaced by a continuous medium, the characteristics of which may vary almost continuously from volume to volume.

A basic question is what dimensions a sample must have to be representative of the rock mass, notably as regards its permeability. These dimensions should be such that the sample contains a sufficiently large number of fractures with the different orientations, openings, and infillings. Thus, in the case of a rock mass with a single family of continuous fractures assumed to have the same opening and infilling throughout, the sample must contain enough fractures for its permeability to be near the permeability of the rock mass. This means that in samples with increasing volumes $V_1$, $V_2$, $V_3, \ldots$ [Fig. 3(a)] their permeabilities—e.g., their coefficients of permeability $K$ along the plane of the fractures—will initially present wide fluctuations but will then tend to a constant value [Fig. 3(b)]. Thus a sample will be representative if its volume exceeds $V_r$, the value of which will depend on the accuracy with which permeability is to be determined.

If the opening of the fractures is variable, the sample must have a volume ensuring that it represents the distribution of openings in the rock mass; i.e., each interval of openings $e$, $e + \Delta e$ must be represented by a sufficiently large number of fractures. In the case of clean fractures, the contribution of

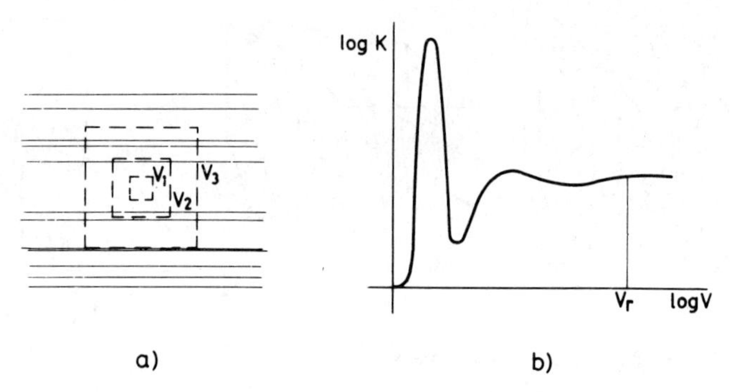


**Fig. 3.** Variation of the permeability coefficient with the volume of the sample

which to permeability changes with the cube of the opening, the representativeness of the largest openings should especially be taken into account.

The same obviously applies to the cases of two, three, or more families of fractures with given orientations.

In the general case of fractures presenting an arbitrary space distribution, a sample will not be representative unless it contains enough fractures representing each of the families of fractures corresponding to normals contained in a given solid-angle element. In other words, as a general rule a system of fractures in a representative sample can be resolved into families of near-parallel fractures. Additionally, the sample must ensure the representativeness of the openings and infillings present in each family.

Thus, a representative sample must usually contain very numerous fractures. That is why in practice one has very often to accept samples with a poor representativeness as is usual in the characterization of other properties of rock masses.

Since in the method described in this chapter rock masses are sampled by means of boreholes, the sampling quality must be discussed. For this purpose, let us consider a family of fractures the normal of which makes an angle $\theta$ with the axis of a borehole (Fig. 4). The fracture spacing being $l$, the number $n$ of fractures in a length $L$ of the borehole is

$$n = \frac{L}{l} \cos \theta$$

Consequently, when $\theta$ tends to 90° the number $n$ tends to zero, even if $L$ is large. This means that sampling is necessarily poor for families nearly parallel to the borehole, as is well known.

Therefore, when fractures are assembled in families with well-defined orientations, the boreholes must meet all the families, along angles ensuring the best sampling for those families whose permeability is more important.

In the case of an arbitrary space distribution, boreholes must be parallel

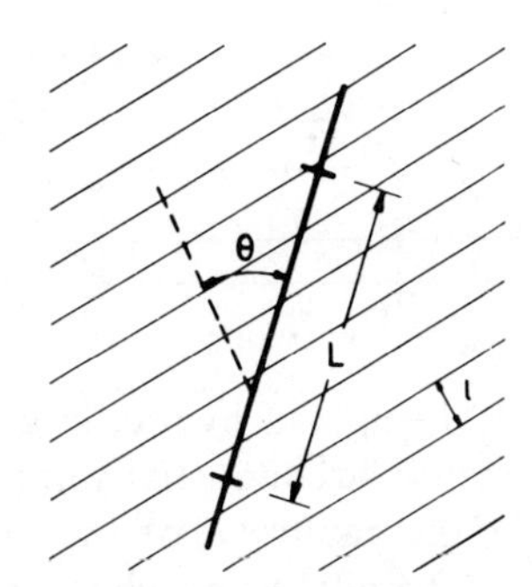


**Fig. 4.** Sampling of a family of fractures

to the planes of the fractures less important for permeability, i.e., those with the widest spacing and (or) the least opening and (or) the least permeable infilling. Notice that thus even the accuracy of the permeability in the direction of the borehole will not be appreciably affected, since the most important contributions to that value will be those of fractures not nearly parallel to the borehole.

To improve the quality of the sampling, $L$ should be high, in accordance with the anticipated values of $\theta$ and $l$. As integral samples are as a rule less than 3 m in length, it is often advisable to consider as a single sample different samples from the same borehole or from parallel boreholes.

## 4. Permeability of a System of Fractures

Consider a representative volume element of a rock mass subjected to percolation and let the hydraulic potential be $\phi$ and the hydraulic gradient $\mathbf{J} = -\text{grad}\,\phi$. Owing to the anisotropy, the mean percolation velocity vector $\mathbf{V}$ is in general not parallel to $\mathbf{J}$. Characterizing the permeability of the rock mass is to define a relationship by means of which the direction and magnitude of $\mathbf{V}$ can be determined from a known $\mathbf{J}$. As will be seen, this relationship is defined by a tensor represented by $||K||$, which will be called the permeability tensor:

$$\mathbf{V} = ||K||\mathbf{J}.$$

In the following section the permeability through a family of parallel fractures is determined from the laws governing the percolation through a fracture; then the case of several families is dealt with, and finally the general case of fractures with any distribution is considered.

### *4.1*

The flow being assumed laminar, the mean percolation velocity $\mathbf{V}$ in a clean fracture (Fig. 5); i.e., the unit discharge through the borehole is

$$\mathbf{V} = K_f \mathbf{J}_f, \tag{1}$$

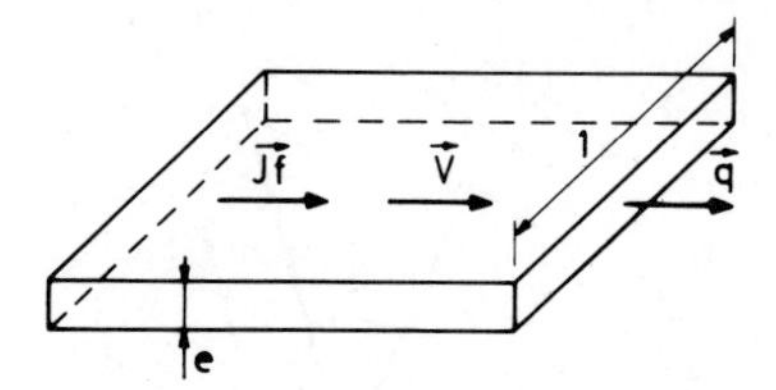


**Fig. 5.** Flow in a fracture

$\mathbf{J}_f$ being the hydraulic gradient on the plane of the fracture and $K_f$ the hydraulic conductivity of the fracture. This coefficient depends on the opening of the fracture $e$, on the coefficient of kinematic viscosity of the liquid $\nu$, and on the relative roughness of the walls of the fracture $r = h/2e$, where $h$ is the absolute roughness, i.e., the mean height of the unneveness; we shall choose for $K_f$ the empirical expression [4]

$$K_f = Ce^2, \tag{2}$$

where

$$C = \frac{g}{12\nu(1 + 8.8r^{1.5})},$$

$g$ being the acceleration of gravity. As can be seen in Fig. 6, the coefficient $C$

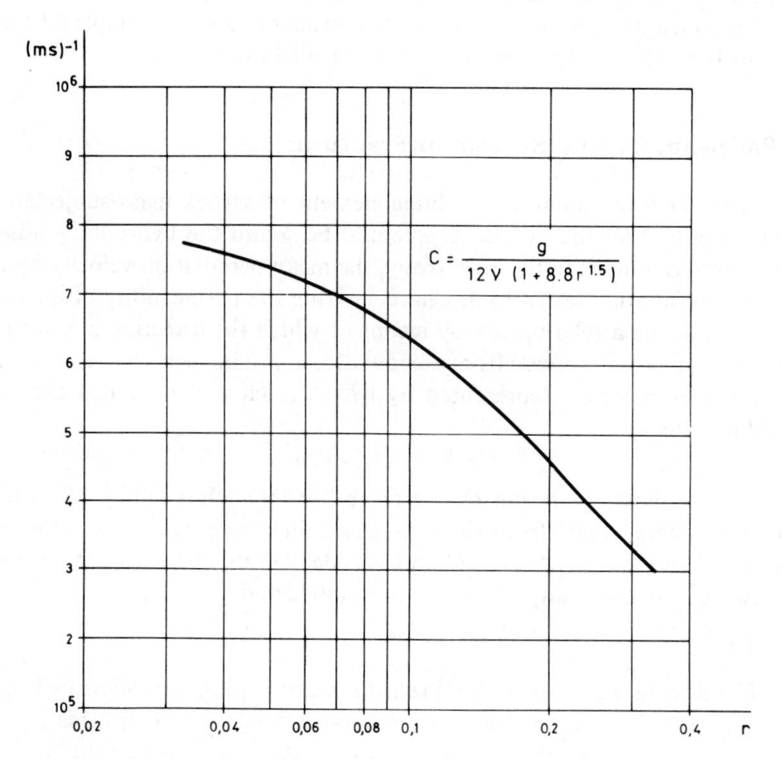


**Fig. 6.** Variation of the coefficient $C$ with the relative roughness $r$

is more influenced by the roughness when $r$ exceeds a value of about 0.1, being as high as $3 \times 10^5$ (m-s)$^{-1}$ for $r = 0.33$, the upper roughness limit considered by Louis [4]. The deviations of $K_f$ due to inaccurate values of $r$ will be taken into account by means of the correcting factors mentioned in Sec. 5.1.

Thus, the discharge per unit width of the fracture **q** will be

$$\mathbf{q} = K_f e \mathbf{J}_f, \tag{3}$$

and, consequently,

$$\mathbf{q} = Ce^3 \mathbf{J}_f.$$

If the fractures are infilled, Eqs. (1) and (3) remain valid, $K_f$ becoming the coefficient of permeability of the infilling material.

### *4.2*

Consider a rock mass with a family of infilled or clean fractures with openings $e_i$ and coefficients $K_{fi}$ under a hydraulic gradient $\mathbf{J}_f$ parallel to the fractures (Fig. 7). The unit discharge through the rock mass, i.e., the mean percolation velocity **V**, will be

$$\mathbf{V} = \frac{1}{L} \sum \mathbf{q}_i = \frac{\sum K_{fi} e_i}{L} \mathbf{J}_f,$$

where $L$ is a straight-line segment perpendicular to the fractures sufficiently long for the corresponding volume to be representative of the permeability of the rock mass. Since $K$ is the coefficient of permeability of the rock mass along the fractures,

$$\mathbf{V} = K \mathbf{J}_f, \tag{4}$$

where

$$K = \frac{\sum K_{fi} e_i}{L}. \tag{5}$$

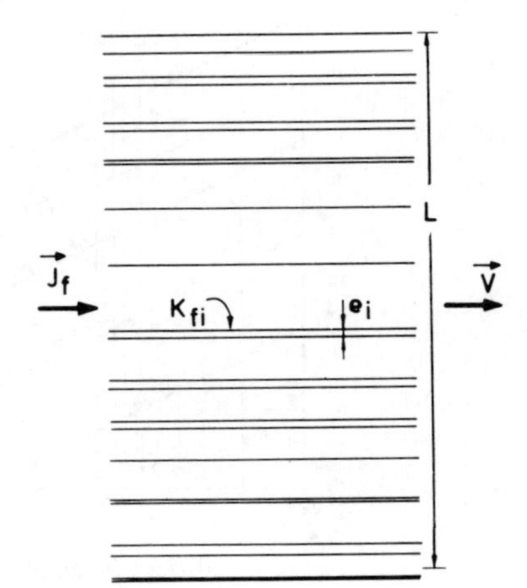


**Fig. 7.** Percolation through one family of fractures

We may write

$$K = K_1 + K_2 + \ldots + K_i + \ldots$$

with

$$K_i = \frac{K_{fi} e_i}{L}.$$

That is, the coefficient of permeability of the rock mass equals the sum of the coefficients of permeability $K_1, K_2, \ldots$ corresponding to separate families, each consisting of the repetition of each sampled fracture, with a mean spacing $L$. This accurately reflects the concept that a sampling with a length $L$ is representative of the fracturing in the rock mass.

In the case of a family of clean fractures, and taking Eq. (2) into account, we obtain

$$K = \frac{\sum C_i e_i^3}{L}.$$

If both the opening and the roughness of the fractures are constant, the expression above becomes

$$K = \frac{Ce^3}{l},$$

$l = L/n$ being the mean spacing of the fractures and $n$ the number of fractures within the length $L$. The coefficient of permeability $K$ as a function of the mean spacing $l$ of the fractures is presented in Fig. 8 for $C = 3 \times 10^5$ (m-s)$^{-1}$.

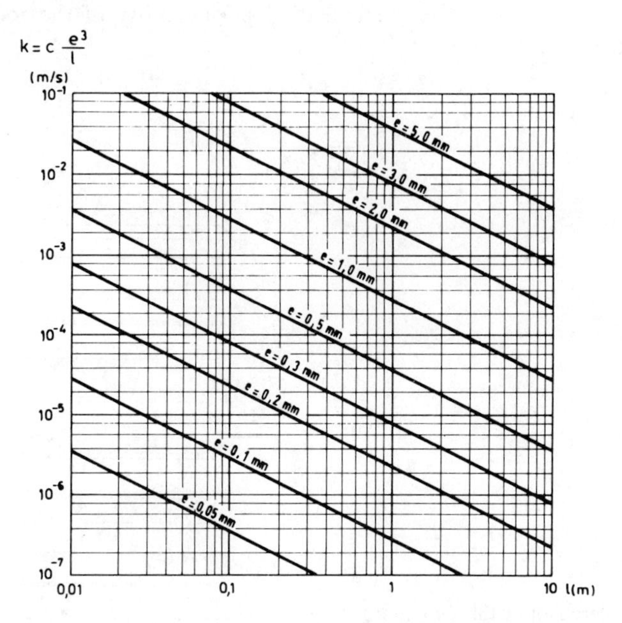


**Fig. 8.** Coefficient of permeability of a family of fractures

For a family of fractures infilled with the same material with a coefficient of permeability $K_f$ and the same opening,

$$K = K_f \frac{e}{l}.$$

Thus, considering two rock masses with fractures having the same spacing and the same opening but with fractures clean in one case and infilled with a material with a coefficient of permeability $K_f$ in the other, the ratio of the coefficients of permeability of the two rock masses is

$$A = \frac{C}{K_f} e^2.$$

The ratio $A$ as a function of the openings of the fractures is presented in Fig. 9 for $C = 3 \times 10^5$ (m-s)$^{-1}$. According to the figure, permeability through infilled fractures is negligible with respect to permeability through clean fractures, even for considerably high values of $K_f$. Thus, the contribution of infilled fractures to the permeability of the rock mass is often not worth considering.

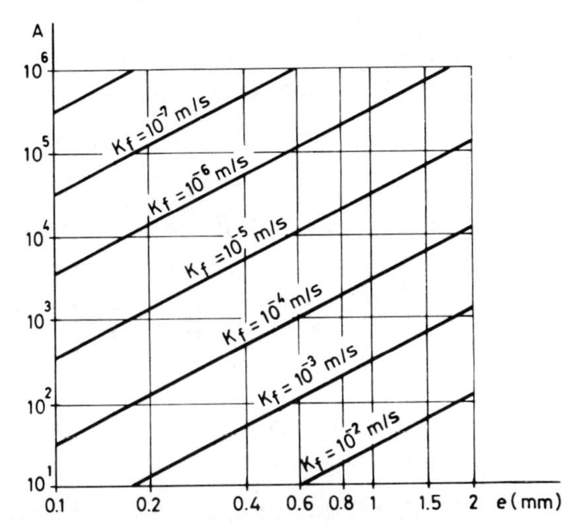


**Fig. 9.** Ratio of the coefficients of permeability of families of fractures, clean and infilled with a material with a coefficient of permeability $K_f$

#### *4.3*

So far the hydraulic gradient has been assumed to be parallel to the plane of the fractures forming a family. In the general case, the hydraulic gradient of the percolation makes an angle with the normal **n** to the fractures (Fig. 10). The magnitude of the hydraulic gradient is $J = -(d\phi/ds)$, and the gradient in the plane of the fracture has a magnitude $J_f = -(d\phi/ds) \sin \epsilon = J \sin \epsilon$.

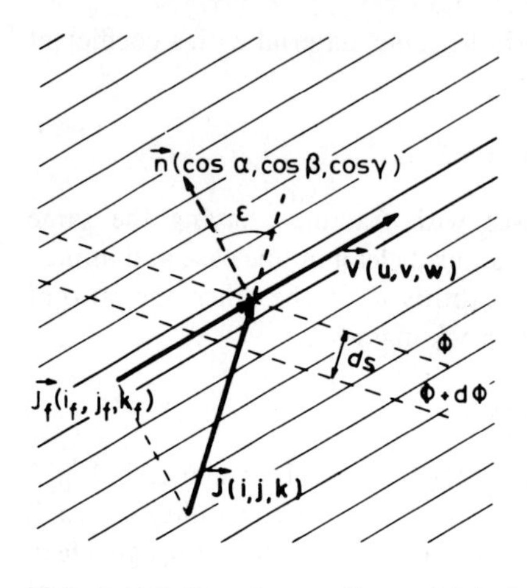


**Fig. 10.** General case of percolation through a family of fractures

This means that the gradient which determines the flow through the fractures is the projection $\mathbf{J}_f$ of $\mathbf{J}$ on the plane of the fractures. Thus, Eqs. (1) and (4) remain valid for a fracture and a family of fractures, respectively, $\mathbf{J}_f$ being the projection of $\mathbf{J}$.

The components of $\mathbf{J}_f(i_f, j_f, k_f)$ in an orthogonal coordinate system can be expressed as follows as a function of the components of $J(i, j, k)$:

$$
\begin{aligned}
i_f &= i(\cos^2 \beta + \cos^2 \gamma) - j \cos \alpha \cos \beta - k \cos \alpha \cos \gamma, \\
j_f &= -i \cos \beta \cos \alpha + j(\cos^2 \alpha + \cos^2 \gamma) - k \cos \beta \cos \gamma, \\
k_f &= -i \cos \gamma \cos \alpha - j \cos \gamma \cos \beta + k(\cos^2 \alpha + \cos^2 \beta),
\end{aligned} \tag{6}
$$

$\cos \alpha$, $\cos \beta$, $\cos \gamma$ being the direction cosines of the unit vector normal to the fractures $\mathbf{n}(\cos \alpha, \cos \beta, \cos \gamma)$. Consequently, the components of the unit discharge through the rock mass $\mathbf{V}$ $(u, v, w)$ are, taking Eq. (4) into account,

$$
\begin{aligned}
u &= Ki_f, \\
v &= Ki_f, \\
w &= Kk_f,
\end{aligned}
$$

$K$ being given by Eq. (5), where $L$ is a straight-line segment perpendicular to the fractures. As fracturing in the rock mass is sampled by means of boreholes, calling $L$ the length of the sample (Fig. 4) from a borehole whose axis makes an angle $\theta$ with the normal to the fractures, the expression of $K$ becomes

$$K = \frac{\sum K_{fi} e_i}{L \cos \theta}.$$

Consequently,

$$K = K_1 + K_2 + \ldots + K_i + \ldots$$

with

$$K_i = \frac{K_{fi} e_i}{L \cos \theta}, \tag{7}$$

$L$ being the length of the sampling, and, according to Eq. (2),

$$K_{fi} = C_i e_i^2$$

for a clean fracture; otherwise, $K_{fi}$ is the coefficient of permeability of the infilling material.

Thus, in tensor notation vectors $\mathbf{V}$ and $\mathbf{J}$ are related by a symmetric tensor $||K||$, which will be called the permeability tensor of the rock mass,

$$\mathbf{V} = ||K||\mathbf{J} \tag{8}$$

with

$$||K|| = ||K_1|| + ||K_2|| + \ldots + ||K_i|| + \ldots,$$

where $||K_1||, ||K_2||, \ldots, ||K_i||, \ldots$, denoting the tensors which represent the contribution of each fracture to the permeability, are

$$||K_i|| = \begin{Vmatrix} K_{xxi} & K_{xyi} & K_{xzi} \\ K_{yxi} & K_{yyi} & K_{yzi} \\ K_{zxi} & K_{zyi} & K_{zzi} \end{Vmatrix} \tag{9}$$

with

$$K_{xxi} = K_i(\cos^2 \beta + \cos^2 \gamma), \quad K_{xyi} = K_{yxi} = -K_i \cos \alpha \cos \beta,$$
$$K_{yyi} = K_i(\cos^2 \alpha + \cos^2 \gamma), \quad K_{yzi} = K_{zyi} = -K_i \cos \beta \cos \gamma,$$
$$K_{zzi} = K_i(\cos^2 \alpha + \cos^2 \beta), \quad K_{zxi} = K_{xzi} = -K_i \cos \alpha \cos \gamma,$$

$K_i$ being given by Eq. (7).

Notice that tensor $||K_i||$ concerning the fracture $i$ can be considered as the permeability tensor of a family of fractures with the same characteristics ($K_{fi}$, $e_i$) and a mean spacing $L \cos \theta$ as in the case of the hydraulic gradient parallel to the fracutres.

In practice, it is advisable to have the axis $Oz$ lying downward along the axis of the borehole and the axis $Ox$ on the vertical plane through the borehole axis [Fig. 11(a)]. Additionally, the unit vector $\mathbf{n}$ should be defined

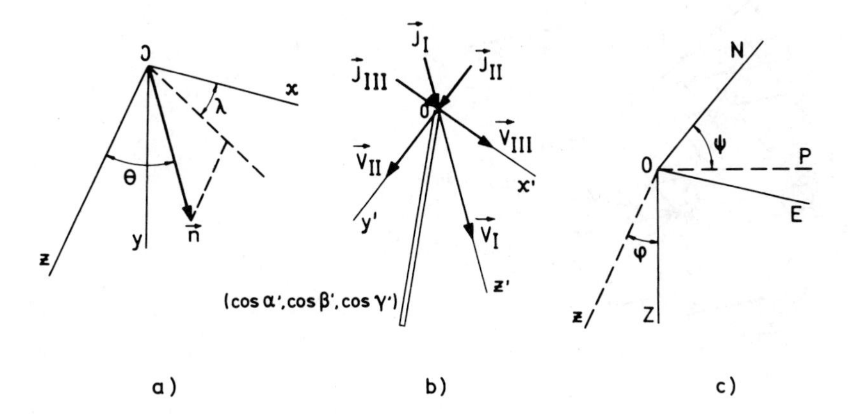


**Fig. 11.** Coordinate systems

from the angle $\theta = \gamma$ and the angle $\lambda$ of axis $Ox$ with the projection of $\mathbf{n}$ on the plane $Oxy$. Since

$$\cos\alpha = \sin\theta \cdot \cos\lambda,$$
$$\cos\beta = \sin\theta \cdot \sin\lambda,$$
$$\cos\gamma = \cos\theta,$$

the components of the tensor of the contribution of each fracture to the permeability become

$$K_{xxi} = K_i(\sin^2\lambda + \cos^2\theta \cdot \cos^2\lambda), \qquad K_{xyi} = K_{yxi} = -K_i \sin^2\theta \cos\lambda \sin\lambda,$$
$$K_{yyi} = K_i(\sin^2\theta \cos^2\lambda + \cos^2\theta), \qquad K_{yzi} = K_{zyi} = -K_i \sin\theta \cos\theta \sin\lambda,$$
$$K_{zzi} = K_i \sin^2\theta, \qquad K_{zxi} = K_{xzi} = -K_i \sin\theta \cos\theta \cos\lambda, \tag{10}$$

$K_i$ being a function of $\theta$ according to Eq. (7).

Thus, each component of the tensor of each fracture has an expression

$$\frac{K_{fi}e_i}{L\cos\theta} f(\lambda, \theta),$$

where $f(\lambda, \theta)$ is a function of the angles defining the direction of the fractures, which is variable with the component concerned.

### 4.4

Let us consider the case of a rock mass with several families of fractures (Fig. 12). It is assumed that under a given hydraulic gradient $\mathbf{J}$ the mean percolation velocity $\mathbf{V}$ through the rock mass is

$$\mathbf{V} = \mathbf{V}' + \mathbf{V}'' + \ldots,$$

$\mathbf{V}', \mathbf{V}'', \ldots$ being the mean percolation velocity of each family of fractures;

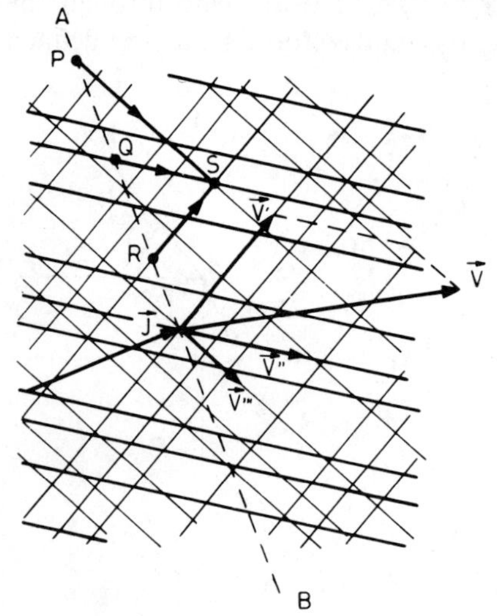


**Fig. 12.** Percolation through several families of fractures

i.e., head losses at the intersection lines of fractures belonging to different families are not taken into account. It is important to note that, according to the assumed continuity and constant opening of each fracture, if the hydraulic potential $\phi$ is constant along a plane $AB$ (Fig. 12), the potential at an intersection point $S$ is the same whatever the fracture through which the liquid reaches the point; for instance, the liquid path could be $PS$, $QS$, or $RS$. This means that potentials at the intersection points of fractures are compatible, even if a three-dimensional distribution of the families is taken into account. The correction to be discussed in Sec. 5.1 will help to take into consideration the above-mentioned head losses.

The former assumption being accepted and Eq. (8) being taken into account, we obtain

$$\mathbf{V} = ||K'||\mathbf{J} + ||K''||\mathbf{J} + \ldots = ||K||\mathbf{J}; \tag{11}$$

i.e., there is a permeability tensor of the rock mass $||K||$ which is a symmetric tensor given by

$$||K|| = ||K'|| + ||K''|| + \ldots,$$

$||K'||, ||K''||, \ldots$ being the tensors of the different families of fractures.

As each of these tensors can be resolved into the tensors of each fracture of the family,

$$||K|| = ||K_1|| + ||K_2|| + \ldots + ||K_i|| + \ldots, \tag{12}$$

where $||K_1||, ||K_2||, \ldots, ||K_i||, \ldots$ are the tensors of each of the joints within a given sampling length $L$. Thus, taking into account Eq. (10),

$$||K_i|| = \left\| \begin{matrix} K_i(\sin^2 \lambda_i + \cos^2 \theta_i \cos^2 \lambda_i) & -K_i \sin^2 \theta_i \cos \lambda_i \sin \lambda_i & -K_i \sin \theta_i \cos \theta_i \cos \lambda_i \\ -K_i \sin^2 \theta_i \cos \lambda_i \sin \lambda_i & K_i(\sin^2 \theta_i \cos^2 \lambda_i + \cos^2 \lambda_i) & -K_i \sin \theta_i \cos \theta_i \sin \lambda_i \\ -K_i \sin \theta_i \cos \theta_i \cos \lambda_i & -K_i \sin \theta_i \cos \theta_i \sin \lambda_i & K_i \sin^2 \theta_i \end{matrix} \right\|, \tag{13}$$

where

$$K_i = \frac{K_{fi} e_i}{L \cos \theta_i} \tag{14}$$

with

$$K_{fi} = C e_i^2$$

for clean fractures.

Summing up, provided the straight-line segment $L$ ensures a representative sampling, tensor $||K||$ will characterize the permeability of the rock mass as a continous medium.

#### 4.5

In the general case of the fractures in the rock mass having an arbitrary space distribution, they can be grouped in families such that each family includes the fractures the normals to which lie within a given solid-angle element, as mentioned in Sec. 3; a sampling with a length $L$ will be representative if it includes enough fractures of each family. Thus, the general case under consideration reduces to the case of several families of fractures dealt with above, where it was concluded that the permeability tensor $||K||$ is obtained by superposition of the contributions of each sampled fracture considered separately, according to Eq. (12).

Another way to draw the same conclusion consists of assuming that each fracture in a sampling $L$ belongs to a family of fractures with the same orientation, the same characteristics ($K_{fi}$, $e_i$), and a mean spacing $L \cos \theta_i$. For such an assumption to be valid, it suffices that the sampling with a length $L$ is representative.

### 4.6

So far only percolation through fractures has been considered; i.e., the flow through the rock itself was neglected, as is usually acceptable in practice.

In the special case of it being otherwise, the unit discharge through the rock will be

$$\mathbf{V} = K_r \mathbf{J},$$

$K_r$ being the coefficient of permeability of the rock material. Thus, Eq. (11) becomes

$$\mathbf{V} = ||K||\mathbf{J} + K_r \mathbf{J}$$

provided the superposition of the discharges is assumed to be valid. Consequently,

$$\mathbf{V} = (||K|| + K_r)\mathbf{J}.$$

The flow in the plane of the fractures was assumed in Sec. 4.1 to be isotropic. If in fact it is anisotropic and if the anisotropic permeability is defined, e.g., by the principal coefficients of permeability and the principal directions, the permeability of the system of fractures can be obtained by methods similar to those used above. Nevertheless, no conditions arise in practice which make it necessary to take such an anisotropy into account.

It was also assumed in Sec. 4.1 that the flow is laminar. For the hydraulic gradients usual in structures, velocities are sufficiently low for the flow to be laminar even in fractures with considerable openings, to which the noncontinuity of the fractures strongly contributes [2]. Additionally, taking nonlinearity into account makes permeability analysis of fracture systems much more complex. In fact let us assume as usual that the flow through a fracture is governed by a law of the type

$$V = K'_f J_f^{\alpha},$$

where $J_f$ is the magnitude of the hydraulic gradient in the plane of the fracture, $K'_f$ is the turbulent hydraulic conductivity, and $\alpha$ is an exponent ranging from 1 to 0.5. Equation (1) becomes

$$\mathbf{V} = K'_f J_f^{\alpha} \frac{\mathbf{J}_f}{J_f},$$

where $\mathbf{J}_f / J_f$ is a unit vector with the same direction as $\mathbf{J}_f$. Therefore,

$$\mathbf{V} = K'_f J_f^{\alpha - 1} \mathbf{J}_f. \tag{15}$$

From $J_f^{\alpha-1} = \sqrt{(i_f^2 + j_f^2 + k_f^2)^{\alpha-1}}$ and Eqs. (6), one concludes there is no linear relationship between the components of $\mathbf{V}$ and $\mathbf{J}$. To obtain the mean percolation velocity through a system of fractures, one must calculate by means of Eq. (15) the value of $\mathbf{V}(u, v, w)$ for each fracture and for each value of $\mathbf{J}(i, j, k)$ and add up the contributions of the fractures of the system to $u$, $v$, $w$. This is a very arduous procedure.

### 4.7

The permeability tensor $\|K\|$ being symmetric, there are eigenvectors, i.e., there are three mutually orthogonal directions $Ox'$, $Oy'$, $Oz'$ [Fig. 11(b)], along which the hydraulic gradient $\mathbf{J}$ and the resulting mean percolation velocity $\mathbf{V}$ have the same direction:

$$\begin{aligned} \mathbf{V}_{\mathrm{I}} &= K_{\mathrm{I}} \mathbf{J}_{\mathrm{I}} \\ \mathbf{V}_{\mathrm{II}} &= K_{\mathrm{II}} \mathbf{J}_{\mathrm{II}} \\ \mathbf{V}_{\mathrm{III}} &= K_{\mathrm{III}} \mathbf{J}_{\mathrm{III}}. \end{aligned} \tag{16}$$

The directions of $\mathbf{J}_{\mathrm{I}}$, $\mathbf{J}_{\mathrm{II}}$, $\mathbf{J}_{\mathrm{III}}$ are the principal directions of permeability, and $K_{\mathrm{I}}$, $K_{\mathrm{II}}$, $K_{\mathrm{III}}$ are the principal coefficients of permeability. Among the principal coefficients of permeability there are, as is known, the maximum and the minimum coefficient of permeability.

The principal coefficients of permeability and their directions are determined, as is usual, from their defining equation,

$$K_{\mathrm{I,II,III}} \mathbf{J} = \|K\| \mathbf{J}, \tag{17}$$

which has the three solutions given in Eqs. (16).

## 5. Experimental Correction of the Permeability Tensor

### 5.1

In the method here described for characterizing the permeability of rock masses, it is very important to apply correcting factors derived from the comparison of results of permeability tests in boreholes with the values obtained from the analysis just presented.

The need of a correction is mainly due to the assumed continuity of the fractures. The correcting factors will also compensate deviations due to other assumptions, particularly that roughness is $r = 0.33$ and that head losses at fracture intersections are negligible.

In rock masses with well-defined families of fractures, each family may have different characteristics, especially the development of each fracture in its plane—i.e., its continuity—and the roughness. It is then advisable to apply a correcting factor to each markedly different family of fractures.

Let us consider first the simplest case, in which it is considered sufficient to apply a single correcting factor $\rho$ to the coefficient $K_{fi}$ ascribed to clean or infilled fractures. Therefore, coefficients $K_i$ given by Eq. (14) become

$$K_i = \rho \frac{K_{fi} e_i}{L \cos \theta_i},$$

and, from Eqs. (13) and (17), one concludes that $\rho$ multiplies the components of tensor $||K||$ and the principal permeabilities, which become $\rho K_{\text{I}}$, $\rho K_{\text{II}}$, $\rho K_{\text{III}}$, whereas the principal directions remain unchanged.

Let us suppose that a borehole with an arbitrary direction defined by direction cosines $\cos \alpha'$, $\cos \beta'$, $\cos \gamma'$ [Fig. 11(b)] is subjected to a pressure test of the usual type. Let $d$ denote the borehole diameter, $L$ the length of the tested chamber, and $Q$ the discharge, i.e., the volume of water absorbed in the unit time under pressure $H$, measured in water height. The correcting factor $\rho$ will be determined so as to make the discharge $Q$ equal to the values corresponding to the principal permeabilities $\rho K_{\text{I}}$, $\rho K_{\text{II}}$, $\rho K_{\text{III}}$ and the direction of the borehole.

To express $Q$ in terms of the principal permeabilities, we shall resort to the well-known affine transformation of the anisotropic medium, with respect to the coordinate system $Ox'y'z'$ [Fig. 11(b)]:

$$\xi = \sqrt{\frac{K}{K_{\text{I}}}}\, x',$$
$$\eta = \sqrt{\frac{K}{K_{\text{II}}}}\, y', \qquad (18)$$
$$\zeta = \sqrt{\frac{K}{K_{\text{III}}}}\, z',$$

with $K = \sqrt[3]{K_{\text{I}} K_{\text{II}} K_{\text{III}}}$. As is known, this transformation yields an isotropic medium with a permeability $K$, and if the boundary conditions in the initial medium are applied on homologous points of the transformed medium, the total discharges through homologous surfaces of both media are the same [8].

Applying this transformation to the pressure test, the length of the tests chamber becomes

$$\bar{L} = L \sqrt{\sqrt[3]{K_{\text{I}} K_{\text{II}} K_{\text{III}}} \left( \frac{\cos^2 \alpha'}{K_{\text{I}}} + \frac{\cos^2 \beta'}{K_{\text{II}}} + \frac{\cos^2 \gamma'}{K_{\text{III}}} \right)},$$

which is obtained by taking Eqs. (18) into account.

When this transformation is applied, the cross section of the borehole becomes elliptical and ceases to be normal to the axis of the borehole unless this is parallel to one of the principal directions of permeability, e.g., $Oz'$. This is assumed to be at least roughly true, which in practice is not difficult to ensure. Regarding the flow in a borehole with an elliptical cross section with axes $d_1$ and $d_2$ in an isotropic medium, electric analogy tests, carried out according to a technique developed by Franciss [2], have shown that the discharge is not appreciably changed when the elliptical cross section is replaced by a circular cross section with a diameter

$$\bar{d} = \sqrt{d_1 d_2}.$$

Thus, for a ratio $d_1/d_2$ of $10^3$ the error is no more than 17%. Therefore, taking Eq. (18) into account, the elliptical cross section of the transformed medium can be replaced by a circular cross section with a diameter

$$\bar{d} = \sqrt{\frac{\sqrt[3]{K_{\mathrm{I}}K_{\mathrm{II}}K_{\mathrm{III}}}}{\sqrt{K_{\mathrm{I}}K_{\mathrm{II}}}}}\, d.$$

Owing to the properties of the transformation used, it can be stated that the discharge, under a pressure $H$, through the transformed medium, which is isotropic with a coefficient of permeability

$$K = \rho \sqrt[3]{K_{\mathrm{I}}K_{\mathrm{II}}K_{\mathrm{III}}},$$

remains equal to $Q$. Taking into account that the coefficient of permeability of a medium assumed to be continuous and isotropic can be calculated by the expression [1]

$$K = \frac{Q}{2\pi H \bar{L}} \operatorname{long}_n 1.32 \frac{\bar{L}}{\bar{d}}, \tag{19}$$

we obtain

$$\rho = \frac{1}{\sqrt[3]{K_{\mathrm{I}}K_{\mathrm{II}}K_{\mathrm{III}}}} \frac{Q}{2\pi H \bar{L}} \operatorname{long}_n 1.32 \frac{\bar{L}}{\bar{d}}. \tag{20}$$

This is how the correcting factor $\rho$ can be calculated from a pressure test, which must be carried out in the same borehole length $L$ from which the integral sample that served to determine the components of the permeability tensor was obtained.

Consider now the case in which the fractures can be divided into two groups as regards the correcting factor to be applied to the coefficient $K_{fi}$. Thus, there will be coefficients $K_i$ given by

$$\rho_1 \frac{K_{fi} e_i}{L \cos \theta_i} \quad \text{and} \quad \rho_2 \frac{K_{fi} e_i}{L \cos \theta_i},$$

the two correcting factors being $\rho_1$ and $\rho_2$. This case may occur, for instance, in sedimentary rock masses in which a family of fractures parallel to the stratification do not have the same characteristics as the other fractures.

We wish to determine $\rho_1$ and $\rho_2$ from pressure tests in two boreholes with different directions. If expressions of $K_{\mathrm{I}}$, $K_{\mathrm{II}}$, $K_{\mathrm{III}}$ in the function of the factors $\rho_1$, $\rho_2$ were known, these factors could be obtained by applying Eq. (19) directly to the results of tests in the two boreholes. But because the expressions in reference are much too complex, it is preferable (1) successively to choose arbitrary pairs of values $\rho_1$, $\rho_2$ and to determine the permeability tensor $||K||$ for each pair; (2) to calculate the principal coefficients of permeability $K_{\text{I}}$, $K_{\text{II}}$, $K_{\text{III}}$ and their directions; and (3) to compute from Eq. (20), as indicated above, the factors $\rho_1^*$ and $\rho_2^*$ corresponding to each of the two tests. The unknown values $\rho_1$, $\rho_2$ are those for which $\rho_1^* = \rho_2^* = 1$. Once $\rho_1$ and $\rho_2$ have been obtained, the principal directions and the principal coefficients of permeability can be determined. As permeability tests are carried out in the boreholes from which integral samples have been obtained, the accuracy of $\rho_1$ and $\rho_2$ will be increased if the permeability tensor, in a given coordinate system, is calculated by taking into account the contributions of the fractures of the two integral samples from the borehole lengths subjected to permeability tests.

The method just described can be extended to more than two correcting factors, but computations become considerable more time-consuming. In the majority of cases it will be sufficient to consider two factors.

When a given rock mass has been subjected to several pressure tests and correcting factors considered representative have been obtained, further tests may be dispensed with, and permeability may be determined from the characteristics of fractures alone.

### 5.2

The components of the permeability tensor and its principal directions are defined in the coordinate system *Oxyz* [Fig. 11(a)], which is associated with the direction of the borehole. To present the final results, it is preferable to use the system connected with the cardinal points indicated in Fig. 11(c), of which one of the axes, *OZ*, is vertical, and the other two point into the north, *ON*, and into the east, *OE*. As axis *Ox* lies on the vertical plane through the axis of the borehole, the new coordinate system can be defined with respect to the system of Fig. 11(a) by means of the angle $\varphi$ of the axis of the borehole with the vertical, and the angle $\psi$ of *ON* with the horizontal line *OP* which lies on the vertical plane through the axis of the borehole. Denoting by $\bar{i}, \bar{j}, \bar{k}$ the components of **J** in system *ONEZ*, we obtain

$$\begin{Bmatrix} i \\ j \\ k \end{Bmatrix} = ||A|| \begin{Bmatrix} \bar{i} \\ \bar{j} \\ \bar{k} \end{Bmatrix}$$

with

$$||A|| = \begin{Vmatrix} \cos\psi\cos\varphi & \sin\psi\cos\varphi & \sin\varphi \\ -\sin\psi & \cos\psi & 0 \\ -\cos\psi\sin\varphi & -\sin\psi\sin\varphi & \cos\varphi \end{Vmatrix}.$$

Consequently, taking Eq. (11) into account, the permeability tensor of the rock mass with respect to the coordinate system *ONEZ* is given by

$$||\bar{K}|| = ||K|| \; ||A||,$$

$||K||$ being the tensor with respect to system *Oxyz*.

The principal directions of permeability will also be expressed with respect to the coordinate system *ONEZ*.

## 6. Determination of the Permeability Tensor from Integral Samples

Provided integral samples of the rock mass are available and fractures are assumed to be plane, continuous, and with constant openings and uniform infillings (if any), the permeability tensor $||K||$ of the rock mass can be determined by adding up the contribution $||K_i||$ of each fracture, according to Eqs. (13) and (14).

For that purpose it is necessary to determine for each fracture the values of coefficient $K_{fi}$, opening $e_i$, and angles $\lambda_i$ and $\theta_i$, defining the orientation of the fracture [Fig. 11(a)].

$K_{fi}$ is given by Eq. (2) in the case of a clean fracture, with $C = 3 \times 10^5$ $(\text{m-s})^{-1}$ when no evidence for a different value is available. When the contribution of infilled fractures to permeability is to be taken into account (Sec. 4.2, Fig. 9), a value must be ascribed to the coefficient of permeability of the infilling material.

The opening $e$ should be determined with particular attention when it is small, say of an order of magnitude of tenths of a millimeter, and above all in clean fractures, where coefficients $K_i$ change with the cube of $e_i$. Openings $e_i$ have been determined with micrometric oculars or by comparison with marks with thicknesses ranging from 0.05 mm on a ruler.

The accuracy of $K_{fi}$ can be checked by means of permeability tests on the fractures themselves—infilled or not—remaining in the integral samples. Such tests are of special interest for defining an adequate technique for measuring $e$ in clean fractures and for estimating the coefficient of permeability in the case of infilled fractures.

Angles $\lambda_i$ and $\theta_i$ have been determined by any of two procedures. In one of them, $\lambda_i$ and $\theta_i$ are calculated from the elevations $z_1, z_2, \ldots, z_6$ of the intersections of the fracture with the six generatrices equally spaced $G_1$ to $G_6$ marked on the surface of the integral sample (Fig. 13); a linear regression yields the most probable plane. The opening of the fracture is measured at the intersection with the generatrices indicated, and thus a mean value can be obtained. The other procedure is an experimental determination of $\lambda_i$ and $\theta_i$ by means of a device consisting of a ring, which can be adjusted on the surface of the sample, and a ruler perpendicular to the plane of the ring

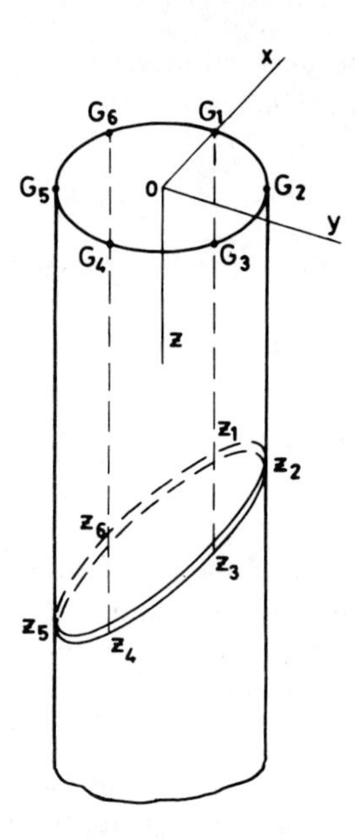


**Fig. 13.** Determination of fracture attitudes from the measured values $z_1, z_2, \ldots, z_6$

(Fig. 14). The angle $\theta_i$ is given by $\tan \theta_i = a_i/d$, where $d$ is the diameter of the sample and $a_i$ is measured on the ruler; the angle $\lambda_i$ is read directly on the ring, with respect to the reference generatrix $G_1$ marked on the integral sample.

Summing up, the routine for determining the permeability tensor is the following:

1. Mark on the sample reference generatrices $G_1$ to $G_6$ (Fig. 13) or generatrix $G_1$ (Fig. 14), $G_1$ being determined by axis $Ox$ [Fig. 11(a)].
2. Determine angles $\lambda_i$, $\theta_i$ for each fracture (Figs. 13 and 14).
3. Determine the opening $e_i$ of each fracture.
4. Calculate coefficients $K_{fi}$ of clean fractures, and ascribe values $K_{fi}$ to infilled fractures.
5. Calculate the components of tensor $||K_i||$ for each fracture.
6. Add up the tensors corresponding to the different fractures in the sample to obtain the permeabilitiy tensor $||K||$ in the coordinate system $Oxyz$.
7. Determine the principal directions of permeability $Oxi$, $Oy'$, $Oz'$ and the principal coefficients of permeability, $K_{\text{I}}$, $K_{\text{II}}$, $K_{\text{III}}$ (Sec. 4.7).
8. Calculate the correcting factors $\rho$ (Sec. 5.1).
9. Determine the components of the permeability tensor and its principal directions in the coordinate system $ONEZ$ (Sec. 5.2).

Computer programs have been developed for the calculations included in this routine.

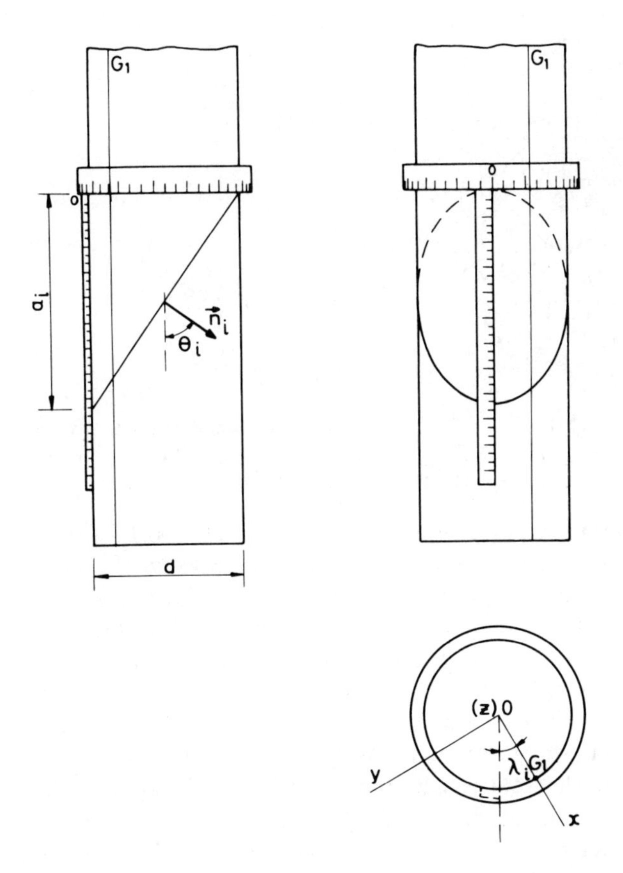


**Fig. 14.** Determination of fracture attitudes from the measured values $a_i$ and $\lambda_i$

## 7. Applications

Figure 15 presents results of a determination of the permeability tensor in a vesicular basalt, from fractures observed in an integral sample with a length $L = 2$ m obtained in a borehole 86 mm in diameter. In the figure are shown the attitudes of the fractures and their openings—distributed in the intervals indicated, with or without infilling—as well as the principal directions of permeability and the corresponding principal permeabilities. The values of these permeabilities were multiplied with a correcting factor $\rho = 0.8$ determined in pressure tests in the same borehole stretch from which the integral sample had been obtained. The results show there is a nearly vertical principal direction, corresponding to the minimum permeability $K_{III} = 0.18 \times 10^{-6}$ m/s, and an almost isotropic horizontal permeability with

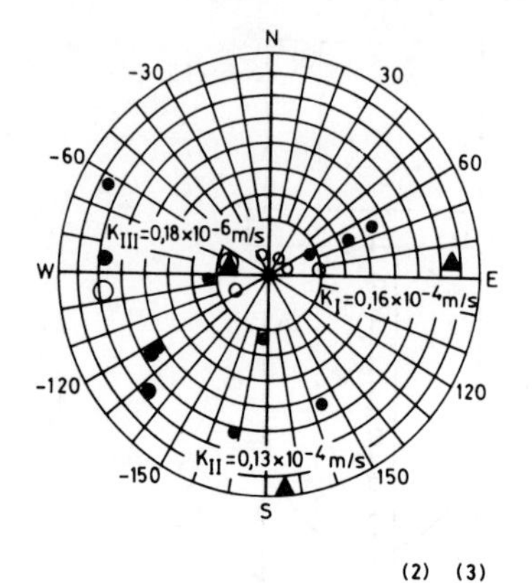


**Fig. 15.** Permeability tensor of vesicular basalt: (1) principal directions, (2) clean fractures, (3) infilled fractures

principal values $K_I = 0.16 \times 10^{-4}$ m/s and $K_{II} = 0.13 \times 10^{-4}$ m/s. Thus, the coefficient of anisotropy, $K_I/K_{III}$, has a high value of about 100.

An extensive program for characterizing permeability in a basaltic formation for the foundation of a concrete dam yielded the results now to be described. About 400 m of integral samples were obtained from boreholes with a diameter of 76 mm, the length of the samples being, as a rule, $L = 3$ m. The values of the correcting factor $\rho$ were calculated from 128 permeability tests. The basaltic formation was made up of layers of compact basalt, vesicular-amygdaloidal basalt, and basaltic breccia. In accordance with the features of the samples, it seemed advisable to distribute them in groups with similar characteristics, within each of the three rock types, which was done by a mathematical method suggested by one of the authors (Franciss and Puccini [3]). To have an idea of the dispersion of permeability, the directions and magnitudes of the principal permeabilities were determined in each sample; then the mean values and the corresponding standard deviations of $K_I$, $K_{II}$, $K_{III}$ were calculated for each group, a log normal distribution being assumed for the magnitudes of the principal permeabilities. Table 1 presents the principal permeabilities as well as the coefficients of anisotropy. As an instance, the solid angles corresponding to the dispersion of the principal directions of permeability are indicated in Fig. 16 for one group of each rock type.

These results entirely agree with the fracturing attitudes in the basaltic rock mass concerned, as is shown by the systematically near-vertical direction of the minimum principal permeability $K_{III}$, and a usually almost isotropic horizontal permeability, with magnitudes considerably above $K_{III}$, on the average. The coefficient of anisotropy $K_I/K_{III}$ lies, as a rule, in the interval 5–50, but two values exceeding 1000 were also obtained. Given the near isotropy in the horizontal plane, it is not surprising that directions $K_I$ and $K_{II}$

**Table 1**

| Compact Basalt | | | Vescular-Amygdaloidal Basalt | | | Basaltic Breccia | | |
|---|---|---|---|---|---|---|---|---|
| *Group* | $K_I, K_{II}, K_{III}$ $(m/s)$ | $\frac{K_I}{K_{III}}$ | *Group* | $K_I, K_{II}, K_{III}$ $(m/s)$ | $\frac{K_I}{K_{III}}$ | *Group* | $K_I, K_{II}, K_{III}$ $(m/s)$ | $\frac{K_I}{K_{III}}$ |
| 1 | $0.295 \times 10^{-4}$ <br> $0.281 \times 10^{-4}$ <br> $0.181 \times 10^{-5}$ | 16 | 1 | $0.389 \times 10^{-5}$ <br> $0.331 \times 10^{-5}$ <br> $0.603 \times 10^{-6}$ | 6 | 1 | $0.331 \times 10^{-5}$ <br> $0.316 \times 10^{-5}$ <br> $0.269 \times 10^{-6}$ | 12 |
| 2 | $0.851 \times 10^{-6}$ <br> $0.776 \times 10^{-6}$ <br> $0.128 \times 10^{-6}$ | 7 | 2 | $0.660 \times 10^{-5}$ <br> $0.562 \times 10^{-5}$ <br> $0.120 \times 10^{-6}$ | 55 | 2 | $0.100 \times 10^{-6}$ <br> $0.525 \times 10^{-6}$ <br> $0.525 \times 10^{-7}$ | 19 |
| 3 | $0.478 \times 10^{-6}$ <br> $0.426 \times 10^{-6}$ <br> $0.741 \times 10^{-7}$ | 6 | 3 | $0.169 \times 10^{-5}$ <br> $0.169 \times 10^{-5}$ <br> $0.158 \times 10^{-8}$ | 1050 | 3 | $0.213 \times 10^{-6}$ <br> $0.204 \times 10^{-6}$ <br> $0.120 \times 10^{-7}$ | 18 |
| 4 | $0.316 \times 10^{-6}$ <br> $0.301 \times 10^{-6}$ <br> $0.119 \times 10^{-7}$ | 27 | 4 | $0.478 \times 10^{-6}$ <br> $0.457 \times 10^{-6}$ <br> $0.197 \times 10^{-7}$ | 25 | 4 | Practically impermeable | — |
| 5 | $0.630 \times 10^{-5}$ <br> $0.619 \times 10^{-5}$ <br> $0.933 \times 10^{-9}$ | 6700 | 5 | Practically impermeable | — | | | |
| 6 | Practically impermeable | — | | | | | | |

present considerable dispersions (Fig. 16), although a trend is observed for $K_I$ to lie in a direction in the neighborhood of NS.

Regarding the correcting factor $\rho$, the values obtained range from about 0.01 to about 50, the values exceeding the unit possibly being due to the high roughness adopted in the calculation and to errors in the measurement of $e$.

Therefore, within each rock type, permeability changes considerably

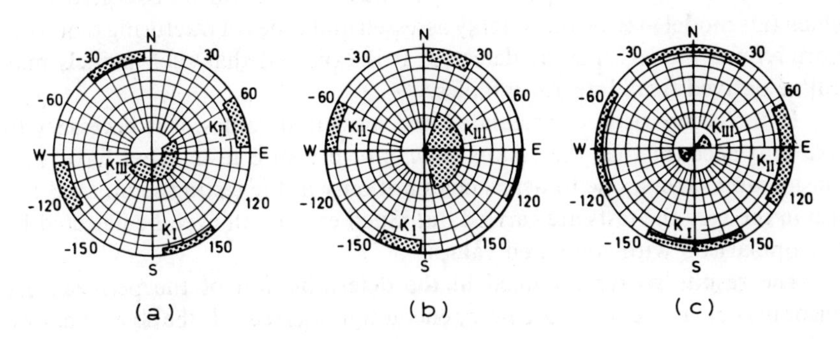


**Fig. 16.** Dispersion of the principal directions of permeability: (a) compact basalt, group 1, (b) vesicular-amygdaloidal basalt, group 2, (c) basaltic breccia, group 3.

from group to group, whereas dispersion within each group is not marked, which shows the possibility of an adequate grouping of the samples before determining the permeability tensor.

## 8. Conclusion

The problem of percolation through rock masses has been the object of systematic research only in the last 15 years, and the results obtained now begin to effectively influence design. On one hand, field observations have undoubtedly shown that percolation phenomena are as a rule continuous, which confirms the presence of interconnected fractures in rock masses; on the other hand, the contribution of laboratory research on percolation through fractures and the great possibilities of a numeric solution for definite problems by the finite element method should be underlined.

One of the difficulties still faced is the indispensable need to characterize permeability as an anisotropic magnitude. In fact the experimental approach by *in situ* tests requires several tests at each point to be characterized (Sec. 1), which has greatly hindered an adequate treatment of percolation problems. Another obstacle is the well-known difficulty in the interpretation of results of pressure tests at points above the groundwater table.

Thus, several authors have considered the advantage of determining permeability from a characterization of the fractures in the rock mass, but so far no adequate technique has been available for the purpose. In this chapter a characterization based on the observation of integral samples is used, the very simplifying assumption being accepted that to each fracture in a sample there corresponds in the rock mass a plane continuous fracture with uniform characteristics. Such a model will have a validity variable from case to case, and it will quite possibly be untenable sometimes. It is therefore necessary that calculated and measured permeability values go on being compared by determining correcting factors $\rho$ (Sec. 5.1). Thus, results will be collected from which this model may be thoroughly assessed and types of fracturing requiring more refined models may be detected. It is expected that such models may still be derived from integral samples.

In the comparison of calculated and measured values, it is necessary to take into account that the results of *in situ* pressure tests often have very considerable errors, due to deficiencies not only in the testing setup used but also in the way the tests are carried out. Such errors can even be detected by the comparison with computed values.

The results so far obtained in the determination of the permeability tensor in rock masses have been very encouraging as regards the determination of both principal directions and magnitudes of principal permeabilities. These present, as a rule, marked dispersion from tested point to tested point, which raises a difficulty—well known when isotropic permeability is assumed —namely how to characterize the permeability of a rock mass from local values with a great dispersion. This is a question which ought to be throughly studied, as the solution of definite percolation problems depends on its being cleared up.

## References

1. Bogomolov, G. V., and A. I. Silin-Bektchourine, "Hydrologie Spécialisée", *Ann. Serv. Inf. Geol.*, No. 37, Paris, 1959, p.1–235.
2. Franciss, F. O., "Contribution à l'étude du mouvement de l'eau à travers les milieux fissurés", Thèse Doctorat, Faculté des Sciences, Université de Grenoble, Grenoble, 1970.
3. Franciss, F. O., and A. L. Puccini, *Technique of Model Group Identification and its Application in Rock Mechanics*", Proceedings of the Second International Congress of the International Association of Engineering Geology, Vol. 2, Associação Brasileira de Geologia de Engenharia, São Paulo, 1974.
4. Louis, C., "A Study of Ground Water Flow in Jointed Rock and its Influence on the Stability of Rock Masses", *Rock Mechanics Report No. 10*, Imperial College, London, Sept. 1969.
5. Louis, C., *Rock Hydraulics*, Bureau de Recherches Géologiques et Minières, Orléans, 1974.
6. Rocha, M., "A Method of Integral Sampling of Rock Masses", *Rock Mech.*, Vol. 3, No. 1, Wien, 1971, p. 1–12.
7. Rocha, M., and M. Barroso, "Some Applications of the New Integral Sampling Method in Rock Masses", *Rock Fracture Symposium International Society for Rock Mechanics*, Nancy, 1971, p. I–21.
8. Schneebeli, G., *Hydraulique Souterraine*, Eyrolles, Paris, 1966.
9. Snow, D. T., "Three-Hole Pressure Test for Anisotropic Foundations Permeability", *Rock Mech. Eng. Geol.*, Vol. IV, No. 4, Wien, 1966, p. 298–316.

# The Role of Theory in Geotechnical Field Observations

RALPH B. PECK* AND DON U. DEERE†

## The Changing Role of Theory

Geotechnical science and geotechnical engineering had many origins. Most engineers would agree that they came to focus in the personality and technical contributions of Karl Terzaghi in the two decades between 1920 and 1940. Hence, Terzaghi's view of the role of theory is of special interest.

In his Presidential Address to the First International Conference on Soil Mechanics and Foundation Engineering in 1936 [1], now considered to be a classical account of the essential features of geotechnical progress, one of the major sections is entitled "Theory vs. Reality." Evidently, when reviewing the history of development of soil mechanics, Terzaghi felt obliged to conclude that, on the whole, theory had been an obstacle to progress. Among his examples were the classical earth pressure theories for cohesionless soil. According to these theories, the pressure against a vertical support should increase linearly with depth from a value of zero at the ground surface. Yet practical experience had indicated that the bracing of open cuts behaved as if the greatest pressures were near the top rather than the bottom of the excavation [2]. Fruitless argument had ensued between several generations of academicians, on one hand, who defended the theories stoutly, and practitioners, on the other, who preferred to believe what they had experienced. Fundamental laboratory tests [3, 4] clarified the principles, but it was not until full-scale field measurements were made on the Berlin Subway open cuts [5] that the case

*Consulting civil engineer, geotechnics, Albuquerque; Professor Emeritus of Foundation Engineering, Lecturer and Research Consultant in Civil Engineering, University of Illinois at Urbana-Champaign, Urbana, Illinois.

†Consulting engineering geologist, Gainesville. Formerly Professor of Civil Engineering and of Geology, University of Illinois at Urbana-Champaign, Urbana, Illinois.

for a nonlinear distribution of pressure became overwhelming. The general wedge theory of earth pressures [6], in which the stress-deformation characteristics of real rather than idealized materials were taken into account, soon followed.

As a result of similar revisions of several other widely used theories, the theoretical basis of soil mechanics was placed in much better order. Advances in knowledge of the properties of real earth and rock materials and the results of many full-scale field observations came about hand in hand with improvements in theory, and rapid progress took place during the next two decades. The beginnings of a realistic theoretical basis for rock mechanics also appeared.

Possibly, today the pre-1936 story may be repeating itself. Theory and, especially, the means for carrying out theoretical calculations have advanced enormously. They have outstripped our present and perhaps our future ability to determine and utilize all the necessary constitutive properties of real masses of soil, weathered rock, and rock. Whether or not we fall victim to excessive excursions into theory will depend to a large extent on our ability to check the predictions by full-scale observations and on the use to which we put the theory.

The interaction between theoretical development and increased knowledge about the behavior of earth materials is obvious, and we shall not dwell on it further. What we wish to emphasize is the proper use of theory in the design and construction of difficult geotechnical works and the role that theory plays in guiding us into carrying out useful and meaningful field observations and in profiting from them directly.

## Fundamental Aspects of Geotechnical Engineering

Two fundamental factors at play in geotechnical engineering govern the role of theory.

The first is the nature of geotechnical materials. We deal with materials that are complex with respect to their physical and engineering properties; not only are the properties complex, but they are still imperfectly understood. Indeed, although the future may bring as yet unsuspected and spectacular improvements in techniques of geotechnical exploration, we can state with some confidence that the engineering properties of *in situ* masses of geotechnical materials will never be so well known as those of concrete or steel. When we are concerned with the stability of natural slopes, or the stability of subsurface excavations such as tunnels or underground power plants, features that appear to be details from the point of view of exploration may turn out to be decisive from the point of view of safety of construction and from the point of view of the adequacy of design.

The second factor is the manner in which geotechnical works are carried out. They can hardly be classified as manufacturing procedures, such as those used in fabricating and erecting the superstructure of a steel bridge. Geotechnical works are never exactly two of a kind. They are built by men and machines, usually under difficult physical conditions, often under contractual relationships less than ideal, by construction methods that are by no means perfect, with little opportunity for quality control in its usual connotation. If we ignore the conditions under which a tunnel must be built, if we idealize the tunneling procedure on a given project, our design will not conform to reality, no matter how beautiful the theory upon which it is based, and our estimate of cost may turn out to be pure fiction.

These two factors are sometimes regarded as limitations to the application of theory in geotechnical work. Perhaps they are. On the other hand, they constitute challenges to the geotechnical professional, and they determine the proper use of theory in geotechnical works.

## Use of Theory

What might be termed the standard use of theory, one that is applicable under relatively simple geotechnical conditions, is to predict what will happen as a consequence of the proposed construction. Theory permits studying various alternative design and construction procedures and gives the basis for at least tentative design.

A second use, more peculiar to geotechnical engineering, is to provide a basis for comparing the anticipated conditions with reality even when the real conditions are complex. Theory used for this purpose permits us to judge how the real subsurface conditions and the real properties of geotechnical materials vary from those assumed after what may be the best of investigations; indeed, theory used in this fashion permits us to ascertain what are actually the significant real properties. It may help us determine to what extent undesirable behavior, observed during construction, is due to the properties of the geotechnical materials involved and to what extent it is due to unsuitable construction methods or to poor workmanship.

## Early Examples of the Role of Theory in Field Observations

In his early professional years, Terzaghi's appreciation of this second role of theory in geotechnical field observations was almost surely intuitive. Not until he had made use of it on several projects did he begin to sense a methodology that might be formalized.

Typical of his early applications was the determination of the allowance that should be made in the verticality of the turbine shafts at the Svir III hydroelectric station because of the tilt anticipated under the stresses due to filling the reservoir [7]. He computed the tilt of the turbine shafts by a simple application of the theory of elasticity, on the basis of his best estimate of the modulus of elasticity for the materials likely to be stressed. He did not suggest, however, that the shafts should be constructed out of plumb by the computed amount. Instead, he computed the displacements of a number of reference points where observations could be made during other stress-changing operations such as major excavations. He found that the measured displacements were rather uniformly a certain fraction of the computed displacements, and he postulated that the turbine shafts should be constructed out of plumb by the same fraction of their computed tilt. The turbine shafts, after the reservoir was filled, possessed the desired verticality.

More subtle but more significant was Terzaghi's use of the flow net, in itself a graphical solution of pure theory, in assessing the behavior of the Newport News Dry Docks [8]. These unconventional structures consisted of three parallel cellular sheet pile walls, appropriately closed at the ends to form two parallel basins. The floors of the basins, in contrast to the heavy concrete floors of conventional dry docks, were of nominal thickness. They rested on a stratum of marl (a stiff gray clay) overlying a stratum of green fine dense silty sand. A cross section, taken from the original paper, is shown in Fig. 1.

It was obvious that the stability of the dry docks would depend on the uplift pressures against the floors or the underlying impervious marl when the basins were unwatered. To estimate this pressure, Terzaghi drew a conventional flow net, assuming two-dimensional flow in planes perpendicular to the axis of the basins and assuming that the sand with respect to permeability was homogeneous and isotropic. He also assumed as boundary conditions that the sheet pile cells were impervious and that the contact between the cells and the marl was tight. Terzaghi showed the flow net and discussed it in some detail in his report on the project, but he did not think it of sufficient importance to include it in the published paper. Nevertheless, the following two quotations from the paper indicate the manner in which the flow net was actually used:

> The total leakage through the weep holes . . . was several times greater than the quantity computed on the assumption that the water flows toward the concrete floor only through the marl. This finding indicates that a considerable part of the leakage follows the rows of sheet piles in a vertical upward direction.
>
> A constant flow toward the wells can be maintained only by seepage

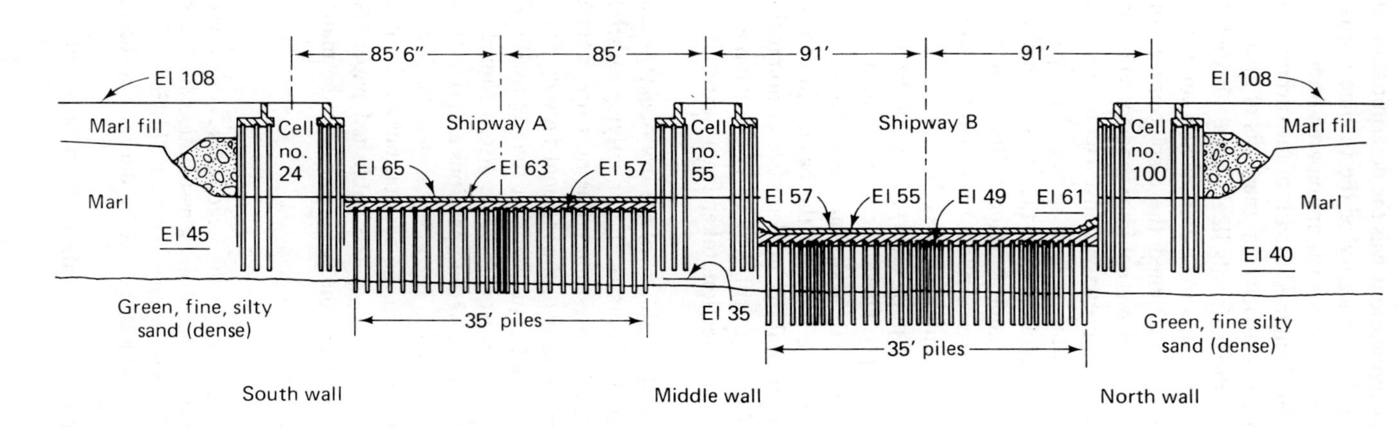


Fig. 1. Newport News shipway cross section (After Ref. 8)

> from permanent sources of water into the cells, partly through the marl stratum which constitutes the base of the fill in the cells and partly through the locks of the sheet piles. Approximate computations based on the flow-net method indicated that the observed rate of flow and the *measured hydraulic gradients** can be accounted for only by assuming that the loss of head associated with the percolation of the water across the rows of sheet piles was negligible.

Pore pressure observations in the sand beneath the floors were a key feature of the observational program. The results disagreed with the values predicted from the flow net. That there was disagreement was in itself of little significance. What was important was the manner in which the equipotential lines of the flow net would have to be altered to agree with the measurements. The required alteration showed conclusively that the assumed boundary conditions were in error.

The use made by Terzaghi of the flow net was thus twofold. It served as a standard against which the observed pore pressures could be compared. But, more important, it demonstrated the manner in which the real conditions must have varied from those assumed. The flow net indicated much more than the mere existence of a discrepancy between computed and observed values. It showed quickly and surely what the significant boundary conditions really were. It is apparent that this use of the flow net, by Terzaghi in 1945, was still intuitive. He did not formally make the point that, although his flow net was erroneous because of the incorrect boundary conditions, it served a most useful purpose, namely, to disclose, when combined with the the results of field observations, what the real field conditions were.

Indeed, a simple flow net drawn on the basis of homogeneity and isotropy, when considered together with the results of pore pressure observations, is a powerful tool for soil exploration. The flow net is undoubtedly erroneous, because real soils are neither homogeneous nor isotropic. Yet, the real conditions of nonhomogeneity and anisotropy cannot be deduced from field observations alone. They require a flow net based on simplifying assumptions. Whether the flow net is constructed graphically or generated by computer is irrelevant; how it is used is what matters.

Although the approach illustrated thus far was developed and utilized to a considerable extent in applied soil mechanics [9], it has truly come into its own in the successful application of rock mechanics. Construction of some of the major underground openings in rock, such as subway stations or large power plants, would not have been feasible except for the adaptation and application of the procedure. Several recent examples in rock engineering will indicate the power of the method.

*Italics ours.

## Background of Observational Method in Rock Engineering

Much of the early work in applied rock mechanics made use of material properties obtained from laboratory tests on intact rock samples and equations from the theory of elasticity. Experience has shown that both are of questionable value if used directly and indiscriminately.

The mechanical properties of an *in situ* rock mass depend not only on the properties of the intact rock in the individual joint blocks but also on the frequency, orientation, and character of the geologic discontinuities (joints, bedding planes, foliation, etc.) that bound the blocks. For example, laboratory tests on a rock core of granite gneiss might give a value of $600 \times 10^3$ $kg/cm^2$ for Young's modulus of elasticity, but *in situ* testing of the rock mass would likely yield values of only 100 to $200 \times 10^3$ $kg/cm^2$. The *in situ* values would depend on the amount of jointing and weathering of the rock. The mechanical properties might also be highly anisotropic; the modulus, for example, in a direction parallel to the prominent joint system or bedding might perhaps be twice that measured in a perpendicular direction.

As the value of *in situ* testing became recognized, a great variety of tests was developed by research organizations and engineering firms. Unfortunately, many of these tests were not of sufficiently large scale to incorporate the effects of jointing, and erroneous or questionable values were obtained and frequently used. The question of scale is still being debated, but the International Society of Rock Mechanics through its Commission on Standardization of Laboratory and Field Tests has recommended for both *in situ* direct shear tests and *in situ* modulus tests that test areas be at least $1m^2$.

Because of the fairly large size of the test area, the loads involved are also large. This fact plus the extensive preparation of the test area, usually in a shaft or test adit, have made *in situ* testing both time-consuming and expensive. Two to four weeks are commonly required and $10,000 per test may be exceeded. Terzaghi [10] in commenting on the excellent paper by John [11] feared that, because of the excessive time and cost of *in situ* testing, the temptation would be to make too few tests and that the results might not be representative and would possibly lead to faulty design.

Zones for *in situ* testing are now carefully selected after detailed geologic studies, and tests are made in several homogeneous areas including those representing both the best and the worst rock quality. Extrapolations of results, and even predictions for other sites, are made by use of indices describing the rock quality. These procedures have largely overcome the undesirable developments feared by Terzaghi. The Illinois school of applied rock mechanics has been one of the leaders in this effort [12].

Equations from the theory of elasticity have been generously used in the past and in many cases still are. One of their common uses is to calculate the stress concentration around a tunnel. Classical results indicate a peaked-up circumferential stress with the maximum value at the tunnel wall and with values decreasing at increasing distances. Through the development this past decade of instrumentation and techniques for determining the stresses at various distances from the tunnel wall, it has been found that the highest stress most often is not at the tunnel wall but at some distance away. Obviously, the rock at the tunnel wall has yielded along joint surfaces and cracks caused by blasting. The yielding has resulted in a redistribution of stress so that the stress peaks farther back from the tunnel wall where the rock strength is greater because of triaxial confinement.

This situation was not fully realized in the early days of rock mechanics, and some erroneous design concepts on occasion have been used. Elastic-plastic theories for simple cases were readily available and, when the need became apparent, were adopted for use with frictional materials including time-dependent behavior [13, 14]. However, the problem remains of determining the constitutive properties of the rock mass in a realistic and representative way.

Another early example of the use of simple elastic theory that led to results later found to be generally in error was to invoke Poisson's ratio $\sigma$ and the factor $\sigma/(1 - \sigma)$ for estimating the state of stress at a given depth in a rock mass. For a horizontal surface the *in situ* vertical rock stress (the major principal stress) was estimated to be equal to the weight of overlying rock and soil, and the horizontal stress to be a fraction of the vertical stress as specified by the factor above. Since Poisson's ratio was normally assumed equal to 0.20 to 0.25, the factor, which was considered to be similar to the coefficient of earth pressure at rest, was computed to be 0.25 to 0.33.

The results accumulated from the last decade of testing indicate that, whereas by far the majority of *in situ* stress determinations show the vertical or near-vertical stress to be a principal stress nearly equal to the overburden weight, the horizontal stresses are on the average equal to or 2 to 3 times greater than the vertical stress, rather than only a fraction of it. There is little doubt that the *in situ* horizontal stress (or so-called residual stress) is a result of inelastic displacements and is a function of the geological history, including erosion, preloading by glaciers, tectonic movements, igneous intrusions, weathering, etc. Since none of these events is known in all its detail, and because of the complexity of the interaction of these several factors, there is little hope that the *in situ* state of stress can be estimated by either theory or geologic knowledge. It must be determined by field measurements.

## Churchill Falls Underground Powerhouse

The Churchill Falls (Labrador) underground powerhouse exemplifies the enlightened and extensive use of rock mechanics in both design and construction [15]. The underground powerhouse cavern, housing eleven 475-MW generators, is one of the largest in the world. It is located at a depth of 1000 ft and measures 81 ft wide, 972 ft long, and about 150 ft high at its deepest portion. Construction began in 1966, and first power was on the line in 1972.

In addition to surface geologic mapping and several deep vertical and inclined borings into the cavern area, the exploration included borehole photography performed to determine the orientation of the different joint sets and the foliation of the granite gneiss bedrock. The core recovery from the borings was essentially 100% and the RQD averaged over 94%; thus, the quality of the rock mass appeared excellent. Three sets or families of joints were noted from the surface mapping and borehole photography, but Lugeon-type water pressure tests, which showed negligible water losses, indicated that the joints were tight. Laboratory testing of the rock cores revealed average values of the unconfined compressive strength of a little more than 1000 $kg/cm^2$ and Young's modulus of elasticity of $550 \times 10^3$ $kg/cm^2$.

Because of the generally high quality of the rock mass, it was believed that the rock would behave essentially as an elastic medium except possibly that joint blocks would loosen at intersections and at adversely oriented joints dipping out of the walls. To minimize this type of behavior the specifications required that all excavation headings be of limited size and that tensioned rock bolts be placed close to the face following blasting. Moreover,

> . . . a two-dimensional elastic finite elements computer model was used extensively as a "design tool" to develop and optimize suitable shapes, sizes and spacing of openings. The combination of the generally level topography of the overlying plateau, together with the symmetry and depth of the proposed openings, supplied relatively simple boundary conditions for the model [15].

Figure 2 illustrates alternative shapes, positions, and pillar widths studied for the transformer gallery, powerhouse cavern, and surge chamber. Attempts were made in designing the chambers to minimize the occurrence and depth of any zones of tensile stress and also to keep the magnitude of the compressive stresses at the walls well below the unconfined compressive strength of the rock.

At the time of the design of the cavities the initial state of stress in the rock mass was not known. Therefore, the ratio of horizontal to vertical stress was varied in the studies from 0.3 to 2.0 with most emphasis given to the values from 0.6 to 1.5. When the cavern area was first entered in the early days of construction, three test galleries were excavated and *in situ* stress determinations were made by stress-relief overcoring methods in boreholes drilled outward from the walls. The principal stresses were found to be essentially vertical and horizontal. The vertical stresses approximated the over-

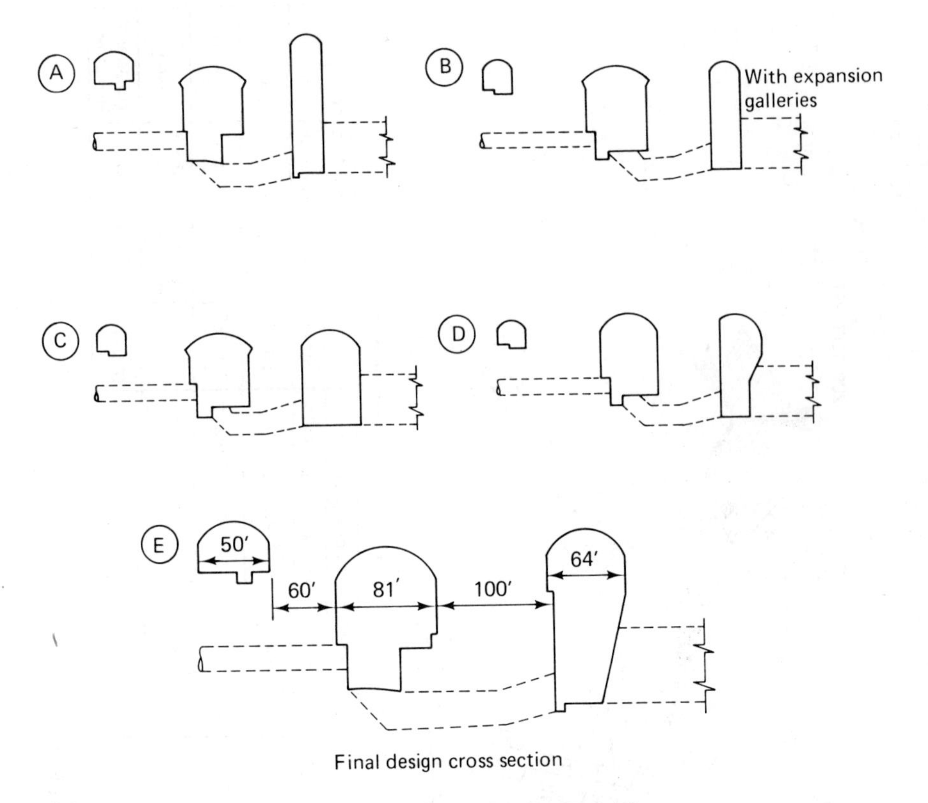


**Fig. 2.** Churchill Falls, alternate shapes studied (After Ref. 15)

burden weight, and the two horizontal stresses were equal and of magnitude equal to 1.1 to 1.9 (average 1.7) times the vertical stress (Fig. 3).

During the design stages the finite element analysis was used to compute expected displacements of the cavern arch and walls at various stages of construction. At this time no *in situ* measurements were available of modulus of elasticity of the rock mass, a quantity needed for the computation. It was realized that the modulus of the rock cores would be too high because the cores did not contain the joint systems of the rock mass. Therefore, for the preliminary designs a value ranging from about $\frac{1}{4}$ to $\frac{1}{2}$ of the rock-core modulus was used. *In situ* tests were made in the test galleries as soon as the construction adits reached the chamber area, and the anticipated range of values was confirmed. However, the first meter or so of the wall rock was often of noticeably lower modulus because of local yielding and destressing.

During construction the principal field monitoring consisted of mapping the geologic discontinuities and observing their effect on overbreak or joint-block loosening, and installation and reading of multiple-position borehole extensometers to indicate the magnitude of rock movement toward the cavity

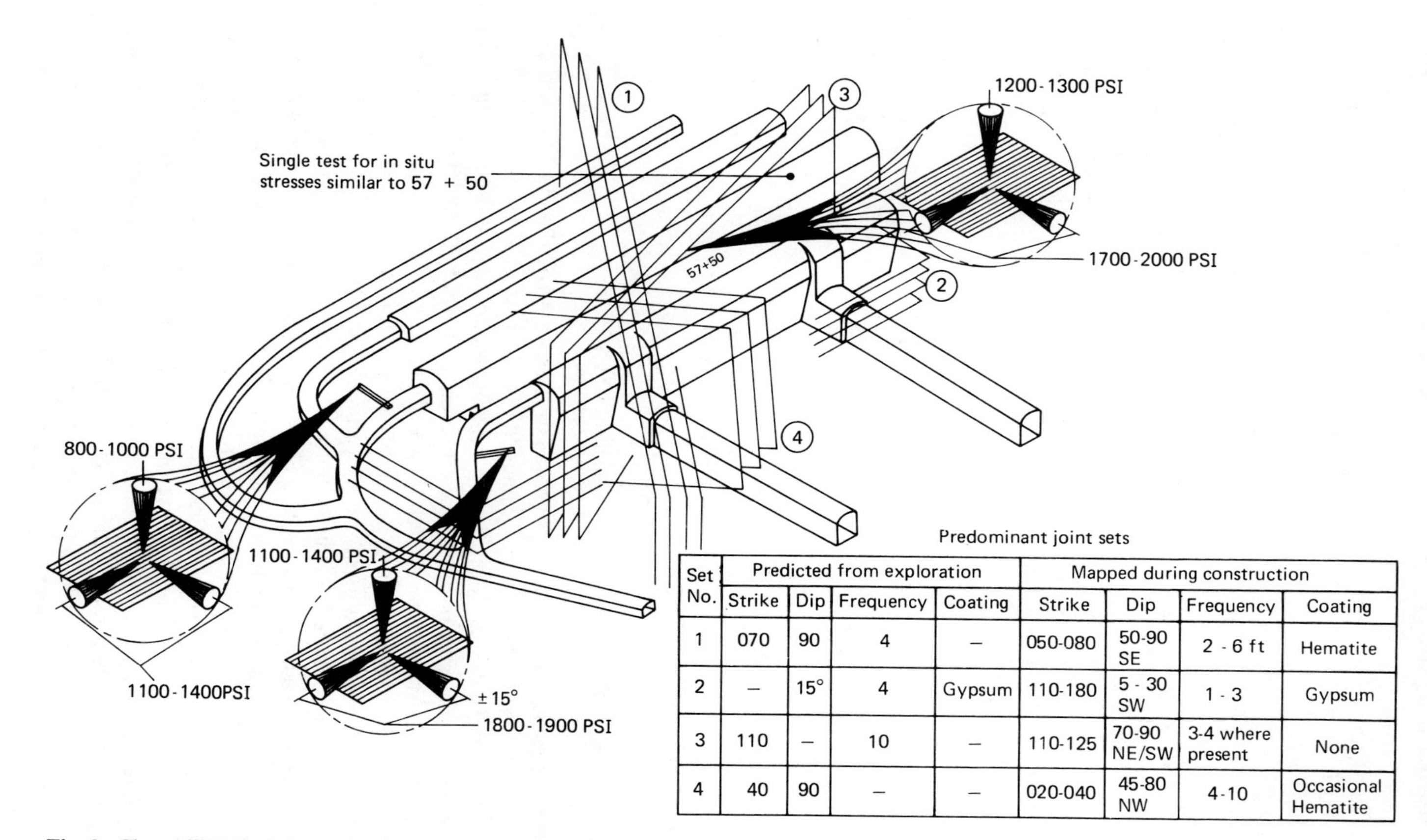


Predominant joint sets

| Set No. | Predicted from exploration | | | | Mapped during construction | | | |
|---|---|---|---|---|---|---|---|---|
| | Strike | Dip | Frequency | Coating | Strike | Dip | Frequency | Coating |
| 1 | 070 | 90 | 4 | – | 050-080 | 50-90 SE | 2 - 6 ft | Hematite |
| 2 | – | 15° | 4 | Gypsum | 110-180 | 5 - 30 SW | 1 - 3 | Gypsum |
| 3 | 110 | – | 10 | – | 110-125 | 70-90 NE/SW | 3-4 where present | None |
| 4 | 40 | 90 | – | – | 020-040 | 45-80 NW | 4-10 | Occasional Hematite |

**Fig. 3.** Churchill Falls, joint systems and *in situ* stresses (After Ref. 15)

at different distances into the rock mass. The geologic mapping allowed the rock bolt pattern and blasting procedures to be modified as needed. The borehole extensometer readings showed the depths behind the arch and walls at which movements of the rock into the cavern were taking place and allowed the measured magnitudes to be compared with the predicted ones. Reference 15 states

> . . . During excavation, 19 multiple-position extensometers were installed in the arch of the powerhouse and 5 in the surge chamber arch to monitor deformations. Downward movements of a maximum of 0.4 inches were recorded, and generally the movement was less than 0.15 inches. . . . Measured movement into the cavities was of the general magnitude predicted by the elastic model, but in several areas of lower quality rock was 2 to 3 times the elastic prediction.

A total of 170 borehole extensometers were installed in the walls and in critical areas where the finite element analysis showed there would be high stresses, such as at intersections of openings and in the draft tube pillars. At several locations the movements exceeded those predicted on the basis of elastic behavior. These observations indicated that within the rock mass there were discontinuous inelastic movements requiring the installation of extra bolts. Although predicted and measured movements were generally less than 0.3 in., the maximum displacement measured before stabilizing with the extra bolts was 0.6 in.

Near the end of the excavation period, when the complex underground excavation geometry had been established, several *in situ* stress measurements were made by overcoring techniques in critical areas where certain values of compressive stresses were needed to balance penstock pressures. The values determined were essentially the same as those predicted by the finite element solution and were judged sufficient to resist the penstock pressure safely.

Thus, the Churchill Falls case history illustrates the manner in which rock mechanics aids in design, in construction monitoring for safety and stability, and in checking on design assumptions. The role of theory is clear; it shows what quantities to monitor, where critical monitoring is necessary, and what values are indicative of elastic and of inelastic behavior. The role of field observations is also clear. The *in situ* tests define the *in situ* state of stress, and the multiple-position borehole extensometers allow the depth of inelastic movement to be determined so that corrective rock bolting can be designed.

## Dupont Circle Subway Station, Washington, D.C.

The Dupont Circle station is a horseshoe-shaped excavation 775 ft long, 77 ft wide, and 44 ft high [16]. Although it is not so large as the Churchill

Falls cavern, its stability during construction was more critical because of its closeness to the surface (65 ft) and its considerable width compared to the thickness of hard rock above the arch, only 25 to 30 ft. Thirty-five feet of weathered rock and soil overlaid the hard rock. The rock quality in the station area was judged fair to good with occasional zones of poor quality. Because of the shallow cover and the weathering that parts of the rock mass had undergone, it was anticipated that the *in situ* horizontal stresses would be small and that careful excavation and support would be required to prevent fallout of joint blocks and possibly complete breakdown of the thin natural rock arch.

The design and construction specifications required that the excavation be done in multiple headings and that the arch in one heading be stabilized by long rock bolts and shotcrete, or by temporary posts if necessary, before an adjacent heading was opened up. By this procedure, segments of the arch were supported and reinforced by the long rock bolts before the arch was opened to its full width. Within a few hours after excavating the arch to its full width over a length of 5 ft, the permanent support of rock bolts, shotcrete, and steel rib was emplaced.

An extensive monitoring system was designed to measure displacements of the rock at various distances above the arch and back from the walls. Borehole extensometers were used [17], some of which were installed from the ground surface before excavation and others from within the excavation, either from the pilot tunnel or close to the face of one of the headings (Fig. 4).

Contrary to the Churchill Falls case, no *in situ* measurements were contemplated or made for determining the *in situ* state of stress or rock mass modulus. Because of the shallow depth and extensive weathering, the ratio of lateral to vertical pressure was judged to be small. Estimates were made of the expected displacements by using equations of elastic theory with grossly simplified boundary conditions. Displacements of $\frac{1}{4}$ to $\frac{1}{2}$ in. were visualized.

The questions to be answered by the instrumentation program, which was conducted by the University of Illinois under contract to Washington Metro, were [17]

1. How do the rock displacements develop as the various excavation sequences are carried out?
2. Are the excavation sequences and initial supports effective in minimizing rock movements?
3. What effect do the major discontinuities have on rock movements and initial support problems at the heading before the chamber is opened to its full width?
4. What is the relation of rock displacement to the loads that develop in the lining when the chamber is opened to its full width?

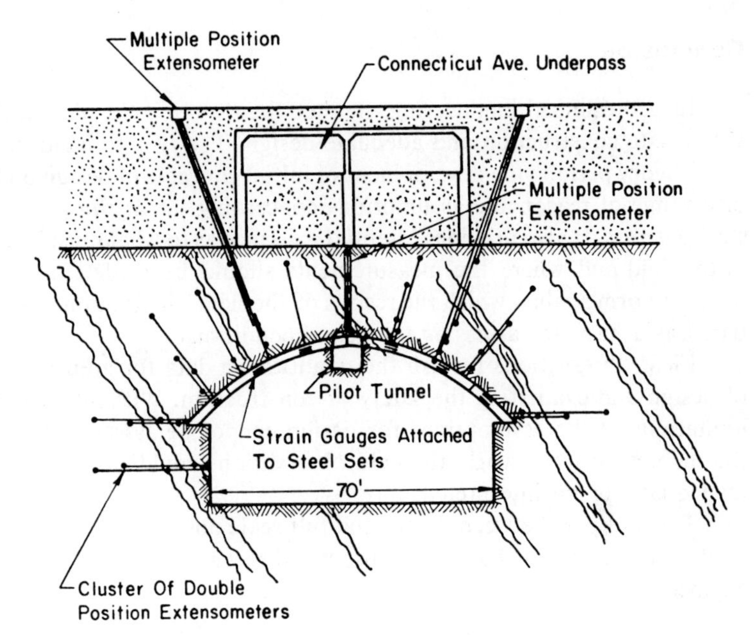


**Fig. 4.** Special test section, Dupont Circle Station, Washington Metro (After Ref. 17)

5. What is the effective stiffness of the blocking and the rock walls as the lining deflects?
6. Are the assumed design loads reasonable?
7. How do the major shear zones affect the distribution of thrust and moment in the lining?

It can thus be seen that the construction monitoring program was designed not only to measure displacements and assess stability but to provide data for checking design assumptions for the Metro station as well as the validity of the general design procedures.

The extensometers gave evidence of loosening and movement of discrete joint blocks and also demonstrated the pattern of continuing loosening at successively greater depths if additional rock bolts of sufficient length were not promptly installed. The magnitude of movements ranged from $\frac{1}{4}$ in. to $1\frac{1}{2}$ or 2 in. where progressive movements occurred. It was found that the rate of movements and the pattern of movements with depth were more significant in assessing the need for greater support than the magnitude of movement alone. It was also noted that continuing movements in the side wall resulted in renewed activity of the arch. Numerous bolts of 20- to 30-ft lengths were added in the side walls for this reason.

## Conclusion

In geotechnical engineering, neither theory nor field observations can assure safe construction and adequate design. The two go hand in hand.

Theory permits the development of initial concepts of design on the basis of a range of reasonable assumptions concerning the *in situ* properties and state of stress. It also provides essential guidance as to what must be measured in the field and where the measurements should be made. Finally, it furnishes a norm against which the results of the field observations can be compared as a basis for assessing the actual conditions.

Field observations furnish the quantitative data for adjusting the basis of design and evaluating the safety of construction. Without such data, the limitations of the assumptions for design cannot be assessed. Yet, without the theoretical framework, the field observations could easily be irrelevant, inadequate, or misinterpreted.

The interplay between theory and full-scale observations is characteristic of all civil engineering but is perhaps most direct and apparent in geotechnical engineering.

## References


1. TERZAGHI, K., "Relation Between Soil Mechanics and Foundation Engineering," *Proc. 1st Int. Conf. Soil Mech., Cambridge*, Vol. 3, 1936, pp. 13–18.
2. MEEM, J. C., "Pressure, Resistance, and Stability of Earth," *Trans. ASCE*, Vol. 70, (1910, pp. 352–411.
3. TERZAGHI, K., "Old Earth-Pressure Theories and New Test Results," *Eng. News-Rec.*, Vol. 85, No. 14, 1920, pp. 632–637.
4. TERZAGHI, K., "Large Retaining-Wall Tests," *Eng. News-Rec.*, Vol. 112, No, 5, 1934, pp. 136–140.
5. SPILKER, A., "Mitteilung über die messung der Kräfte in einer baugruben aussteifung," *Bautechnik*, Vol. 15, 1937, pp. 16–18.
6. TERZAGHI, K., "General Wedge Theory of Earth Pressure," *Trans. ASCE*, Vol. 106, 1941, pp. 68–97.
7. GRAFTIO, H., "Some Features in Connection with the Foundation of Svir III Hydroelectric Power Development," *Proc. 1st Int. Conf. Soil Mech., Cambridge*, Vol. 1, 1936, pp. 284–290.
8. FITZ HUGH, M. M., J. S. MILLER, and K. TERZAGHI, "Shipways with Cellular Walls on a Marl Foundation," *Trans. ASCE*, Vol. 112, 1947, pp. 298–324.
9. PECK, R. B., "Advantages and Limitations of the Observational Method in Soil Mechanics," *Géotechnique*, Vol. 19, 1969, pp. 171–187.
10. TERZAGHI, K., "Discussions on: K. John, An approach to Rock Mechanics," *Proc. ASCE*, Vol. 89, No. SM 1, 1963, pp. 295–300.
11. JOHN, K., "An Approach to Rock Mechanics," *Proc. ASCE*, Vol. 88, No. SM 4, 1962, pp. 1–30.

12. DEERE, D. U., A. J. HENDRON, F. D. PATTON, and E. J. CORDING, "Design of Surface and Near-Surface Construction in Rock," in *Failure and Breakage of Rock*, Fairhurst, ed., AIME, New York. 1968, pp. 237–302.
13. SEMPLE, R. M., A. J. HENDRON, and G. MESRI, "The Effect of Time-Dependent Properties of Altered Rock on Tunnel Support Requirements, Abstract," in *Proceedings, 2nd Rapid Excavation and Tunneling Conference*, AIME, New York, 1974, pp. 1371–1372.
14. SEMPLE, R. M., "The Effect of Time-Dependent Properties of Altered Rock on Tunnel Support Requirements," Ph. D. thesis, University of Illinois at Urbana-Champaign, Urbana, 1973, 215 pp.
15. BENSON, R. P., R. J. CONLON, A. H. MERRITT, P. JOLI-COEUR, and D. U. DEERE, "Rock Mechanics at Churchill Falls," in *Underground Rock Chambers*, ASCE, New York, 1971, pp. 407–486.
16. BAWA, K. S., "Design and Instrumentation of an Underground Station for Washington Metro System," in *Large Permanent Underground Openings*, Brekke, T. and F. Jörstad, eds. Universitets for Laget, Oslo, 1970, pp. 31–42.
17. CORDING E. J., and D. U. DEERE, "Rock Tunnel Supports and Field Measurements," in *Proceedings, North American Rapid Excavation and Tunneling Conference*, AIME New York, 1972, pp. 601–622.

# Soil-Structure Interaction Effects in the Design of Nuclear Power Plants

H. BOLTON SEED,* ROBERT V. WHITMAN,† AND JOHN LYSMER‡

## Introduction

One of the most discussed aspects of the design of nuclear power plants in recent years has been that of evaluating the effects of soil-structure interaction on the seismic response. In its broadest sense, this involves the assessment of the relationship between the characteristics of the earthquake ground motions, the local soil and geologic conditions at the site, and the response of the structure to the ground motions. Two important aspects of this assessment involve the following considerations:

1. The local soil and geologic conditions may affect the characteristics of the ground motions developed at a site, both in terms of the peak acceleration developed, the frequency content of the motions, and the spatial distribution of the motion characteristics, and it is desirable to evaluate the possible extent of these effects in order to establish meaningful design criteria.
2. The structures will interact with the soils below and adjacent to them during the earthquake, and it is necessary to evaluate the effects of this interaction on the motions developed in the structures.

In considering these aspects of seismic design it is necessary to keep in mind the fact that soils are generally nonuniform in characteristics due to

*Professor of Civil Engineering, University of California, Berkeley, California.
†Professor of Civil Engineering, Massachusetts Institute of Technology, Cambridge, Massachusetts.
‡Associate Professor of Civil Engineering, University of California, Berkeley, California.

their mode of formation, that their properties as measured in laboratory tests are invariably influenced to some extent by boring and sampling operations, and that measurements of *in situ* characteristics cannot usually be performed with a very high degree of accuracy. Thus, considerable judgment is required to determine representative soil characteristics, and it will usually be necessary to consider ranges of properties for analysis purposes.

At the present time there appears to be widespread agreement that the characteristics of the ground surface motions developed at any given site are influenced by the local soil conditions [2,8,12,13,31,40–42,48] and that the ground motions used for design should be specified by a site-dependent spectrum [17,24,30,34,43,45], developed at a point on the ground surface in the free field. However, because many nuclear power plants are constructed on rock or stiff soil conditions, a single spectrum shape is applicable for the majority of cases considered [32, 52], and the actual design motion spectrum is scaled in accordance with the peak design acceleration considered appropriate for the seismicity of the plant site.

Having thus specified the design motion, the problem of accounting for soil-structure interaction may be defined as follows (see Fig. 1): Given the earthquake ground motions that would occur on the surface of the ground if the structure were not present (the control or design motions), find the dynamic response of the structure.

In the case of a structure supported at the ground surface, little need be known about the variation of ground motions with depth, but for embedded structures, some knowledge of this variation is essential. Other desirable features of a high-quality analysis are

1. It should consider the three-dimensional nature of the problem.
2. It should consider the effects of nearby structures on each other.

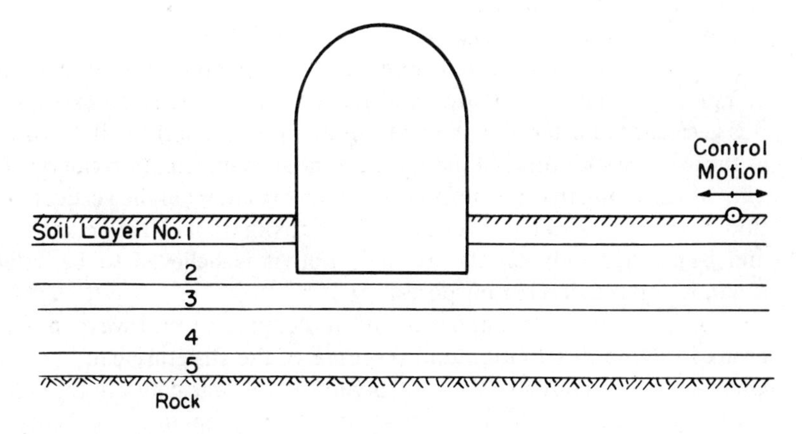


**Fig. 1.** Soil structure interaction problem

3. It should consider the variation of soil characteristics with depth.
4. It should consider the nonlinear stress-strain and energy-absorbing characteristics of the soils.

The potential significance of all these features has not yet been fully ascertained. However, they provide a basis for considering the strengths and weaknesses of analysis procedures currently available and thereby enable the engineer to select a method of analysis appropriate for the structure under investigation.

## Methods of Analyzing Soil-Structure Interaction Effects for Embedded Nuclear Power Plants

The methods of analysis that have been used for analyzing soil-structure interaction effects on the seismic response of nuclear power plants embedded in the ground can be divided into two basic approaches: complete interaction analyses and inertial interaction analyses. The general features of these two basic approaches are outlined below.

### *Complete Interaction Analysis*

The approach involves the solution to the complete problem specified in Fig. 1 and illustrated schematically in Fig. 2(a). In fact the soil-structure system is subjected to earthquake ground motions which vary from point to point even in rock well below the structure and travel in some unknown way across the base of the soil-structure system.

This admittedly complex problem is usually idealized for purposes of analysis so that motions in the near-surface soils are considered to be due to vertical propagation of motions from below, producing a uniform pattern of motions in the near-surface soils, as shown in Fig. 2(b). Solution of this problem provides an idealized complete solution, and it is only this degree of complexity which can be considered at the present time. To achieve a solution, it is necessary to determine the motions at all points in the soil deposit as well as those in the structure. At the present time such information can be obtained only by assuming that the motions in the soil result from the vertical propagation of shear waves. This is clearly an approximation of the actual condition and is justified only on the grounds that it is believed to be sufficiently accurate for engineering purposes.

On the basis of this approximation there are several ways in which the ground motion distribution and response of the structure can be evaluated. One way is to deconvolve the control motion to some depth in the soil profile such as a soil-rock interface. One-dimensional amplification theory can be used for this purpose [10,38,39]. Then the motion computed at this depth is

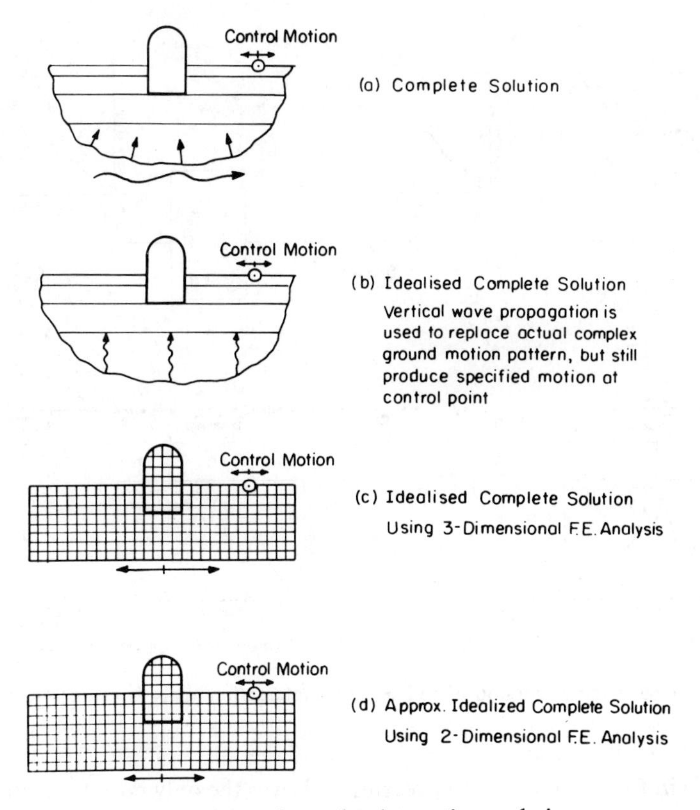


**Fig. 2.** Types of complete interaction analysis

used as input to a three-dimensional mathematical model of the overlying soil structure, as illustrated in Fig. 3 [44]. Another way is to compute transfer functions relating the motions and forces at desired points in the soil or structure to the control motion applied at a point on the surface of the soil well away from the structure [23]. In either case the analysis would be done iteratively to allow for the strain-dependent nature of the nonlinear soil characteristics [38,41]. In each iteration the analysis is linear, but the soil properties are adjusted from iteration to iteration until the computed strains are compatible with the soil properties. In principle, a number of different solution techniques might be used to accomplish the necessary numerical work. Today, only finite element methods [28] [Fig. 2(c)] are readily adaptable for accomplishing all the necessary steps, including iteration on the level of strains. However, finite-difference methods and the method of characteristics [46] have also been proposed for analysis of these problems.

A somewhat more approximate version of this analysis is obtained if the soil-structure system is analyzed as a two-dimensional finite-element system

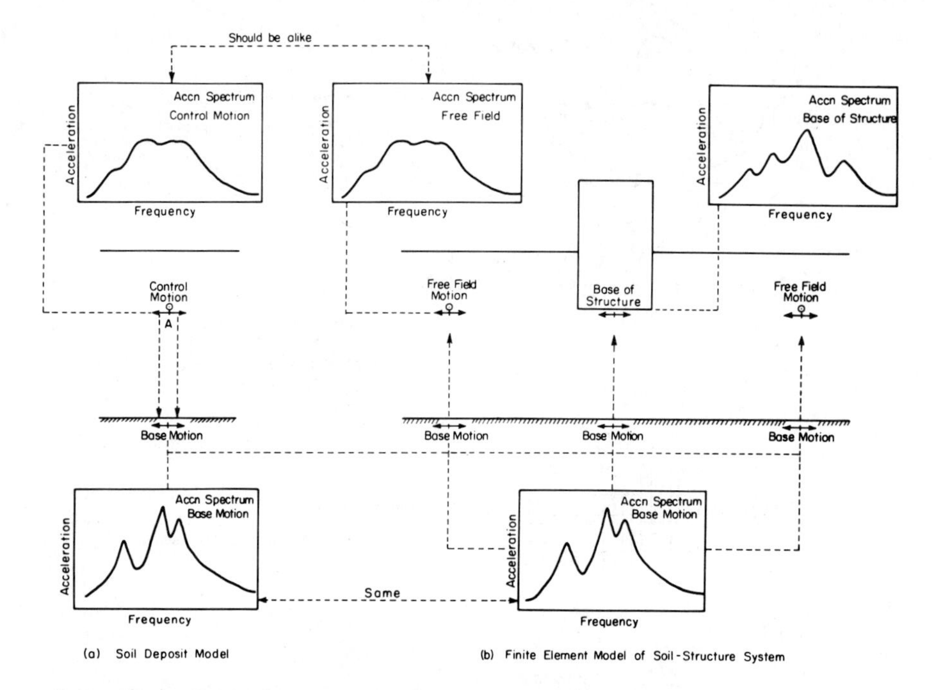


**Fig. 3.** Schematic representation of soil-structure interaction analysis using finite element model

as shown in Fig. 2(d). Until very recently this was the only possible method of obtaining a complete solution for embedded structures, and this approach has been widely used for analysis purposes.

At the present time, idealized versions of the complete interaction analysis (idealized in the sense that ground motions are considered to be some approximate form of the actual ground motions) can be made for the cases shown in Table 1.

Comparative studies using these different approaches suggest that computer costs may vary widely depending on the complexity of the analysis used and the efficiency of the computer program adopted; furthermore, these comparisons show that it is usually possible to model three-dimensional effects using two-dimensional systems. Thus, the two-dimensional analytical model with three-dimensional energy-absorbing boundaries shown in Fig. 4 appears to provide a sufficiently accurate method of analysis for virtually any design condition [27].

However, in all cases it is important that the analytical model be formulated so as to preserve the frequencies and waveforms of primary interest. For this reason it is essential to recognize that the nature of damping in soil makes

Table 1

| *Idealized Ground Motion* | *Structure-Soil Geometry* | *Soil Conditions* |
|---|---|---|
| Vertically propagating body waves | Three-dimensional axisymmetric systems with extensive soil deposit [5–6] | Layered soil systems having any distribution of moduli and material damping simulating nonlinear behavior |
| | Three-dimensional axisymmetric systems with transmitting boundaries to represent extensive soil deposits [21] | Layered soil systems having any distribution of moduli and material damping simulating nonlinear behavior |
| | Three-dimensional systems with multiple buildings having approximately the same lateral dimension and lying within elongated strip in plan [18,27,29] | Layered soil systems having any distribution of moduli and material damping simulating nonlinear behavior |
| | Two-dimensional plane-strain systems with extensive soil deposit or with transmitting boundaries to represent extensive soil deposit [28,44] | Layered soil systems having any distribution of moduli and material damping simulating nonlinear behavior |
| Vertically propagating body waves traveling along horizontal base | Two-dimensional plane-strain systems with extensive soil deposit [50,51] | Layered soil systems having any distribution of moduli and material damping simulating nonlinear behavior |
| Horizontally propagating waves of specified form on the vertical section | Two-dimensional plane-strain systems with extensive soil deposit [19] | Layered soil systems having any distribution of moduli and material damping simulating nonlinear behavior |

some forms of solution more suitable than others. The energy loss within soil results primarily from hysteresis, and for a given strain level the energy loss per cycle is more or less independent of frequency. To simulate this behavior using linear viscoelasticity, it is necessary to have viscosity coefficients which vary inversely with frequency. This in turn implies the necessity of solution in the frequency domain using the techniques of Fourier analysis. Solutions in the time domain, using Rayleigh damping, may not properly represent damping over a broad band of frequency content.

It may be noted that a complete analysis of the types described above,

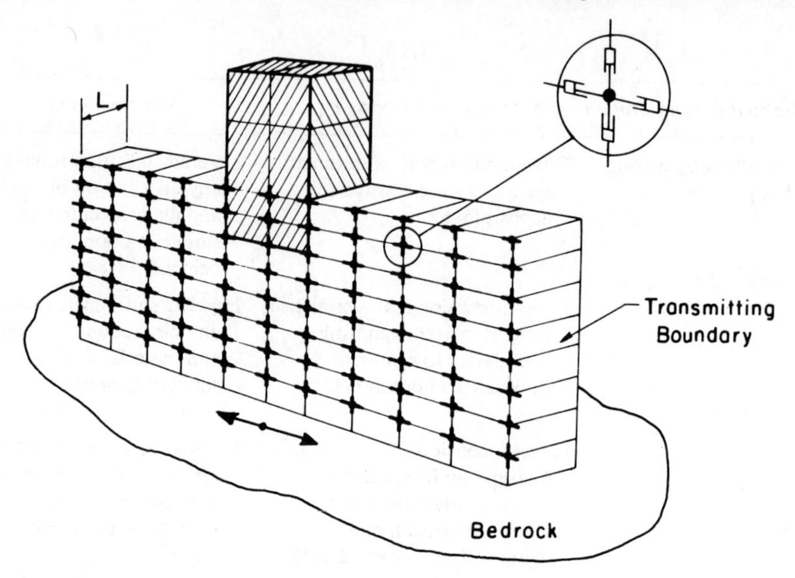


**Fig. 4.** Schematic view of a simplified 3-D model

involving the assessment of ground motions in the soil below and adjacent to a structure as well as those of the structure itself, can also be carried out in two steps [54], as indicated in Fig. 5:

1. In the first step, it is assumed that the structure has no mass but has stiffness and damping. The acceleration time history of each point of the structure is computed as well as the forces in the structure.

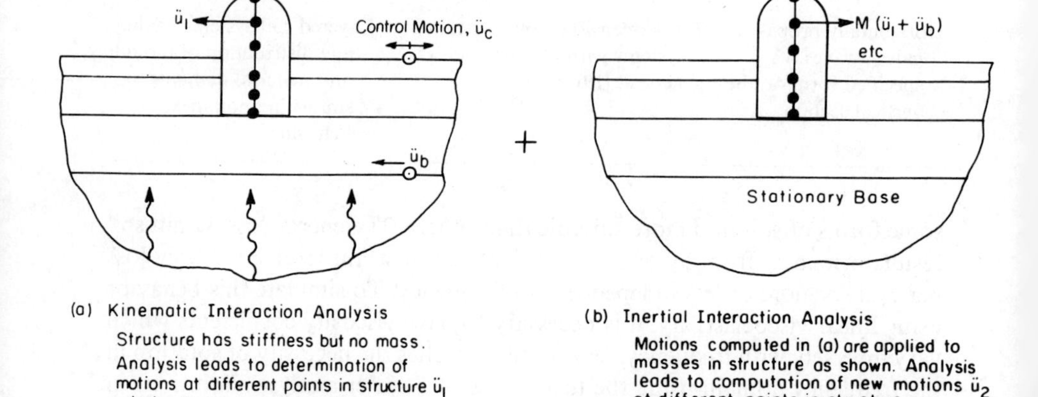


**Fig. 5.** Idealized complete solution—two step method using kinematic and inertial interaction analyses

2. In the second step, time-varying inertial forces are applied at each point of the structure; the force at each point is the product of the mass at the point and the acceleration determined by adding the acceleration determined in step 1 to the base rock acceleration. The motions of and forces in the structure, as caused by this loading, are computed and added to those computed in step 1.

Note that the mass and stiffness of the soil and the stiffness of the structure are considered in the analyses in both steps. This superposition principle of course applies only for a linear system, that is, to each step of an iterative procedure.

This superposition theorem may also be expressed mathematically as follows. The equations of motion in matrix form are

$$[M]\{\ddot{u}\} + [K]\{u\} = -[M]\ddot{u}_g \tag{1}$$

where $[M]$ is the mass matrix; $[K]$ is stifiness matrix involving complex, frequency-dependent terms; $\{u\}$ is a vector of relative motions between points in the soil or structure and the top of the rock; and $u_g$ is the motion of the rock. This set of equations may be broken into two parts:

$$[M_{so}]\{\ddot{u}_1\} + [K]\{u_1\} = -[M_{so}]\ddot{u}_g, \tag{2}$$

$$[M]\{u_2\} + [K]\{u_2\} = -[M_{st}]\{\ddot{u}_1 + \ddot{u}_g\}, \tag{3}$$

where $u = u_1 + u_2$, $[M_{so}]$ is the mass matrix assuming that the structure has no mass but that the soil does have mass, and $[M_{st}]$ is the mass matrix assuming that the structure has mass but that the soil has no mass. By definition,

$$[M_{so}] + [M_{st}] = [M].$$

$u_1$ is the motion (relative to the motion of the rock) if the structure has no mass, and $u_2$ is the additional relative motion caused by the mass (and hence dynamic response) of the structure. Note that Eq. (2) describes the problem depicted in part (a) of Fig. 5, whereas Eq. (3) describes the problem depicted in part (b). Addition of Eqs. (2) and (3) gives Eq. (1).

The presence of the structure modifies the free-field ground motions in both parts of the two-step analysis depicted in Fig. 5. In the first step [part (a) of the figure] the horizontal motions of the base of the structure and on the side of the structure at ground level are different from the motions at the corresponding elevations in the free field. In addition, there is also rocking of the structure-soil interface. These modifications to the free-field ground motions are the result of *kinematic interaction.* Additional motions of the structure-soil interface occur in the second part of the analysis [part (b) of Fig. 5]; these additional motions are the result of *inertial interaction.* Adding the motions computed in the two steps gives the correct total motions.

The superposition principle described in the previous paragraphs is not necessarily of great usefulness in simplying calculations. Clearly, the first step might just as well be performed including the mass of the structure, making it a complete interaction analysis and thereby eliminating the need for step 2. However, the main value of the principle lies in the insight which it gives to the phenomenon of soil-structure interaction, as illustrated by the following discussion.

#### *Inertial Interaction Analysis*

The second basic approach for analyzing soil-structure interaction effects is that in which kinematic interaction effects are ignored or approximated so that only inertial interaction need be included in the analysis. The dynamic forces applied to the structure are then simply the product of the design ground motions and the mass of the structure (see Fig. 6). Alternatively, the same analysis can be made by imagining that the foundation is supported by springs and that the support for the springs experiences the design ground motion. The two ways shown in Fig. 6 for depicting the loading on the structure are mathematically equivalent if the base of the structure can be considered rigid.

It is apparent that this approach is perfectly justified in the case of a surface structure on a linear-elastic material since kinematic interaction effects are zero in this case (if the input consists of vertically propagating body waves) and the motions in the structure are exactly equal to those produced by the control motion. The method is also good for surface structures on nonlinear soils if the properties of the soil in the inertial interaction model are selected to be compatible with the strains developed by the ground motions. Thus, any correct mathematical model for inertial interaction effects only will provide good results for a surface structure—the validity depending only on the accuracy of the assumptions made in establishing the model.

For embedded structures, however, kinematic interaction effects are not negligible, and for these conditions, the assumption that an inertial interac-

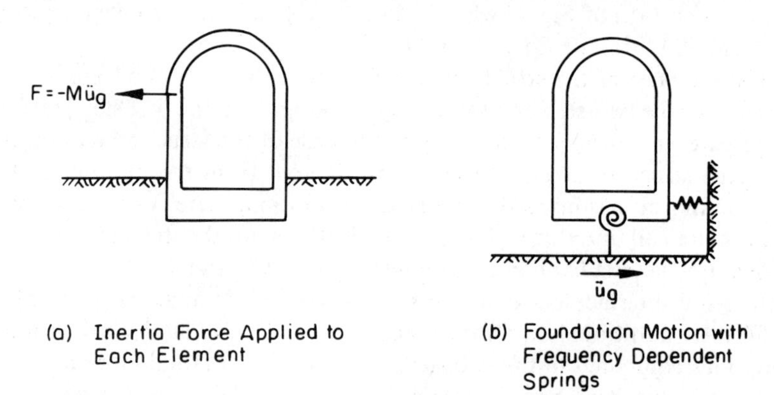


**Fig. 6.** Equivalent formulations of inertial interaction analysis

tion analysis can provide accurate results is formally equivalent to assuming that, for the kinematic interaction analysis, the soil above the base of the structure is rigid, as illustrated in Fig. 7; in this case the motions developed in the structure will be equal to those caused by the control motion as before. Intuitively, an inertial interaction analysis treats the control motion as some undefined average motion in the free field around the structure.

Once it has been decided to use the control motion as the exciting force for the inertial interaction analysis, there are several ways in which the soil can be represented. These are listed in Table 2. The following comments also apply:

1. A finite element mesh may be coupled directly to the mathematical model of the structure, and the response of the entire system may be analyzed together. With this method, it is not necessary to assume that the structure-soil interface is rigid; the actual flexibility of the foundation may be included in the model. However, if this approach is followed, it is essentially just as simple to make a complete interaction analysis.
2. Frequency-dependent foundation compliance functions [15,20,22, 25,35,53] may be used. It is usual to assume that the translation mode and the rocking mode of the soil-structure interface are uncoupled in which case only one function is needed for each type of motion that the soil-structure interface may experience. This method is strictly applicable only when the soil-structure interface moves as a rigid body. Exact stiffness functions may be obtained by
   (a) Using a finite element mesh to represent the effect of embedment and vertical variation in soil properties [22].
   (b) If the structure rests at or near the surface, using the appropriate theory for a viscoelastic half-space or a viscoelastic layered system. The half-space and layered system theories may also be used to generate approximate functions for embedded structures [4]. However, further approximations must necessarily be introduced even for near-surface structures if the half-space theory used for analysis does not include consideration of the material damping in the soil.
3. Frequency-independent foundation springs and dashpots may be used [37,49]. Various methods may be used to estimate these approximate representations of the soil behavior.

In general, inertial interaction analyses have usually been based on theories in which the soil is represented as some type of half-space. Until very recently it was only possible to represent the soil as an elastic half-space with one or two layers and no internal damping characteristics. This degree of idealization led to a high degree of approximation in the practical application

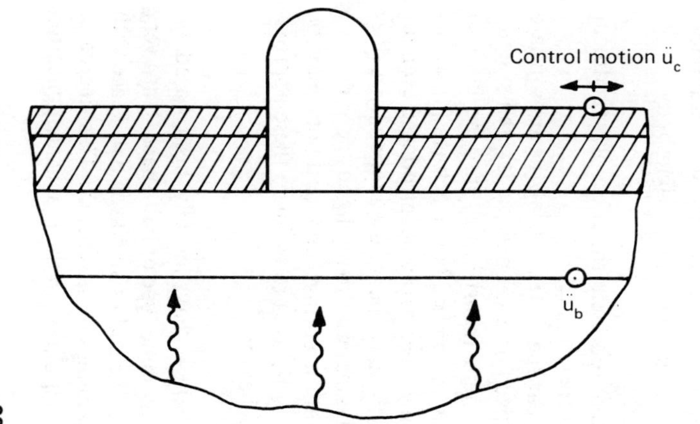


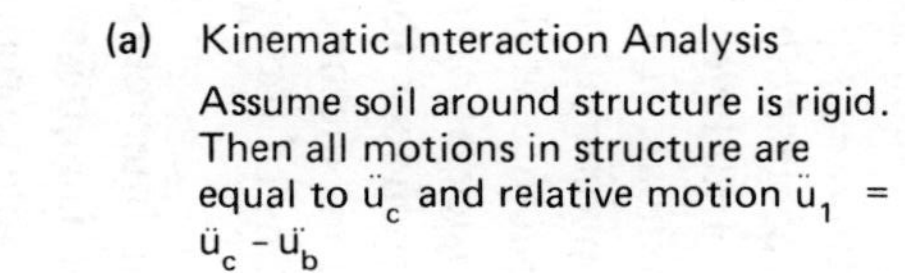

(a) Kinematic Interaction Analysis

Assume soil around structure is rigid. Then all motions in structure are equal to $\ddot{u}_c$ and relative motion $\ddot{u}_1 = \ddot{u}_c - \ddot{u}_b$

+

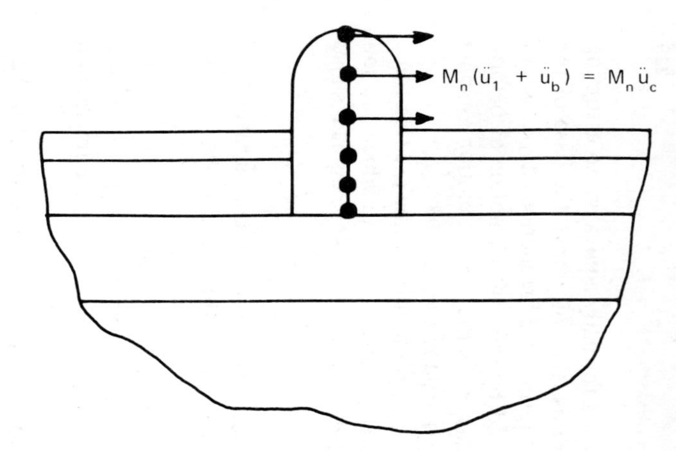


(b) Inertial Interaction Analysis

Apply control motions to masses in structure as shown. Compute resulting response. Results vary depending on method of analysis used
e.g. Finite element analysis
Impedance functions
Interaction springs, etc
and consideration of soil properties
e.g. Elastic or visco-elastic
Constant or strain-dependent moduli, etc
Other than finite element analyses, only approximate solutions are available for embedded structures.

**Fig. 7.** Approximate solutions—inertial interaction only

**Table 2**
**Representations of Soil for Inertial Interaction Anlaysis**

1. Finite element mesh coupled directly to model of structure.
2. Frequency-dependent foundation compliance functions
   a. From finite element model.
   b. From theory for viscoelastic uniform or layered half-space or elastic strata.
3. Frequency-independent springs and dashpots
   a. Deduced from frequency-dependent compliance functions.
   b. Using formulas applicable to typical situations.
   c. Derived from tests and experience.

of the results. However, in recent years analyses have been developed in which the half-space can be represented by a multilayered viscoelastic material [14,25,53]. These new theories can also be used in conjunction with equivalent linear soil properties to approximate nonlinear soil behavior as in the "complete interaction analysis" approach. It is important, however, in order to obtain good results, that the analytical procedure should correctly simulate the soil layering and the hysteretic nature of damping in the soils; thus, a viscoelastic solution, with viscosity inversely proportional to frequency, should be used.

Replacing the soil by "static springs" and dashpots permits great simplifications in an inertial analysis of a structure-soil system [55]. Not only is the size of the computer program greatly reduced, but it is possible to use simplified, approximate techniques of solution—such as modal analysis with weighted modal damping [36,49]. If good judgment is used in the selection of the springs and dashpots, good results can be obtained. However, errors in assessement of spring constants, damping values, and the mass to be used in the analysis, particularly where the mass of excavated soil is considerable, can lead to large differences in the computed response, and guides to judgment in this respect are urgently needed [44].

Usually the value of a foundation stiffness function at zero frequency is used for the spring constant. By introducing an effective inertia, a good parabolic fit can be made to actual stiffness functions over some range of frequencies; however, the effective inertia suitable at small frequencies may lead to a considerable underestimate of foundation stiffness at high frequencies. For this reason effective inertias should not be used. The damping portion of the foundation stiffness function can be made correct only at one frequency; usually this is taken as the fundamental frequency of the soil-structure system. Fortunately, many of the frequency-dependent foundation damping curves are more or less constant over a wide range of frequencies, especially when the effect of the internal damping within the soil is included.

Nevertheless, considerable difficulties may be introduced through the use of approximations in the inertial interaction type of analysis, for example, in the selection of appropriate values for spring constants and damping factors to be used in the more approximate versions of the method. Spring constants are sometimes determined by the use of formulas developed for foundation vibration problems or by methods neglecting strain compatibility in selecting a modulus for the foundation soils. Thus, wide variations in spring constants can be determined by different engineering organizations. Similarly, analytical procedures do not always include the effects of material damping so that some approximate estimate of the effects of this factor must be made. Overall damping values have often been estimated very conservatively (10% damping for both horizontal and rocking vibrations has commonly been used in the past) so that the computed results are quite conservative.

It is especially important therefore in using inertial interaction analyses to evaluate soil-structure interaction effects that special care be given to the selection of methods for determining these parameters, that computations be made for potential variations in these parameters, and that the results be evaluated with a considerable degree of engineering judgment.

When using an inertial interaction analysis, it is necessary to use some auxiliary analysis to determine the appropriate modulus and damping. One possible form of auxiliary analysis is a one-dimensional amplification analysis. The damping from such an analysis will in many cases not differ much from the damping values computed near the structure in a complete interaction analysis.

## Comparison of Methods of Analysis

The foregoing discussion has emphasized that the commonly encountered methods of analysis are distinguished by the way in which the input ground motion is treated, that is, whether or not kinematic interaction is explicitly considered. No distinction has been made on the basis of the technique of analysis, that is, continuum or finite-element methods. Indeed, it has been shown that both continuum and finite-element methods may, in principle, be used with either the complete or inertial interaction methods, though, in fact, any type of complete interaction analysis for embedded structures can only be made using finite-element procedures at the present time.

It is further apparent from the preceding discussion that the essential difference, at the present time, between the idealized complete interaction analysis and the inertial interaction analysis lies in their treatment of embedded structures.

For surface structures good results can be obtained by either method of analysis provided it is formulated properly and takes into account the three-dimensional nature of the problem, the influence of adjacent structures, the stratification of the soil and variation of the properties with depth, and the nonlinear nature of the stress-strain and damping characteristics of the soils. However, it is now within the capability of both approaches to account for all these factors satisfactorily, and thus either approach can provide excellent results. This should not be construed to mean that all results for surface structures are satisfactory in accuracy. There are so many approximations of the best analysis in general use that the results of any analysis whether of the complete or inertial interaction variety should be scrutinized carefully to ensure that it conforms to the best standards for such analyses, as outlined above.

For embedded structures, the complete interaction analysis is clearly superior from a theoretical viewpoint in that, provided the analysis is carried out properly, the complete interaction analysis comes closest to representing, in a rational way, all the important aspects of the problem. Its principal limitation is the cost of the analysis, but this factor is becoming less significant with the development of more efficient computer programs. It is also apparent that there are some aspects of the variation of the free-field motion with distance that the typical complete interaction analysis does not simulate correctly. Free-field motions do not consist simply of *SH* waves propagating vertically, and one-dimensional amplification analysis may overestimate the rate at which peak acceleration and the amplitude of certain frequency components decrease with depth. Thus, to obtain reliable design motions it is necessary to limit the rate at which these characteristics of ground motions are reduced with depth by applying good engineering judgment to the results of such computations.

At the same time it is important to recognize that there is a growing body of observational data to show that ground motions do indeed decrease significantly with depth and that failure to recognize this leads to undue conservatism in evaluations of structural response. Figure 8, for example, shows the marked decrease in peak acceleration with depth of embedment for motions recorded at the bases of structures in Tokyo in the Higashi-Matsuyama earthquake of July 1, 1968 [33]. The marked differences in spectral accelerations with depth as obtained by averaging spectra for several ground surface records and several records obtained at a depth of 40 ft are also readily apparent.

More recently records of ground motion were obtained in the buildings of the Humboldt Bay Nuclear Power Station in the Ferndale, California, earthquake of June 7, 1975. Values of peak acceleration recorded at the ground surface (0.26$g$ and 0.35$g$) were substantially higher than those recorded at the base of the refueling building (0.13$g$) at a depth of about 80 ft, as shown in Fig. 9. It is interesting to note that these peak accelerations are almost exactly the same as those computed by an "idealized complete interaction analysis" of this plant, using a two-dimensional analytical model

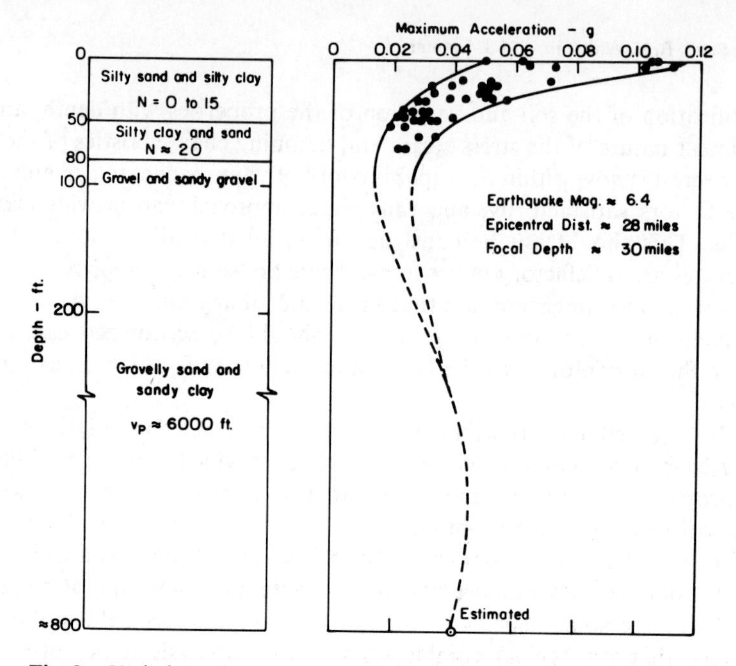


**Fig. 8a.** Variation of recorded maximum acceleration with depth for building in Tokyo—Higashi-Matsuyama earthquake, 1 July, 1968

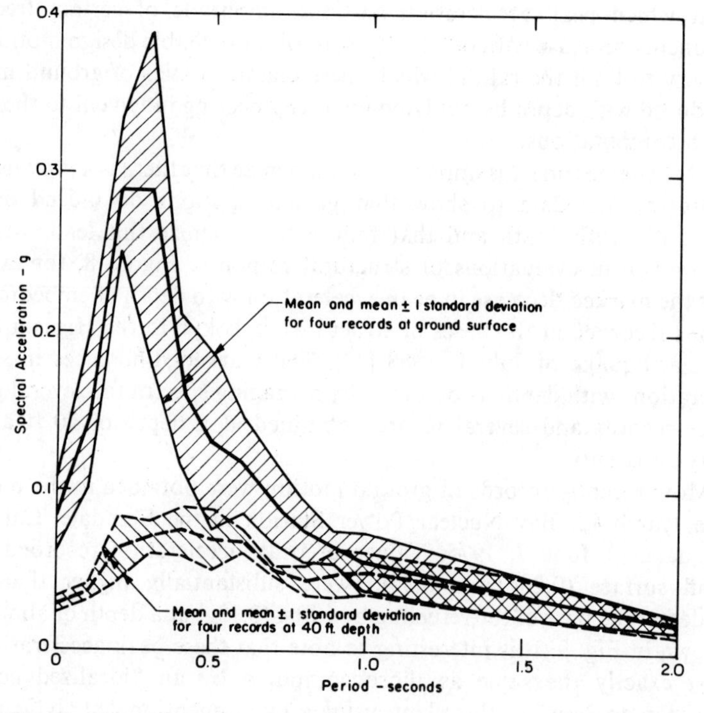


**Fig. 8b.** Comparison of response spectra for motions recorded at ground surface and 40 ft depth

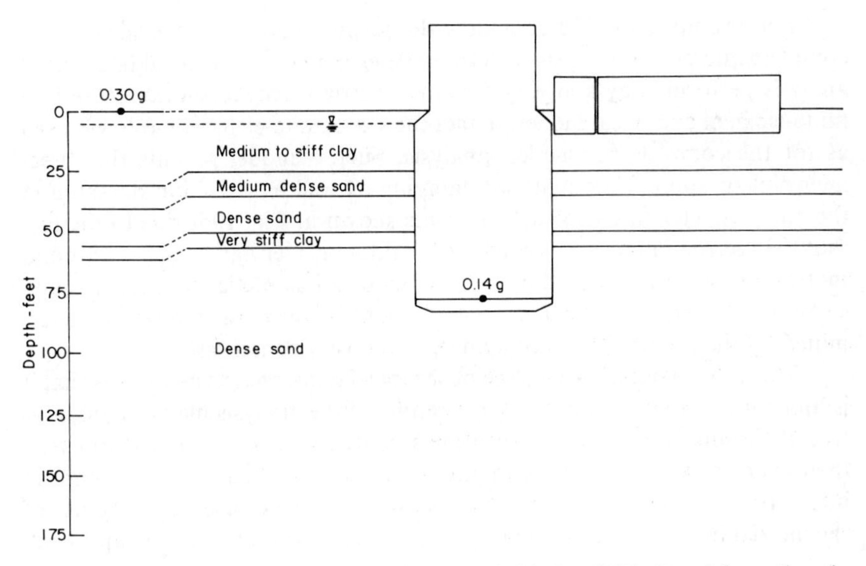


**Fig. 9.** Maximum accelerations recorded at Humboldt Bay NPS—Ferndale earthquake, June 7, 1975

and the procedure illustrated in Fig. 3, made about 6 months before the earthquake occurred. Preliminary studies indicate that a similarly good comparison between computed and recorded base motion response spectra for the refueling building may be anticipated.

It should also be noted that there is a growing body of analytical data indicating that although ground motions do not consist simply of vertically propagating shear waves, but undoubtedly include shear waves propagating at an angle to the vertical and Rayleigh waves propagating horizontally, the effects of these other forms of wave motions are similar to those of vertically propagating shear waves. For example, Chen [9], using a theory developed by Lysmer [26], found almost identical surface motion characteristics in computing surface motions by shear wave analyses and Rayleigh wave analyses, while other similarities in effects are reported by Tazime [47], Haskell [16], Allam [1], Asada [3], and Dobry et al. [11]. Thus, it seems likely that ground motions computed by vertical wave propagation theory can provide an adequate representation of the general seismic environment and the variations in the characteristics of ground motions with depth.

On the other hand, the value of an inertial interaction analysis for embedded structures is clearly limited since it omits this important part of the problem, i.e., kinematic interaction. Since this analysis thus fails to consider the variation of ground motion with depth, both observational data (see Figs. 8 and 9) and theoretical considerations show that it usually tends to be conservative. For deeply embedded structures this conservatism may be quite significant.

For example, Fig. 10 compares the response spectra determined by a complete interaction analysis with those determined by an inertial interaction analysis performed by applying dynamic inertia forces to the structure in a finite-element analytical model; in fact the same finite-element mesh was used as for the complete interaction analysis. Such a model permits the direct inclusion of appropriate material damping as well as radiation damping in the analysis. The difference in the results shown in Fig. 10 is due to the fact that the inertial interaction analysis does not consider any change in ground motion with depth, as would be determined by a kinematic interaction analysis or a complete interaction analysis. It may be seen that the results determined by the inertial interaction analysis are very conservative.

Thus, the major disadvantage of the inertial interaction analysis is that it is difficult to know by how much the results of the analysis may be conservative. If the aim is to obtain an accurate assessment of probable performance, then even more judgement is required with its use than for the complete interaction approach. If unknown conservatism can be accepted, then use of the inertial interaction approach may be an acceptable engineering approach

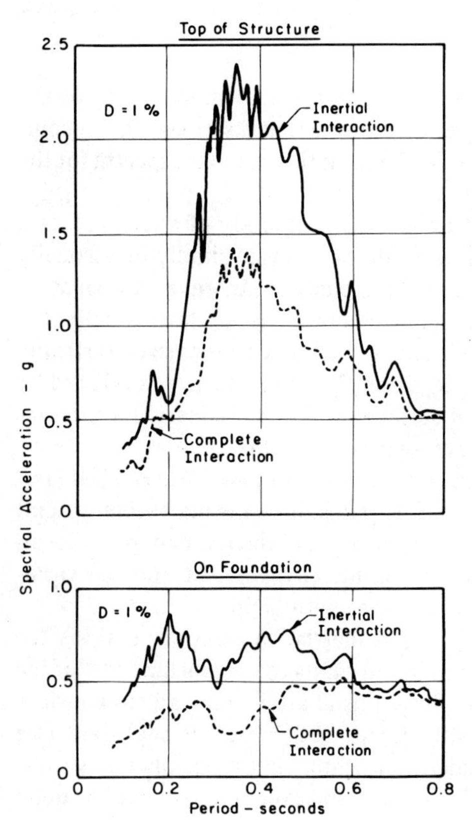


**Fig. 10.** Comparison of response spectra for complete and inertial interaction analyses. Structure embedded at 55 ft depth. Data courtesy E. Kausel, Stone and Webster Engineering Corporation.

for design purposes. The major advantage of the inertial interaction method is that it readily permits the use of approximations which greatly reduce computational time and expense.

In the long run, it is to be hoped that approximate and simplified methods—possibly some version of the inertial interaction analysis—can be used for design analyses with greater knowledge of accuracy and conservatism than at present. To achieve this goal it is first necessary to generate the "most correct" solutions for a number of problems, which can then be used as a standard of comparison to judge the correctness and reliability of simpler, approximate analyses. The "most correct" solutions for embedded structures are at this time obtained by idealized complete three-dimensional interaction analyses using the finite-element method. For each problem a series of such analyses is necessary so that parameters may be varied to cover uncertainty in the choice of these parameters. The series should also include analyses made with several different techniques of modeling and solution, so that the shortcomings of individual techniques can be understood. Then judgment must be applied to determining the "most correct" interpretation of the series of results. Finally, after several such studies, guidelines for making simpler analyses can be developed and made available to the profession.

Until such studies are conducted, for the design of embedded structures there exists a choice between (1) a complete interaction analysis with an adequate variation of parameters study and with use of engineering judgement to avoid possible unconservatism and (2) an inertial interaction analysis which is probably, but not certainly, very conservative to some unknown degree. The choice will depend on the designers' ability to exercise proper judgment and willingness to accept conservative results.

## Acknowledgments

Much of the material for this chapter was prepared by the authors as part of an ASCE committee report on the state-of-the-art of evaluating soil-structure interaction effects in the design of nuclear power plants. Accordingly, it has benefited considerably from the constructive comments and suggestions of the other committee members: I. M. Idriss, P. K. Agrawal, R. P. Kennedy, and A. H. Hadjian, whose helpful comments and discussions are gratefully acknowledged.

## References

1. Allam, A. M., *An Investigation into the Nature of Microtremors Through Experimental Studies of Seismic Waves*, University of Tokyo, Tokyo, 1969.
2. Ambraseys, N. N., "Dynamics and Response of Foundation Materials in

Epicentral Regions of Strong Earthquakes," Proceedings of the Fifth World Conference on Earthquake Engineering, Rome, 1973, pp. cxxvi–cxlviii.

3. Asada, A., F. Kawakami, and M. Kamiyama, "On the Characteristics of Seismic Motion in Soft Soil Layers," Proceedings of the Fifth World Conference on Earthquake Engineering, Rome, 1973, pp. 319–328.
4. Beredugo, Y. O., and M. Novak, "Coupled Horizontal and Rocking Vibration of Embedded Footings," *Can. Geotech. J.*, Nov. 1972, pp. 477–497.
5. Berger, E., "Seismic Response of Axisymmetric Soil-Structure Systems," Ph.D. dissertation, University of California, Berkeley, Fall 1975.
6. Berger, E., J. Lysmer, and H. B. Seed, "ALUSH—A Computer Program for Seismic Response Analysis of Axisymmetric Soil-Structure Systems," *Report No. EERC 75–31*, Earthquake Engineering Research Center, University of California, Berkeley, Nov. 1975.
7. Berger, E., J. Lysmer, and H. B. Seed, "Comparison of Plane Strain and Axisymmetric Soil-Structure Interaction Analyses," Second ASCE Specialty Conference on Structural Design of Nuclear Plant Facilities, Vol. 1-A, New Orleans, Dec. 1975, pp. 809–825.
8. Blume, J. A., R. L. Sharpe, and J. S. Dalal, *Recommendations for Shape of Earthquake Response Spectra*, John A. Blume & Associates, Engrs., San Francisco, USAEC Contract No. AT(49–5)–3011, Feb. 1973.
9. Chen, J.-C., Personal communication, 1975.
10. Dobry, R., R. V. Whitman, and J. M. Roesset, "Soil Properties and the One-Dimensional Theory of Earthquake Amplification," *Research Report R71–18*, Department of Civil Engineering, Cambridge, Mass., 1971.
11. Dobry, R., R. V. Whitman, and J. M. Roesset, "Computation of Site Amplification Parameters from Seismographs Recorded in Borehole Arrays," 1975, in Press.
12. Donovan, N. C., "A Statistical Evaluation of Strong Motion Data Including the Feb. 9, 1971 San Fernando Earthquake," Proceedings of the Fifth World Conference on Earthquake Engineering, Rome, 1973, pp. 1252–1261.
13. Duke, C. M., K. E. Johnsen, L. E. Larson, and D. C. Engman, "Effects of Site Classification and Distance on Instrumental Indices in the San Fernando Earthquake," *UCLA Eng-7247*, University of California, Los Angeles, June 1972.
14. Gazetas, G. C., "Dynamic Stiffness Functions of Strip and Rectangular Footings on Layered Soil," S. M. thesis, Department of Civil Engineering, Massachusetts Institute of Technology, Cambridge, 1975.
15. Hadjian, A. H., J. E. Luco, and N. C. Tsai, "Soil-Structure Interaction: Continuum or Finite Elements," *Nuclear Eng. Des.*, Vol. 31, No. 2, Dec. 1974, pp. 151–167.
16. Haskell, N. A., "Crustial Reflection of Plane *SH* Waves," *J. Geophys. Res.*, Vol. 65, No. 12, Dec. 1960.
17. Hayashi, S., H. Tsuchida, and E. Kurata, "Average Response Spectra for Various Subsoil Conditions," Third Joint Meeting, U.S.-Japan Panel on Wind and Seismic Effects, UJNR, Tokyo, May 10–12, 1971.
18. Hwang, R., J. Lysmer, E. Berger, "A Simplified Three-Dimensional Soil-Structure Interaction Study," Proceedings of the Second ASCE Specialty Con-

ference on Structural Design of Nuclear Plant Facilities, Vol. 1-A, New Orleans, Dec. 1975, pp. 786–808.

19. ISENBERG, J., "Interaction Between Soil and Nuclear Reactor Foundations During Earthquakes," Report to the Research Foundation, University of Toledo, Toledo, Ohio, Agbabian-Jacobsen Assocs., Los Angeles, June 1970.
20. KAUSEL, E., "Forced Vibrations of Circular Foundations on Layered Media," *Soils Publication No. 336*, Department of Civil Engineering, Massachusetts Institute of Technology, Cambridge, Jan. 1974.
21. KAUSEL, E., and J. M. ROESSET, "Soil-Structure-Interaction Problems for Nuclear Containment Structures," ASCE Power Division Specialty Conference, Denver, Aug. 1974.
22. KAUSEL, E., and J. M. ROESSET, "Dynamic Stiffness of Circular Foundations," *J. Eng. Mech. Div. ASCE*, Vol. 101, No. EM6, Dec. 1975, pp. 771–785.
23. KAUSEL, E., J. M. ROESSET, and G. WAAS, "Dynamic Analysis of Circular Footings on Layered Media," *J. Eng. Mech. Div. ASCE*, Vol. 101, No. EM5, Oct. 1975, pp. 679–693.
24. KURIBAYASHI, E., T. IWASAKI, Y. IIDA, and K. TUJI, "Effects of Seismic and Subsoil Conditions on Earthquake Response Spectra," Proceedings, of International Conference on Microzontation, Seattle, 1972, pp. 499–512.
25. LUCO, J. E., "Impedance Functions for a Rigid Foundation on a Layered Medium," *Nuclear Eng. Des.*, Vol. 31, No. 2, 1974, pp. 204–217.
26. LYSMER, J., "Lumped Mass Method for Rayleigh Waves," *Bull. Seism. Soc. Am.*, Vol. 60, No. 1, Feb. 1970, pp. 89–104.
27. LYSMER, J., H. B. SEED, T. UDAKA, and R. N. HWANG, "Efficient Finite Element Analysis of Seismic Structure-Soil-Structure Interaction," Second ASCE Specialty Conference on Structural Design of Nuclear Plant Facilities, New Orleans, Dec. 1975. To be published in Vol. 2 of the proceedings.
28. LYSMER, J., T. UDAKA, H. B. SEED, and R. HWANG, "LUSH—A Computer Program for Complex Response Analysis of Soil-Structure Systems," *Report No. EERC 74–4*, Earthquake Engineering Research Center, University of California, Berkeley, April 1974.
29. LYSMER, J., T. UDAKA, C.-F. TSAI, and H. B. SEED, "FLUSH—A Computer Program for Approximate 3-D Analysis of Soil-Structure Interaction Problems" *Report No. EERC 75–30*, Earthquake Engineering Research Center, University of California, Berkeley, Nov. 1975.
30. MOHRAZ, B., *A Study of Earthquake Response Spectra for Different Geological Conditions*, Civil and Mechanical Engineering Department, Institute of Technology, Southern Methodist University, Dallas, 1975.
31. MOHRAZ B., W. J. HALL, and N. M. NEWMARK, "A Study of Vertical and Horizontal Earthquake Spectra," USAEC Contract No. AT(49–5)–2667, Nathan M. Newmark Consulting Engineering Services, Urbana, Ill., 1972.
32. NEWMARK, N. M., J. A. BLUME, and K. KAPUR, "Design Response Spectra for Nuclear Power Plants," Paper presented at the Structural Engineers ASCE Conference, San Francisco, April 1973.
33. OHSAKI, Y., and T. HAGIWARA, "On Effects of Soils and Foundations upon Earthquake Inputs to Buildings," *Building Research Institute Paper No. 41*, Ministry of Construction, Japanese Government, June 1970.

34. PAGE, R. A., J. A. BLUME, and W. B. JOYNER, "Earthquake Shaking and Damage to Buildings," *Science*, Vol. 189, No. 4203, Aug. 1975.
35. RICHART, F. E., JR., J. R. HALL, JR., and R. D. WOODS, *Vibrations of Soils and Foundations*, Prentice-Hall, Englewood Cliffs, N. J., 1970.
36. ROESSET, J. M., R. V. WHITMAN, and R. DOBRY, "Modal Analysis for Structures with Foundation Interaction," *J. Struct. Eng. Div. ASCE*, Vol. 99, No. ST3, 1973, pp. 389–416.
37. SARRAZIN, M. A., J. M. ROESSET, and R. V. WHITMAN, "Dynamic Soil-Structure Interaction," *J. Struct. Eng. Div. ASCE*, Vol. 98, No. ST7, 1972, pp. 1525–1544.
38. SCHNABEL, P. B., J. LYSMER, and H. B. SEED, "SHAKE—A Computer Program for Earthquake Response Analysis of Horizontally Layered Sites," *Report No. EERC 72–12*, Earthquake Engineering Research Center, University of California, Berkeley, Dec. 1972.
39. SCHNABEL, P., H. B. SEED, and J. LYSMER, "Modifications of Seismograph Records for Effects of Local Soil Conditions," *Bull. Seism. Soc. Am.*, Vol. 62, No. 6, Dec. 1972, pp. 1649–1664.
40. SEED, H. B., "The Influence of Local Soil Conditions on Earthquake Damage," Proceedings of Special Session on Soil Dynamics, International Conference on Soil Mechanics and Foundation Engineering, Mexico City, 1969, pp. 33–66.
41. SEED, H. B., and I. M. IDRISS, "Influence of Soil Conditions on Ground Motions During Earthquakes," *J. Soil Mech. Found. Div. ASCE*, Vol. 94, No. SM1, Jan. 1969.
42. SEED, H. B., R. MURARKA, J. LYSMER, and I. M. IDRISS, "Relationships Between Maximum Acceleration, Maximum Velocity, Distance from Source and Local Site Conditions for Moderately Strong Earthquakes," *Report No. EERC 75–17*, Earthquake Engineering Research Center, University of California, Berkeley, July 1975.
43. SEED, H. B., C. UGAS, and J. LYSMER, "Site Dependent Spectra for Earthquake Resistant Design," *Report No. EERC 74–12*, Earthquake Engineering Research Center, University of California, Berkeley, Nov. 1974.
44. SEED, H. B., J. LYSMER, and R. HWANG, "Soil-Structure Interaction Analyses for Seismic Response," *J. Geotech. Eng. Div. ASCE*, Vol. 101, No. GT, May 1975.
45. SHANNON & WILSON, Inc. and Agbabian Associates, "Soil Behavior Under Earthquake Loading Conditions," Procedures for Evaluation of Vibratory Ground Motions of Soil Deposits for Nuclear Power Plant Sites prepared for U.S. Atomic Energy Commission, Division of Reactor Safety Research, June 1974.
46. STREETER, W. L., E.B . WYLIE, and F. E. RICHART, JR., "Soil Motion Computations by Characteristics Method," *J. Geotech. Eng. Div. ASCE*, Vol. 100, No. GT3, March 1974, pp. 247–263.
47. TAZIME, K., "Minimum Group Velocity, Maximum Aplitude and Quarter Wave-Length Law—Love-Waves in Doubly Stratified Layers," *J. Phys. Earth*, Vol. 5, No. 1, 1957.
48. TRIFUNAC, M. D., and A. G. BRADY, "Correlations of Peak Acceleration Velocity and Displacement with Earthquake Magnitude, Distance and Site Conditions," to be published in *Earthquake Eng. Struct. Dynamics J.*, 1975.

49. TSAI, N. C., D. NIEHOFF, M. SWATTA, and A. H. HADJIAN, "The Use of Frequency-Independent Soil-Structure Interaction Parameters," *Nuclear Eng. Des.*, Vol. 31, No. 2, 1974, pp. 168–183.
50. UDAKA, T., "Analysis of Response of Large Embankments to Travelling Base Motions," Doctoral dissertation, College of Engineering, University of California, Berkeley, Fall 1975.
51. UDAKA, T., J. LYSMER, and H. B. SEED, "TRIP and TRAVEL—Computer Programs for Soil-Structure Interaction Analysis with Horizontally Travelling Waves," *Report No. EERC 75–32*, Earthquake Engineering Research Center, University of California, Berkeley, Dec. 1975.
52. U.S. Atomic Energy Commission, "Design Response Spectra for Seismic Design of Nuclear Power Plants," *Regulatory Guide 1.60*, Directorate of Regulatory Standards, Rev. 1, Washington, D.C., 1973.
53. VELETSOS, A. S., and B. VERBIC, "Basic Response Functions for Elastic Foundations," *J. Eng. Mech. Div. ASCE*, Vol. 100, No. EM2, April 1974, pp. 189–202.
54. WHITMAN, R. V., Discussion presented at First ASCE Specialty Conference on Structural Design in Nuclear Plant Facilities, Chicago, Dec. 1973.
55. WHITMAN, R. V., and F. E. RICHART, "Design Procedures for Dynamically Loaded Foundations," *J. Soil Mech. Found. Div. ASCE*, Vol. 93, No. SM6, Nov. 1969.

# Engineering of Rock Blasting on Civil Projects

A. J. HENDRON, JR.*

## Introduction

Controlled blasting is used at some time during most civil engineering projects where there is rock excavation. Controlled blasting is often necessary because the blasting must take place in the near proximity of adjacent structures. In other instances, the blasting is controlled because a smooth perimeter is desired to minimize rock support and overbreak. The construction of tunnels and shafts for subways, rock excavations for foundations, and the excavation of road cuts for interstate highways sometimes require blasting operations which must be conducted in an urban environment. Unfortunately, blasting operations produce unwanted sounds and vibration along with their beneficial effects. Thus, in the writing of specifications for blasting in an urban environment, potential damage to adjacent structures by ground vibrations must be considered, possible damage to windows from airblasts must be considered, potential damage and safety problems from fly rock must be considered, and the discomfort to people from ground vibrations, airblast, and noise must be taken into account. In some instances the potential interruption in service of delicate equipment housed in adjacent structures must be considered; this equipment may be electronic computers or other electronic gear with sensitive relays in the circuits.

The contractor or the owner's engineer is faced with determining the maximum weight of explosives which may be detonated without damage to structures on adjacent property. If the weight of explosive is overestimated, the resulting damage to adjacent structures may result in costly losses. But, if the engineer or contractor is too conservative, and the weight of explosive

*Professor of Civil Engineering, University of Illinois at Urbana-Champaign, Urbana, Illinois.

becomes too restrictive, progress of the project may be curtailed, and the cost of excavation will increase accordingly.

Because people are so sensitive to sounds and vibrations produced by blasting, complaints and damage claims quite commonly arise within the range of perceptibility of these effects, even when no actual structural damage is done. This situation is likely to become even more critical in the future because of the recent emphasis placed on pollution of the environment, which has resulted in efforts to isolate the individual from intrusions of noise and vibration.

Blasting rounds are controlled on many civil engineering projects in order to achieve a smooth wall around the perimeter of the excavation with a minimum of overbreak. Smooth wall excavations minimize the rock support and can be utilized to minimize the amount of concrete used on structures such as spillways. In open excavations, such as portal cuts for tunnels, spillway cuts, highway cuts, and basement excavations in metropolitan areas, controlled blasting techniques such as presplitting, cushion blasting, or line drilling can be used to advantage. Smooth walls in underground excavations, such as underground powerhouses and tunnels, can be achieved by a technique called smooth wall blasting. Properly executed smooth wall blasting results in less temporary support and more economical permanent liners in tunnels. Deep (50–70 ft) basement excavations in metropolitan areas are very special cases which must be treated with extreme care. In many instances they are located within several feet or inches from existing structures and the construction procedure requires blasting immediately adjacent to the structures as well as the installation of high-capacity rock anchors for stability. In this situation it is most important to install the anchors as soon as possible and to carefully control the unsupported length and height of the open excavation. Although blasting vibrations need to be considered, they are an item of secondary priority in comparison to the consideration of the overall stability of the cut. Thus, the inspection forces in the field must allocate their time and energies accordingly.

To achieve the desired result, the engineer must know the technical state-of-the-art for all of the types of controlled blasting mentioned above. But, equally important, the construction specifications and bid documents must be written in such a way that it is possible to achieve the desired result. The specifications must be written in such a way that the contractor knows beforehand what is expected. This will permit the contractor to be responsive and include the proper items and expenses in his bid for the controlled rock excavation. Much controversy has resulted from specifications for controlled blasting because many of them have been so vague that the contractor could not ascertain before bidding the nature of the procedures which would be required by the engineer. It should also be pointed out that the specifications should not be so restrictive that they eliminate the contractor's flexilibity and restrict any contributions he may make to the job from his past experience and ingenuity. For some problems, such as the excavation of high vertical walls adjacent to occupied buildings, the engineer and owner may justifiably feel that other measures are necessary in addition to a well-written and technically sound specification accompanied by diligent inspection. Since the final result is primarily influenced by the knowledge, experience, and responsible performance of the contractor, the engineer may indeed make his most valuable contribution to the job by writing a good prequalification specification which the contractor must satisfy to become a bidder. This mechanism has been used with success on projects where the owners have been both private parties and government agencies.

In this chapter, the technical aspects and the current state-of-the-art in controlled blasting will be reviewed. In addition, guidelines will be set forth and suggestions will be made on how to incorporate these ideas into the specifications so that the desired results will be achieved.

## Vibration Criteria

### *General*

The problem of predetermining the quantity of explosives which may be used without damaging an existing structure may be resolved into two parts. First, the engineer must be able to predict the intensity of ground vibration as a function of charge weight, distance from the detonation, and properties of the transmitting medium. Second, it is necessary to know the level of ground vibration which can be tolerated by different types of structures without causing damage. The available information relating to both parts of this problem is discussed below.

### *Ground Vibrations from Blasting*

Part of the energy released in the detonation of a blasting round is transmitted directly into the surrounding rock mass in the form of stress waves. The ground motions observed at a given point are dependent on the weight of explosive detonated per delay, the distance from the detonation point to the observation point, and the transmission characteristics of the rock mass. Since an acceptable theoretical approach has not yet been developed for calculating ground motions in rock, the scaling of field measurements is used almost exclusively for predicting ground motions from explosions. Available data for estimating these motions have been measured from quarry blasting, contruction blasting, and blasting in open pit mines. Similar measurements have been obtained in connection with nuclear and chemical explosions tests conducted for the development of design procedures for protective military structures [12].

The empirical scaling of shock phenomena from explosions involves the comparison of dynamic measurements obtained at various distances from a wide range of charge sizes. Ambraseys and Hendron [1] have suggested the use of cube-root scaling to compare particle velocity measurements made from different-sized explosions. Such a correlation of data is shown in Fig. 1, where the measured particle velocity is plotted versus the scaled range, which

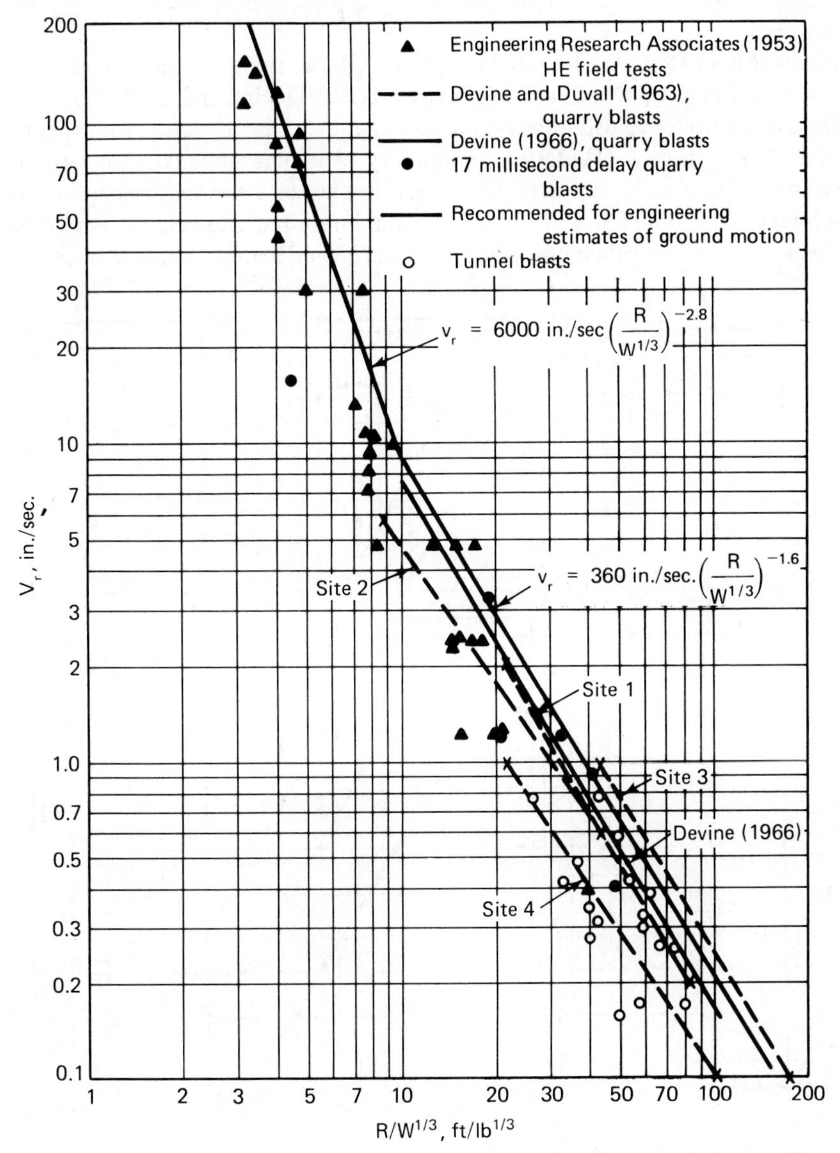


**Fig. 1.** Maximum particle velocity versus scaled range according to cube root scaling

is the slant range in feet divided by the cube root of the maximum weight of charge per delay in $lb^{1/3}$. In this figure, experience from many jobs is shown. For preliminary estimates of maximum radial particle velocity, it is suggested that, for scaled ranges greater than 10 $ft/lb^{1/3}$, the upper-bound line on Fig. 1 be used. This line is described by the following equation:

$$v_r = 360 \frac{\text{in.}}{\text{sec}} \left( \frac{R}{W^{1/3}} \right)^{-1.6}, \tag{1}$$

where $R$ is in feet, and $W$ is the maximum charge per delay in pounds.

Other investigators, such as Oriard [18,19], Devine and Duvall [1], and Devine [7], prefer to use square-root scaling rather than the cube-root scaling as shown in Fig. 1. Thus, for preliminary estimates of maximum particle velocity, Oriard [18,19] uses the upper bound of previous measurements shown by line $B$ in Fig. 2. In Fig. 2 the maximum particle velocity is plotted against the scaled range according to square-root scaling. Line $D$ in Fig. 2

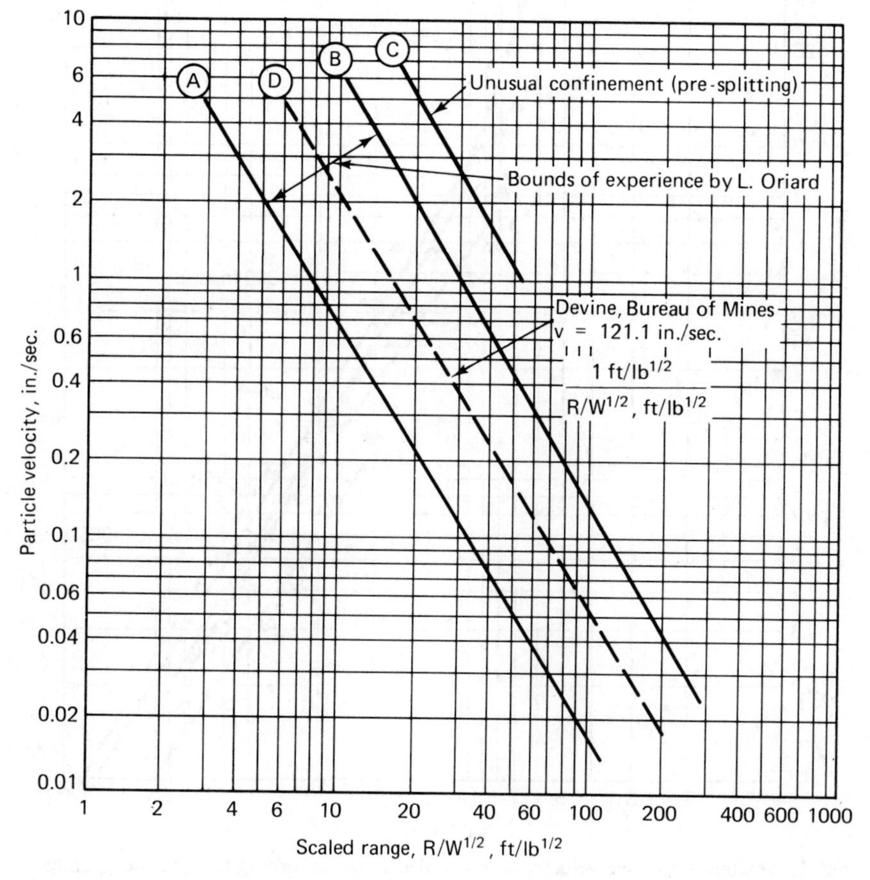


**Fig. 2.** Maximum particle velocity versus scaled range, according to square root scaling

represents the best fit to many measurements of radial particle velocity obtained from quarry blasts by Devine [6]. It should be noted that line *D* falls nearly in the middle of the range of Oriard's experience, which falls between lines *A* and *B*. The range shown between lines *A* and *B* is typical for data obtained from downhole blasting and represents the scatter that is typical from vibrations produced by blasting. In such cases where there is unusual confinement, such as in the first holes which are detonated in the cut round of a tunnel or the holes which are detonated simultaneously down a presplit line, line *C* shown in Fig. 2 gives an appropriate estimate of the maximum particle velocity as a function of scaled range.

The relative merits of cube-root and square-root scaling will not be debated in this chapter, but the differences which result in practical applications will be discussed below. The relations between the maximum charge per delay and range which produce given maximum particle velocities are shown in Fig. 3 for various scaling techniques. Note that line 4 in Fig. 3 is the

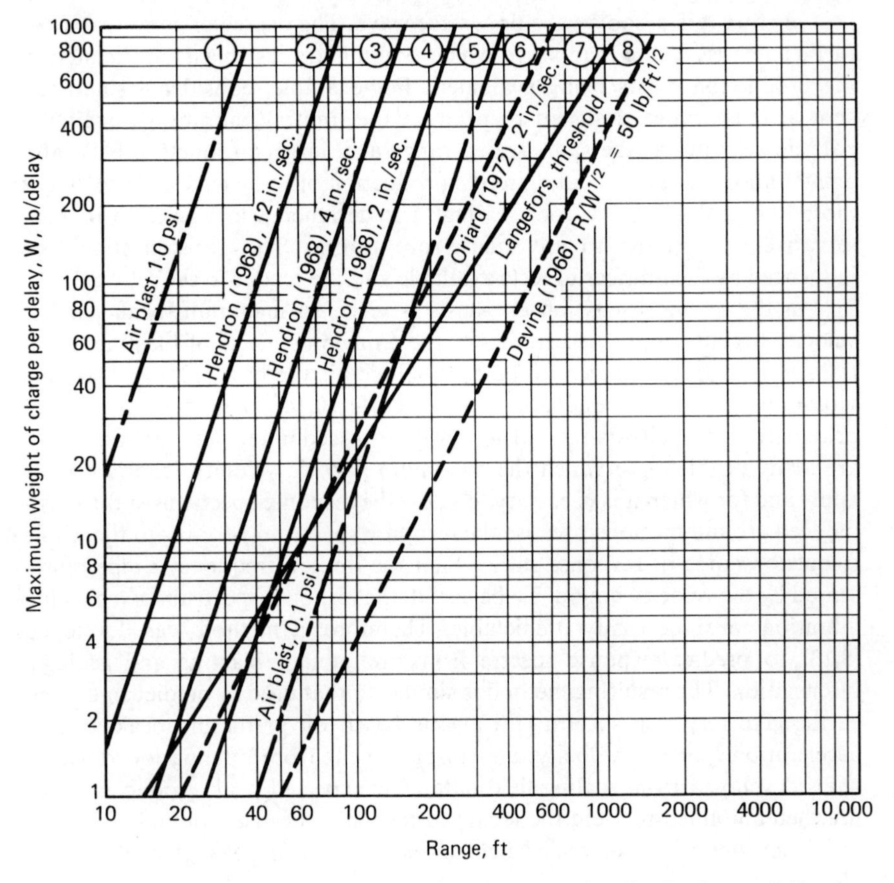


**Fig. 3.** Relation between charge per delay and range for various levels of ground vibration

relationship between the maximum charge per delay and range which gives a maximum particle velocity of 2 in./sec according to the data scaled by cube-root scaling in Fig. 1 [1]. The relationship given by line 6 in Fig. 3 is the combination of maximum charge weights per delay and range which will result in a maximum particle velocity of 2 in./sec according to square-root scaling from curve *B* in Fig. 2 [18,19]. It should be noted that the differences between lines 4 and 6 are not significant for practical applications where the range is between 20 and 100 ft. In general, the relationship given by square-root scaling (line 6) becomes increasingly more conservative, with respect to the relationship given by cube-root scaling (line 4), as the range increases. For ranges closer than about 45 ft, the relationship given by cube-root scaling (line 4) is more conservative for determining allowable charges per delay than the relationship derived from square-root scaling (line 6).

In all instances, the reader is cautioned to explore thoroughly the responses of the project site in question and to study the relationship between different scaling techniques and the type of seismic waves under consideration, i.e., whether it is a body wave or surface wave. The degree of conservatism is further related to the manner in which preliminary test blasts are related to the production blasts being evaluated. For example, consider a small test shot at close range designed to produce the limiting vibration (maximum particle velocity) at the same scaled range as a larger production blast at a greater absolute range. Scaling to the production blast by cube-root scaling is more liberal than square-root scaling. The designer who wishes to be conservative may choose to use square-root scaling. The decision should be influenced by the number of tests available and the scatter in the results.

In the above discussion emphasis is given to maximum peak particle velocity because controlled studies of the damaging effects of blasting vibrations have indicated that peak particle velocity is the best index for blasting vibration damage to residential structures [4,10,14]. The development of peak particle velocity damage criteria will be traced in the next section. There are many problems to which the maximum particle velocity criteria do not apply and for which it is necessary to know the response spectrum of the blast-induced ground motions because the response spectrum pertains to the whole frequency range of response rather than the limited frequency range represented by the velocity bound. To be useful, the response spectrum of a blasting vibration must be easily predictable. Therefore, a method was developed [8,13] to predict response spectra from preliminary blasting and geologic information. The resulting method is similar to that used to predict smoothed earthquake response spectra [17] and is based on predicting peak ground acceleration, particle velocity, and displacement from attenuation relationships developed from scaling field data. The expected peak ground motions are then amplified to yield the idealized response spectrum bounds.

The attenuation of scaled field measurements of peak ground motion (particle displacement, $\delta$, particle velocity, $v$; and particle acceleration, $a$) with increasing scaled distance, $R(\rho c^2)^{1/3}/W^{1/3}$, is presented in Fig. 4, where $R$ is the range in feet, $\rho$ is the mass density per unit of volume in slugs per cubic foot, $c$ is the seismic velocity in feet per second, and $W$ is the maximum weight of explosive per delay in pounds. The basis in dimensional analysis for the scaling used is given by Hendron and Ambraseys [1], Newmark [16], Dowding [8], Hendron and Dowding [13], and Hendron [12]. The plots shown in Fig. 4 were derived from 12 separate field studies involving open cut, tunnel, and shaft blasts with maximum explosive weights per delay ranging from 2.4 to 19,625 lb [8,13]. The average scaled-distance-attenuation relationships shown in Fig. 4 for peak values of blast-generated displacements, velocities, and accelerations may be expressed as

$$\delta = \frac{3}{1000}\,\text{in.}\left[\frac{100\text{ ft}}{R}\right]^{1.1}\left[\frac{10{,}000\text{ ft/sec}}{c}\right]^{1.4}\left[\frac{W}{10\text{ lb}}\right]^{0.7}\left[\frac{5.25}{\rho}\right]^{0.7}, \tag{2}$$

$$v = \frac{3}{4}\,\frac{\text{in.}}{\text{sec}}\left[\frac{100\text{ ft}}{R}\right]^{1.5}\left[\frac{W}{10\text{ lb}}\right]^{0.5}\left[\frac{5.25}{\rho}\right]^{0.5}, \tag{3}$$

$$a = \frac{2}{3}\,\text{g}\left[\frac{100\text{ ft}}{R}\right]^{1.9}\left[\frac{c}{10{,}000\text{ fps}}\right]^{1.4}\left[\frac{W}{10\text{ lb}}\right]^{0.3}\left[\frac{5.25}{\rho}\right]^{0.3}, \tag{4}$$

Proper units for $\rho$ are obtained by dividing the unit weight of the rock in pounds per cubic foot by the acceleration of gravity (32.2 ft/sec), although $\rho$ will vary so little in rock that this factor can safely be ignored. The maximum values given by Eqs. (2), (3), and (4) are a conservative estimate for motions produced by bench blasts to a free face or by the later delays in a tunnel round. These values should be doubled for a conservative estimate of the motions produced by confined blasts such as presplit rounds, the cut portion of a tunnel round, or the initial cuts in an open excavation.

A study of the actual response spectra of many construction blasts [8] has shown that the following procedure can be used for constructing a smooth response spectrum for the ground vibrations produced by such blasts:

1. Estimate $\rho$, $c$, $W^{1/3}$, and $R$ and obtain $\delta$, $v$, $a$ from Eqs. (2), (3) and (4).
2. The peak ground motions should be plotted on tripartite paper to yield a trapezoidal ground motion spectrum.
3. The principal spectrum frequency, $\omega_0$, is defined as the center of the ground motion spectrum.
4. The response spectrum for frequencies lower than $\frac{1}{4}\omega_0$ can be obtained by multiplying the ground displacement by the appropriate amplification factor $A_\delta$.
5. The response spectrum for frequencies between $\frac{1}{2}\omega_0$ and $1\frac{1}{2}\omega_0$ can be obtained by multiplying the maximum ground velocity by the appropriate amplification factor $A_v$. If the blast is detonated with delays at a

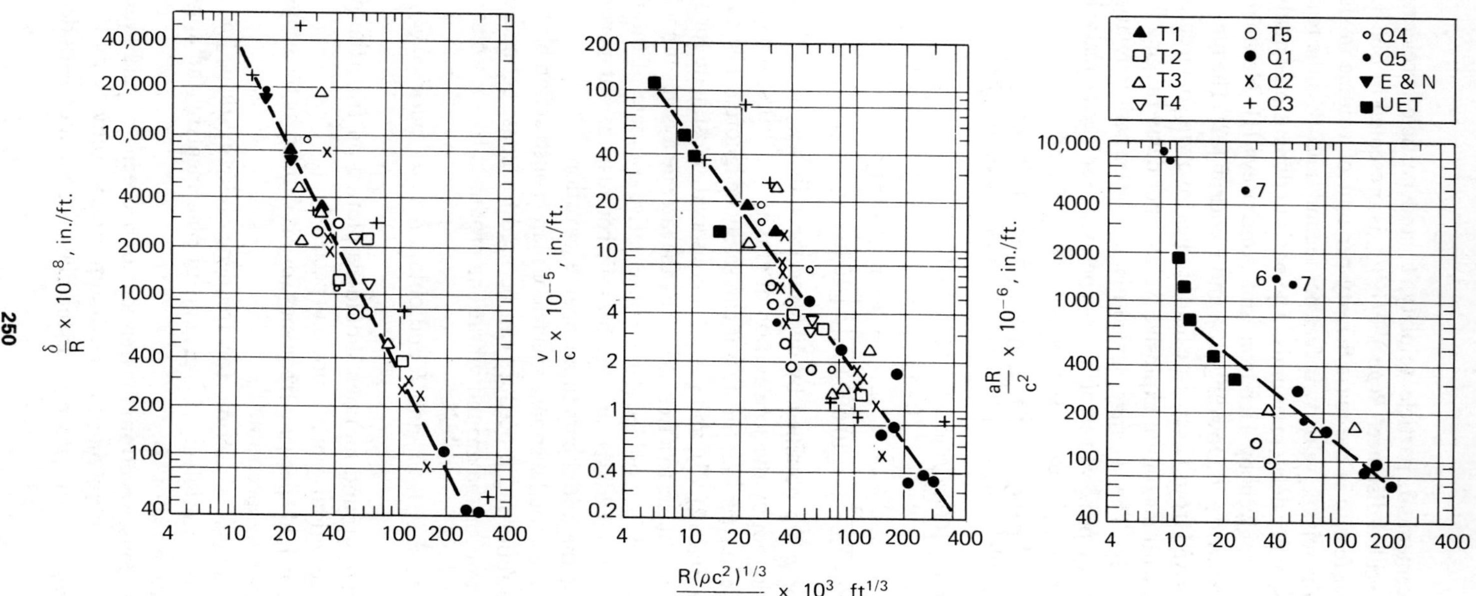


Fig. 4. Scaled field measurements of radial particle displacement, velocity, and acceleration versus scaled range

constant interval, the velocity bound must include the frequency corresponding to the delay interval.

6. The response spectrum for frequencies greater than $2\omega_0$ is obtained by multiplying the maximum ground acceleration by the appropriate amplification factor $A_a$.

7. The amplified spectrum displacement, velocity, and acceleration bounds should be connected to complete the spectrum.

The amplification factors $A_\delta$, $A_v$, and $A_a$ are given in Fig. 5 (after Dowding [8]) as a function of scaled range for 3% critical damping. Note that the factors $A_a$ and $A_\delta$ do not vary with scaled range, whereas the value of $A_v$ varies with scaled range. It should also be noted that the value of $A_v$ is dependent on whether the blast is a single or multiple delay blast. Experience has shown that the upper relationship for $A_v$ should be used if the number of delays is greater than 3. If the response spectrum is desired for values other than 3% of critical damping, the values of $A_\delta$, $A_v$, and $A_a$ from Fig. 5 should be multiplied by the following factors:

| *% Critical Damping* | $A_\delta$ | $A_v$ | $A_a$ |
|---|---|---|---|
| 2 | 1.05 | 1.10 | 1.20 |
| 5 | 0.83 | 0.76 | 0.72 |
| 10 | 0.65 | 0.52 | 0.42 |

Observations by Dowding [8] on a significant number of structures subject to blasting vibrations indicate that most structures behaved as if 3% of critical damping was appropriate for the intensity of motions produced by blasting vibrations less than 2 in./sec.

As an example of the procedure described above, the response spectrum (for $\beta = 3\%$) for the ground motions 220 ft from a blast consisting of seven 200-lb delays at 34-msec intervals will be calculated. The seismic velocity will be assumed to be 13,000 ft/sec, and the soil overburden at the point of interest is assumed to be negligible. From Eqs. (2), (3), and (4) the maximum ground displacement, velocity, and acceleration are 0.0073 in., 1.0 in./sec, and 0.65 g, respectively. When the ground motions are plotted on tripartite paper as shown in Fig. 6, the principal spectral frequency, $\omega_0$, is found to be 30 cps. The frequency corresponding to the delay interval is 29 cps and is located within the frequency limits of the velocity bound. Therefore, the velocity bound need not be extended to cover the frequency corresponding to the delay interval. The appropriate amplification factors for the multiple delay, constant-interval shot are $A_\delta = 1.2$, $A_v = 3.8$, and $A_a = 2.5$, for $R(\rho c^2)^{1/3}/W^{1/3} = 35 \text{ ft}^{1/3}$, from Fig. 5. In Fig. 6 the amplified velocity bound extends

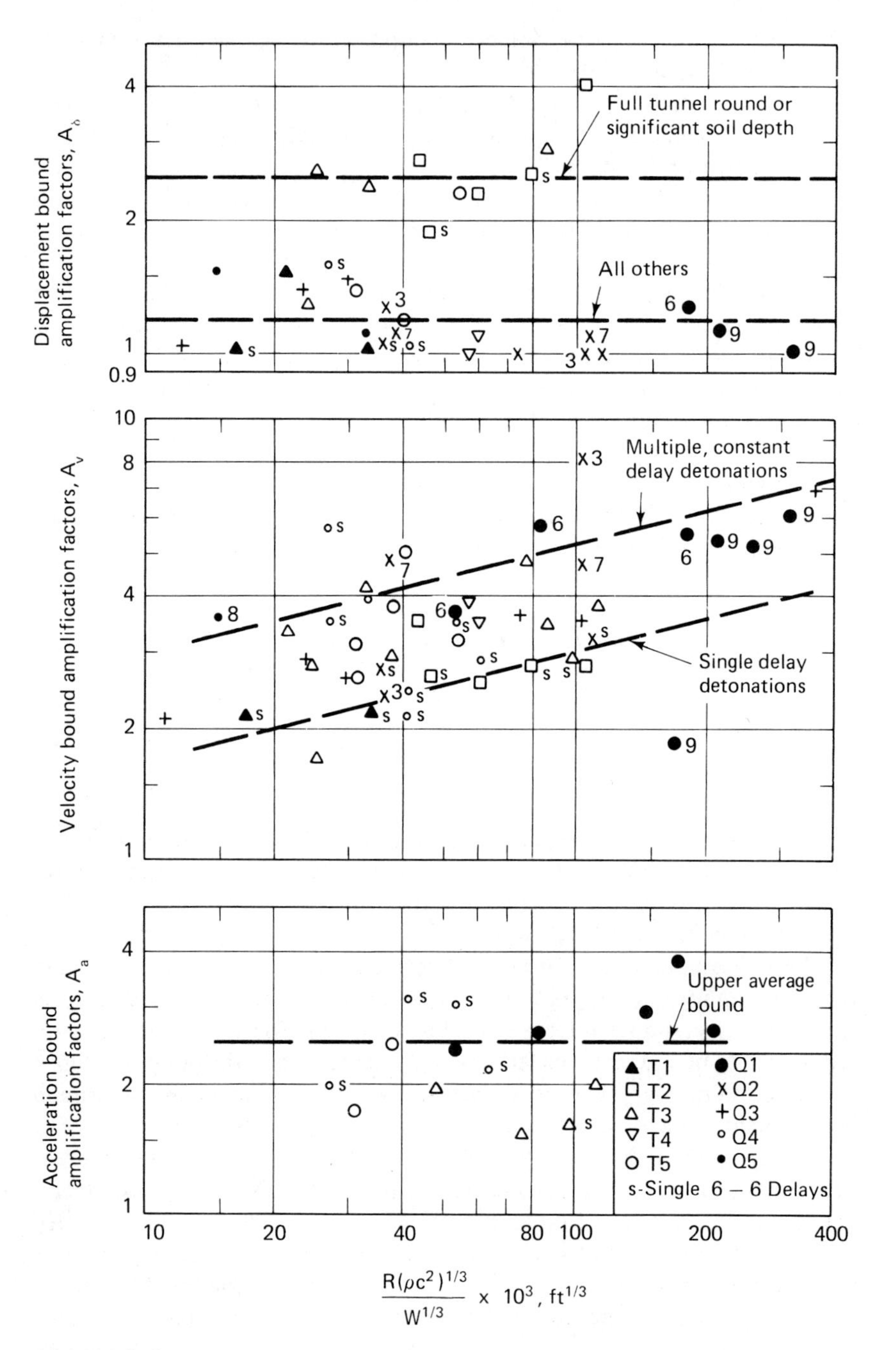


**Fig. 5.** Displacement-, velocity-, and acceleration-bound amplification factors versus scaled range ($\beta = 0.03$)

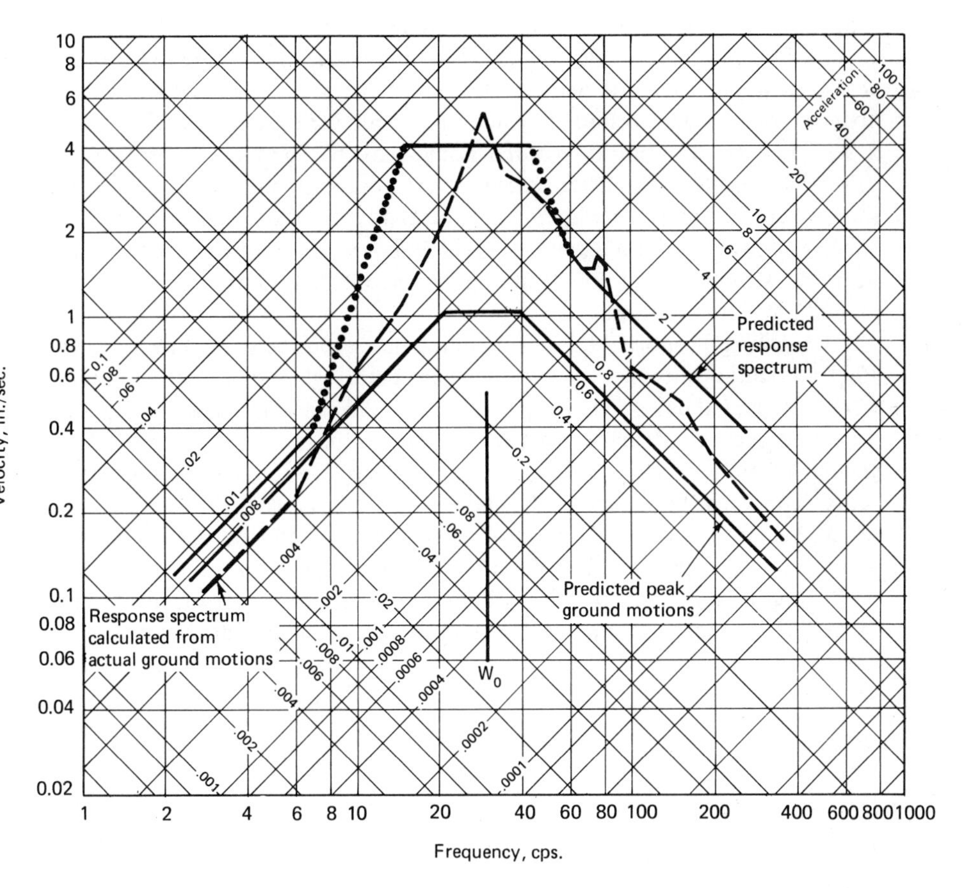


**Fig. 6.** Comparison of the simplified, predicted response spectra with the actual calculated response spectra

from 15 to 45 cps, the amplified displacement bound applies to frequencies below 7 cps, and the amplified acceleration bound applies to frequencies above 60 cps. These bounds are then connected by the inclined dotted lines (Fig. 6) to form the complete 3% critically damped response spectrum. The dashed irregular line in Fig. 6 is the actual response spectrum calculated from the ground motions from a blast corresponding to the assumptions of the hypothetical case. This example was taken from field study *Q*2 as described by Dowding [8].

### *Damage Criteria*

The intensity of ground motion which can be tolerated by various structures must be determined by the engineer before estimates of permissible charge weights can be determined. Obviously, the level of ground motion required to damage structures is not the same for different types of structures. In addition, the "acceptable" damage level may depend more on the use of a structure rather than the actual integrity of the structure. For example, a given set of ground motions may not structurally affect either a residence or a steel framed warehouse, but the home may be "damaged" because the distortion resulted in plaster cracks objectionable to the owner. Thus, the limiting ground motions which cause various types of damage can be established only by experience from cases where the ground motions are measured near the structure and the resulting damage can be correlated with the magnitude of the motions.

Crandell [4] reported the results of a comprehensive study in which over 1000 residential homes, two-story business buildings, schools, and churches were investigated before and after blasting. On the basis of this study, Crandell presented the first damage criterion which was based on measurements of ground motions in the vicinity of the structure. He found that the energy ratio, defined as the square of the ratio of maximum acceleration in feet per square second to frequency in cycles per second, could be correlated with damage. An energy ratio of 3 or below was considered safe, and the danger of producing damage was considered highly probable for energy ratios greater than 6, If harmonic motion is assumed for the ground vibrations, the following relations exist among maximum acceleration $a_{max}$, maximum particle velocity $v_{max}$, maximum displacement $\delta_{max}$, and frequency $f$:

$$v_{max} = 2\pi f \delta_{max}, \tag{5}$$

$$a_{max} = 4\pi^2 f^2 \delta_{max}, \tag{6}$$

$$a_{max} = 2\pi f v_{max}. \tag{7}$$

Thus from Eq. (7) it is apparent that the energy ratio is proportional to the square of the maximum particle velocity $v_{max}$. A damage criterion based on energy ratio is therefore the same as a criterion based on maximum particle velocity. Calculations show that energy ratios of 3 and 6 correspond to maximum particle velocities of 3.3 and 4.7 in./sec, respectively.

Langefors et al. [15] reported the results of an investigation similar to Crandell's, except that they measured displacement and frequency in the vicinity of the structure rather than acceleration and frequency as measured by Crandell. They found that damage to structures could be correlated with the product of maximum displacement and frequency. Since maximum particle velocity is proportional to the product of maximum displacement and frequency, this damage criterion is also equivalent to a maximum particle velocity criterion. Based on these data, Langefors et al. concluded that maximum particle velocities below 2.8 in./sec would not produce damage. Edwards and Northwood [10] concluded from similar studies that a particle velocity criteria could be used for damage control and that a maximum particle velocity of 2 in./sec would not produce damage.

Duvall and Fogelson [9] statistically analyzed the vibration measurements and damage correlations made by Edwards and Northwood [10], Langefors et al. [15], and Thoenen and Windes [23]. Although the three studies analyzed were made at different times in three different countries, they showed remarkable agreement. The statistical analysis showed that for a maximum particle velocity of 7.6 in./sec the probability of producing major damage (fall of plaster, serious cracking) is 50% and that the probability of producing minor damage (fine plaster cracks, opening of old cracks) is slightly less than 50% at a particle velocity of 5.4 in./sec. In all 124 cases analyzed, damage was not observed from blasting vibrations if the particle velocity was below 2 in./sec. The damage criteria given above are recommended because they resulted from a thorough analysis of a considerable body of damage data on residential type structures.

Langefors and Kihlstrom [14] also give particle velocity criteria for damage to tunnels in rock. A particle velocity of 12 in./sec is given as a criterion for the "fall of rock in unlined tunnels," and a particle velocity of 24 in./sec is correlated with the formation of new cracks in rock. These criteria are consistent with the experience of the author for unlined tunnels near nuclear detonations. Unlined tunnels rarely experience visible damage at ranges where the free-field ground motions are on the order of 1–2 ft/sec, unless a loosened piece of rock is detached from the roof by the shaking.

The observations of Langefors and Kihlstrom [14] concerning rock tunnels are not contrary to the results of the Underground Explosion Tests (UET) which were conducted by Engineering Research Associates [11] for the Corps of Engineers during the period from 1948 to 1952.

In the underground explosion tests a considerable number of TNT explosions were detonated at scaled depths of about 0.38 $ft/lb^{1/3}$ in sandstone, granite, and limestone. The most comprehensive set of these tests was conducted in sandstone, and one of the variables in this series of tests included a study of damage to unlined tunnels which were mined to pass directly below the point of detonation. Generally, the tunnel size was selected to be in proportion to the cube root of the corresponding charge weight used in the test. A full-scale tunnel was taken to be approximately 30 ft in diameter and the corresponding full-scale charge weight for a tunnel of this size was 320,000 lb. A brief summary of the underground explosion tests is given in Table 1.

From the UET program, four zones of failure were empirically defined from the observations of damage to unlined tunnels. Zone I was described as tight closure of the tunnel. Zone I failure appeared for a length along the tunnel roughly as shown in Fig. 7. Zone II was also a region of fairly tight closure, but the degrees of tightness decreased progressively with range; thus, zones I and II were sometimes difficult to distinguish, and in many reports no effort was made to delineate between them. Zone III was characterized by continuous damage to the tunnel surface, but this damage decreased with

**Table 1**
**Brief Summary of UET Tests**

| *Rock Type* | *No. of Tests* | *Weight of TNT (lb)* |
|---|---|---|
| Limestone | 2 | 320 |
| Granite | 10 | 320 |
| | 2 | 2,560 |
| Sandstone | 8 | 320 |
| | 1 | 1,080 |
| | 3 | 2,560 |
| | 1 | 10,000 |
| | 3 | 40,000 |
| | 1 | 320,000 |

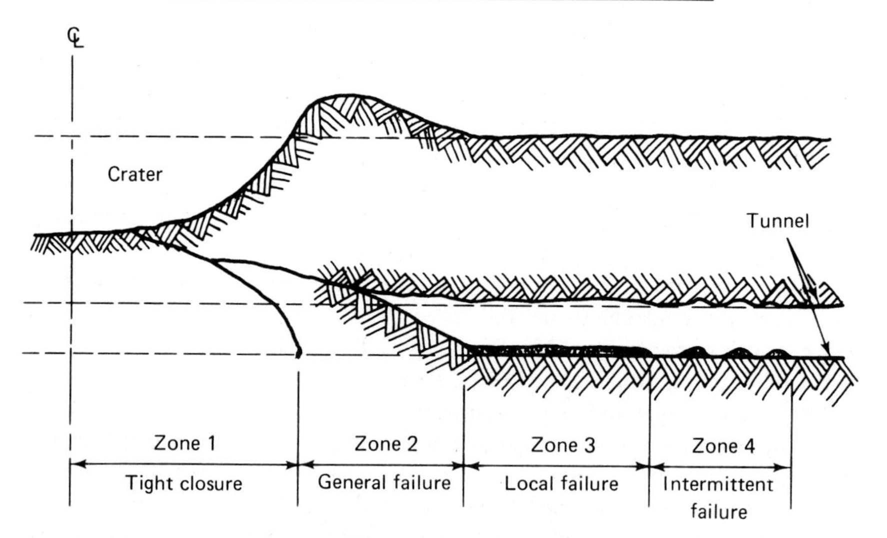


**Fig. 7.** Damage zones from UET program

increase in distance from the explosion. Finally, zone IV encompassed a region of intermittent failure of the tunnel surface with its maximum extent being the limit of observable damage. Table 2 gives a summary of the empirical designation of damage zones for all the tests conducted over unlined tunnels in sandstone. It should be noted at the bottom of Table 2 that the average scaled distances for zone I, zone II, zone III, and zone IV damage limits are 1.3, 2.0, 3.3, and 5.1 ft/lb$^3$, respectively. The peak radial strains measured as a function of scaled range for explosions in sandstone are shown by the line given in Fig. 8. The measured peak radial particle velocities versus scaled range are shown by the lines given in Fig. 9. A general summary of the behavior of unlined tunnels in sandstone in the Underground Explosion Tests is given in Table 3. In Table 3 it is shown that the outer limit of zone I corresponds to a

**Table 2**
**Scale Damage Distance in Tunnels**

| Round | *Scale Distance* $(ft/lb^{1/3})$ *from Charge to* Tunnel Portal | Tunnel Face | Nearest Point of Tunnel | Number of Observers | *Scale Damage Distances,* $R/W^{1/3}$ $(ft/lb^{1/3})$ Zone I | | Zone II | | Zone III | | Zone IV | |
|---|---|---|---|---|---|---|---|---|---|---|---|---|
| 807 | 13.4 | 1.8 | 1.19 | 3 | 1.2 | 1.3 | 1.9 | — | 2.7 | — | 3.1 | — |
| 808 | 7.4 | 7.8 | 1.75 | 3 | — | — | 1.8 | 1.8 | 2.2 | 2.2 | 3.8 | 4.8 |
| 809 | 7.5 | 4.6 | 3.32 | 2 | — | — | — | — | — | — | 4.3 | — |
| 810 | 16.5 | 7.2 | 3.29 | 3 | — | — | — | — | 4.0 | 3.3 | 5.2 | 4.5 |
| 811 | 10.2 | 13.6 | 1.82 | 2 | — | — | 2.4 | 2.0 | 3.5 | 3.6 | 5.0 | 5.3 |
| 812 | 5.3 | 17.6 | 1.32 | 4 | — | — | 1.6 | 1.3 | 2.5 | 2.6 | 4.0 | 4.0 |
| 813 | 9.0 | 5.8 | 1.71 | 2 | — | — | 2.0 | 2.1 | 3.4 | 3.4 | 4.8 | 4.5 |
| 814 | — | 6.4 | 2.76 | 3 | — | — | 3.8 | 2.8 | 4.2 | 3.1 | 8.7 | — |
| 814"A" | 4.4 | 7.2 | 3.51 | 3 | — | — | — | — | 3.7 | 3.7 | — | 5.3 |
| 815 | — | 1.9 | 1.17 | 4 | 1.2 | 1.3 | 1.7 | — | 4.0 | — | 6.4 | — |
| 816 | — | 8.0 | 1.43 | 4 | 1.5 | 1.5 | 1.9 | 2.0 | 3.7 | 3.5 | 7.3 | — |
| 817 | 4.8 | — | 1.75 | 5 | — | — | 2.6 | 2.2 | 3.6 | — | — | — |
| 817"A" | 2.5 | 3.4 | 1.75 | 5 | — | — | 1.8 | 1.9 | — | 2.8 | — | — |
| 817"B" | 2.1 | 1.2 | 0.85 | 5 | — | — | 1.3 | — | — | — | — | — |
| | | | | | Average | | | | Average | | | |
| | | | | | 1.3 | 1.4 | 2.0 | 2.0 | 3.4 | 3.1 | 5.3 | 4.7 |
| | | | | | 1.3 | | 2.0 | | 3.3 | | 5.1 | |

free-field strain of about 1%. The outer limit of zone III corresponds to a radial strain of about 0.0012, and the other limit of zone IV corresponds to a free-field radial strain of about 0.0004.

From Table 3 it is apparent that particle velocities on the order of 3–6 fps were associated with the limit of occasional rock drops from the roof in an unlined tunnel. This type of failure would not occur in a lined tunnel. Thus, it seems that the UET test data indicate that the Langefors and Kihlstrom [14] damage criteria for tunnels in rock (10 in./sec) is conservative enough to be used in practice for both lined and unlined tunnels.

For residential-type structures the writer has used 2 in./sec as a damage criterion for controlling blasting operations. The relationship between charge weights per delay and distance for 2 in./sec from Ambraseys and Hendron [1] and Oriard [18,19] are given in Fig. 3. Note that the Ambraseys-Hendron and Oriard curves for 2 in./sec (Fig. 3) fall very close to the Langefors-Kihlstrom threshold relationship given by line 7 in Fig. 3. This criterion has not resulted in damage and also allows the contractor to excavate the rock as long as the blasting operation is greater than about 30 ft from the structure in question. For distances closer than about 30 ft it is usually found that a

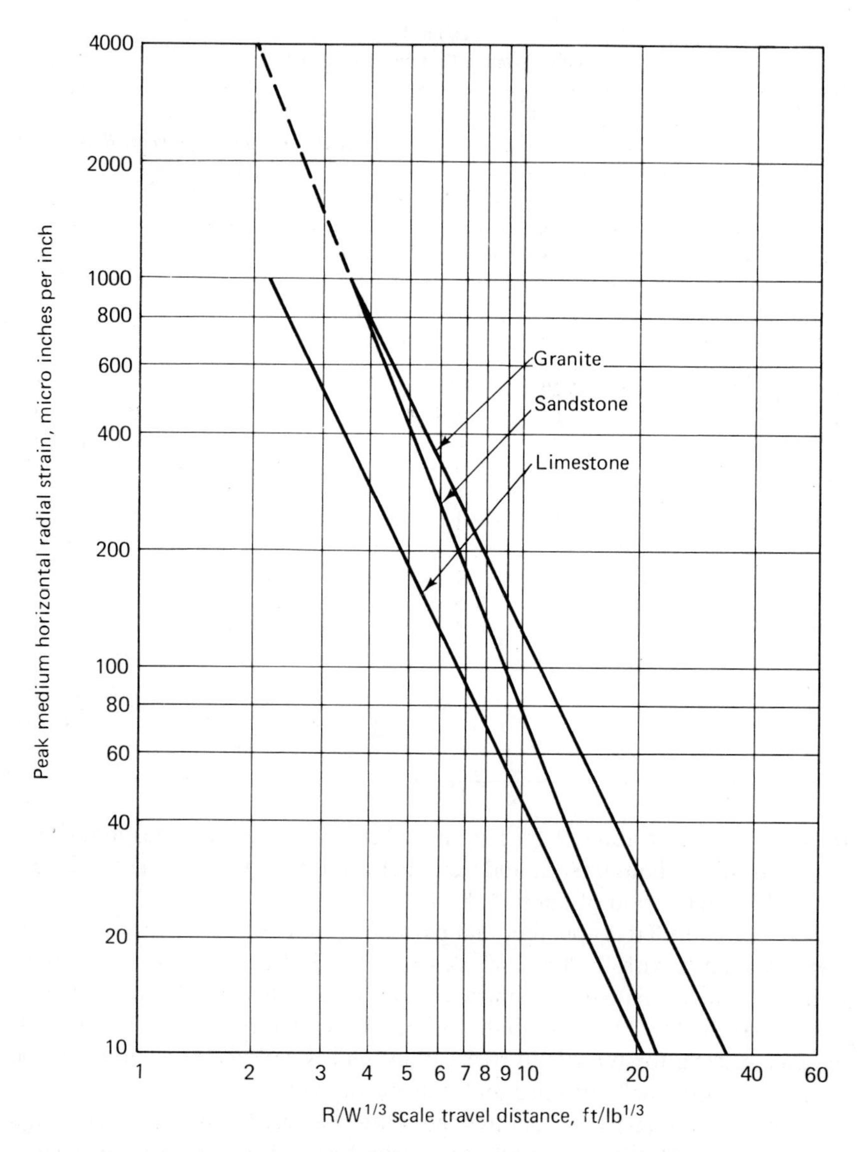


**Fig. 8.** Variation of average peak medium horizontal radial strain with scale travel distance in granite, limestone, and sandstone

2-in./sec criterion will severely restrict the contractor's operations. It has been the experience of the writer that these structures can tolerate a higher particle velocity without damage for small charges close to the structure because the motion occurs at a high frequency (40–150 cps), whereas the empirical criterion of 2 in./sec was developed for more distant blasts where the pre-

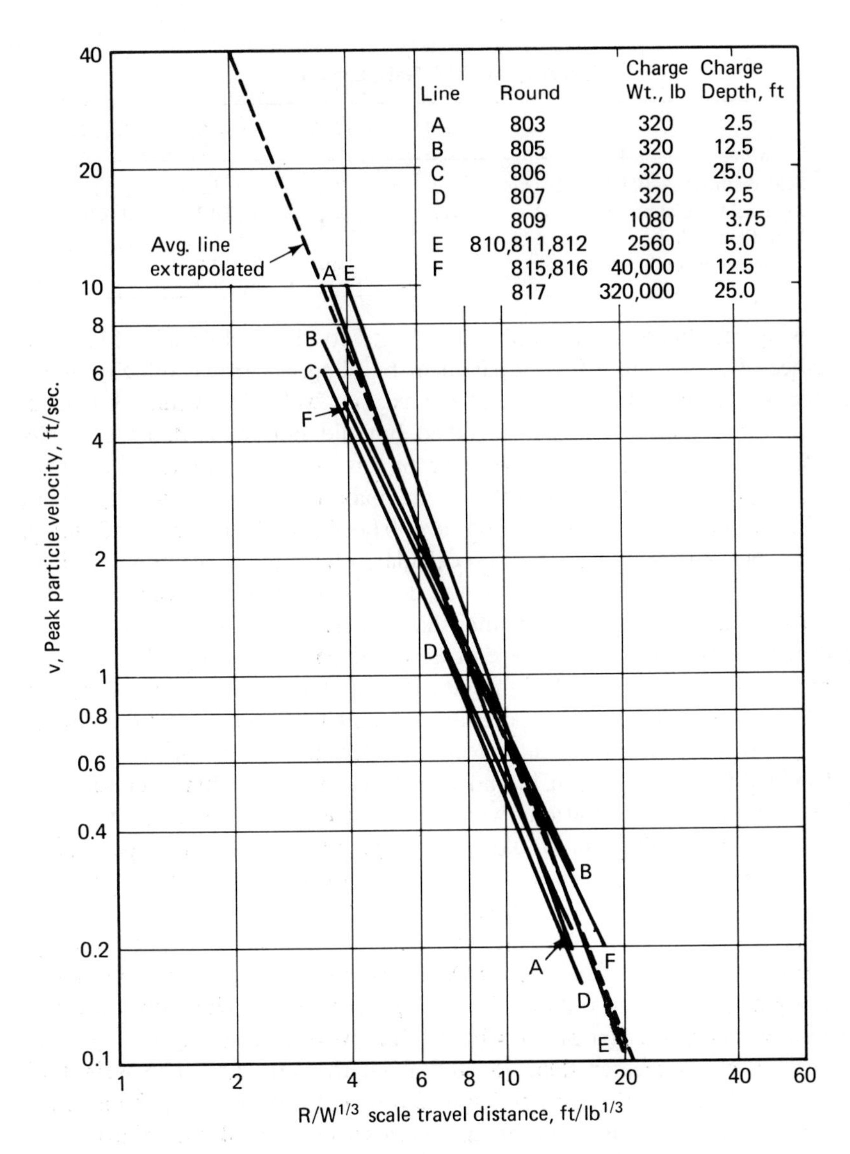


**Fig. 9.** Variation of peak particle velocity with scale travel distance

dominant ground motion frequencies were more nearly coincident with the frequency (about 10 cps) of the single-story structures studied. In such instances the response spectrum of the blasting vibrations can be used as a basis for determining permissible charge weights per delay for close-in blasts.

The application of the response spectrum for determining the allowable charge per delay for close-in blasting as discussed above is illustrated by the

**Table 3**
**Summary of UET Tests, Sandstone**

| | *Zone I* | *Zone II* | *Zone III* | *Zone IV* |
|---|---|---|---|---|
| Scaled range, $R/W^{1/3}$, ft/lb$^{1/3}$ | 1.3 | 2.0 | 3.3 | 5.1 |
| Free-field radial strain | 0.012 | 0.004 | 0.0012 | 0.0004 |
| Free-field radial particle velocity, fps | | 40 | 13 | 3–6 |

following case history of a job in New York City. For a 4 lb/delay blast at a distance of 25 ft from a brick apartment building, a particle velocity of 3.5 in./sec was measured at the base of the exterior wall. This value, of course, was in excess of the 2 in./sec specified but did not cause damage to the building. If the peak ground vibrations for this case are computed from Eqs. (2), (3), and (4) for $c = 10{,}000$ fps, the maximum ground displacement, particle velocity, and acceleration are 0.0066 in., 3.4 in./sec, and 6.5 g, respectively. The response spectrum calculated from the procedure described previously is shown in Fig. 10. It was determined that the structure had a frequency of less than 10 cps and that the responses of masonry walls between columns and floors were at about 30 cps. Thus, from Fig. 10 it is apparent that the response of the structure and wall was governed by the displacement bound to the spectrum. Thus, the structure should not be damaged or the wall cracked if the response spectrum of subsequent blasts did not exceed the displacement bound in Fig. 10. Thus, for blasts closer than 25 ft, charge-distance relations were determined from Eq. (2) such that a displacement of 0.0066 in. would not be exceeded. This charge per delay-distance relationship is shown in Table 4 along with the expected maximum particle velocity. This guideline was used for the remainder of the job and enabled the contractor to excavate the rock with no damage to the building.

For blasting near reinforced tie back retaining walls, bridge abutments, bridge piers, engineered industrial buildings, and semigravity dam sections a maximum velocity criterion of 4 in./sec has been successfully used by the writer for blasts greater than 25–30 ft from the structure. The weight of charge per delay as a function of distance which can be used in such instances is given by curve 3 in Fig. 3. For distances closer than 25–30 ft the charges can be increased above those given by curve 3 of Fig. 3 on a case-by-case basis by using the response spectrum approach with the pertinent properties of the structure involved. The application of the approach as indicated above for a semigravity dam section led to the charge per delay-distance relationship as shown in Table 5 for distances closer than 50 ft.

For unusual problems without precedent the response spectrum approach may be the only available method upon which engineering decisions can be based. Such an example is the consideration of damage or loss of service of electrical equipment in adjacent buildings. The engineer will simply have to

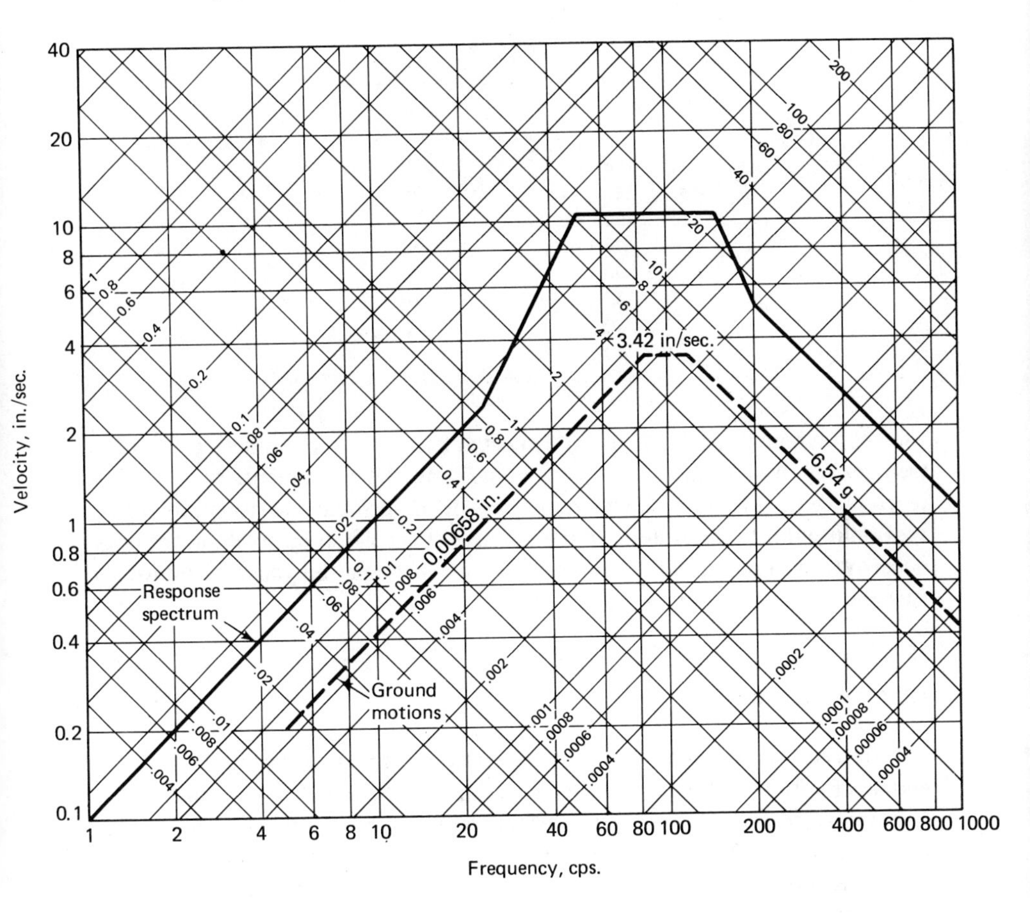


**Fig. 10.** Predicted response spectrum at 25 ft. from a 4 lb /delay blast

**Table 4**

| *Distance (R) to Blast (ft)* | *Maximum Permissible Charge Per Delay (lb/delay)* | *Maximum* Permissible Particle Velocity (in./sec)* |
|---|---|---|
| <5 | — | — |
| 5–10 | 0.5 | 12.0 |
| 10–15 | 1.0 | 6.7 |
| 15–20 | 2.0 | 5.2 |
| 20–25 | 3.0 | 4.1 |
| 25–30 | 4.0 | 3.4 |
| 30–35 | 5.0 | 2.9 |
| >35 | | 2.0 |

*Largest single velocity component.

Table 5

| $R$ (*ft*) | $W$ (*lb/delay*) |
|---|---|
| 150 | 200 |
| 125 | 125 |
| 100 | 80 |
| 75 | 50 |
| 50 | 20 |
| 30 | 10 |
| 20 | 5 |
| 10 | 2 |

use the response spectrum of the expected motions in conjunction with the frequencies of the racks or mounts containing the equipment. The fragility level of the equipment can then be used to determine the acceptable base motion input into the system. In the absence of specific fragility data, the peak acceleration transmitted to the equipment through the racks, mounts, or suspended floors should be less than 1 g.

## Airblast Effects

In typical downhole blasting operations, airwaves are not likely to endanger any structures. Occasionally, however, such a hazard may exist. Examples are operations where surface charges are detonated, where large quantities of primacord are exposed at the surface, where no stemming is used (such as tunnel or shafting rounds), or where demolition is above ground. Ordinary structures, such as single-story homes, could have new plaster cracks formed with airblast overpressures on the order of 1 psi. Overpressures on the order of 1 psi would also most certainly break all windows. The data shown in Fig. 11 indicate that nearly all windows less than 60 $ft^2$ in area, if properly mounted, are safe from breaking at airblast pressures less than about 0.1 psi. There have been observations in practice, however, where occasional windows have been broken at pressure levels corresponding to about 0.1 psi where the windows have been poorly mounted.

In Fig. 12, relationships are given between peak overpressure in psi and the scaled range in $ft/lb^{1/3}$ for blasts at various depths of burial. The three shaded curves represent data from experiments with spherical charges in clay and in rock at scaled depths of burial of $\frac{1}{2}$ $ft/lb^{1/3}$ and 1 $ft/lb^{1/3}$. Also shown on the same diagram are data from single delay quarry blasts and multiple delay quarry blasts. It should be noted that the data from the single delay and multiple delay quarry blasts fall quite close to the data from the single spherical charges detonated at a scaled depth of 1 $ft/lb^{1/3}$ if the quarry blast

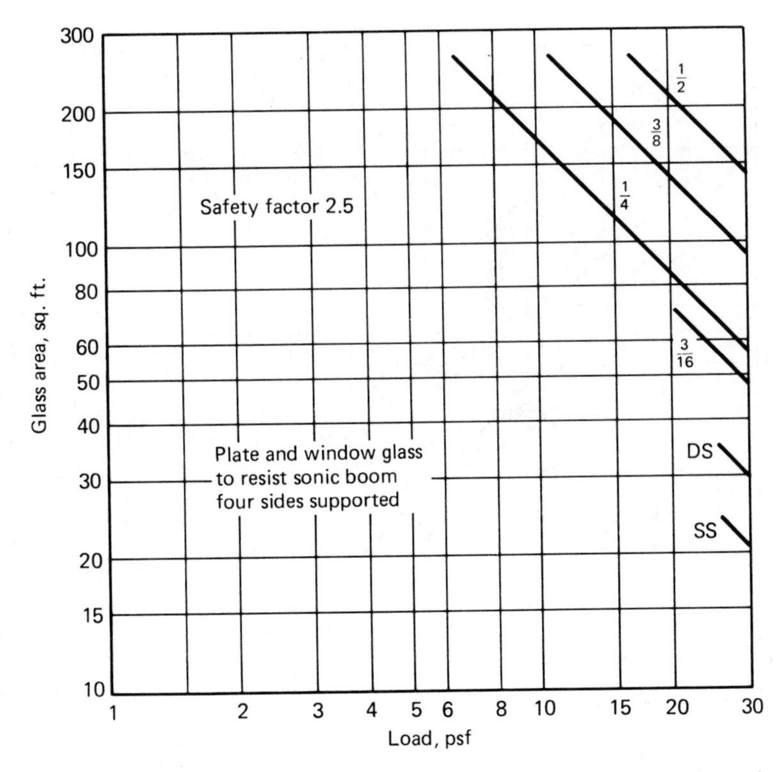


**Fig. 11.** Relation between window area and safe sonic boom pressure for various glass thickness. (After PPG Industries, 1969)

data are scaled using the weight of charge in the group of holes which are shot on the same delay interval closest to the point where the airblast was measured. The solid line given in Fig. 12 is a suggested approximate relationship to determine the overpressure for the various scaled ranges from the group of holes with the maximum charge per delay. Note that an overpressure of 1 psi occurs at a scaled range of 4 $ft/lb^{1/3}$ and that an overpressure of 0.1 psi occurs at a scaled range of 40 $ft/lb^{1/3}$. Figure 12 should not be used to predict airblast from shafting or tunnel rounds or for bench blasting with primacord rather than electric blasting caps.

In Fig. 3, the relationship between the maximum charge per delay and the scaled range which yields an airblast pressure of 1 psi is shown by line 1. The relationship between maximum charge per delay and the range which yields an airblast pressure of 0.1 psi is given by line 5. The relationship given by line 1 shows that an airblast pressure of 1 psi occurs at much closer ranges than the ground velocities which are likely to damage a structure. Thus, plaster cracking should never be caused by airblast for downhole blasting with electric caps and most probably would be caused by ground vibration. It does

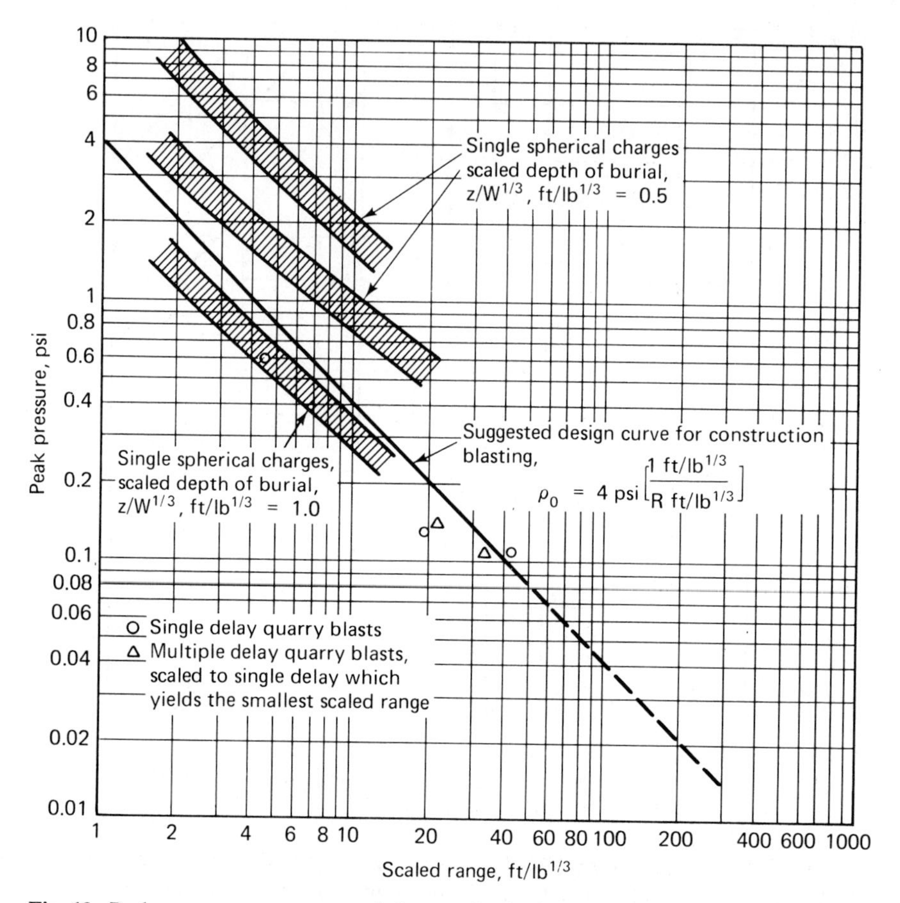


**Fig. 12.** Peak overpressure versus scaled range for buried explosions

appear, however, that the relationship shown on line 5 (Fig. 3) for 0.1 psi, that airblast pressures of 0.1 psi can extend out as far as ranges corresponding to a ground velocity of 2 in./sec. Thus, occasional windows could be broken, if very poorly mounted, at ranges corresponding to a ground velocity of 2 in./sec.

## Human Response

A simple statement regarding the potential hazard of vibrations to structures does not begin to describe or satisfy the overall problem of blasting in a populated area. One of the chief difficulties is the sensitivity of people to sounds and vibrations and their lack of knowledge of the normal static nonvibratory physical forces which are involved in their daily lives. Consequently, one must at least consider the reaction of people as well as the response of the structures.

The response of humans to vibration has been studied by Reiher and Meister [22]. They studied the response of people to steady-state vibrations. Crandell [4] published curves on the level of human response to transient vibration. And more recently, Rathbone [21] and Bollinger [3] discussed the perceptibility of people to transient motion. A simplified summary of the response of people to steady-state motion is given in Fig. 13(a). The response of people to transient vibratory motion, without noise, is given in Fig. 13(b). Note that people can notice transient motions as low as 0.06 in./sec, that the

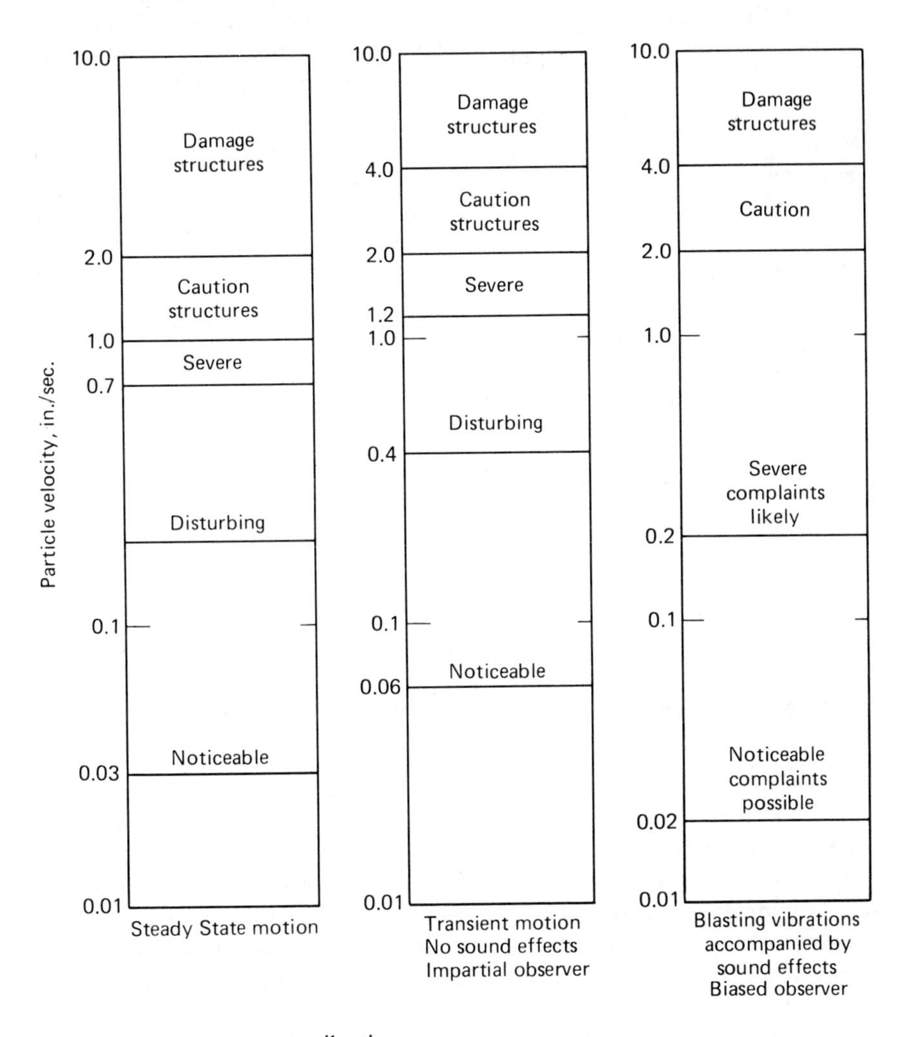


**Fig. 13.** Human response to vibrations

motion becomes disturbing at 0.4 in./sec, and that it feels severe to people at 1.2 in./sec. In actual practice, however, all rules for predicting motion response fall apart when sound effects accompany the motion and when the motion is of short duration. In some instances, the average person forms a judgment based largely on his psychoacoustic responses and is usually unaware of the important distinction between the characteristics of the motion alone and the sound effects that accompany that motion. One type of sound effect is produced by a blast which generates a very large noise at the source of the explosion. Such a blast is often regarded as severe and damaging when damage did not occur and when motion was not perceptible. To the average layman, the loud noise is sufficient to prove severity. Similarly, a blast may be accompanied by an inaudible airwave that has sufficient energy to cause loose windows and doors to rattle. The motion may be imperceptible, but the building occupant can be expected to judge the intensity of the blast by what he heard. Simply stated, he thinks the building was subject to strong vibration because he heard the sound of vibration of parts of the structure.

In Fig. 13(c), a simplified guideline is given for human response for blasting vibrations accompanied by sound effects for an observer who is slightly biased and is cognizant of the fact that blasting is going on in the area. For this combination, the blasting is noticeable at 0.02 in./sec and is often judged to be severe, and complaints are likely at a particle velocity as low as 0.2 in./sec. It may be in planning some blasting operations that these factors, rather than structural damage considerations, may govern.

## Controlled Perimeter Blasting

### *General*

Line drilling, cushion blasting, and presplitting are controlled blasting techniques for producing smooth walls on the perimeter of surface excavations in rock. Smooth wall blasting is a procedure used to produce smooth perimeters in tunnel excavations. A general description of the methods and guidelines for practical application of these methods are given below.

### *Line Drilling*

Line drilling consists of a single row of closely spaced, unloaded, small-diameter holes along the perimeter of the excavation, as shown in Fig. 14. The line of line drill holes provides a plane of weakness to which the production blast can break. Line drill holes should be about 2 to 3 in. in diameter, and the spacing between holes should be 2–4 times the hole diameter. The distance between the line drill holes and the adjacent row of holes is usually 50–75% of the normal burden. The spacing of holes in the row adjacent to the perimeter is also commonly reduced to 50–75% of the normal spacing, and the load-

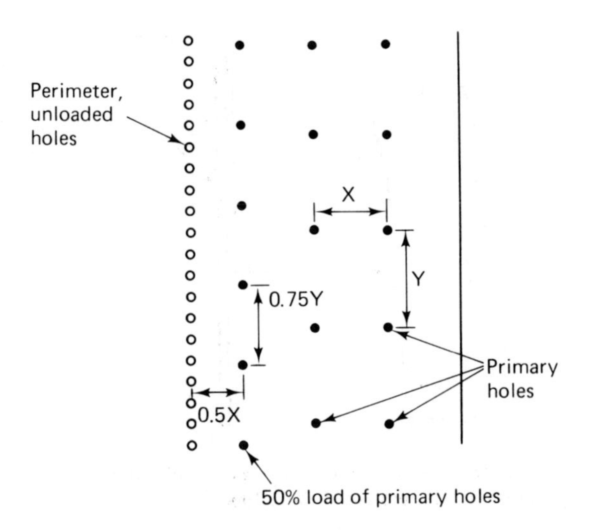


**Fig. 14.** Typical hole pattern for line drilling. (After Du-Pont Blasters Handbook, 1966)

ing of holes in this row is about 50% of the loading used in the primary holes. One of the most important factors affecting the results on a job where the line drilling technique is used is the drill hole alignment. Holes should not deviate out of a vertical plane more than 6 in. Drilling accuracy usually is the main factor which controls the maximum depth to which one set of line drilled holes should be drilled.

Line drilling is used on nearly all perimeters immediately adjacent to existing structures in an urban environment. In some instances the unloaded perimeter holes may be drilled very close to form an open slot. This is done by inserting steel pipe into the last hole drilled and drilling the next hole adjacent to the pipe. This is called channel drilling.

### *Cushion Blasting*

Cushion blasting involves the use of a single row of holes along the perimeter of the excavation. Cushion blast holes are loaded with light, distributed charges which are stemmed and fired after the primary excavation is removed. The holes are fired with a minimum delay between holes such that the detonation tends to shear the rock between holes and give a smooth wall. After the primary cut is removed, a minimum burden should be left in front of the final excavation line, as shown in Fig. 15. The burden will vary with the hole diameter being used. Table 6 gives guidelines for drill hole spacing and loadings for various drill hole diameters. Note that the spacing between holes should always be less than the burden. The loadings given in Table 6 may be obtained by string-loading dynamite cartridges down primacord downlines

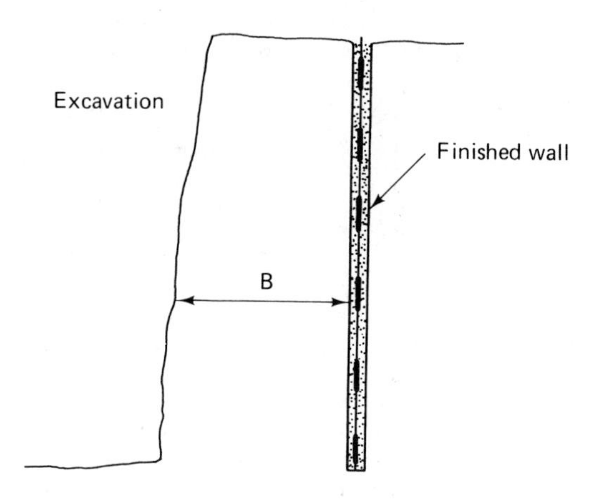


**Fig. 15.** Typical layout for cushion blasting. (After DuPont Blasters Handbook, 1966)

as shown in Fig. 15. Two to three times the loading used in the upper part of the hole should be used at the bottom of the hole to ensure shearing at the bottom of the hole. Sand or pea gravel is commonly used to stem the hole. The top 2 or 3 ft of the hole should be completely stemmed and not loaded. Primacord trunklines are normally used to get a minimum delay between holes, but if noise and ground vibrations must be controlled, MS delays can be used.

**Table 6***

| *Hole Diameter (in.)* | *Spacing (ft)* | *Burden (ft)* | *Hole Loading (lb/ft)* |
|---|---|---|---|
| 2–2½ | 3 | 4 | 0.08–0.25 |
| 3–3½ | 4 | 5 | 0.13–0.50 |
| 4–4½ | 5 | 6 | 0.25–0.75 |

*After *Blasters Handbook* [2].

### *Presplitting*

Presplitting consists of a single row of holes, 2 to 4 in. in diameter, drilled along the perimeter of the excavation. In most cases, all the holes are loaded. Presplitting is different from line drilling and cushion blasting because the holes are fired before the adjacent primary excavation is blasted, as shown in Fig. 16. In presplitting, the row of holes is shot simultaneously, and the web between holes is subjected to tensile stresses which cause cracking along the line of presplit holes on the perimeter of the excavation. This presplit surface

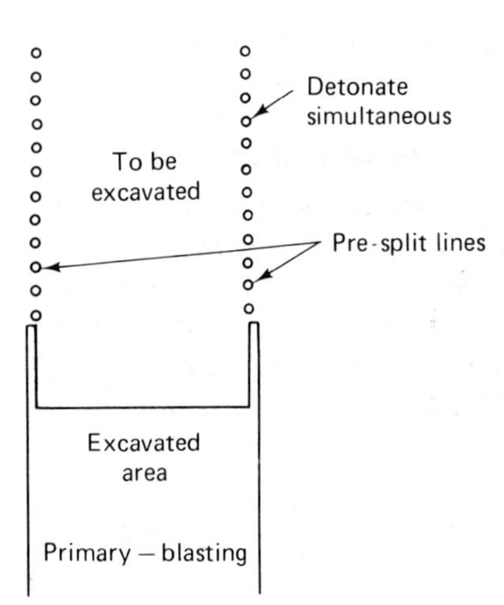


**Fig. 16.** Typical layout for presplit holes. (After DuPont Blasters Handbook, 1966)

is the smooth surface desired for the final excavation if the proper hole loadings and hole spacings are used.

Presplit holes are string-loaded, similar to cushion blasting holes, to obtain the average loadings shown in Table 7. The holes are usually fired simultaneously with a primacord trunkline, but if noise or ground vibrations are a consideration, sections of the presplit line can be fired with MS delays. The average spacings of presplit holes as a function of drill hole diameter are given in Table 7. All presplit holes should be completely stemmed as in cushion blasting and should be loaded to about twice the average loading in the bottom few feet of the hole to ensure shearing at the bottom of the hole.

**Table 7**
**Typical Loads and Spacings for Presplitting**

| *Hole Diameter (in.)* | *Spacing (ft)* | *Explosive Charge (lb/ft)* |
|---|---|---|
| 2–2½ | 1½–2 | 0.08–0.25 |
| 3–3½ | 1½–3 | 0.13–0.50 |
| 4 | 2–4 | 0.25–0.75 |

*After *Blasters Handbook* [2].

The depth that can be presplit at one time is primarily dependent on drilling accuracy. Depths of 20–40 ft are commonly used for drill hole sizes ranging from 2 to 4 in. The author has found that 3-in.-diameter holes on a 2-ft spacing loaded at about 0.25 lb/ft give good results for fairly average rock conditions.

Presplitting should not be used adjacent to existing structures because the gas pressures tend to heave the rock at shallow depths. The confinement and large number of holes detonated simultaneously also produce intense vibrations close to the presplit line.

### *Smooth Wall Blasting*

Smooth wall blasting is used in tunnels to obtain a smooth perimeter. The technique is very similar to cushion blasting in that holes are drilled at a fairly close spacing around the perimeter; these holes are lightly loaded and shot simultaneously to remove the final burden in the tunnel round. A typical tunnel round, designed to produce smooth walls, is shown in Fig. 17. In Fig. 17, the number by each drill hole denotes the number of the standard tunnel

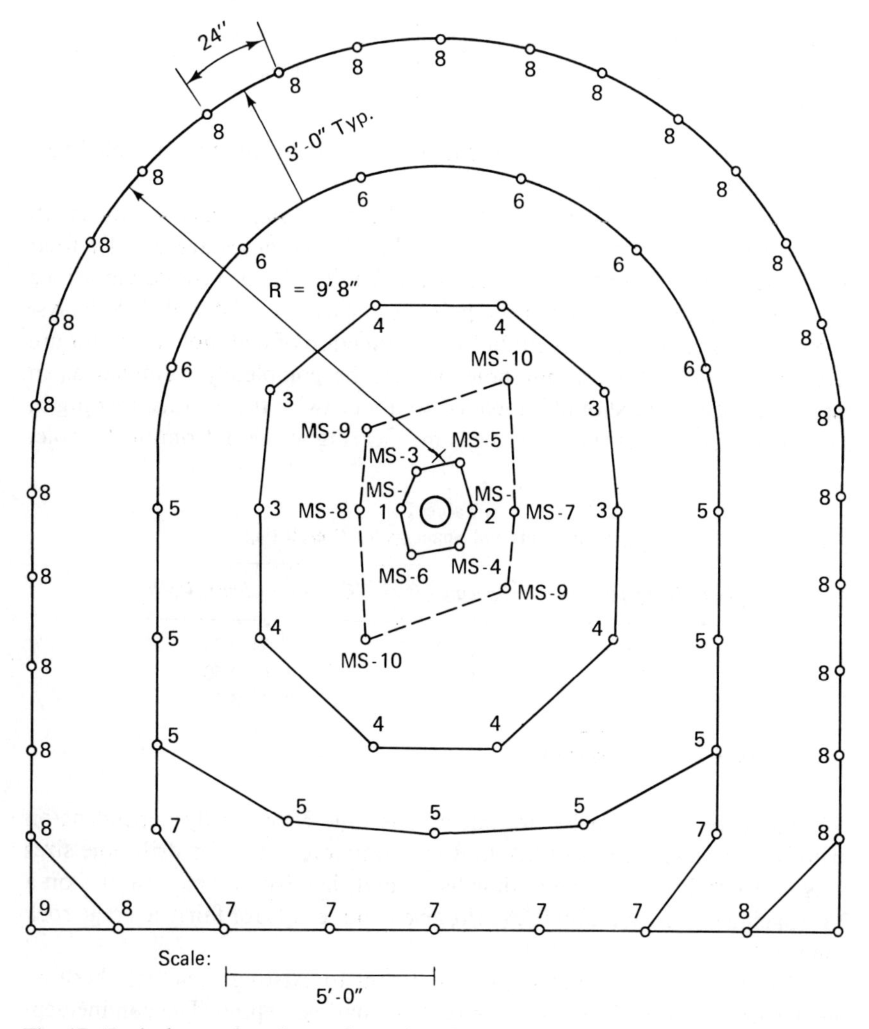


**Fig. 17.** Typical smooth wall tunnel round. (After Deere, 1972)

delay interval on which the hole is to be fired. If the letters MS are placed before the number, the hole is to be fired on that particular delay interval using millisecond delays. For the round shown in Fig. 17, the perimeter holes are shot simultaneously on the number 8 standard tunnel delay. The tunnel round should be designed such that the perimeter holes are fired on the lowest number delay possible. In general, the scatter in firing times increases as the delay number increases for electric caps; thus, the perimeter holes will be fired more nearly simultaneously if the delay used in the perimeter holes is as small as possible. One method of designing a tunnel round to reduce the delay number used on the perimeter holes is to use millisecond delays in the cut portion of the tunnel round. Note in Fig. 17 that the first 10-msec delay intervals were used to detonate the 12 holes used in the double spiral cut [14].

For smooth wall blasting, the spacing of the perimeter holes should be about 15 times the drill hole diameter, and the perimeter holes should be loaded with light, distributed charges ranging from $\frac{1}{8}$ to $\frac{1}{4}$ lb/ft of hole. Small-diameter cartridges are commercially available which will give these loadings. The burden on the perimeter holes at the time of firing should always be greater than the spacing of the perimeter holes. A burden of 1.5 times the spacing of the perimeter holes is commonly used but may have to be altered slightly for various rock conditions. For the round shown in Fig. 17, a hole spacing of 2 ft was used on the perimeter holes and a burden of 3 ft was employed.

## Blasting Specifications

### *General*

Blasting specifications for a civil engineering project are usually written in two parts. The first part of the specification covers the general blasting procedures, and a second part entitled Specific Requirements usually covers such special topics as the controlled blasting techniques discussed in this chapter. The items which should be included in these two parts of the blasting specifications are discussed below.

### *Specifications on General Blasting Procedures*

The specifications on general blasting procedure usually include those items which apply to all blasting operations. For example, in this section it is usually required that the contractor provide the services of at least one person qualified in the use of explosives for designing each blast and directing the execution of the blast. The qualifications of such persons are commonly required to be transmitted to the engineer for approval. If for one reason or another the blasting operations affect other aspects of a construction job, there should also be a requirement in these general specifications that the contractor must notify the engineer within some stated minimum time before blasting is to commence. This notification will permit the rescheduling of other operations and enable the engineer to control the use of such items as two-way radios which may be hazardous in the vicinity of electric blasting caps.

It is also common to specify in the general blasting specifications that the contractor submit the design of a blast to the engineer for approval before drilling and loading is begun. Such a plan should include the following information:

1. Number, location, diameter, and depth of drill holes shown on a plan drawn to scale.
2. Type and grade of explosive, size of cartridge, and weight of explosive in each hole.
3. Total amount of explosives in the blast and maximum pounds of explosive per delay interval.
4. Delay arrangement scheme showing delay interval proposed for each hole. Type and brand of delays should also be shown.
5. Character and source of firing current, size and length of lead lines, current requirement, and the combined resistance of the complete blasting circuit.

In each specification, it should be stated specifically what "approval" of the blasting plan by the engineer implies. Although the engineer may be extremely interested in inspecting the blasting plans regarding the adequacy of a round for obtaining a smooth perimeter, he may not be concerned about the design of a production blast to obtain adequate breakage so that the excavated rock can be handled by the type of equipment the contractor has on the job. Thus, as an example, a statement can be added to the specification stating that "approval of the blast design and plan by the engineer shall not relieve the contractor of his responsibility for the accuracy or adequacy of the plan for obtaining adequate breakage." Other examples may also be cited, but the significant point is that the specifications should clearly state the division of responsibility between the engineer and the contractor if the blasting plan is "approved."

Safety precautions should also be covered in the general specifications. The contractor is usually made completely responsible for safety in this portion of the specifications. All items regarding the safe handling, storage, and firing of explosives which are required in addition to the applicable federal, state, and municipal statutes should be covered. Such items may include the restriction of two-way radios, special precautions if stray currents have been detected on the site, procedures for clearing a danger area before blasting, and provisions for special inspection of equipment required if certain free-running blasting agents are used in place of cartridged explosives, and many other items too numerous to mention. One of the most important items to include in this section is the requirement of blasting mats if structures and people will be close enough such that fly rock is a problem.

### *Specific Blasting Specifications*

Specific requirements, which are necessary for achieving the desired results and which affect the contractor's costs, should be clearly stated in this section of the specifications. Specifications for vibration control, line drilling, presplitting, cushion blasting, and smooth wall blasting should be covered in this section of the specification. In addition, in many civil engineering jobs, limits may also be placed on some aspects of the production blasting. For example, if the engineer may wish to specify "small hole" blasting, there should be a statement in this section of the specification requiring that the blast holes be less than a certain diameter; that maximum diameter may be about 4 to 5 in. If a maximum diameter is not stated, the contracter may bid the job on the basis of large blast holes on large spacings, and restriction to smaller holes at a later date could possibly cause a contractual dispute.

Such items as the maximum depth of lift and the maximum depth of subdrilling permitted should also be treated in this portion of the specification. On jobs involving the installation of high-capacity tendons to tie back vertical cuts adjacent to structures the maximum depth of lift is extremely important since it governs the maximum unsupported height of cut immediately after each bench blast near the perimeter.

It has been the experience of the writer that the best way to cover vibration limitations *for blasts greater than about 30 ft away from a structure* is to specify the allowable vibration limit, not the quantity of explosive, and to specify the critical locations which will be monitored and the methods of monitoring. Specifying explosive quantities is not desirable. If the engineer is too liberal, he may actually exceed the vibration limits and get damage. It is more likely that the engineer will be too conservative and large sums of money will be wasted because his quantity limits are unnecessarily low. It is more desirable to let the contractor and his consultants demonstrate a little ingenuity. They may know of techniques for accomplishing the work more efficiently than the engineer anticipated and still stay within the limit the engineer really wants, namely a vibration limit (usually in terms of a maximum particle velocity). The writer has found it useful, however, to include a table in the specifications giving the approximate pounds per delay which will correspond to the specified velocity at various distances. Although this table may not be binding on either party, it does prevent the contractor from being totally surprised at the small charges required for some jobs. This type of contractor should be eliminated by a prequalification specification, however, if the owner's lawyers will permit.

When vibration limits are given in the specifications which are not to be exceeded at various locations of structures around the perimeter of the job, the owner should also make available in the bid documents any vibration data from test blasts in the immediate area. This will enable the contractor and his consultants to make the best prebid estimate of the procedures which they will use. If prebid test blasts are not available, then the specifications should provide for the job to be started with four or five test blasts for which the contractor should be paid. This will allow him to approach the vibration limits gradually and will enable him to adjust his production patterns on the basis of vibration data obtained on the site. Usually the engineer will provide the equipment and personnel to monitor the initial locations. But, on some jobs, it may be desirable for the contractor to make the vibration measurements. If this is the case, the specifications must specify the type of equipment, frequency response, etc., which will be satisfactory for accurately measuring the ground vibrations expected.

As shown previously in this chapter, it may be necessary to allow higher particle velocities as blasting gets closer than 30 ft from a structure. In such cases the engineer and the contractor should work out the charge-distance relations, as in Table 4, on the basis of seismograph measurements from initial blasts at distances farther than 30 ft from the structures of concern. Until this information is obtained the values in Table 4 or Table 5 could be used as a guide.

For the controlled perimeter blasting methods of line drilling, presplitting, and cushion blasting, the specifications should cover the following items:

1. The diameter, depth, and spacing of the perimeter holes should be specified for all three types of controlled blasting (line drilling, cushion blasting, and presplitting). This enables the contractor to estimate drilling costs.
2. An approximate range should be given of the charge per foot of hole for the presplit and cushion blast perimeter holes. For line drilling, it should be stated that the perimeter holes are unloaded.
3. Stemming materials should be specified for the presplit and cushion blast holes.
4. Hole alignment tolerances should be given for the perimeter holes for all three methods of controlled blasting (holes should not deviate more than 6 in. out of plane).
5. Simultaneous firing of the perimeter holes should be specified for cushion blasting and presplitting, unless simultaneous firing produces too much ground vibration. If ground vibrations control, then the perimeter holes should be shot with MS delays.
6. The approximate range of burden values should be suggested for cushion blasting.
7. The spacing and loading of the two holes adjacent to the perimeter holes should be suggested for line drilling.

For smooth wall blasting in tunnels, the following items should be included in the specifications:

1. The diameter and spacing of the perimeter holes should be specified.
2. The approximate burden on the perimeter holes should be suggested (1.1 to 1.5 times the spacing of the perimeter holes).
3. It should be required that all the perimeter holes, except the lifters, be fired on the last delay period used in the round.
4. The approximate loading in the perimeter holes should be suggested in the specifications.

## Conclusions

In this chapter, the technical aspects of controlling construction blasting to prevent damage to adjacent structures from ground vibrations and airblast has been discussed. Controlled blasting techniques available for producing smooth perimeters on both surface and tunnel excavations have also been reviewed. In addition, the items which should be covered in a good blasting specification have been set forth. The author feels that one of the most significant things that the reader should have learned from this chapter is that most of our knowledge about controlled blasting is empirical. Enough experience has been accumulated, however, that we are technically capable of achieving good controlled blasting for almost all situations where controlled blasting is required. In most situations where experience with controlled blasting has been poor, it can usually be traced to vague specifications which did not state either the result to be achieved or the detailed method to accomplish the desired result. The objective of this chapter was to give some of the detail which must be considered before a good specification can be written. It should be obvious that the specification writer must have at his disposal a knowledge of many of the construction details of blasting to permit the writing of an acceptable specification.

The writer has also found that a knowledge of the response spectrum of ground motions produced by blasting vibrations is valuable for making design decisions affecting the specifications for those cases where we are presently lacking precedent.

## References

1. Ambraseys, N. R., and A. J. Hendron, Jr., "Dynamic Behavior of Rock Masses," *Rock Mechanics in Engineering Practice*, K. G. Stagg and O. C. Zienkiewicz, eds., Wiley, New York, 1968, pp. 203–27.
2. *Blasters Handbook*, E. I. duPont de Nemours and Company, Inc., Wilmington, 1966.

3. Bollinger, G. A., "Blast Vibration Analysis," manuscript to Sprengnether Instrument Company. (Private communication.)
4. Crandell, F. J., "Ground Vibration Due to Blasting and Its Effect Upon Structures," *J. Boston Soc., Civil Eng.* Vol. 36, No. 2, 1949, pp. 206–229.
5. Deere, D. U., personal communication, 1972.
6. Devine, J. R., "Avoiding Damage to Residences from Blasting Vibrations," *Highway Research Record No. 135*, Highway Research Board, National Research Council, National Academy of Sciences, Washington, D.C., 1966.
7. Devine, J. F., and W. I. Duvall, "Effect of Charge Weight on Vibration Levels for Millisecond Delayed Quarry Blasts," *Earthquake Notes Seism. Soc. Am.*, Vol. 34, No. 2, 1963, p. 17.
8. Dowding, C. H., "Response of Buildings to Ground Vibrations Resulting from Construction Blasting," Ph.D. thesis, University of Illinois, Urbana, 1971.
9. Duvall, W. I., and D. E. Fogelson, "Review of Criteria for Estimating Damage to Residences from Blasting Vibrations," *Report of Investigations 5968*, Bureau of Mines Report, Denver, 1962, 19 pp.
10. Edwards, A. T., and T. D. Northwood, "Experimental Studies of the Effects of Blasting on Structures," *The Engineer*, Vol. 210, Sept. 30, 1960.
11. Engineering Research Associates, "Underground Explosion Test Program, Final Report," Vol. II: Rock, 1953.
12. Hendron, A. J., Jr., "Scaling of Ground Motions from Contained Explosions in Rock for Estimating Direct Ground Shock from Surface Bursts on Rock," *Technical Report No. 15*, Omaha District, Corps of Engineers, Omaha, 1973.
13. Hendron, A. J., Jr., and C. H. Dowding, "Ground and Structural Response Due to Blasting," *Proceedings, 3rd Congress of the International Society of Rock Mechanics*, Vol. II-B, National Academy of Sciences, Washington, D.C., 1974, pp. 1359–1364.
14. Langefors, U., and B. Kihlstrom, *The Modern Technique of Rock Blasting*, Wiley, New York, and Almqvist & Wiksell, Stockholm, 1963, 405 pp.
15. Langefors, U., B. Kihlstrom, and H. Westerburg, "Ground Vibrations in Blasting," *Water Power*, Feb, 1958, pp. 335–338, 390–395, 421–424.
16. Newmark, N. M., "Problems in Wave Propagation in Soil and Rock," *Proceedings of International Symposium on Wave Propagation and Dynamic Properties of Earth Materials*, University of New Mexico Press, Albuquerque, 1968, pp. 7–26.
17. Newmark, N. M., and W. J. Hall, "Seismic Design Criteria for Nuclear Reactor Facilities," *Proceedings, 4th World Conference on Earthquake Engineering, Santiago, Vol. 2*, IAEA, 1969, pp. 37–50.
18. Oriard, L. L., "Blasting Effects and Their Control in Open Pit Mining," Symposium and Speciality Seminar on Stability in Open Pit Mines, University of British Columbia, Vancouver, Nov. 1971.
19. Oriard, L. L., "Blasting Operations in the Urban Environment," *Bull. Assoc. Eng. Geol.*, Winter 1971.
20. PPG Industries, "Glass Product Recommendations, Structural," *PPG Industries Technical Service Report No. 101*, Pittsburgh, 1969.
21. Rathbone, T. C., "Human Sensitivity to Product Vibration," *Product Eng.*, 1963.

22. Reiher, H., and F. J. Meister, "Die Empfindlichkeit des Menschen gegen Erschutterungen (Human Sensitivity to Vibration)," *Forsch. Gebiete Ing.*, Vol. 2, No. 11, 1931, pp. 381–386.
23. Thoenen, S. R., and S. L. Windes, "Seismic Effects of Quarry Blasting," *Bulletin 442*, Bureau of Mines, Denver, 1942, 83 pp.

# The Representation and Use of Design Specifications *

S. J. FENVES** AND R. N. WRIGHT†

## Abstract

*Design specifications are presented as the primary communication and control tool for the design and construction industry. Requisite properties of completeness, uniqueness, and correctness are identified, and the role of performance and limit state concepts in specifying intent of the specifications are emphasized. Formal representational methods are presented at three levels: decision tables for specification provisions, an information network for related provisions, and argument trees for organizing and outlining. An idealized process for specification development is presented, and the use of the representational tools for checking specifications and providing strategies for textual expression is described and illustrated. Development of computer aids for specification processing in design and conformance checking is described.*

## I. Introduction

We use the term design specifications to encompass all types of formal documents used for the evaluation of engineering or architectural design. These include

- Legal building codes;
- Model building codes such as the BOCA Basic Building Code [5];



**Professor of Civil Engineering, Carnegie-Mellon University, Pittsburgh, Pennsylvania.

†Director, Center for Building Technology, National Bureau of Standards, Washington, D.C.

- Consensus standards such as the ACI Building Code Requirements for Reinforced Concrete [2];
- Proprietary or trade association specifications such as the AISC Specification for the Design, Fabrication and Erection of Structural Steel for Buildings [4]; and
- Specifications of agencies or owners, such as the U.S. Department of Housing and Urban Development Minimum Property Standards for Federal Housing Administration mortgages [11].

Our discussion specifically excludes project specifications and other specifications used in contractual relationships and product specifications describing existing products or systems.

Design specifications are the primary communication tools and control mechanisms for the design and construction industry. They provide for effective expression of intent between owners, designers, public authorities, builders, and users of buildings. The quality of the built environment, including its functionality and safety, is directly dependent on the quality of the specifications controlling its design. Ventre [21] has argued that because of the "diverse, dispersed, detached, and discontinuous" nature of the building industry, specifications, and especially their legal embodiments in building codes, represent essentially the only "collective memory" of the industry.

Design specifications represent the culmination of a broad professional concern. Generally, design specifications intend to assure the functionality of a building or system and to protect the public health, safety, and welfare during construction and use. Designers and building regulatory officials use design specifications to achieve a common understanding in order to effectively control designs. Specification writers translate knowledge of the environment, structural behavior, and requirements for functionality and safety into usable requirements or practices in specification form. Most civil engineering researchers aim to improve design and construction practices; much of the output of this research is implemented through new or revised specifications. Siess [20] has described the mutual interaction and reinforcement among research, practice, and specifications.

While most researchers are concerned with improving the content of specifications by basing them on more rational models of material and structural behavior, our concern is primarily with the format of specifications. It will be shown that the two aspects of content and format are closely interrelated and that methods designed to improve their format can also yield better content.

At the present, there are no recognized formal methods for generating or reviewing proposed new specifications or modifications of existing ones. Notwithstanding the importance of design specifications to the building industry and the cost of producing them, there is no methodology, beyond informal peer review and occasional test comparisons with previous specifications, for making any quantitative evaluation of proposed specifications. Furthermore, while an increasing fraction of processing of design information against specifications is performed by computer programs, the entire responsibility for the correctness of these programs, including the selection of provisions to be included and the detailed interpretation of these provisions, rests with the computer program developers. Neither the users of these programs nor building officials required to pass judgment on their output have any ready means to ascertain that programs perform in all cases as intended by the specification writers.

We shall show here that rigorous mathematical foundations exist on which efficient, formalized procedures for developing and using specifications may be built. These methods apply to three distinct processes:

- *Formulation*, the development of the information content of the specification;
- *Expression*, the exposition of the information content in both conventional textual form and in forms adaptable for computer processing; and
- *Use*, the interpretation and application of the specification to the evaluation of designs in both manual and computer-aided processes.

Our objective is to improve engineering practices through better specifications and better methods for their use. We shall present the bases for a systematic approach to the formulation, expression, and use of specifications which assure three requisite properties:

- *Completeness*, that the specification explicitly applies in any possible situation;
- *Uniqueness*, that the specification yields one and only one result in any possible situation; and
- *Correctness*, that the result is that intended by the specification writers.

The methods presented are suitable for both manual and computer-aided applications by specification writers, designers, and reviewers for building regulatory authorities. With slight modifications, the methods are equally applicable to three types of design specifications:

- *Performance specifications*, which state the required attributes in a scheme-independent manner, such as the Guide Criteria for Operation BREAKTHROUGH [10];
- *Procedural specifications*, which state required attributes and procedures for their evaluation in a scheme-dependent manner, such as the ACI and AISC specifications; and

- *Prescriptive specifications*, which state required dimensions or properties in a manner completely defining the acceptable configurations or procedures in a scheme-dependent manner, such as the One and Two Family Dwelling Code [19].

## II. Background

The investigation of the properties of completeness and uniqueness of specification provisions is closely related to the aspect of linguistics called *syntax*, dealing with language organization. Correctness, on the other hand, deals with meaning and intent and is therefore related to *semantics*. The formalization of the semantic aspect of specifications is aided by two powerful concepts.

First, the performance concept involves stating the attribute satisfying user needs without prescribing the materials, components, or systems to be employed. J. R. Wright [22] describes the evolution of the performance concept from its apparent beginnings at the Building Research Station in the United Kingdom in the 1930s. As will be shown, performance is important for all specifications, not only performance specifications, since it gives explicit attention to the attributes the designer intends to provide.

The limit state concept is a second formalism appropriate to the semantics of specifications. As described by Allen [1], limit states describe those conditions for which systems or elements would no longer fit their intended purposes. A limit state is not synonymous with a performance attribute, since the condition may deal with a response related to the intended performance, such as cracking, but not occurring in all possible solution schemes.

Neither the performance attributes of interest nor the limit states of concern are explicitly expressed in most existing specifications. This lack of clarity has made it difficult to improve specifications through research, as there can be no certainty that a specification provision is improved if neither the response of concern nor the desired performance attribute is clearly defined.

The proper syntax or organization of the information in specifications is also vital to the transmittal of intent from writers to the users. Frequent complaints of practitioners and students alike indicate that specifications are "too complex" and "hard to follow." It will be shown that many of these valid complaints can be removed by the use of formal methods to assure that the intent of the specification writers is maintained in the textual expression.

The methods presented here are primarily based on the writers' cooperative efforts over a long period. In 1966, Fenves [6] identified the applicability of decision tables, a then-recent program development tool, to the representation of provisions of procedural design specifications. With Gaylord and Goel, he presented in decision table form the AISC Specification [8]. Decision table formulations of other design specifications have been developed by Seeberg [19] and Noland [13].

The AISC study [8] also revealed that the information content of the specification is topologically related in a hierarchical network; this observation led to a prototype computer program for the review of designs [9]. Wright et al. [23] recognized that the topological relationship of data provided a key to the efficient formulation and processing of constraints in computer-aided design programs. The implication of these studies on computer-aided design was summarized by Fenves [7]. Fenves and Wright investigated the application of the concepts developed to the restructuring of the textual expression of the AISC Specification [16, 24]. Based on this work, Nyman and Fenves [14] explored algorithms and computer aids for organizing the information content of specifications and its textual expression. The methodology has been advanced substantially in work continuing at Carnegie-Mellon University, the National Bureau of Standards, and the University of Illinois. In this chapter we shall summarize the technologies and present recent advances.

## III. Analysis of Specifications

The concepts outlined in the preceding sections are best illustrated by applying them to the analysis of selected portions of the AISC Specification [4]. The AISC Specification, as most specifications in use today, is an outgrowth of a long historical development started decades before the concepts of performance and limit states were introduced. Thus, a part of the analysis is to locate and identify these qualities.

### *3.1 Development*

In performance terminology, the AISC Specification deals with the entity "structure" or "structural system" and the two major attribute categories of "safety" and "serviceability." Within "safety," the environment of concern is the effect of external loads, while for "serviceability," the concern is with fitness for erection and use. To achieve these performance attributes, the design must guard against applicable limit states.

The entity "structure" must be further subdivided. A major category is that of "member," which is readily distinguished from other categories, such as "connection" and "connector," dealt with in the specification. The entity "member," however, is still too general, in that specific limit states cannot be directly associated with it. Since limit states are related to response, it is convenient to introduce a subdivision of members by stress type, such as "tension," "compression," etc. It is to be noted that stress type is not a strict subdivision of members (at different stages of the design process, a member may be investigated for different stress types or combinations) but a common property of members which acts as a selector to associate members with the applicable limit states.

For the subdivision of "tension members," the applicable limit states under "safety" are "yielding" and "rupture," whereas under "serviceability," the AISC Commentary specifically mentions "undesirable lateral movement ('slapping' or 'vibration')" [3].

Finally, it is necessary to prescribe a measure which will ensure satisfactory performance. In dealing with members, the AISC Specification handles the safety attribute by specifying a maximum allowable stress and satisfies the serviceability attribute by limiting the slenderness ratio.

Thus, we arrive at the two provisions of the AISC Specification dealing with tension members, reproduced verbatim from Ref. 4:

> "1.5.1.1 Tension [allowable stress]
>
> On the net section, except at pin holes:
>
> $$F_t = 0.60F_y$$
>
> but not more than 0.5 times the minimum tensile strength of the steel.
>
> On the net section at pin holes in eyebars, pin-connected plates or build-up members:
>
> $$F_t = 0.45F_y."$$
>
> "1.8.4 Maximum Ratios
>
> The slenderness ratio, $Kl/r$, of compression members shall not exceed 200.
>
> The slenderness ratio, $Kl/r$, of tension members, other than rods, preferably should not exceed:
>
> For main members ................................. 240
>
> For bracing and other secondary members.............. 300."

### 3.2 Representation

In this section we shall deal with the formal representation of specification provisions and their relations, using as examples the provisions identified above. Three representational tools are used, corresponding to three levels of abstraction of specification.

*Provision Level.* At the level of a single provision, the technique of decision logic tables, or *decision tables* for short, is used. The decision table representation of Section 1.5.1 is shown in Table 1. As can be seen, the table is divided into four sections. The upper left section, called *condition stub*, is a list of all Boolean conditions (in this case, the single condition "at pinhole?"). The lower left section, called *action stub*, is a list of all applicable actions. The upper right section, called *condition entry*, contains entries of Y (yes) or N (no) corresponding to the conditions, organized into vertical columns

**Table 1**
**Allowable Tension Stress**

| At Pinhole | N | Y |
|---|---|---|
| $F_t = \text{min. } (0.60F_y, 0.50F_{ts})$ | Y | |
| $F_t = 0.45F_y$ | | Y |

called *rules*. A particular rule governs if the given data (values of the Boolean conditions) match the values given in that rule of the condition entry. Finally, the lower right section, called *action entry*, contains entries of Y and blank indicating that the corresponding action is or is not to be executed in a given rule. The table is to be read by proceeding down within a rule and across for each succeeding rule as follows: "If not at pinhole, then $F_t = \text{min. } (0.6F_y, 0.5F_{ts})$; if at pinhole, then $F_t = 0.45F_y$." For tables with more than one condition, it is understood that the conditions are related by the logical operator *and*.

Section 1.8.4 is represented by Table 2. Several new symbols may be noted in the condition entry. First, a number of conditions are immaterial (I) in certain rules (e.g., the question "main member?" is immaterial for compression members). Second, the symbols Y* and N* are introduced to

**Table 2**
**Slenderness Ratio Criterion**

| Compression member | Y | Y | N | N | N | N | N | N | E |
|---|---|---|---|---|---|---|---|---|---|
| Member a rod | I | I | Y | N | N | N | N | N | |
| Check for max. ratio desired | Y | Y | I | N | Y | Y | Y | Y | |
| Main member | I | I | I | I | Y | Y | N | N | |
| $Kl/r \leq 200$ | Y | N | I | I | I | I | I | N* | |
| $Kl/r \leq 240$ | Y* | I | I | I | Y | N | I | N* | |
| $Kl/r \leq 300$ | Y* | I | I | I | Y* | I | Y | N | |
| Section 1.8.4. satisfied | Y | | Y | Y | Y | | Y | | |
| Section 1.8.4 not satisfied | | Y | | | | Y | | Y | |
| Else action | | | | | | | | | Y |

denote implicit entries, that is, entries known to be yes or no from other conditions (e.g., if "$Kl/r \leq 200$" is true, it implies that "$Kl/r \leq 240$" and "$Kl/r \leq 300$" are also true). Finally, the last column, denoted E for *else*, covers all possible combinations not matched by the other rules; the corresponding action, designated *else action*, indicates that there are combinations of conditions not covered in the provision.

The decision table corresponding to Section 1.5.3 (compressive stress, of Ref. 4, not reproduced here, is shown as Table 3. The first four conditions are mutually exclusive; that is, a compression member can only be one of the four types covered in the provision; thus, in every rule, only one of the first four entries is yes, the other three being implicit no's.

Each table generates only one item of data, which can be a numeric value, such as $F_t$, or a Boolean datum, such as "Section 1.5.1 satisfied." This restriction to a single output, absent from our early work [8], is necessary for the proper interaction with the information network to be discussed. The result generated in one table can be used in conditions of other, higher-level tables (Table 4). Here, a single value of $F_t$ is used, regardless of which rule of Table 1 generated it. Finally, all provisions for a tension member can

**Table 3**
**Allowable Compressive Stress**

| | | | | | | | | |
|---|---|---|---|---|---|---|---|---|
| Main member | Y | Y | N* | N* | N* | N* | N* | N* |
| Bracing or secondary members | N* | N* | Y | Y | Y | Y | N* | N* |
| Plate girder stiffener | N* | N* | N* | N* | N* | N* | Y | N* |
| Web of rolled shape | N* | N* | N* | N* | N* | N* | N* | Y |
| $Kl/r \leq C_c$ | Y | N | Y | N | Y | N | I | I |
| $l/r \leq 120$ | I | I | Y | Y | N | N | I | I |
| $F_a$ by Eq. 1.5–1 | Y | | Y | | | | | |
| $F_a$ by Eq. 1.5–2 | | Y | | Y | | | | |
| $F_{as}$ by Eqs. 1.5–1, 1.5–3 | | | | | Y | | | |
| $F_{as}$ by Eqs. 1.5–2, 1.5–3 | | | | | | Y | | |
| $F_a = 0.60F_y$ | | | | | | | Y | |
| $F_a = 0.75F_y$ | | | | | | | | Y |

be combined in one table (Table 5). In this table, a compound condition is used to indicate that both the stress and maximum slenderness ratio criteria must be satisfied for the member to be acceptable.

**Table 4**
**Stress Criterion for Tension Member**

| $f_t \leq F_t$ | Y | N |
|---|---|---|
| Section 1.5.1.1 satisfied | Y | |
| Section 1.5.1.1 not satisfied | | Y |

**Table 5**
**Conformance Criteria for Tension Member**

| Section 1.5.1.1 satisfied and Section 1.8.4 satisfied | Y | N |
|---|---|---|
| Tension member conforms | Y | |
| Tension member does not conform | | Y |

*Information Network.* At the next level of representation, we are concerned with the information flow between related provisions, specifically, the manner in which data generated or defined in one provision are used in other provisions in order to represent the hierarchical sequences of definitions, computations, and tests comprising the specification.

The logical relations between items of data are described by two relationships, that of *ingredience* and *dependence*. The ingredients of an item are all data items needed to evaluate that item. Referring to Table 1, the ingredients of $F_t$ are $F_y$, $F_{ts}$, and the Boolean variable "at pinhole." Conversely, the dependents of an item are all data items which are a function of the data item in question.

A convenient representational tool for these interrelations is a directed graph or *information network*, obtained by assigning a node to each data item and assigning a directed branch from the data node to each of its dependents. Since, as discussed earlier, each decision table produces only one data item, it is not necessary to distinguish in the graph between nodes generated by a formula or by a decision table.

A somewhat condensed information network for the three provisions discussed above is shown in Fig. 1. More detailed networks, which include the intermediate computations and tests within a provision, are given in Ref. 15. Larger networks, including the global network of an entire specification, can be built up from subnetworks, or, more precisely, from the ingredients or dependents of the individual data items. As an illustration, the network

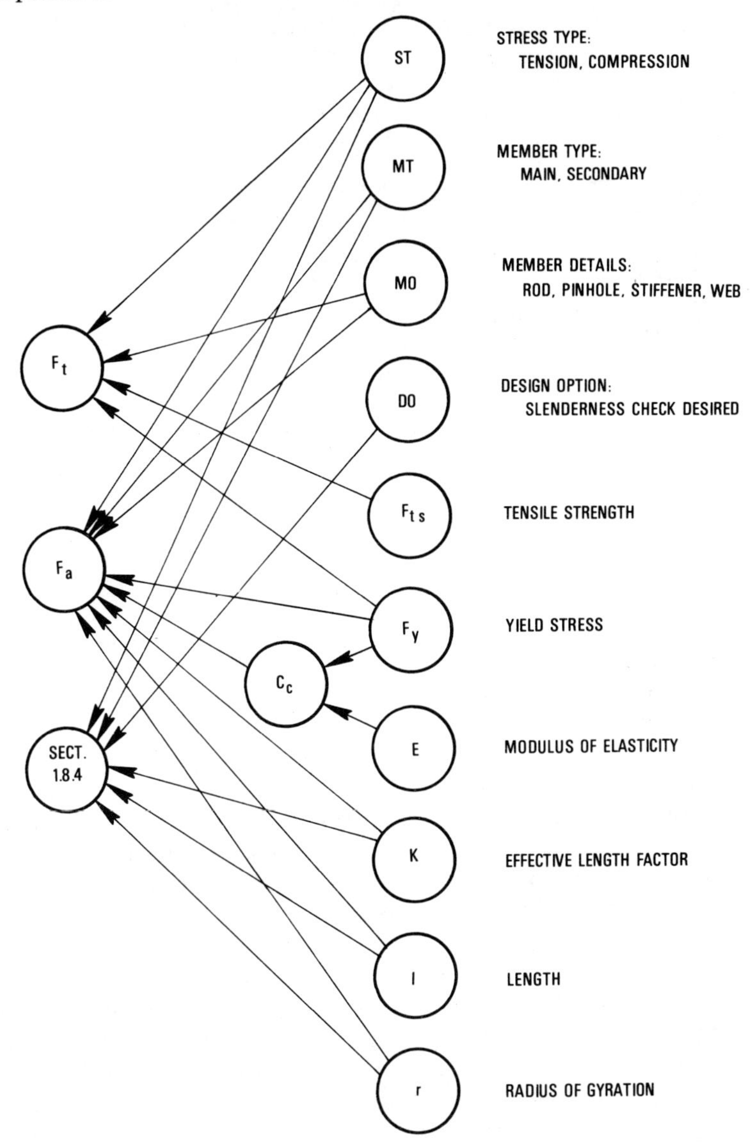


**Fig. 1.** Information network for allowable stress and slenderness ratio criteria

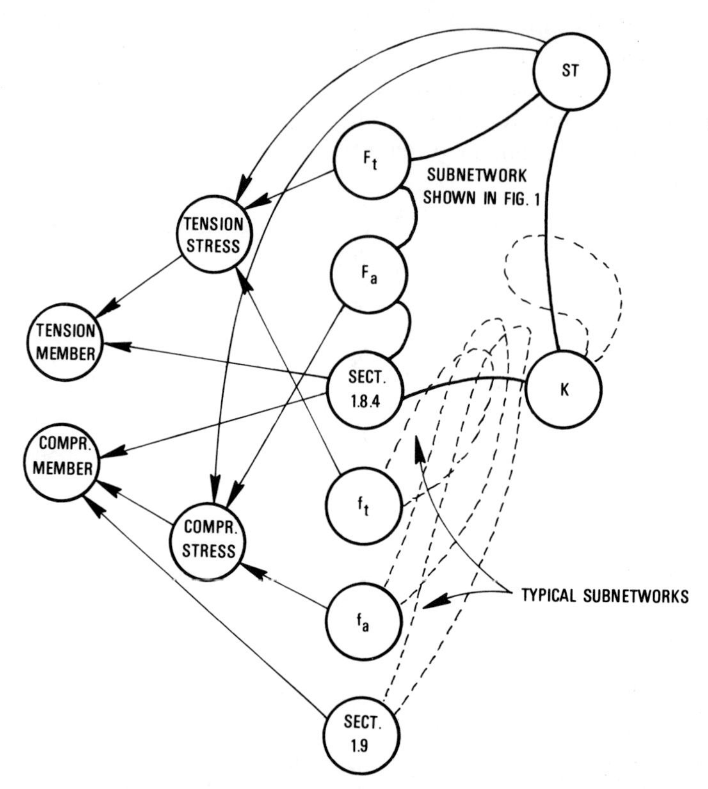


**Fig. 2.** Schematic information network for tension and compression member criteria

for tension and compression member criteria is sketched in Fig. 2. The sketch is intended to illustrate that the effective length factor, $K$, taken as a simple ingredient in Fig. 1, is, in fact, the terminal node of a subnetwork and that the evaluation of the members also requires computation of the actual stresses $f_t$ and $f_a$, involving definitions of net and gross areas, and the like, and checking of Section 1.9 for limiting proportions of column elements. The subnetworks indicated by dashed lines intersect the network shown in Fig. 1, i.e., share some of their ingredients.

*Organizational Level.* Finally, at the topmost level of representation, our concern is with identifying key words or *arguments* which concisely describe the scope or range of applicability of a provision, and their interrelationships, which may be used to organize or outline the entire specification. These arguments can be represented as hierarchically structured *argument trees*. Figure 3(a) represents the segment of the attribute tree for the physical component descriptions encountered in the AISC Specification provisions

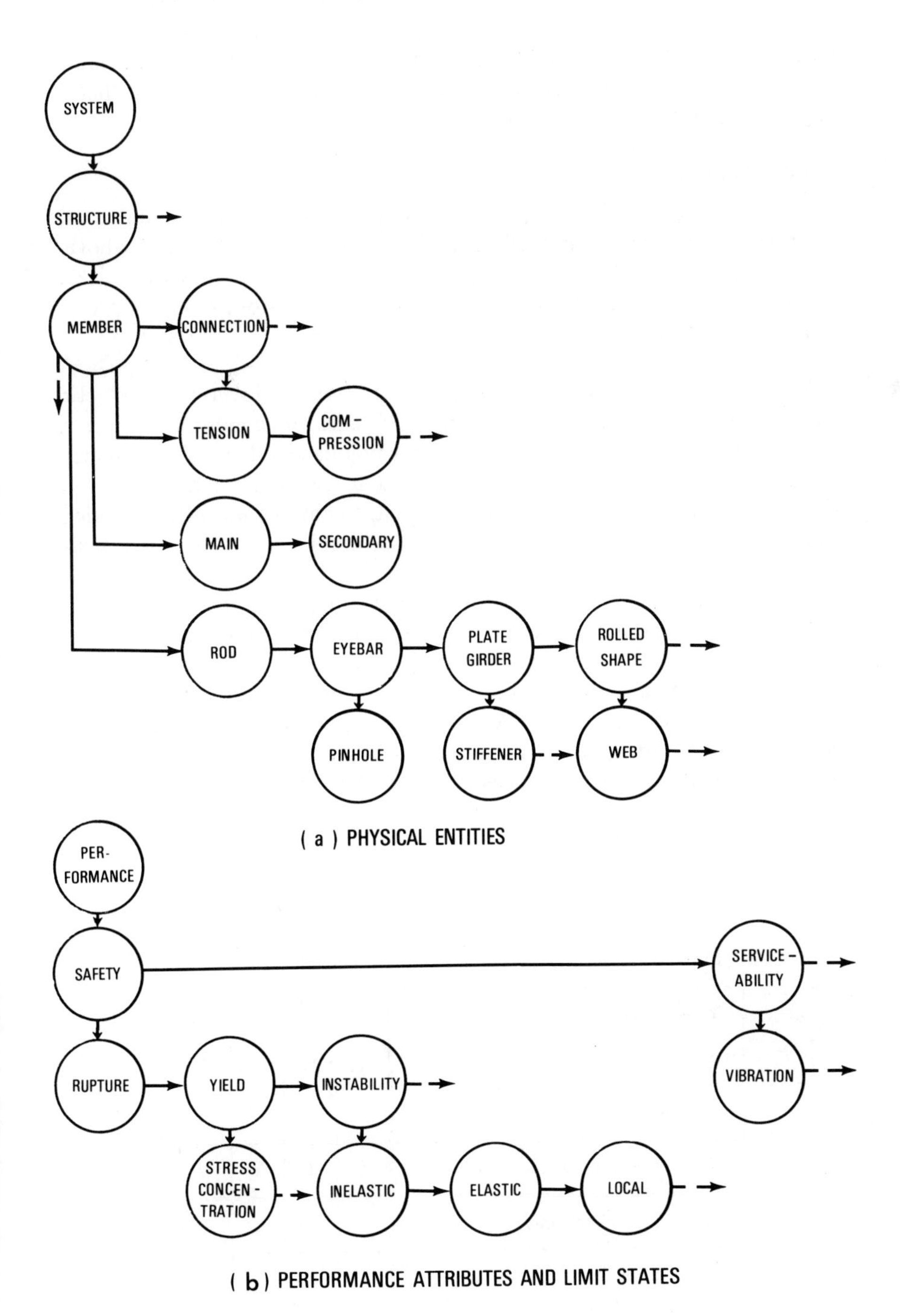


**Fig. 3.** Argument trees

discussed above. It is to be noted that a member may have only one attribute at any one level (e.g., a member is either "main" or "secondary") but that it may have attributes from several levels.

### 3.3 Analysis

Analysis for the three requisites of uniqueness, correctness, and completeness can be carried out at each of the three levels discussed above. Furthermore, the analysis deals both with syntax, that is, "how to do it?", and with semantics, that is, the "why?" for each provision, group of provisions, or the entire specification.

*Provision Level.* Decision tables lend themselves directly to syntactic analysis for uniqueness and completeness. Because the condition entry is a matrix of Boolean variables, formal tests for uniqueness (lack of redundancy or contradiction) and completeness are available [18]. For example, analysis of Table 2 shows that it is incomplete, in that it contains no rules for which condition 1 ("compression member") is yes and condition 3 ("check for maximum ratio desired") is no. However, a review of the specification and commentary indicates that the table is functionally complete since the limitation of $Kl/r \leq 200$ is mandatory, and not optional as for tension members.

From a semantic standpoint, a major shortcoming of the present AISC Specification is, as discussed before, the absence of explicit reference to performance attributes and applicable limit states. Provisions for tension members could, for example, be restructured according to the decision table shown in Table 6, with appropriate measures identified for the controlling limit states.

**Table 6**
**Conformance Criteria for Tension Member (modified)**

| | | | | |
|---|---|---|---|---|
| Stress concentration present | N | N | Y | Y |
| Yield criterion$_1$ satisfied and Rupture criterion satisfied and Slenderness criterion satisfied | Y | N | I | I |
| Yield criterion$_2$ satisfied | I | I | Y | N |
| Tension member conforms | Y | | Y | |
| Tension member does not conform | | Y | | Y |

*Information Network.* At the information network level, the directed graph can again be used for syntactic analysis. In particular, for completeness and uniqueness, the graph must be

- Connected, that is, there can be no data items which are not ingredients or dependents of other items; and
- Acyclic, that is, there can be no closed directed paths in the network, as this would imply either circular definitions or iterative computations.

These two properties can be ascertained by standard network traversal algorithms. The information network cannot be formally analyzed for correctness and semantics. As will be shown in Sec. 5.2, a major source of incorrect interpretation arises from the textual expression of the network.

*Organizational Level.* At the organizational level, the directed tree of arguments is again well suited for analyzing completeness and uniqueness, which require that at each level the arguments be

- Exhaustive, that is, cover all possibilities*; and
- Mutually exclusive, that is, a given element should match only one argument.

To properly address the semantics of the specification, the argument tree of physical component descriptions must be complemented by a second, independent argument tree of performance attribute and limit state descriptors, as shown in Fig. 3(b). Each of the criteria can then be uniquely identified by the applicable entries from the two argument trees, as illustrated in Table 7.

## IV. Network Representation of Specifications

In this section, the representational tools discussed in Sec. 3.2 in connection with a segment of a specific specification are formally summarized.

*Provision Level.* The logical content of a specification provision is represented by a decision table. The decision table, in turn, can be converted to a *decision tree*, which is a graph having the following properties:

- There is a single entry node with one exit branch;
- All intermediate nodes have one entering branch and two exit

*In Fig. 3, dashed horizontal branches are used to indicate that the arguments shown do not constitute an exhaustive set.

**Table 7**
**Classification of AISC Criteria**

| | Physical Entity | | | | | | | | | | | Performance Attribute/Limit State | | | | | | | | | | |
|---|---|---|---|---|---|---|---|---|---|---|---|---|---|---|---|---|---|---|---|---|---|---|
| Criterion | Tension | Compression | Main | Secondary | Rod | Eyebar | Pinhole | Plate Girder | Stiffness | Rolled Edge | Web | Safety | Rupture | Yield | Stress Concentration | Instability | Inelastic | Elastic | Local | Serviceability | Vibration | Measure |
| 1 | ✓ | | | | | | | | | | | | | ✓ | | | | | | | | $f_t \leq 0.6F_y$ |
| 2 | ✓ | | | | | | | | | | | | ✓ | | | | | | | | | $f_t \leq 0.5F_{ts}$ |
| 3 | ✓ | | ✓ | | | | | | | | | | | | | | | | | | ✓ | $Kl/r \leq 240$ |
| 4 | ✓ | | | ✓ | | | | | | | | | | | | | | | | | ✓ | $Kl/r \leq 300$ |
| 5 | ✓ | | | | ✓ | | | | | | | | | | | | | | | | ✓ | No requirement |
| 6 | ✓ | | | | | | ✓ | | | | | | | ✓ | | | | | | | | $f_t \leq 0.45F_y$ |
| 7 | | ✓ | ✓ | | | | | | | | | | | | | | ✓ | | | | | $f_a \leq F_a$ by Eq. 1.5–1 |
| 8 | | ✓ | ✓ | | | | | | | | | | | | | | | ✓ | | | | $f_a \leq F_a$ by Eq. 1.5–2 |
| 9 | | ✓ | | ✓ | | | | | | | | | | | | | ✓ | | | | | $f_a \leq F_a$ by Eqs. 1.5–1, 1.5–3 |
| 10 | | ✓ | | ✓ | | | | | | | | | | | | | | ✓ | | | | $f_a \leq F_a$ by Eqs. 1.5–2, 1.5–3 |
| 11 | | ✓ | | | | | | | | | | | | | | | | | ✓ | | | Limitations of Section 1.9 |
| 12 | | ✓ | | | | | | | | | | | | | | | | | | | ✓ | $Kl/r \leq 200$ |
| 13 | | ✓ | | | | | | | ✓ | | | | | | | | ✓ | | | | | $f_a \leq 0.75F_y$ |
| 14 | | ✓ | | | | | | | | | ✓ | | | | | | ✓ | | | | | $f_a \leq 0.75F_y$ |

branches, corresponding to the two outcomes (yes or no) of the condition represented by the node; and

- Terminal nodes have one entering branch and no exit branches and correspond to the rules of the decision table.

Each decision table produces one data item, the rules identifying only alternate methods or formulas for deriving the item. A degenerate decision table is a function, containing no conditions and represented by a single node. A decision tree representation of Table 2 is shown in Fig. 4. As discussed in Sec. 3.3, there is a terminal node corresponding to the else rule. As can be seen from the figure, the decision tree resembles a conventional flow diagram and is thus familiar to programmers. On the other hand, a decision tree always implies a specific sequence of testing the conditions, whereas the table is independent of sequence. The use of alternate sequences for different textual expressions is discussed in Sec. 5.2.

*Information Network.* The hierarchical interrelationship among data items appearing in a specification can be represented by two sets of compact lists, the ingredience and dependence lists. Formally, for each data item $d_i$, the *ingredience list*

$$I(d_i) = \{d_k, d_l, \dots, d_m\}$$

is the list of data items directly entering into the determination of $d_i$. Conversly, the *dependence list*

$$D(d_i) = \{d_p, d_q, \dots, d_r\}$$

is the list of data items which directly depend on $d_i$, i.e., for which $d_i$ is an ingredient. These lists can be represented in graph or network form by assigning a node to each datum and a branch from each datum to all elements of its dependence list. Global dependents of a datum can be traced out by traversing the network from the datum in question to all nodes reachable in the direction of the branches. Global ingredients of a datum can be similarly located by traversing the network in the direction opposite to that of the branches. Data items having no ingredients are basic parameters which must be independently defined for the written expression of the specification or input directly for computer processing. Data items having no dependents are the criteria which must be evaluated to ascertain conformance with the specification.

*Organizational Level.* Finally, for organizing, outlining, and indexing purposes, a number of descriptors or arguments are associated with each criterion. The arguments form argument trees, representing the logical subdivisions of the organizational bases. In every specification, there are at least two disjoint argument trees, corresponding to the subdivisions of the physical entities addressed and the performance attributes sought, respectively, as

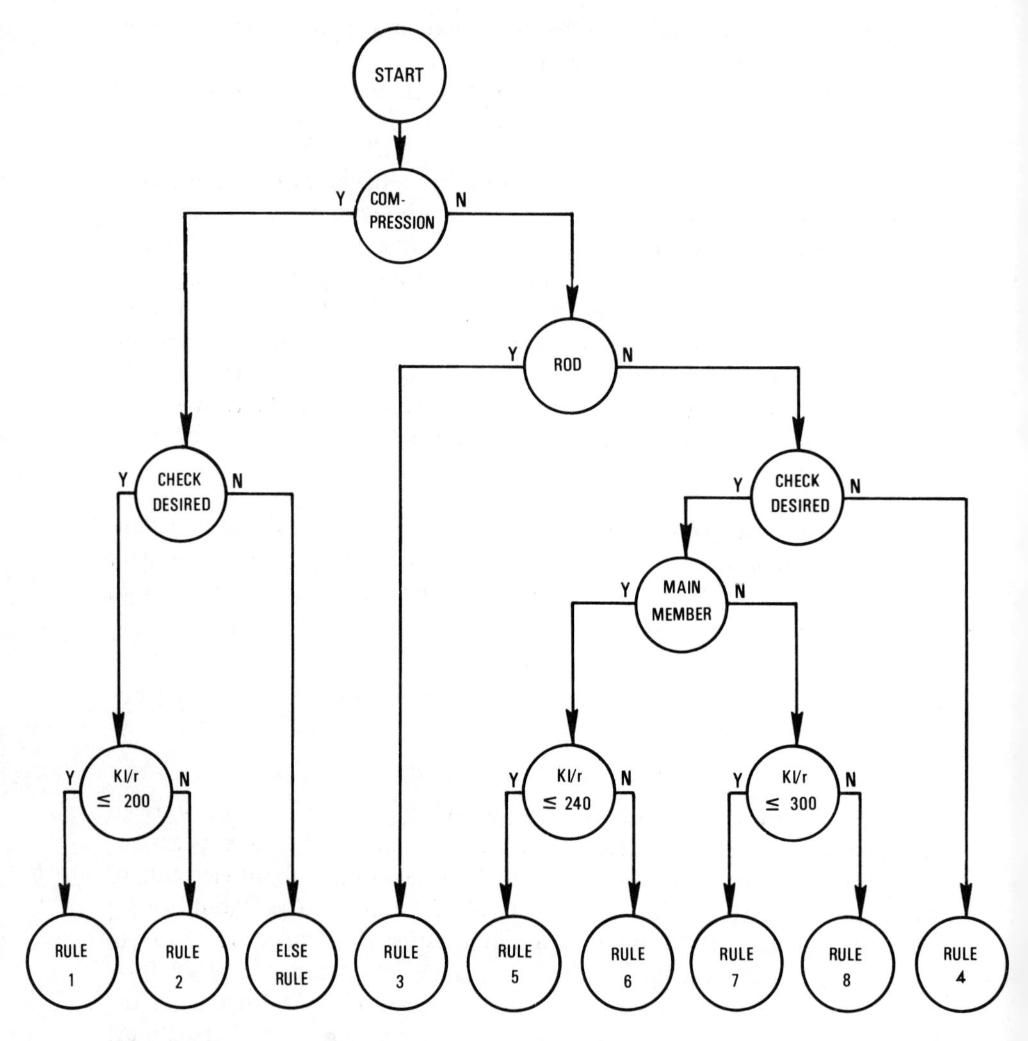


**Fig. 4.** Decision tree for maximum slenderness ratio criterion

illustrated in Fig. 3. Additional argument trees may be introduced where provisions deal with certain common properties which do not strictly correspond to physical subdivisions or performance attributes. Formally, for each criterion, the *argument list*

$$A(d_i) = \{a_k, a_l, \ldots, a_m\}$$

is the list of all arguments applicable to the criterion. The list contains only the terminal argument from each attribute tree applicable to the criterion; the path to that argument from the root of the tree is uniquely determined by the requirement that arguments have unique names. Conversely, for each argument, $a_k$, the *scope list*

$$S(a_k) = \{d_i, d_j, \ldots, d_o\}$$

is the list of all criteria for which the argument appears. Table 7, read row-wise, represents the argument sets of the 14 criteria shown; read columnwise, it represents the scope list of each terminal argument.

## V. Synthesis of Specifications

In synthesizing or developing a new design specification, many concurrent activities of groups of professionals occur. Generally, it is not possible to completely separate the contents of the proposed specification from its format, nor can one clearly distinguish the activities of generating the information base of the specification and of writing the text expressing this information. The development process is frequently iterative, where new concepts, even the need for new research, emerge as portions of the specification are developed. Nevertheless, it is useful to postulate a simplified, linearized model of the synthesis process, the first stage, formulation, dealing with the development of the information content and the generation of its formal representation, and the second stage, expression, dealing with the formatting of that representation.

### *5.1 Formulation*

A linearized model of the formulation process consists of five successive activities. All specifications deal, explicitly or implicitly, with performance objectives. Thus, as a first step, the performance attributes to be achieved must be defined. Design specifications and building codes have traditionally dealt with the overall objectives of maintaining health and life safety; more recently, additional attributes, such as energy conservation or operability after natural disasters, have been introduced as requisites. An attribute such as "maintenance of life safety" is too broad a concept for developing specification provisions. Therefore, the environments or factors within each attribute have to be further isolated and identified. For example, "safety" may be subdivided into "internal effects," such as explosions and other potential causes of progressive collapse, and "external effects," such as wind, earthquake, and the like. This leads to the identification of the anticipated response of the system to the adverse environment and to the definition of the limit states, that is, the conditions under which the anticipated response renders the structure or system unfit for its intended purpose.

As the second step, it becomes necessary to identify the physical entities which are susceptible to failure or dysfunction corresponding to the limit states considered. As mentioned earlier, it is advantageous at this stage to introduce common abstract properties, such as "tension stress" for certain ultimate limit states or "horizontal surfaces" for the limit state of ponding, rather than attempting to exhaustively enumerate all possible components or configurations susceptible to a given limit state. The intersection of limit states, common properties, and physical elements identifies the criteria that have to be met.

The third step involves the definition of measures quantifying each criterion, from simple statements that a certain device or item shall be provided to limits or ranges on critical parameters. As a fourth step in the formulation process, evaluation procedures must be developed to ascertain each of the measures defined previously. In performance specifications, these procedures are treated separately from the criteria, whereas procedural specifications consist largely of the detailed exposition of such procedures.

Throughout the formulation process outlined, the growing information base of the specification being developed can be directly incorporated into the formal representation. Specifically, the first step involves the development of the attribute argument tree, such as the one given in Fig. 3(b). The second step consists essentially of the development of the physical entity argument tree, the definition of criteria, and the establishment of the argument and scope lists. The third and fourth steps involve the development of the information network among the related criteria, measures, and evaluation procedures and the generation of the decision tables for the individual provisions.

The final step in the formulation process consists of the application of the analysis tools described to the representation, in order to ascertain the requisite properties of completeness, uniqueness, and correctness. At the risk of repetitiousness, we emphasize that such analyses will inevitably reveal violations of the above properties and require additional iterations on the formulation process.

### 5.2 Expression

We call expression the process of converting the abstract representation into usable forms for a readable textual format and for the generation of computer aids. The latter topic will be discussed in Section VI after some additional topics are introduced.

The difficulties of achieving a usable, readable text arise because the text must follow a linear sequence, whereas the information it contains is highly nonsequential, consisting of disjoint argument trees terminating in criteria, which in turn depend on an information network with many multiple connections, the nodes of which themselves may consist of substantial decision trees. Expression is, therefore, the task of unraveling this complex structure into a linear format that is easy and convenient to use, that gives confidence to the designers that they are following the specification writers' intent, and that similarly gives assurance to the specification writers that the provisions are correctly interpreted and executed.

We are convinced that many of the complaints concerning present specifications, and often the resistance to the introduction of new ones, are the result of poor textual expression, as evidenced by awkward outlines and uniformative provision headings, lack of proper cross-referencing among related provisions, procedural sequences poorly related to the design process, and badly composed provisions which are hard to interpret and follow.

We are not in a position to propose universally applicable methods for expression, but we have developed strategies which may be explored by specification writers in order to achieve better textual expression and computer aids which allow exploring alternatives without the danger of losing the intended coverage and meaning. These strategies are essentially means for transforming the complex representation into different linear sequences.

*Provision Level.* Here, the problem is that of converting a decision table into a decision tree, which can then be expressed as one or more sentences containing conditional clauses. The literature on decision table processing discusses two basic strategies, called *immediate decision*, where the objective is to isolate rules as quickly as possible, and *delayed decision*, where the objective is to reduce the number of possible rules roughly in half with each test [18] (the numerical analyst will recognize the analogy of the two strategies to searching by iteration and searching by interval halving, respectively). These two strategies can be directly applied to the expression of provisions: In the immediate decision method, the simplest rules (containing the largest number of immaterials), unique rules (differing in one condition from all other rules), or the most common rules could be listed prior to the other rules; in contrast, by following the delayed decision method, provisions could be systematically broken into shorter subprovisions of roughly equal scope.

*Information Network.* At the intermediate level, the problem is that of representing the graph of the information network by a suitable spanning tree (i.e., a subgraph which contains all the nodes of the original graph but only as many branches as necessary to provide a single path from any node to any other node) and then to display the nodes of the tree in a linear sequence. By the nature of the information network, all branches not in the spanning tree become cross-references among the data items. Two strategies for generating such a spanning tree are available, involving a simple graph traversal algorithm. Assume that a fictitious "end" node is made a dependent of all terminal (criterion) nodes, that a fictitious "start" node is made an ingredient of all input (basic parameter) nodes, and that all branches are of "length" one. If the nodes are ordered by increasing longest path from the "start" node, one obtains a sequence, which we call *direct execution*, in which every term, formula, test, etc., is defined just before it is first used, yielding concise, specific sequential instructions, with all cross-references pointing to terms previously defined. The strategy can, however, become lengthy and tedious for an experienced user thoroughly familiar with the specification. By contrast, if the nodes are ordered by increasing longest path from the "end" node, one obtains a sequence, which we call *conditional execution*, where the criterion to be checked is given first, followed by its ingredient subcriteria, and so on, until finally the basic data elements are defined. Such a strategy permits an experienced user to read only as far down as necessary to locate the controlling provision or test; however, if necessary, by reading further he can refresh his memory on more detailed provisions. Variants of these two strategies are further discussed in Ref. 14.

*Organizational Level.* In generating the outline and overall organization of the specification, it is necessary to linearly sequence criteria which are indexed and only partially ordered by the nodes of disjoint attribute trees, as illustrated in Table 7. We have not yet developed general strategies for this phase of expression. It is to be noted, however, that here syntax and semantics interact very strongly: A sequencing which orders first on attributes and limit states, with the physical classification in a secondary role, is likely to be more appealing to the researcher and theoretically inclined designer, whereas the opposite strategy is likely to be more familiar and convenient to the average designer.

The three sets of strategies discussed should be taken as boundary values on a continuum of possible expressions, rather than as absolute alternates. Any given specification is likely to contain a mixture of all the above strategies. It is also possible that eventually frequently used specifications may be expressed in one form for a specific use, say, for designers, and that alternate form may be provided for alternate uses, say, one for students and another one for building regulatory officials, with full confidence that the contents and meaning will be preserved.

## VI. Use of Specifications

In the introduction, we refer to use as the application of specifications to the evaluation of designs in both manual and computer-aided processes. It is to be hoped that manual processing can be improved by the application of the formulation and expression strategies discussed. Computer-aided processing can also benefit significantly from these methods, as will be demonstrated in this section.

In computer-aided processing, one deals with constraints, rather than criteria. A constraint is a particular application of a design criterion. It is particular in the sense that it is a criterion applied to a particluar entity or point for a particular loading or environmental condition. Usually, each design criterion results in many constraints.

Systematic approaches can be provided for the computer-aided development of programs for constraint processing. These aids are significant because manual programming is extremely expensive and subject to mistakes in the interpretation of the intent of specifications. The cost of preparation of new computer aids for constraint processing appears to have become a major impediment to the implementation of research knowledge in improved specifications.

### *6.1 Extensions of Representation*

To accommodate constraint processing, the representation presented in Sec. IV has to be extended in three ways.

First, in representing criteria, we treated a particular datum (e.g., member length, $l$, stress, $F_a$, etc.) as an individual item. In actual design use, these quantities would be subscripted variables (e.g., the length of the $i$th member, the stress at station $k$ of member $i$ in loading condition $l$, etc.). All such subscripted variables are stored in some data structure which is accessed by the design and analysis routines as well as the constraint processor. The logical data of the specification must be related to the subscripted data of the files for computer-aided data processing. This relationship cannot be a fixed property of the specification, since it should be possible to use the specification with a variety of project data structures. Therefore, we have presented elsewhere generalized procedures for generating constraint processors compatible with rational, but essentially arbitrary, file structures [23,24]. The significant feature of these procedures is that additional ingredients, called *pointer vectors*, are appended to the ingredient lists. A typical pointer vector would, for example, relate stations along the member to the member designation. The extended representation only shows that a pointer vector is needed to access the stations where the stress constraint is to be checked; the actual form and content of the vector would depend entirely on the data file structure for the particular project.

Second, the ingredience and dependence relationships themselves must be extended to account for the subscripted nature of the actual design data. In the work cited [23,24], we have developed a calculus of subscript calculations, so that the subscripts of the dependents can be automatically obtained from the subscripts of the ingredients and vice versa. This approach can significantly decrease the cost of developing computer aids for constraint processing.

Finally, in design, data also have a temporal character. In our early work, we made use of the concept of *status* [9]. The status of a datum is *valid* if it has been calculated in accord with the current values of all the data in its global ingredients. The status of a datum is *void* if it has not yet been calculated or if changes have been made in one or more of the items of data in its global ingredience since the datum was computed. More recently we have introduced the concept of *permanence levels* to distinguish between levels of definition of data [25]. For instance, data being used by a number of different groups of the design team, such as the architects, structural engineers, and mechanical engineers, might be given a permanence level 1, data used solely by one of the disciplines might be given level 2, and data used in a more transient fashion by one of these disciplines might be designated level 3. A trial structural design might be conducted at level 3; the gradient calculations used to determine whether an improvement in the design is possible might be conducted at permanence level 4; when the trial design is determined to have converged its data might be relabeled to level 2; and when the structural design is deemed consistent with the current work of the architects and mechanical engineers it could be relabeled at permanence level 1.

### 6.2 Computer Aids for Constraint Processing

The computer aids available for efficient constraint processing can again be discussed at the three levels used previously.

*Provision Level.* Two direct uses can be made of the decision table representation of specification provisions. First, decision tables can be used directly as a programming language; efficient preprocessors exist which convert decision tables to procedural language statements using the strategies discussed in Sec. 5.2, thereby significantly reducing programming costs [18]. Alternatively, the decision tables can be used as data by a general-purpose interpretive program [9], thereby providing great flexibility in experimenting with alternate specification provisions, as only the data would have to be changed.

Second, wherever a specification provision deals with several entities, or allows designer choices or alternatives, and a particular organization knows a priori which of these entities or choices it intends to use, the application programs can be drastically reduced in size by the systematic elimination of options not wanted. As an example, Table 2, introduced previously, could be systematically reduced to the following programs:

- Compression members only (one condition, two rules).
- All tension members (five conditions, six rules).
- Tension members with slenderness check (five conditions, five rules).
- Tension members without check (table eliminated altogether).

*Information Network.* The two strategies, direct and conditional execution, discussed in Sec. 5.2 are directly applicable to constraint processing. Conditional execution begins with the particular constraint to be evaluated, tests whether it can be evaluated directly from its ingredients, and proceeds with the evaluation of ingredient data only when some are unknown. Direct execution begins with the known input quantities and proceeds to evaluate all higher-level data starting with the data directly dependent on the input.

Conditional execution is appropriate when the computer is used to check only a few of the possible constraints where a criterion applies; this is the usual mode of use in design and in review. Direct execution is suitable when substantially all derived properties are needed for the given values of the input data. This may occur in certain large-volume, low-level design and detailing applications and in review for some types of specifications. Systematic approaches to efficient data processing for both strategies are briefly discussed below.

For conditional execution, we have developed a single general operator, called SEEK [7,23], which uses the information network and the status indicator discussed in the preceding section to recursively compute only the ingredients actually needed and set their status to valid.

Another elemental activity in design is to change the value of a design variable. Use of the information network allows a recursive WARN procedure [7,23] to set to void the status of each datum which would be affected by the change. It would be possible to reevaluate the affected data immediately. However, if a number of data are to be altered, immediate reevaluation would be wasteful. When data are needed again, SEEK will selectively reevaluate only the data affected by the changes.

When the criteria to be evaluated can be restricted to a relatively small number defined in advance, it is entirely feasible to develop an efficient constraint processor using direct execution. The order of computation may be generated directly by expressing the global information network of the required portions of the specification in post order [12]. Then, using the subscripted ingredience relationships defined above, computations may be carried out systematically to evaluate all dependents, rising in the information network from the input data to the highest level criteria.

*Organizational Level.* In constraint processing, the organizational level acts as a switching network or directory to lead the process to the execution of the appropriate constraints. In conditional execution, especially in an interactive (time-shared) environment, the user can specify the node(s) of the argument trees where he intends to begin constraint processing. For direct execution, the argument trees are used directly to sequence the computations for efficient processing. As with the other two levels, the application programs can be substantially improved in size and speed by prespecifying the subtrees comprising the criteria to be incorporated into the programs.

## VII. Summary and Conclusions

We have presented an abstract representational model of design specifications and have identified the formal properties of completeness, uniqueness, and correctness which every design specification should possess. The formal representation consists of decision tables or derived decision trees for the provisions, an information network for interrelated provisions, definitions and evaluation procedures, and argument trees for organizing and outlining. We have identified methods for formulating specifications and tools for checking them for the requisite properties. We described a number of strategies for expressing specifications in textual form and the relative advantages of each. Finally, we have shown the extensions necessary to apply the procedures discussed to the generation of computer aids for processing project design data against specifications for design and conformance checking.

Our study demonstrates that the concepts of performance and limit states need to be an integral part of specification development to ensure that the users know the intent of the specification and can correctly apply its writers' intentions. We have indicated how the formal representation may be used to generate alternate formats for distinct users, say, for experienced designers, students, and building officials. We have shown how computer aids may be used in formulation and expression to reduce the cost and uncertainties in specification developments. While the prime use of these tools is in the synthesis of new specifications, the benefits accrued from the formal representation and purposeful expression may be great enough to warrant review and clarification of existing specifications without major changes in scope or technical content. We have also demonstrated that the generation of computer aids based on the specifications can and should be made an integral part of specification development.

The methods presented have been tested in the analysis of a number of diverse specifications and are considered reliable. There is need, however, for further systematic studies in formulation and expression of specifications, especially in the evaluation of the strategies of expression described.

It is our hope that through the methods presented specification development can become a much more integral part of the transmission and implementation of research results and that design specifications will no longer be looked upon by designers as a necessary evil but as a constructive aid in achieving design objectives.

## Acknowledgments

The work reported herein has benefited from the contribution and comments of many people. We wish to acknowledge specifically our colleagues, Professors E. H. Gaylord, Jr., J. W. Melin, R. L. Tavis, and Mr. R. J. Kapsch, and our former students, Drs. S. K. Goel and D. J. Nyman. The American Institute of Steel Construction provided the initial financial support and practical perspectives to this work. The University of Illinois, Carnegie-Mellon University, the Center for Building Technology of the National Bureau of Standards and the Office of Naval Research also have supported these studies.

## References

1. Allen, D. E., "Limit State Design—A Unified Procedure for the Design of Structures," *Eng. J. (Can.)*, Vol. 53, No. 2, Feb. 1970, pp. 18–25.
2. American Concrete Institute, *Building Code Requirements for Reinforced Concrete*, (ACI 318–71), American Concrete Institute, Detroit, 1971.
3. American Institute of Steel Construction, *Commentary on the Specification for the Design, Fabrication and Erection of Structural Steel for Buildings*, American Institute of Steel Construction, New York, 1969.
4. American Institute of Steel Construction, *Specification for the Design, Fabrication and Erection of Structural Steel for Buildings*, American Institute of Steel Construction, New York, 1969.
5. *Building Officials and Code Administrators Basic Building Code*, Building Officials and Code Administrators, Inc., Chicago, 1975 edition.
6. Fenves, S. J., "Tabular Decision Logic for Structural Design," *J. Struct. Div., ASCE*, Vol. 92, No. ST6, Dec. 1966, pp. 473–490.
7. Fenves, S. J., "Representation of the Computer-Aided Design Process by a Network of Decision Tables," *Computers and Structures*, Vol. 3, No. 5, Sept. 1973, pp. 1099–1107.
8. Fenves, S. J., E. H. Gaylord, Jr., and S. K. Goel, "Decision Table Formulation of the 1969 American Institute of Steel Construction Specification," *Civil Engineering Studies, No. SRS 347*, University of Illinois, Urbana, Aug. 1969.
9. Goel, S. K., and S. J. Fenves, "Computer-Aided Processing of Design Specifications," *J. Struct. Div. ASCE*, Vol. 97, No. ST1, Jan. 1971, pp. 463–479.
10. *Guide Criteria for the Evaluation and Design of Operation BREAKTHROUGH Housing Systems*, Report 10200, 4 volumes, National Bureau of Standards, Washington, D.C., Sept. 1970.
11. *HUD Minimum Property Standards*, One and Two Family Dwellings (No. 4900.1), and Multifamily Housing (No. 4910.1), U.S. Department of Housing and Urban Development, Washington D.C., 1973.
12. Knuth, D. E., *The Art of Computer Programming*, Vol. I: Fundamental Algorithms, Addison-Wesley, Reading, Mass., 1968.
13. Noland, J. L., and C. C. Feng, "American Concrete Institute Building Code in Decision Logic Table Format," *J. Struct. Div. ASCE*, Vol. 101, No. ST4, April 1975, pp. 677–696.
14. Nyman, D. J., and S. J. Fenves, "An Organization Model for Design Specifications, *J. Struct. Div. ASCE*, Vol. 101, No. ST4, April 1973, pp. 697–716.
15. Nyman, D. J., and S. J. Fenves, "An Organizational Model for Design Specifications," *Report R73–4*, Department of Civil Engineering, Carnegie-Mellon University, Pittsburgh, Sept. 1973.
16. Nyman, D. J., S. J. Fenves, and R. N. Wright, "Restructuring Study of the American Institute of Steel Construction Specifications," *Civil Engineering Studies, No. SRS 393*, University of Illinois, Urbana, Jan. 1973.
17. *One and Two Family Dwelling Code*, Promulgated by Building Officials and Code Administrators, American Insurance Association, Southern Building Code Congress, and International Congress of Building Officials, 1971 edition.

18. POLLOCK, S. L., *Decision Tables: Theory and Practice*, Wiley-Interscience, New York, 1971.
19. SEEBERG, P., "Decision Table Formulation of the Specification for the Design of Cold-Formed Steel Structural Members," Department of Civil Engineering, University of Wisconsin, Milwaukee, July 1971.
20. SIESS, C. P., "Research, Building Codes, and Engineering Practice," *J. Am. Concrete Inst.*, Vol. 31, No. 11, May 1960, pp. 1105–1122.
21. VENTRE, F. T., *Social Control of Technological Innovation: The Regulation of Building Construction*, unpublished doctoral dissertation, Department of Urban Studies and Planning, Massachusetts Institute of Technology, Cambridge, May 1973.
22. WRIGHT, J. R., "Performance Criteria in Buildings," *Sci. Am.*, Vol. 224, No. 3, March 1971, pp. 16–25.
23. WRIGHT, R. N., L. T. BOYER, and J. W. MELIN, "Constraint Processing in Design," *J. Struct. Div. ASCE*, Vol. 98, No. ST1, Jan. 1971, pp. 481–494.
24. WRIGHT, R. N., D. J. NYMAN, and S. J. FENVES, "Restructuring Study of American Institute of Steel Construction Specification," unpublished progress report, University of Illinois, Urbana, June 1971.
25. YANG, J. M., and S. J. FENVES, "Representation of Information in the Design-Construction Process," *Report R74–1*, Department of Civil Engineering, Carnegie-Mellon University, Pittsburgh, June 1974.

# Uses of Observation in Earthquake-Resistant Design of Reinforced Concrete

METE A. SOZEN* AND HIROYUKI AOYAMA†

The watershed for the current complex of design bases for earthquake-resistant reinforced concrete structures may be placed, with respect to time, at the first printing of *Design of Multistory Reinforced Concrete Buildings for Earthquake Motions* [6], which brought together analytical concepts of nonlinear dynamic response with available knowledge on inelastic behavior of reinforced concrete, leading to design methods covering the range from determination of forces to provision of special reinforcing details. Agitated by the questions as well as by the answers in that work and under the intermittent pressure of earthquake disasters, an impressive amount of experimental research has been carried out since then to establish behavioral characteristics of reinforced concrete relevant to earthquake-resistant design. This chapter is concerned with the current and future uses of this research.

To trace the transfer of information from the laboratory to practice, an attempt is first made to categorize the processes of research and design. The chapter then covers briefly the important shift in emphasis from behavior under steadily increased loading to that under displacement reversals of varying magnitude. Shear strength is singled out as the topic which will require fundamental changes in design concept as a result of experimental observations. Earthquake simulation in the laboratory is discussed to demonstrate its use in developing methods of analysis related to design. Finally, the task of structural evaluation of the completely designed building is considered.

Coverage is admittedly biased. It is influenced strongly by some of the research and design problems with which the writers have had direct experience. Another limitation, introduced to meet space requirements, is the

*Department of Civil Engineering, University of Illinois, Urbana, Illinois.

†Faculty of Engineering, University of Tokyo, 7–3–1 Hongo, Bunkyo-ku, Tokyo 113, Japan.

ignoring of out-of-vertical-plane events such as building torsion and triaxial loading of elements. Because experimental work in these areas has not yet gathered sufficient momentum to influence practice, this neglect may not be totally negligent.

## Structural Testing

### *The Alpha and Omega Tests*

Observations in experimental research are not initiated, at least on the surface, with self-evident or intelligible truths. Rather, they start with fundamental units of knowledge with which it is possible to construct other "less fundamental" phenomena. The criteria for "fundamentalness" are traditional and relate primarily to the limits of scientific interest of the profession.

Thus, there is the particular unit of test for which the input and the output are known, to the limits of the sensors which have been considered pertinent and used, and the observed relationship between the input and the output is accepted at face value without analysis. This will be referred to as the *Alpha* test.

The *omega* test is at the other end of the scale. The relationship between the input and the output is analyzed with the help of fundamental units of knowledge from alpha tests.

Common examples of the alpha test are coupon tests of materials taken for granted to be primordial within the domain of traditional structural engineering interest. However, not all examples of alpha tests are that compact and convenient. Any bond test is expected to lead to a fundamental unit of information of some generality. The standard "load test," where a structure is loaded to a prescribed level to check its performance, is an alpha test: Its results are accepted without any analysis in most cases. The intuitive judgment of the profession emanating from past experience is often in the category of the alpha test.

A simple example of the omega test is the test of an externally determinate reinforced concrete beam failing in flexure. Measured strength and deformation are related explicitly, with causality adopted casually, to the fundamental parameters obtained from alpha tests. Even in this simple application, the logical syntax is not all what it may appear to be. It is well known that the basic parameters may be combined in more than one way to reproduce some of the observed phenomena. Furthermore, not all parts of the synthesis procedure are independent of observations from the beam test. For example, the principles of plane geometry are independent of the test, but the assumption of linear strain distribution over a partially cracked section is not. Nor is it emphatically evident that, over and above the scatter to be expected in the distribution of material properties, the basic units of information from the coupon tests may not be correctly projected to apply to the conditions in the beam (a unit stress-strain relationship obtained without strain gradient does not necessarily describe phenomena with strain gradient).

It is difficult to classify all tests in strict accordance with the implied characteristics of alpha and omega tests. Just as an observed stress-strain relationship is susceptible to analysis if one is willing to go beyond what may be regarded as the limits of scientific interest for structural engineering, there is often a feature, not necessarily obvious, in the analysis of an omega test which does not readily follow from observations in alpha tests. That is one of the reasons for not being able to do away with omega tests in the laboratory, for not being able to synthesize confidently the results of complex phenomena from alpha tests, and for projecting results with great caution from the experimental to the field environment.

### *Levels*

The range of structural testing, from the coupon tests to tests of entire structures, may be divided into five levels approximately in relation to the complexity of parameter combinations involved in the input, as indicated in Fig. 1.

At each level, an effort is made to express the observations in an intelligible statement of as wide an application as possible: A conceptual model is created which makes analysis of the observed phenomenon as well as prediction by synthesis of more complex phenomena possible.

The first level includes the material tests. In relation to earthquake-resistant design, these tests can be considerably more complicated than the measurement of a force-displacement relationship at a constant rate of strain and at a given temperature. To provide data for analyzing results obtained at higher levels of testing, history and amplitude of strain of stress applications must also be considered.

The second level refers to tests of externally determinate elements subjected to actions which increase or decrease maintaining a constant ratio among them, as in the test of a simple beam subjected to a set of loads which increase at the same rate.

The third level differs from the second primarily in that the external actions vary at different rates. Both levels four and five refer to tests of structures composed of a number of discrete elements, except that level four excludes dynamic testing.

As mentioned earlier, alpha or omega tests may be encountered at any level. The projection of information up or down from any one level has to be treated skeptically, unless the results can be explicitly traced down to alpha tests of the first level. For the same reason, it is preferable wherever possible to design the tests at the higher levels, particularly at level five, so that the

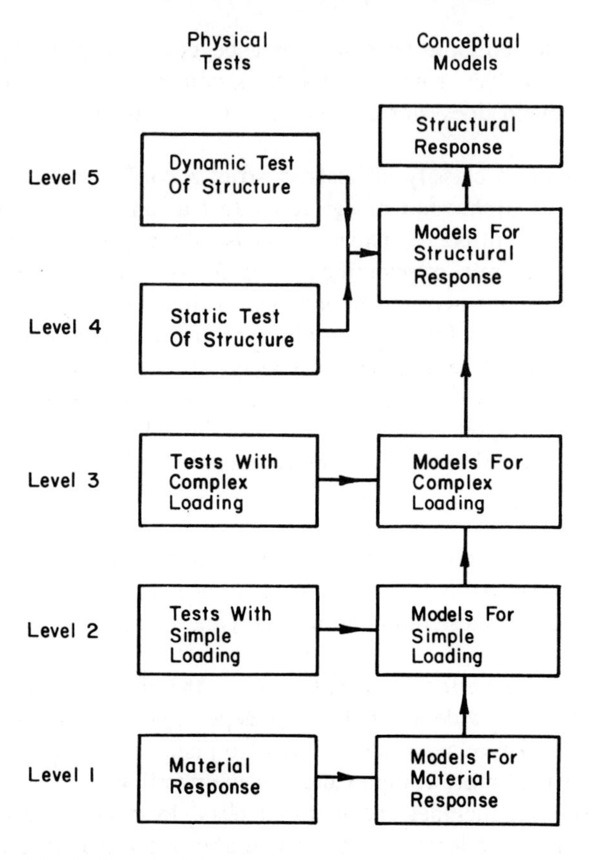


**Fig. 1.** Structural tests

phenomena affecting the results of the test can be analyzed in terms of data from first-level tests.

It is important to note that for problems related to gravity loads level three has not been considered critical, except in few instances of questions related to shear strength in the vicinity of plastic hinges. Consequently, it tends to be taken for granted also in experimental analysis related to earthquake-resistant design where it is known that, for example, points of contraflexure may move along the length of a member in both directions during a particular loading jointly with variations in the axial load.

## Structural Design

A simplified flow chart for structural design is shown in Fig. 2. Given an initial configuration for the structure, a choice of material, and a series of loadings, design forces or required stiffnesses are determined by analysis

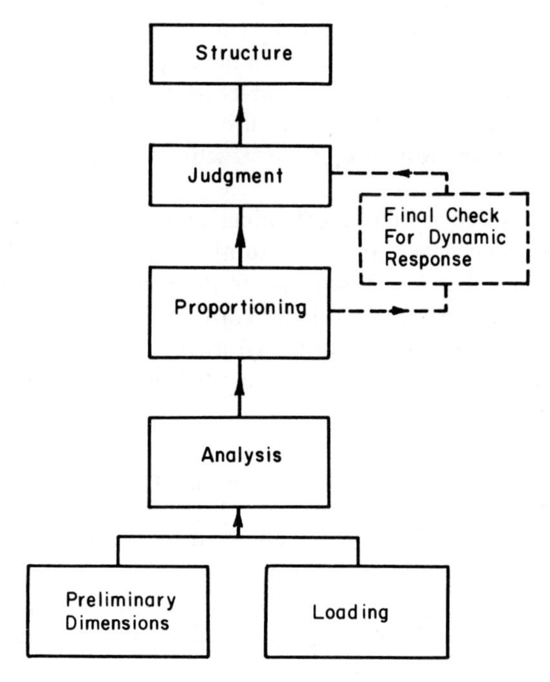


**Fig. 2.** Structural design

leading to member proportions and reinforcing details. Presumably, critical features of the resulting structure are subjected to the judgment of the designer before the drawings are sent to the construction site.

In this process, two different classes of structural analysis are involved: analysis for forces (or required stiffnesses) and analysis for member sizes and amount and arrangement of reinforcement. The first one may be considered external to the structure and will be referred to as analysis. The second one is internal and, given certain basic parameters, more or less automatic. It will be referred to as "proportioning."

To put the two processes in perspective, it must be noted that structural design does not always require analysis, as, for example, in the case of accommodating foundation settlement. Proportioning of the members takes care of the problem in usual cases. The same approach is not unthinkable for earthquake resistance. "Tying the structure together" and not worrying about the design forces does have some intellectual basis or at least successful precedent, but it cannot be recommended for earthquake-resistant design in general because the response of building structures, with the exception of extremely stiff or extremely flexible ones, falls in the range of what Professor Cross called "Hybrid Structural Action" [9]: Changes in stiffness, mass, and strength distribution affect the force and displacement distribution. Analysis is desirable in all cases and essential in most, even though the model for analysis is often no more than an effigy of the actual structure, with the understanding that the object of the analysis is to choose a reasonable strength (or stiffness) for each level of the structure to fulfill the design requirements and not to predict the response of the structure in the unlikely event of the design earthquake.

The main objective of proportioning, or internal analysis, is to place the proportions and details of a structural element in such ranges that the strength of the member is least sensitive to those parameters which are most likely to vary in the course of ordinary construction practice. Wherever possible, this is done explicitly, as in the efforts to minimize the possibility of bond failure by overdesign or as in the limitation of tensile reinforcement in a section.

## Impact of Experimental Observations on Design

The main impact of knowledge obtained from traditional static testing is on proportioning of structural elements, including minima and maxima on important parameters such as member sizes, amount or spacing of transverse and longitudinal reinforcement, splice lengths and locations, and material properties, which decisions may influence the final structure more critically than, say, the choice of the design response spectrum.

The main impact of knowledge obtained from dynamic tests is on modeling of the structure for analysis toward the determination of design forces, stiffness requirements, and the necessity of special details to ensure a stable hysteresis loop in the inelastic range.

During the last 15 years, there have been significant changes in design specifications related to proportioning as a result of laboratory investigations, made more meaningful for the profession by observed earthquake damage, or as a result of observed damage interpreted by laboratory investigations. In contrast, changes in modeling for analysis have been due not to experimental observations but to the increasing accessibility of digital computers and popularization of dynamic analysis.

The notable change in proportioning concepts has been the promotion of transverse reinforcement to first-rank consideration. The problem of reinforcement has taken on a new dimension. Whereas structural elements were treated as having primary reinforcement in the longitudinal direction and secondary reinforcement in the transverse direction, they are currently reinforced in both directions with equal emphasis. The strong interest in transverse reinforcement is due to the full realization of the need for confinement of the concrete and the longitudinal reinforcement to resist normal as well as transverse forces under large deformation reversals into the nonlinear range of response.

## Hysteresis

Prior to the 1950s, there was relatively little interest in the deformation characteristics of reinforced concrete elements in the inelastic range [24]. The substantial experimental work carried out in the 1950s and early 1960s was designed to answer questions raised by problems related to limit design and energy absorption of reinforced concrete structures. Consequently, the majority of the tests for beam or column deformation were conducted in the same vein as tests for material properties: Load was increased continually to failure over a short period of time. Furthermore, most of the data were obtained with a portion of the test specimen subjected to constant bending moment. These experimental conditions are attractive theoretically because, for beams moderately reinforced with common grades of reinforcement, they result in a nearly elastoplastic relationship between moment and angular strain (unit curvature), and they are also attractive experimentally because, besides being relatively easy to achieve in the laboratory, they are the very models of an omega test. The results can be synthesized with reasonable success using stress-strain data from simple coupon tests, which condition creates an aura of rigor. For want of a better term, the moment-curvature relationship obtained under these conditions will be called the "quarter-cycle $M$-$\Phi$" curve in the following discussion.

Because knowledge on static deformation characteristics of reinforced concrete construction was normalized with respect to the quarter-cycle $M$-$\Phi$ curve, concepts of nonlinear response to earthquake motions (which were investigated and organized in the theoretical domain using idealized force-displacement relationships) were initially adapted to apply to reinforced concrete using the quarter-cycle $M$-$\Phi$ curve.

Some of the questions about using the quarter-cycle $M$-$\Phi$ curve as a central, rational, and irrevocable measure of behavior are discussed below with the help of Fig. 3, which shows the shear-displacement response of two comparable reinforced concrete cantilevers, one with a constant axial load and one without [32], The cantilevers were subjected to several cycles of constant displacement. Only the first two cycles are shown for each specimen.

As would be expected, the quarter-cycle $M$-$\Phi$ curve [Fig. 3(b)] based on measured material properties and the assumption of linear strain distribution has a shape very close to elastoplastic, but this is not reflected in the shear-deflection curve [Fig. 3(c) and (d)] for the first quarter cycle of loading, which has a finite slope after yielding. The reasons for this apparent discrepancy are that the concrete data, obtained under different conditions of loading, are irrelevant to this case and the strain distribution over the depth of the section is quite nonlinear. Even for the first quarter cycle, the orthodox $M$-$\Phi$ curve is a statement with rather limited application. The cantilever test is

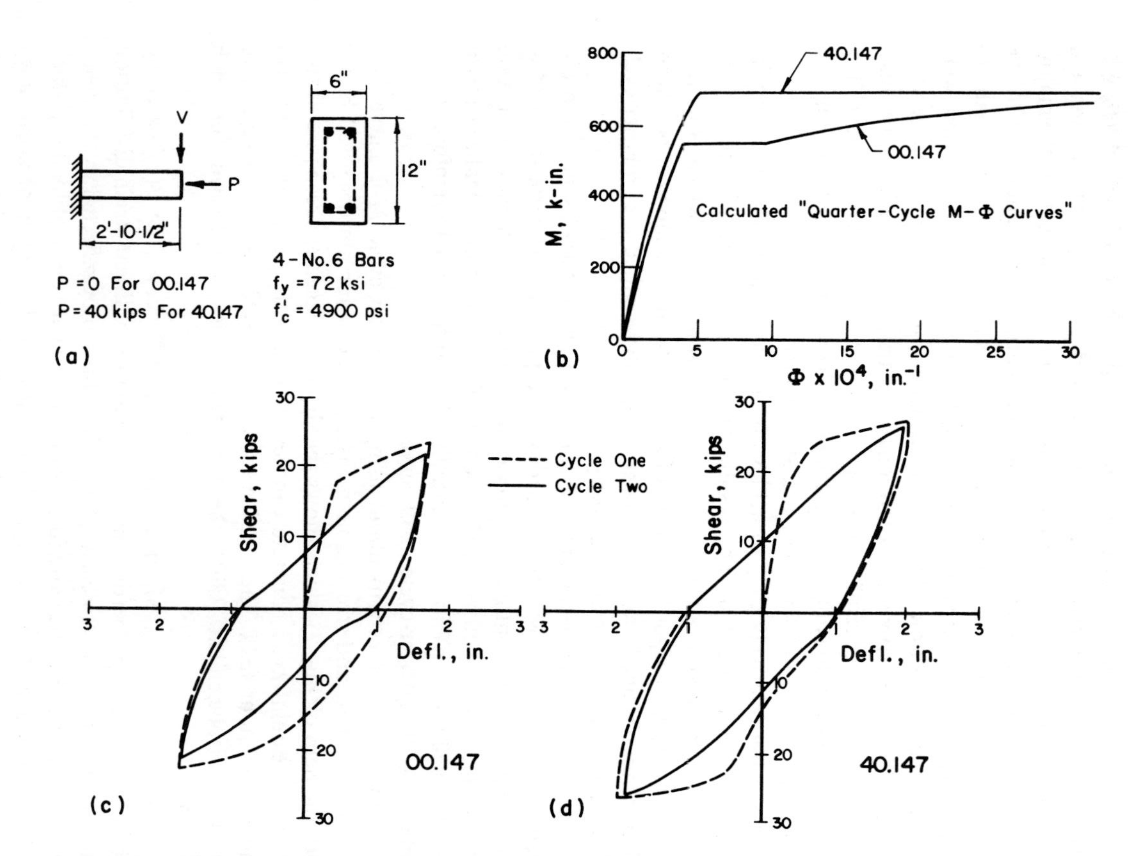


Fig. 3. Examples of hysteresis in the inelastic range of response (After Ref. 32)

effectively an alpha test. Information from "lower" tests does not suffice to explain its results completely.

Consider the shape of the first and second cycles of the force-displacement curves. Even though not elastoplastic, the first cycles have a reasonably well-defined yield, but the second cycles do not. The much sought "well-defined yield point" is erased in the first excursion into the inelastic range and does not return unless larger displacements are incurred in the same direction. This discrepancy between the implication of the quarter-cycle $M$-$\Phi$ curve and actual force-displacement response is important because it tends to make unrealistic the demand for a well-defined yield point in the steel, at least as it is justified in terms of the $M$-$\Phi$ curve.

Because the quarter-cycle $M$-$\Phi$ curve does not explain the response of structural elements subjected to loads or deformations generated by earthquake motions, definitions such as "balanced reinforcement ratio" do not have the same validity for earthquake-resistant design as they do for design to resist gravity forces. Considering that the shell of a column is very likely to spall off in the first major inelastic displacement, the standard definition of the "balance load" based on total section and unconfined concrete properties and that the core concrete is typically confined has little meaning for a column designed to dissipate energy in the inelastic range of response.

For calculating the response history of a structure, the inadequacy of the quarter-cycle $M$-$\Phi$ curve is readily apparent. Because of this weakness, emphasis in research has shifted to studies of the hysteretic response of reinforced concrete elements [26]. However, such a change has not taken place in practice, as indicated by design specifications which continue to treat the quarter-cycle $M$-$\Phi$ curve as a reliable benchmark rather than as a set of index values.

## Shear

In a reinforced concrete element subjected to reversals of large displacements into the inelastic range, transverse reinforcement may perform several functions. In proper amounts and placement, it makes it possible for the concrete to sustain stress at large compressive deformations. It provides lateral support for the longitudinal bars, after spalling of the shell concrete. It restrains the tensile "bursting" forces set up by stress transfer between the bars and the concrete. It helps the member carry transverse forces.

The first three functions it performs best in continuous helical form (spiral reinforcement). Despite a series of confirmations of the positive influence of spiral reinforcement, its quantitative effect on confined concrete has not yet been systematically investigated for types of loadings associated with earthquake effects. In contrast, the influence on concrete behavior of rectilinear transverse reinforcement, which is manifestly less efficient in confining concrete, has attracted more interest in the laboratory. In the case of either type of transverse reinforcement, drastic changes in practice with respect to confinement are not anticipated in the near future, despite the primitiveness of the available information. But with respect to the fourth function, shear resistance, changes in concept and practice are likely in view of the extensive amount of relevant experimental work carried out in the past few years in Japan and the United States.

It is interesting to note that in the initial phase of experimental research into the deformation capacity of reinforced concrete elements, problems related to shear were deliberately relegated to the background by overdesigning the amount of web reinforcement in the test specimens. This conservative measure, which was quite proper for the investigations aimed at flexural properties, did delay the perception of problems related to shear in structural elements displaced well into the nonlinear range.

A rash of failures of stubby reinforced concrete columns, constrained by deep spandrel beams, resulting from the Tokachioki earthquake of 1968 led Japanese investigators to study the shear strength of reinforced concrete elements under repetitions of large lateral displacement reversals. Initial results by Hisada et al. [12], Ikeda [14], and Kanoh et al. [15] indicated in effect that the modified truss analogy failed to serve as a satisfactory design method for web reinforcement under conditions of loading related to earthquakes. Their findings were confirmed by further research [8,18,32], which suggests a reevaluation of the current approach to the design of transverse reinforcement for shear resistance.

The truss analogy was the earliest concept by which calculations for stresses in the web reinforcement were organized. The reinforced concrete beam was imagined to be a truss with "compression diagonals" of concrete with transverse reinforcement acting as tensile web members. The angle of inclination of the "compression diagonals" was set at 45° after some study of various alternatives [19] but primarily because it was simple and plausible.

Several series of tests [19,20,25] indicated a consistent discrepancy between measured maximum strains in the transverse reinforcement and those calculated using the truss analogy. Two similar expressions were proposed to reconcile the difference:

$$v = C_1 + C_2 \rho_w f_v, \tag{1}$$

$$v = (C_3 + C_4 \rho_w) f_v, \tag{2}$$

where $v = V/b_j d$; $V =$ total shear force; $b =$ width of rectangular beam; $d =$ effective depth; $j =$ ratio of the distance between centroids of cross-sectional tensile and compressive forces ("straight-line formula") to the effective depth, approximately $\frac{7}{8}$; $\rho_w =$ web reinforcement ratio; $f_v =$ unit stress in transverse reinforcement; $C_1$ and $C_3 =$ experimental constants; and

$C_2$ and $C_4$ = constants which may be derived from truss analogy (1.0 for vertical stirrups).

Equation (1) proposed by Richart [19], eventually was selected for use in design. Because $C_1$ was expressed as a function of concrete strength, it encouraged the operational concept of part of the shear being "carried" by the concrete and part by the steel. When the ACI Code was revised to refer to strength rather than stress [1], the available strength data were organized in deference to Eq. (1), the only difference being the involvement of material strength rather than permissible stresses.

Two features of this development are of significance. First, the modified truss analogy [Eq. (1)] does not and was never meant to describe the physical mechanism of shear resistance. Viewed in this light, it is not even in the class of, say, a simple expression for anchorage of a plain bar which is directly dependent on experimental factors of limited application but nevertheless describes, if crudely, the phenomenon to which it refers. Second, the scales might just as well have tilted in favor of Eq. (2), proposed by Slater et al. [25], in which case the approach would have been closer to that of concrete "carrying" all the shear but as a function of the confining reinforcement.

It is interesting to note that when Arakawa [4] studied essentially the same population of data which led to the current ACI approach [1] and with the same bias of contributions of concrete and steel being independent and additive components [Eq. (1)], he had no scruples about modifying the second term to $C_2\sqrt{p_w f_y}$, which effectively erased all relation to the truss analogy model. Whether this was necessary for static design is debatable, but the important implication of this change is that Eq. (1) does not possess a form, let alone the experimental factors, that cannot be abrogated.

The professional reaction to the observed strength decay in reinforced concrete columns and beams resulting from load reversals in the inelastic range has been to assign all the shear to the transverse reinforcement or to make $C_1 = 0$ in Eq. (1). This stratagem appears to yield acceptable results, at least for elements of moderate and slender proportions (but not for internal design of connections for which the applications of the concepts of beam shear strength are suspect anyway) provided the cross-sectional sizes of the members are "reasonable." However, this design concept of assigning all the shear to the web reinforcement also encourages the structural designer into believing that the size of the concrete section is irrelevant to the shear problem.

It would appear that the truss analogy is an idea whose time has run out for earthquake-resistant design. Further conceptual development is needed in the direction of relating the internal shear stress or principal stress to a reasonably simple failure criterion for the concrete, with the failure criterion expressed as a function, most likely nonlinear, of the transverse reinforcement.

Two test results from a current investigation in Japan* [8] will illustrate this further. Figure 4 shows the measured response of two columns loaded axially and subjected to bending as shown, in one plane. The vertical axis indicates the shear on the column in tons and the horizontal axis the total lateral displacement in millimeters. Both columns, which had a clear height to depth ratio of 4, were reinforced longitudinally with six 16-mm (approximately No. 5) bars ($\rho = 0.02$, total). The transverse reinforcement ratio was 0.0122 for column 7B and 0.0244 for column 7A. To put this in perspective, it would suffice to mention that in accordance with "truss analogy" the lower transverse reinforcement ratio would correspond to a shear strength of approximately 19 tons, more than the maximum shear applied.

In both cases, the flexural capacity of the column was developed at least once. In fact, a lower amount of web reinforcement would have sufficed to accomplish that. However, further cycling into the inelastic range resulted in a decay in strength which was caused by splitting along the longitudinal bars slowly transferring the column into one with unbounded reinforcement along its clear height. Increase of transverse reinforcement improved the hysteretic relationship at large displacement but did not stop completely the process of deterioration. The elimination of the routine shear failure does not necessarily ensure stable hysteretic response at large displacements. Therefore, increasing the amount of transverse reinforcement is not always the solution to strength decay.

## Earthquake Simulation in the Laboratory

The primary attraction of subjecting a structure to an earthquake motion in the laboratory is contained in a promise which is, in itself, something of a contradiction: the promise of controlling a spontaneous event. Testing a structural *model* using a *simulated* earthquake moticn appears preferable to the two other types of physical testing, despite the suspicions created by "model" modifying the structure and "simulated" modifying the earthquake. Earthquake simulation for structural testing offers an option not included in (but does not supplant) "ordinary" structural testing because of the preservation of a semblance of the chance event, the freedom of the structure to respond to a base motion in accordance with its own constraints. It offers

*An extensive investigation of the strength and deformation characteristics of reinforced concrete columns is currently being conducted in Japan by the Building Research Institute, Ministry of Construction, with the cooperation of several universities and construction companies. A total of 166 specimens have already been tested, with each specimen subjected to 48 cycles of lateral deformation to various limits. The length to depth ratio for the columns (Fig. 4) varies from 2 to 4 for most cases, with a few specimens having more slender proportions. Axial loads range from one-eighth to one-fourth of the axial load capacity. The main variables are the amounts of longitudinal and transverse reinforcement.

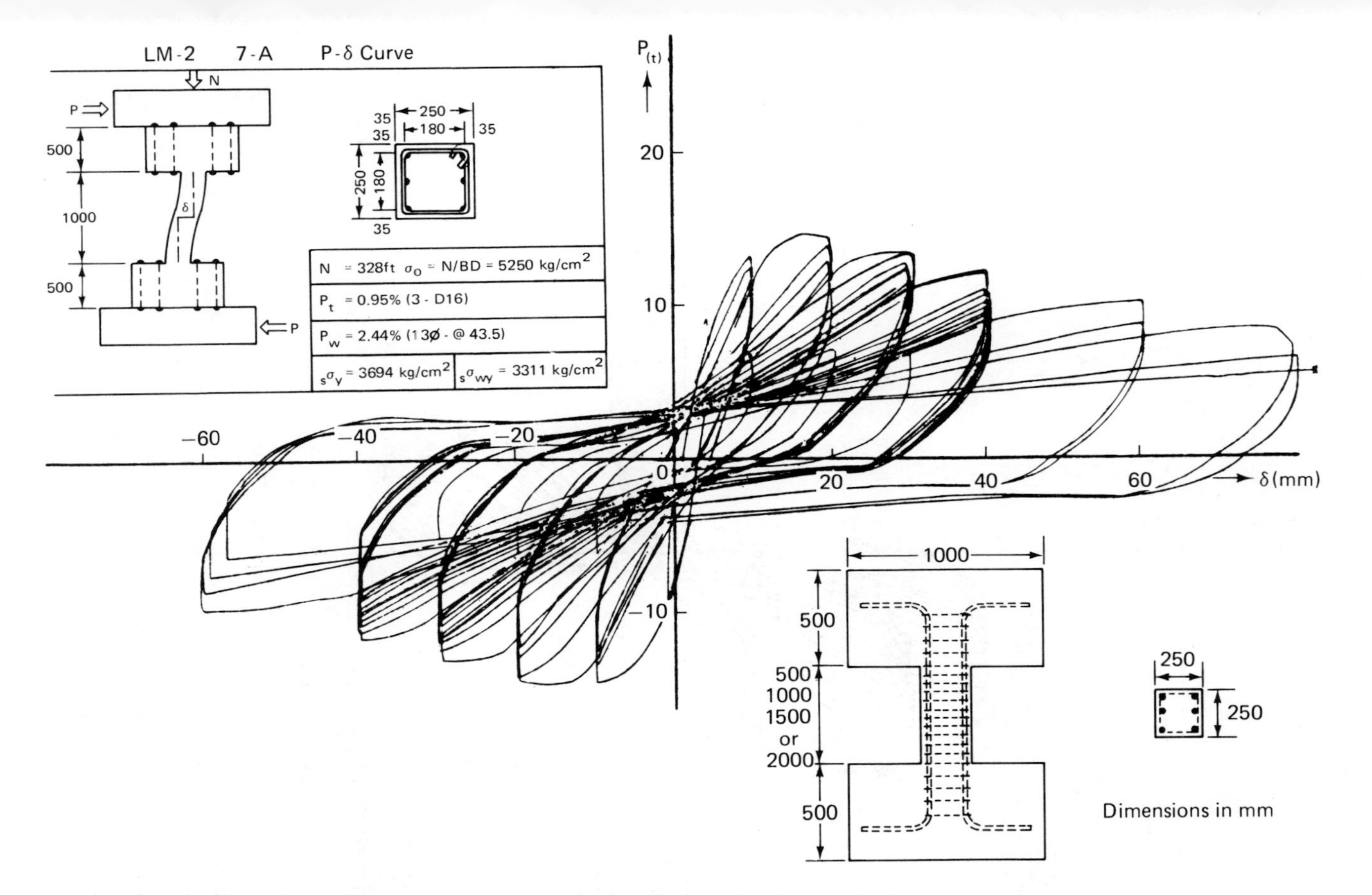


**Fig. 4a.** Load-displacement curves for specimen 7A (Building Research Institute, Japan)

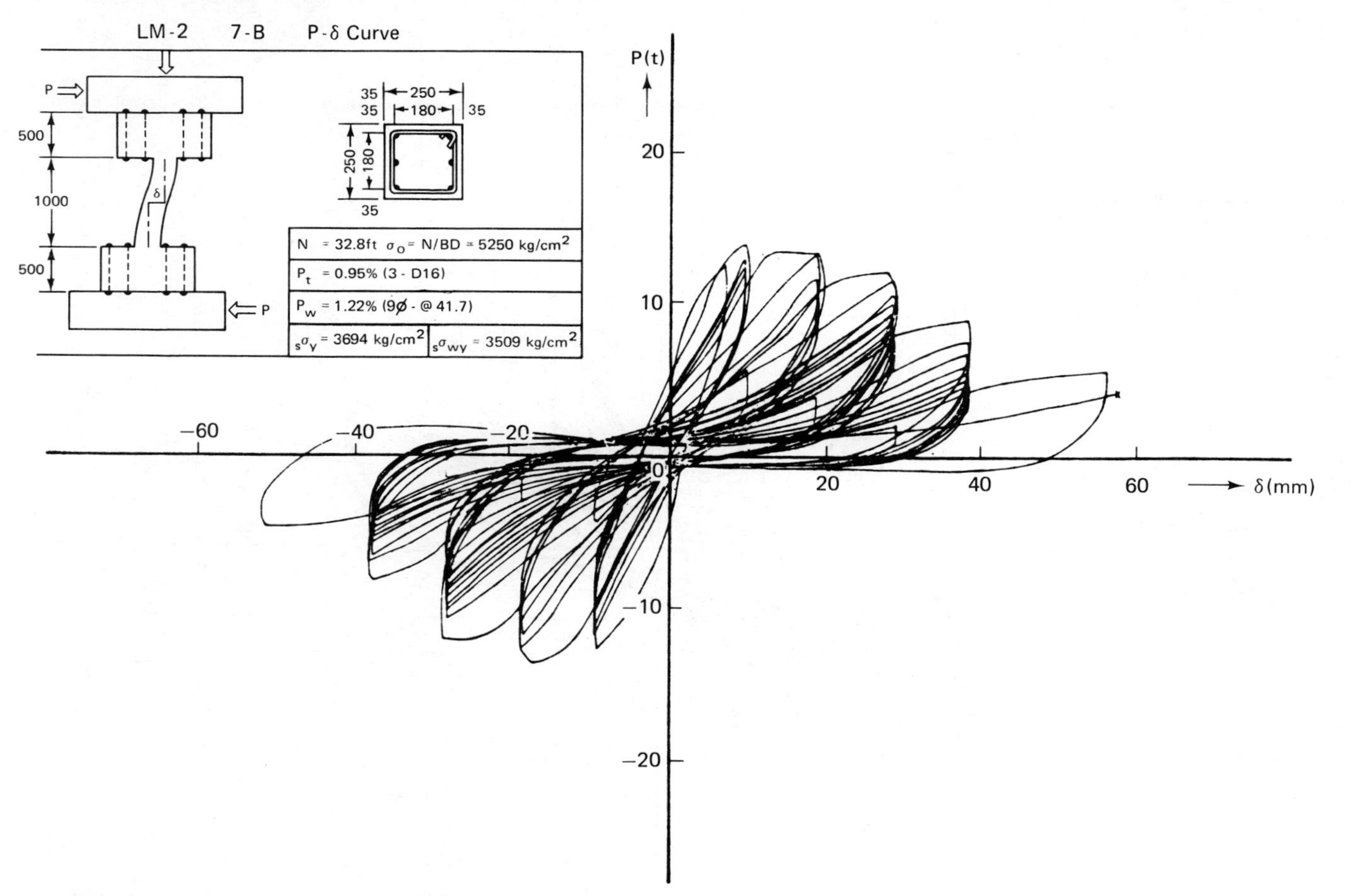


**Fig. 4b.** Load-displacement curves for specimen 7B (Building Research Institute, Japan)

advantages over (but does not supplant) field observations because of the time element for an instrumented building and because of the availability of well-defined information on the motion as well as on the structure for a building studied after earthquake damage.

Recorded attempts at earthquake simulation for structural testing have been made as early as at the turn of the century [21]. But it was only after the middle 1960s, as a result of advances in electrohydraulic controls, computer hardware, and dynamic instrumentation, that it was possible for the structural researcher to concentrate on the test specimen and its behavior rather than on the test equipment. Various testing facilities of modern vintage have been built within the last decade in various countries [16]. The following remarks on the use of earthquake simulation in the laboratory to investigate the behavior of reinforced concrete structure models stem from experience with the University of Illinois Earthquake Simulator, a test facility which can reproduce uniaxial motion or one component of the recorded earthquake motion and which has been in operation since 1967 [27].

### *Acceptance Criteria for the Reproduced Earthquake-Motion Component*

Accepting the synthetic constraints of uniaxial motion and a particular earthquake record, a question that still remains is the fidelity of the reproduced motion. It is desirable that the waveform of the reproduced acceleration history of the platform look precisely like that of the input, but this is not a vital requirement for the success of the test. As a matter of fact, the problem is not one of fidelity of the earthquake motion but of the goodness of the entire production, including the test structure and sensing equipment. The required fidelity of the waveform is primarily a function of the dynamic characteristics of the test structure. The goal is that the reproduced motion contain a range of frequencies at the proper sequences and amplitudes to excite the test structure or test structures as the prototype or prototypes would be excited in an earthquake. The details of the waveform of the acceleration history are not in themselves critical in judging the goodness of reproduced motion.

One of the most obvious tests of the goodness of the platform motion is the response spectrum. This is a necessary but insufficient test as it is rather insensitive and, by definition, does not provide information of the sequence of acceleration pulses.

Experience with the University of Illinois Earthquake Simulator indicates that a direct quantitative method of judging the goodness of a reproduced earthquake-motion component is the linear-oscillator response test [27]. For this test, response histories of linearly elastic single-degree-of-freedom oscillators, at various frequencies covering the anticipated frequencies of the test structure, are calculated for the platform motion as well as the input motion. Comparison of these responses provides the test of "goodness."

### *Structural Models*

Reduction in size of reinforced concrete elements, made necessary by the limits of the earthquake simulation facility, introduces problems in modeling in addition to those readily apparent from principles of similitude recognizing geometrical and physical properties. The interrelationship between shear and flexural strengths of individual elements changes, bond and cracking phenomena vary nonlinearly with the scale factor, and time-dependent variables may introduce spurious effects on short-time response. Briefly, it can be generalized that all behavioral phenomena not explicitly understood in terms of alpha tests at the material level become suspect when member sizes are miniaturized.

Two general principles have been followed in designing the test structures: (1) The physical model is designed to test a theoretical model, rather than a particular building or building type, and (2) the elements of the physical model are designed to minimize effects of shear and bond stresses and phenomena directly related to concrete properties.

The temptation is to ignore the first principle, at least in describing the test results. The geometrical appearance of the model does support referring to it as a building and in fact makes transfer of information from the tests to engineering literature more convenient. But this is a convenience that may give negative results eventually. Viewed as a vehicle for physical testing of a theoretical model, earthquake simulation is a powerful tool with few deficiencies. Viewed as a test structure supposed to represent one in the field, the test structure has a whole host of deficiencies, starting from the foundation to distribution of deadloads.

The second principle pivots on the assurance that as long as response phenomena are related primarily to flexural strength and deformation of reinforced concrete, resulting information can be projected to full-scale buildings with the help of alpha tests in the miniature and full scale. This limitation is made palatable by the facts that (1) shear or bond failures can be investigated in full-scale or nearly full-scale models loaded statically in order to develop criteria for their elimination under dynamic conditions and (2) it is preferable to avoid the possibility of such failures in earthquake-resistant construction.

### *General Observations*

Ideally, the earthquake-simulation test is an omega test. It is designed to spot-check a particular set of results obtained from analytical synthesis of information from "lower" investigations. Actually, it has overtones of the alpha test because the analysis cannot help but be tuned in relation to the results of the rest. A multiplicity of variables influence the analytical model, and, given faith in the experimental results, it is not impossible to make plausible adjustments in the model, which do not necessarily follow from first principles, in order to accommodate the results of the earthquake-simulation test. Therefore, projection of the results to other conditions using as a vehicle nonlinear dynamic analysis must be done very cautiously.

The main purpose of the experimental work on the earthquake simulator is the development of analytical methods for determining the earthquake response of complex structures. An example is SAKE [16] of which results have been confirmed for a particular class of structure: the open regular properly reinforced planar frame. In this domain, it can be used with reasonable confidence. However, its application to, say, a structure with abrupt variation in story stiffness of mass from floor to floor is questionable until this condition has been experimentally verified.

Earthquake-simulation tests also lead to behavioral observations which are of direct value in understanding the response of reinforced concrete structures.

The following trends were observed to be common to the responses of reinforced concrete frames and walls tested [10, 16, 28]. It should be noted that all test structures were designed to minimize torsional oscillations and were subjected to uniaxial horizontal motion.

1. For given types of earthquake motion and test structure, there was a strong correlation between the maximum displacement and specturm intensity [17] modified for the pertinent frequency range.
2. In any test structure subjected to a strong base motion, there was a notable reduction in response frequencies, as a result of cracking of the concrete and yielding and local bond failure of the steel.
3. For types of base motion characterized by El Centro 1940 and Taft 1952, the frequency reduction occurred almost immediately upon initiation of the strong motion. If a single set of frequencies are to be used to interpret or anticipate the response of the structure, the reduced set of frequencies would be more meaningful than the initial set based on calculations or on very-small-amplitude oscillations.
4. The variation in the fundamental frequency could be related quantitatively to the variation of effective stiffness with displacement of the structural system as indicated by static tests.
5. For the test structures, which had been conservatively designed against the possibility of shear or bond failures, the capacity of the system to dissipate energy increased at a decreasing rate with increase in displacement.

These observations led to a method for the calculation of design forces described in the next section.

## The Substitute-Structure Method

The substitute-structure method is a procedure for determining seismic-design forces in multistory reinforced concrete structures. It uses a substitute linear model of the prototype structure which reflects the effects of non-linear response through its modified stiffness and increased damping factor [22]. The method was developed from the observation that the maximum earthquake response of reinforced concrete SDF systems could be closely approximated by a substitute system with appropriately adjusted stiffness and damping characteristics [11].

The procedure starts from two decisions independent of the method: a linear response spectrum of the type shown in Fig. 5 and limits of tolerable

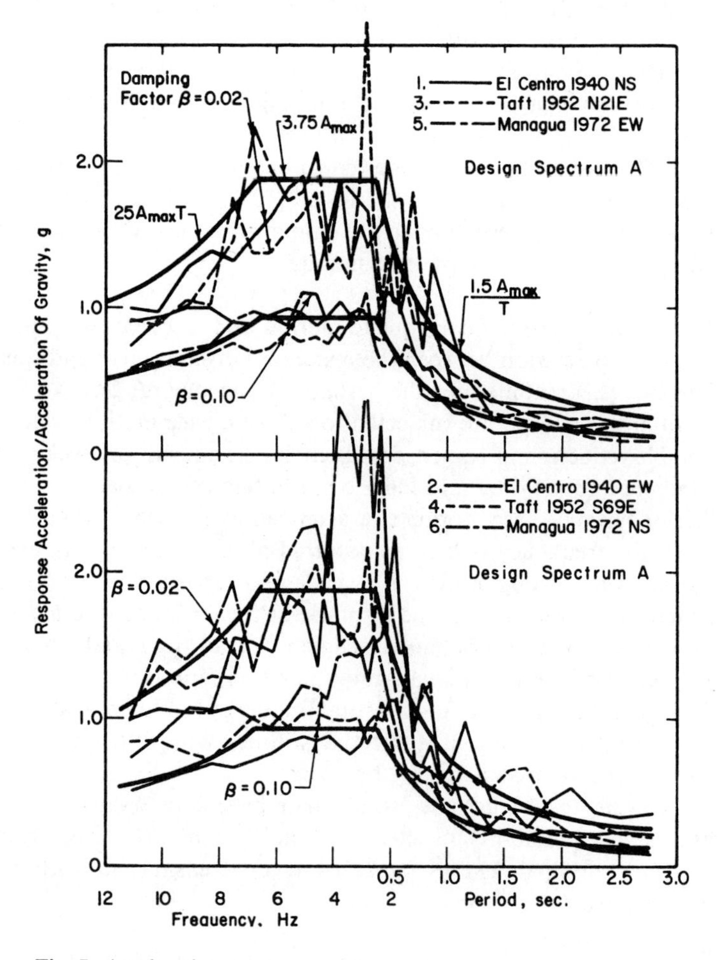


Fig. 5. Acceleration response spectra

member displacement or the tolerable stiffness reduction, $\mu$. The main difference between the routine modal analysis method and the substitute-structure method is in the definition of the structural model and the modal damping factors. The model to be analyzed has its member stiffnesses divided by the assumed values of $\mu$. The modal damping factor is calculated as a function of $\mu$ and the modal shape.

A particular test of the method is illustrated in Figs. 6 and 7. The seismic-design forces in a series of three simple frame structures, having 10 to 3 stories, were determined using spectrum $A$ and values of $\mu$ equal to 6 for the beams and 1 for the columns. Assuming that the yield moments for the various members were identical to those required by the design forces, the frames were "subjected" using SAKE [16] to a series of six strong ground motions, each normalized to a peak acceleration of 0.5$g$. Values of $\mu$ calculated are plotted in Fig. 7.

The design base shear coefficients were 0.54, 0.30, and 0.15 for the 3-, 5-, and 10-story frames, respectively. The first value, 0.54, for the 3-story frame may be treated by itself as an index value of the design system. Despite the relatively high characteristic maximum acceleration of 0.5$g$ which was assumed to normalize the design spectrum, this quantity still appears too high. It is indeed not high, however, if the criterion of no inelastic action in the column is to be satisfied. The design base shear could have been lowered by admitting a value of $\mu$ greater than 1 for the columns.

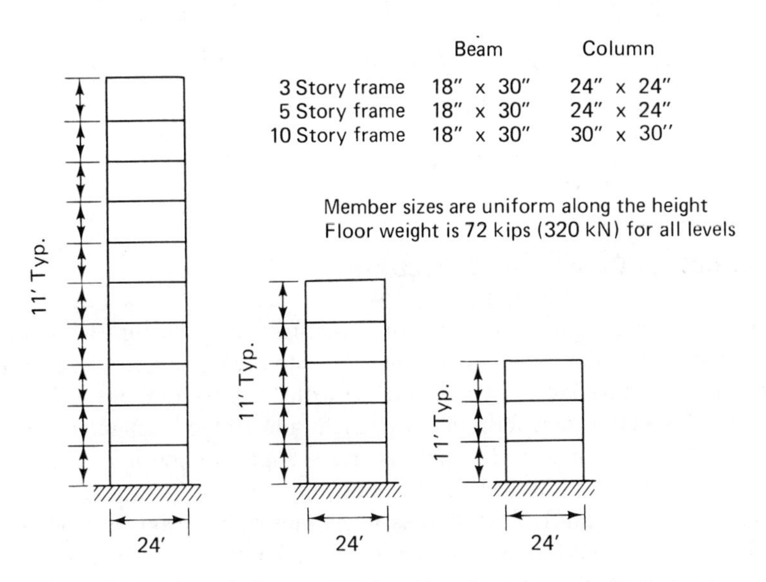


**Fig. 6.** Properties of frames "designed" using the substitute-structure method

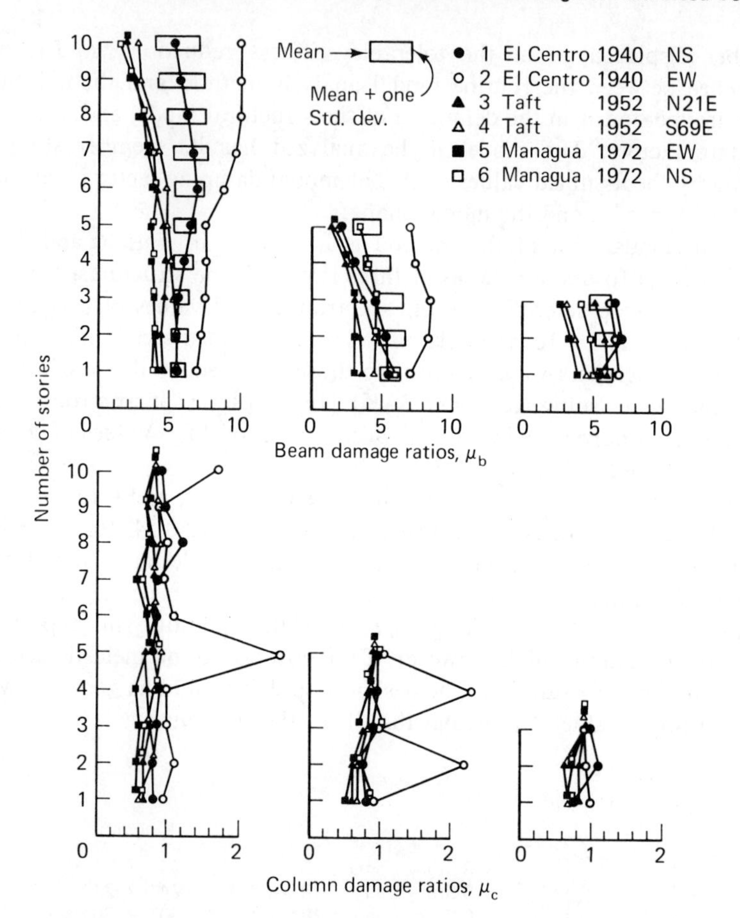


**Fig. 7.** Calculated damage ratios for frames "designed" using the substitute structure method

## Evaluation of Completed Structure

Observed behavior of buildings subjected to strong motions has demonstrated time and again that only in some cases do the response characteristics of the building have close correspondence with the design intent. The absolute values as well as distributions of strength and stiffness often vary palpably from those assumed in the analysis stage. Even discounting the cases of interaction with stiff nonstructural elements, the possibility of the final structure differing significantly from that assumed in seismic design is strong. And yet this problem is seldom confronted in the design process. Furthermore, in making general evaluations of success or failure, the tendency often is to calibrate the observations using the design strengths or stiffnesses implied by the prevailing code when it would obviously be more reasonable, though difficult, to relate it to the actual median characteristics of the structures as built.

Evaluation of the completed design should be a required step in the design process not only for the avoidance of problems unforeseen in the original analysis and proportioning but also for providing a more realistic understanding of the reasons for the good or bad performance record of a building system. A typical example is the main building of the Olive View Hospital Complex in San Fernando, California. Arguments have been made pivoting about the low design base shear (approx. eight percent of the weight of the building, based on working stress design) without acknowledging the fact that even a very conservative estimate of the base shear strength would put it at three times that value [3,5].

The final check need not always be a complicated one. Its extent would depend on the importance, complexity, or novelty of the structure.

### *Story Shear Strength*

The simplest and minimum check is the determination of the story shear strength at the lowest critical level of the structure. This quantity is easily obtained for frames using the limiting strength of the members involved in the governing mechanism for arbitrary or likely distribution of force over the height of the building. Its comparison with the weight of the building would provide a significant item of information for reasonably symmetrical low-rise construction.

The distribution of story shear strength over the height of a low-rise frame would also provide an indication to the designer about the characteristics of the building and possibly reveal undesirable changes in strength distribution.

### *Relative Wall-Area Index*

A simple method, which has been used as the framework for interpretation of experience in Japan, can serve as a very powerful tool in making initial evaluations of the damage susceptibility of low-rise buildings in zones of high seismicity.

Shiga et al. [23] made a quantitative analysis of the observed damage to low-rise buildings, resulting from the Tokachioki earthquake of 1968, by evaluating two parameters for each building: (1) ratio of building weight to sum of cross-sectional areas of walls and columns and (2) ratio of wall area to floor area in a given story. Plotting the position of each building with respect to two coordinate axes representing those parameters indicated significant groupings of buildings with different degrees of damage. Figure 8 shows the same data replotted by Aoyama [30] with the second parameter, plotted along the $x$ axis, modified to be the ratio of the wall area to the total floor area.

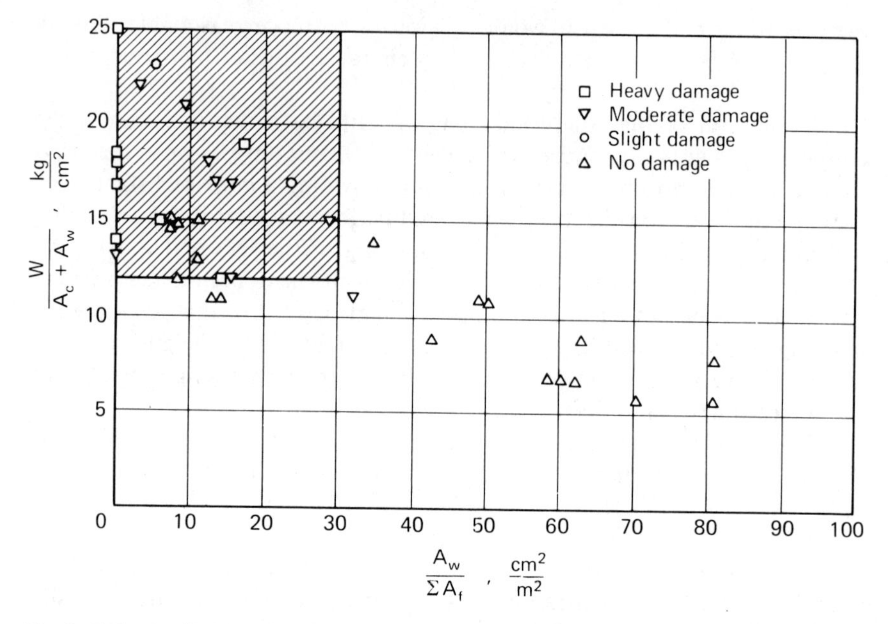


**Fig. 8.** Index for likelihood of damage in low-rise reinforced concrete construction in Japan (Refs. 22 and 30) $W$ = weight of building above level considered; $A_c$ = total column area at level; $A_w$ = total wall area at level; $\Sigma A_f$ = total floor area above level

From Fig. 8 it can be concluded roughly that structures located by these parameters within the hatched area may be susceptible to damage and should be reanalyzed using other techniques if located in a zone of high seismicity.

### *An Intermediate Model for Calculation of Nonlinear Response*

The shear-beam model, with lumped masses, has been used to investigate nonlinear response primarily because it can be handled without a large-capacity digital computer and a large computing budget. The shear-beam model provides satisfactory results if the columns, rather than the girders, yield in a structure without abrupt changes in story shear strength. It leads to incorrect results for frames with beams flexurally weaker than the columns.

The SB model [2] was developed to provide an analytical model that would represent frames with "weak beams" while keeping the digital computation requirements within modest limits. A physical interpretation of the model is shown in Fig. 9(a). As in the shear-beam model, each story mass is coupled directly to the next one, and the first story to the base. In addition, every set of three consecutive levels, with the sets overlapping as shown, are interconnected with a weightless rigid rod hinged at each end and connected with a spring to the intermediate level in the set.

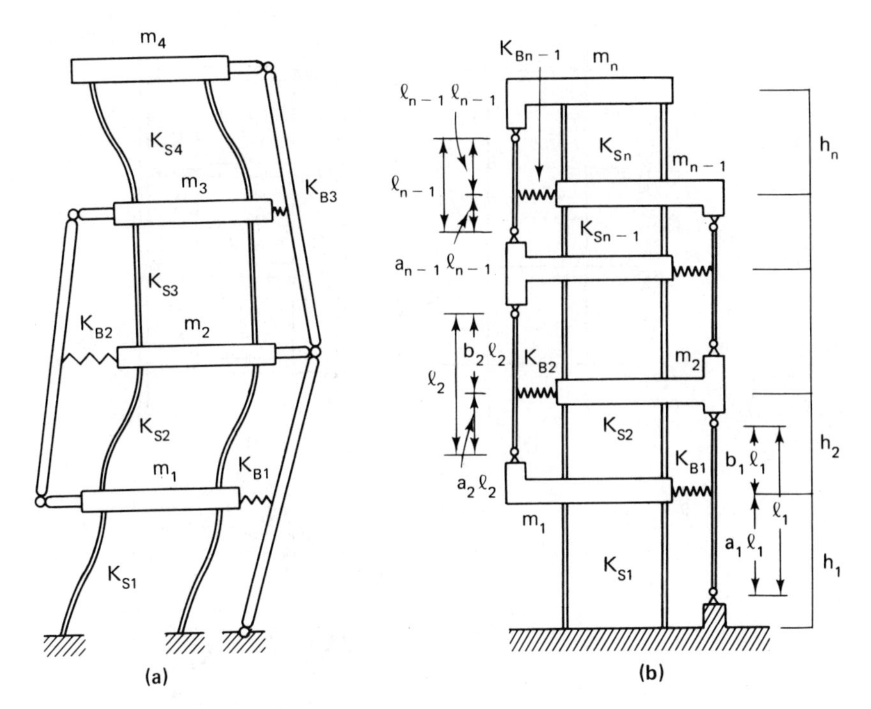


**Fig. 9.** The SB model

In effect, the interstory connections are the shear springs, their stiffness characteristics being determined with the structure displaced into a linear mode shape, and the springs reacting against the rods are the "bending springs" because they are designed to respond when the structure is displaced into a shape different from the linear mode. Thus, the model, which has both shear and bending springs, is called the SB model.

An $n$-story SB model with $n$ masses ($m_1$ to $m_n$), $n$ shear springs ($K_{s1}$ to $K_{sn}$) and $n - 1$ bending springs ($K_{b1}$ to $K_{bn-1}$) is shown in Fig. 9(b). The lengths of each weightless rod above and below the spring are set such that, for a selected deformed shape of the structure such as the linear, the bending springs are not stressed. The resulting stiffness matrix relating story shear to story displacement is tridiagonal.

*Spring Stiffnesses.* Consider the frame shown schematically in Fig. 10(a) with the corresponding SB model shown in Fig. 10(b). When it is displaced in the linear mode [Fig. 10(c)] the stiffness of the prototype frame may be expressed by the reciprocal of the sum of beam and column flexibilities, which gives the stiffness of the shear springs. The bending springs do not participate in this mode. However, when the structure is displaced as shown in

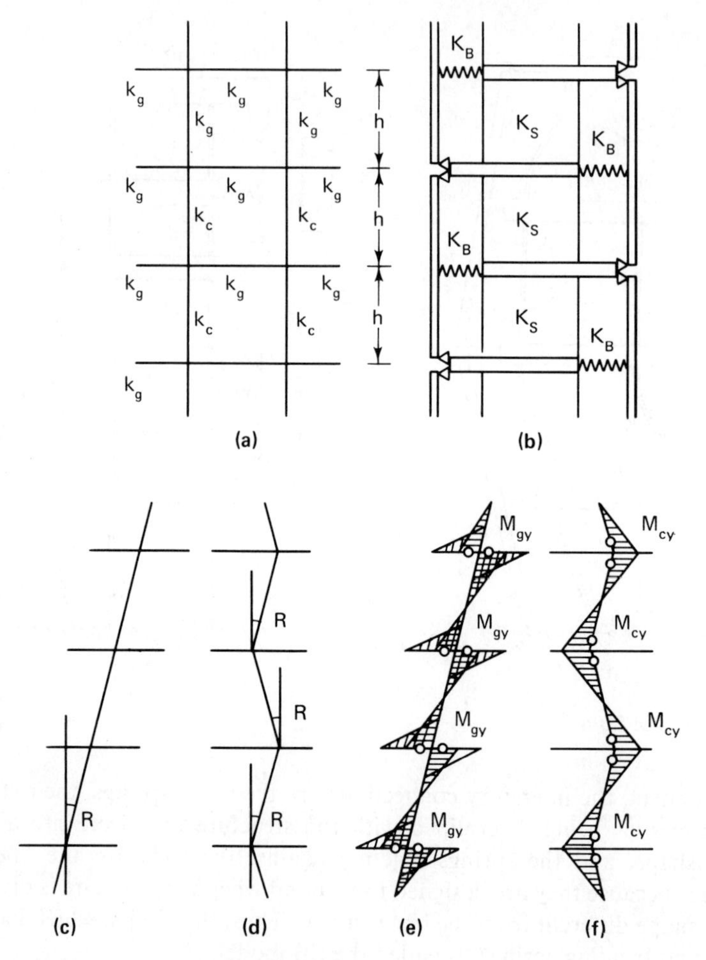


**Fig. 10.** Frame and SB model

Fig. 10(d), both sets of springs react. From this condition, the bending-spring stiffnesses are determined.

*Spring Strengths.* Consider the girder-hinge mechanism shown in Fig. 10(e). The column shears for this mechanism set the limiting strengths of the shear springs. Then consider the column-hinge mechanism in Fig. 10(f). The differences in the story shears lead to the determination of strength limits for the bending springs.

Hysteresis rules for the two types of springs may be different if desired. Calculations of maximum story displacements of low-rise frames using the

SB model [2] have compared quite well with those based on more elaborate models [29,31].

## Concluding Remarks

Although preceded by individual and discontinuous instances of relevant work, the current crop of experimental research on earthquake resistance of reinforced concrete structure has had its beginnings after the publication of Ref. 6, the bulk having been carried out or initiated during the last decade. In a profession with as much inertia as structural engineering, it is remarkable that some of the work has already affected practice and not too surprising that most of it still awaits application, despite the special impetus from earthquakes.

The significant new question that concern for earthquake-resistant design has brought to the laboratory is the one about the behavior of reinforced concrete subjected to reversals of displacement into the inelastic range of response. As a result there have been fundamental changes in the design of experiments as well as in interpretation. Emphasis is placed in evaluation of hysteretic response rather than on the quantification of a single response obtained under continually increasing load. The new vision of force-displacement relationships differs from the old and is yet to have an impact on practice, which is still explicitly calibrated to the immaculate concept of elastoplastic response.

Experimental research, reinforced by field observation, has transformed transverse reinforcement from a consideration of secondary to primary importance in structural design. With respect to one of the functions of transverse reinforcement, that of helping to resist shear, tests under cyclic loading have shown that the modified truss analogy, used for proportioning web reinforcement, has serious weaknesses as a design concept and should be revised.

The most important factor in structural design is successful precedent, evaluated and projected through scientific discipline with help from the laboratory wherever necessary. The major achievement of structural research over the last decade has been the development of information which makes it possible to assemble reasonably realistic dynamic response models of many classes of structures. And yet the profession continues to evaluate past experience in terms of quantities related to code requirements, assigning the discrepancy between elastic response and code-required strength to ductility, when it is well known that in traditional construction actual strength may often exceed that required by minimum code requirements. It is urged that the codes require explicitly a final evaluation of the completed structural design to expose critical changes in design from the initial concept and also to help the designer to interpret past experience less unrealistically.

## Acknowledgment

The writers would like to acknowledge the positive response of the Japan Society for Promotion of Science and the U.S. National Science Foundation to the needs for research on earthquake resistance as well as their active encouragement of cooperation between research workers in Japan and the United States.

## References

1. ACI Committee 326 (Joint with ASCE), "Shear and Diagonal Tension," *Proc. ACI*, Vol. 59, Jan. 1962, pp. 7–30, and *Proc. ACI*, Vol. 59, Feb. 1962, pp. 277–334.
2. AOYAMA, H., "Simple Nonlinear Models for Seismic Response of Reinforced Concrete Buildings," Proceedings, Review Meeting of the U.S.-Japan Cooperative Research Program on Earthquake Engineering with Emphasis on the Safety of School Buildings, Assoc. for Science Documents, Tokyo Inst. of Technology, Tokyo, 1976, pp. 291–309.
3. AOYAMA, H., and M. A. SOZEN, "Dynamic Response of a Reinforced Concrete Structure with Tied and Spiral Columns," Proceedings, Fifth World Conference on Earthquake Engineering, Int. Assoc. of Earthquake Engin., Paper No. 15, Rome, 1973, pp. 137–143.
4. ARAKAWA, T., "Allowable Shearing Stress and Effect of Web Reinforcement in Reinforced Concrete Beams" (in Japanese) *Concrete J.*, Vol. 8, No. 7, July 1970. (See, for English summary, S. Kokusho and K. Ogura, "Shear Strength and Load-Deflection Characteristics of Reinforced Concrete Members," *Proceedings, U.S.-Japan Seminar on Earthquake Engineering with Emphasis on Safety of School Buildings, Sept. 1970*, The Japan Earthquake Engineering Promotion Society, Tokyo, 1971, pp. 364–381.
5. BERTERO, V. V., B. BRESLER, L. G. SELNA, A. K. CHOPRA, and A. V. KORETSKY, "Design Implications of Damage Observed in the Olive View Medical Center Buildings," Proceedings, Fifth World Conference on Earthquake Engineering, Int. Assoc. Earthquake Engin., Paper No. 6, Rome, 1973, pp. 51–59.
6. BLUME, J. A., N. M. NEWMARK, and L. H. CORNING, *Design of Multistory Reinforced Concrete Buildings for Earthquake Motions*, Portland Cement Association, Skokie, 1961.
7. BLUME, J. A., "Early Research in the Dynamic Aspects of Earthquake Engineering," *Dedication, Earthquake Simulator*, Earthquake Engineering Research Center, University of California, Berkeley, 1972, pp. 5–36.
8. Committee on Reinforced Concrete Columns, Building Research Institute of Japan, "Experimental Research on Improving Ductility of Reinforced Concrete Columns Under Cyclic Lateral Loads (in Japanese)," *Concrete J.*, Vol. 13, No. 1., Jan. 1975, pp. 2–18.
9. CROSS, H., "The Relation of Analysis to Structural Design," *Trans. Am. Soc. Civil Eng.*, Vol. 101, 1936, pp. 1363–1374.

10. GULKAN, P., and M. A. SOZEN, "Response and Energy Dissipation of Reinforced Concrete Frames Subjected to Strong Base Motions," *Structural Research Series No. 377*, University of Illinois, Urbana, May 1971, 288 pp.
11. GULKAN, P., and M. A. SOZEN, "Inelastic Response of Reinforced Concrete Structures to Earthquake Motions," *ACI J.*, Vol. 71, No. 12, Dec. 1974, pp. 601–609.
12. HISADA, T. N. OHMORI, and S. BESSHO, *Earthquake Design Considerations in Reinforced Concrete Columns*, Kajima Institute of Construction Technology, Tokyo, Jan. 1972.
13. HOUSNER, G. W., "Behavior of Structures During Earthquakes," *J. Eng. Mech. Div. ASCE*, Vol. 85, No. EM4, Oct. 1959, pp. 108–129.
14. IKEDA, A., "Load-Deformation Characteristics of Reinforced Concrete Columns Subjected to Alternative Loading" (in Japanese), Report of the Training Institute for Engineering Teachers, Yokohama National University, Yokohama, March 1968.
15. KANOH, Y., et al., "Shear Strength of Reinforced Concrete Beams Under Many Cyclic Alternating Loadings" (in Japanese), Research Report, Architectural Institute of Japan, Tokyo, Aug. 1969.
16. OTANI, S., "SAKE, a Computer Program for Inelastic Response of R/C Frames to Earthquakes," *Structural Research Series No. 413*, University of Illinois, Urbana, Nov. 1974, 145 pp.
17. OTANI, S., and M. A. SOZEN, "Behavior of Multistory Reinforced Concrete Frames During Earthquakes," *Structural Research Series No. 392*, University of Illinois, Urbana, Nov. 1972, 551 pp.
18. POPOV, E. P., V. V. BERTERO, and H. KRAWINKLER, "Cyclic Behavior of Three R/C Flexural Members with High Shear," *Report No. 72-S*, Earthquake Research Center, University of California, Berkeley, Oct. 1972.
19. RICHART, F. E., "An Investigation of Web Stresses in Reinforced Concrete Beams," *Bulletin No. 166*, Engineering Experiment Station, University of Illinois, Urbana, June 1927, 106 pp.
20. RICHART, F. E., and L. J. LARSON, "An Investigation of Web Stresses in Reinforced Concrete Beams, Part II," *Bulletin No. 175*, Engineering Experiment Station, University of Illinois, Urbana, April 1928, 74 pp.
21. ROGERS, F. J., "Experiments with a Shaking Machine," *Report of the State Earthquake Investigation Commission, California Earthquake of 18 April 1906*, Vol. 1, Part II, State of California, Sacramento, 1908, pp. 326–335.
22. SHIBATA, A., and M. A. SOZEN, "The Substitute-Structure Method for Earthquake Resistant Design of Reinforced Concrete Frames," *Structural Research Series No. 412*, University of Illinois, Urbana, Oct. 1974, 34 pp.
23. SHIGA, T., A. SHIBATA, and A. TAKAHASHI, "Earthquake Damage and Wall Index of Reinforced Concrete Buildings" (in Japanese), *Tohoku District Symposium No. 12*, Architectural Institute of Japan, Nov. 1968.
24. SIESS, C. P., "Review of Research on Ultimate Strength of Reinforced Concrete Members," *ACI J.*, Vol. 23, No. 10, June 1952 (Proc. V. 48), pp. 833–865.
25. SLATER, W. A., A. R. LORD, and R. R. ZIPPRODT, "Shear Tests of Reinforced Concrete Beams," *Technologic Papers of the Bureau of Standards, No. 314*, U. S. Govt., Washington, D.C., 1926.

26. SOZEN, M. A., "Hysteresis in Structural Elements," *Appl. Mech. Earthquake Eng. ASME*, AMD-Vol. 8, Nov. 1974, pp. 63–98.
27. SOZEN, M. A., and S. OTANI, "Performance of the University of Illinois Earthquake Simulator in Reproducing Scaled Earthquake Motions," *Proceedings, U.S.-Japan Seminar on Earthquake Engineering with Emphasis on the Safety of School Buildings, Sept. 1970*, The Japan Earthquake Engineering Promotion Society, Tokyo, 1971, pp. 278–302.
28. TAKEDA, T., M. A. SOZEN, and N. N. NIELSEN, "Reinforced Concrete Response to Simulated Earthquakes," *J. Struct. Div. ASCE*, Vol. 96, No. ST12, Dec. 1970, pp. 2557–2573.
29. TAKIZAWA, H., "Strong Motion Response Analysis of Reinforced Concrete Buildings" (in Japanese), *Concrete J.*, Vol. 11, No. 2, Feb. 1973.
30. UMEMURA, H., et al., *Dynamic Earthquake-Resistant Design of Reinforced Concrete Buildings* (in Japanese), Giho-do, Tokyo, 1973.
31. UMEMURA, H., H. AOYAMA, and H. TAKIZAWA, "Analysis of the Behavior of Reinforced Concrete Structures During Strong Earthquakes Based on Empirical Estimation of Inelastic Restoring Force Characteristics of Members," Proceedings, Fifth World Conference on Earthquake Engineering, Int. Assoc. of Earthquate Engin., Paper No. 275, Rome, 1973, pp. 2201–2210.
32. WIGHT, J. R., and M. A. SOZEN, "Strength Decay of Reinforced Concrete Columns Under Shear Reversals," *J. Struct. Div. ASCE*, Vol. 101, No. ST5, May 1975, pp. 1053–1065.

# Dynamics of Structure-Foundation Systems

Anestis S. Veletsos*

*Dedicated to Nathan M. Newmark with deep appreciation for the influence he has had on my professional growth and with profound admiration for the significance of his contributions to civil engineering.*

## Introduction

In analyzing the response of structures to dynamic excitations of the ground, it is not uncommon to assume that the motion which is experienced by the base of the structure is the same as the motion which would be obtained at the site under consideration if the structure were not present.

This assumption is justified only for structures supported on essentially rigid ground. For structures supported on soft soil, the foundation motion is generally different from the free-field motion and may include an important rocking component in addition to a lateral or translational component. The rocking component may be particularly significant for tall structures.

The flexibly supported structure differs from the rigidly supported structure in another important respect. Part of its vibrational energy is dissipated into the supporting medium by radiation of waves and by hysteretic action in the medium itself. The importance of the latter factor increases with increasing intensity of ground shaking. There is, of course, no counterpart of this effect of energy dissipation in a rigidly supported structure.

For the purpose of this presentation, the effects of soil-structure interaction will be expressed by the difference in the response of the structure computed on two bases: (1) assuming the motion of the foundation to be the same

*Brown & Root Professor of Engineering, Department of Civil Engineering, Rice University, Houston, Texas.

as the free-field ground motion, and (2) considering the modified or actual motion of the foundation. This difference depends both on the characteristics of the free-field ground motion and on the properties of the structure and the supporting medium.

The soil-structure interaction effects should not be confused with the so-called site effects. The site effects refer to the fact that the characteristics of the free-field ground motion induced by a dynamic event at a given site depend on the properties of the site, whereas the interaction effects refer to the fact that the dynamic response of a structure built on that site depends not only on the characteristics of the free-field ground motion but also on the interrelationship of the structural characteristics and the properties of the underlying soil deposits.

The objective of this chapter is two-fold: (1) to summarize the principal effects of soil-structure interaction for relatively simple structural systems subjected to ground shock and earthquake motions, and (2) to present a simple practical procedure for accounting for these effects when their consideration in design is warranted. The discussion is focused on building structures. The limitations of the proposed procedure are identified, and a brief account is included of areas of further needed research. Also included is a simple criterion for defining the conditions under which the interaction effects are of insufficient importance to warrant consideration in design.

The problem of interaction between a vibrating structure and its supporting medium has been the subject of numerous investigations in recent years. While reference is made to several of these studies, no attempt is made to establish the interrelationship of the material presented herein and information reported previously. This chapter is based almost exclusively on the results of studies carried out at Rice University during the past 5 years.

## System and Method of Analysis

### *Simplest Possible System*

It is desirable to begin with the simplest possible structural system, and to this end we consider the one-story structure shown in Fig. 1. It is a linear structure of mass $m$ and lateral stiffness $k$, which is supported through a foundation of mass $m_o$ at the surface of a half-space composed of a homogeneous, purely elastic or viscoelastic material. The foundation mat is idealized as a rigid circular plate of negligible thickness which is bonded to the half-space, and the columns of the structure are presumed to be massless and axially inextensible. Both the foundation mass and the mass of the structure are assumed to be uniformly distributed over circular areas. The effects of foundation embedment and foundation layering and the uplifting or overturning tendencies of the structure are not considered. More complex, multistory structures are investigated in subsequent sections.

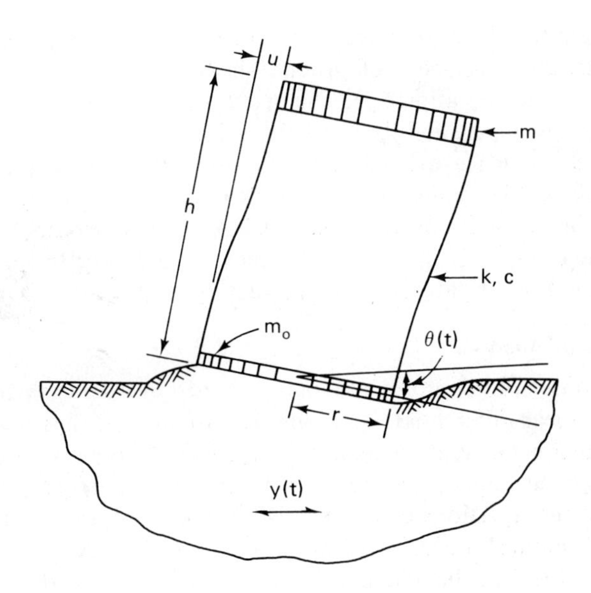


**Fig. 1.** System considered

The foundation medium is characterized by its shear modulus of elasticity, $G$, the mass density, $\rho$, Poisson's ratio, $\nu$, and the specific loss factor, $\Delta W/W$. For a soil specimen in harmonic motion, $\Delta W$ is the area of the elliptical hysteresis loop in the stress-strain diagram [29], and $W$ is the strain energy stored in a purely elastic, linear material which is subjected to the same maximum stress and strain as the viscoelatic material. For a linear material, $\Delta W = 0$.

Depending on the law of viscoelastic action considered for the half-space, $\Delta W$ may be a function of, or independent of, the frequency of vibration. In what follows, $\Delta W/W$ will be considered to be frequency independent, and it will be expressed in the familiar form

$$\frac{\Delta W}{W} = 2\pi \tan \delta \tag{1}$$

in which $\delta$ is a constant representing the phase angle between the stress and the associated strain of the harmonically oscillating soil specimen. Possible ranges of values of $\Delta W/W$ for soils are given in Refs. 6 and 21.

A different model of viscoelastic action, in which $\Delta W/W$ is proportional to the frequency of vibration, was investigated in Ref. 26, where it was shown that the parameters of the two models can be interrelated so that the absolute maximum deformation of the structure to an earthquake excitation is approximately the same in the two cases.

The base excitation is specified by the free-field motion of the ground surface. This is the motion which would be recorded at the surface of the site under consideration if the structure were not present. There is presumed to be only a horizontal component of ground shaking, with displacement $y(t)$, velocity $\dot{y}(t)$, and acceleration $\ddot{y}(t)$. The maximum values of these quantities will be denoted by $y_o$, $\dot{y}_o$, and $\ddot{y}_o$, respectively.

Under the influence of such an excitation, the base of the structure displaces horizontally by an amount $x$ which is generally different from $y$, and, in addition, it rotates by an amount $\theta$. The configuration of the coupled system can then be specified by the displacements $x$ and $\theta$ and by the interfloor deformation, $u$. For a rigidly supported structure, $\theta = 0$ and $x = y$.

### *Methods of Analysis*

The response of the coupled system is governed by a set of three coupled, second-order linear differential equations. The solution of these equations is complicated by the fact that the damping terms which account for the energy dissipated into the half-space are of a form which does not permit the uncoupling of the equations by an expansion of the coordinates in terms of the undamped natural modes of vibration of the system. Also complicating the analysis is the fact that the elastic restraining forces of the supporting medium are functions of the frequency of motion [10,29,32].

Two different approaches have been used to implement the analysis of the system: (1) the Fourier transform technique, in which the response is first evaluated in the frequency domain and then transformed into the time domain, and (2) the convolution integral approach, in which the response is evaluated directly in the time domain.

The first approach, which has been used in the majority of studies conducted so far, requires knowledge of the force-displacement relations of the foundation-soil system in harmonic motion, whereas the second approach requires knowledge of the impulse response functions of the foundation. The latter functions define the displacements induced by impulsive forces, or, conversely, the forces required to induce impulsive displacements. The foundation motions of interest in each case are those due to a horizontal force and an overturning moment. The force-displacement relations for harmonic response have been evaluated both for elastic and viscoelastic representations of the supporting medium [10,29,32], whereas the impulse response functions have been determined only for an elastic half-space [30].

Because it presupposes the applicability of the superposition principle, the Fourier transform approach is, of course, limited to the analysis of linear systems. By contrast, the convolution approach can be and has been applied to the analysis of yielding structures interacting with an elastic half-space [31,33]. The further extension of the latter approach to the more important case of an inelastic structure interacting with a viscoelastic half-space requires the evaluation of the impulse response functions for such a half-space. The determination of these functions has not proved possible to date.

### *Problem Parameters*

The dimensionless parameters which can be used conveniently to characterize the system have been identified in Refs. 24 and 26 and are reproduced in the following in order of more or less decreasing importance:

- The wave parameter

$$\sigma = \frac{c_s T}{h}, \tag{2}$$

which is a measure of the relative stiffness of the foundation medium and the structure. The symbol $c_s$ in this equation denotes the speed of propagation of shear waves in the half-space, and $T$ denotes the fixed-base natural period of the structure. Use also will be made of the inverse of $\sigma$, which is a measure of the relative flexibility of the foundation medium and the superimposed structure.

- The ratio $h/r$ of the height of the structure to the radius of the foundation.
- The frequency parameter $ft_1$, in which $f = 1/T$ is the fixed-base natural frequency of the structure, and $t_1$ is a characteristic time of the excitation.
- The material damping factor for the supporting medium, $\tan \delta$, defined by Eq. (1).
- The damping factor for the structure in its fixed-base condition, $\zeta$.
- The relative mass density for the structure and the supporting medium, defined by

$$\gamma = \frac{m}{\rho \pi r^2 h} \tag{3}$$

in which $\rho$ is the mass density of the half-space material.

- The ratio $m_o/m$ of the foundation mass to the mass of the superstructure.
- Poisson's ratio for the half-space material, $\nu$.

Unless otherwise indicated, for the solutions reported herein the foundation mass is considered to be negligible in comparison to the mass of the superstructure, and $\nu$ is taken as 0.45. Within the ranges of values that are of interest in practical applications, the response of the structure is generally insensitive to variations in these particular parameters.

## Response of System

### *Effective Motion of Foundation*

It is instructive to examine first the relationship between the free-field motion of the ground surface and the motion actually experienced by the foundation of the structure. To this end we consider the differential equation

$$m\ddot{u} + c\dot{u} + ku = -m(\ddot{x} + h\ddot{\theta}), \tag{4}$$

which expresses the dynamic equilibrium of forces acting on the mass $m$. A dot over a symbol denotes one differentiation with respect to time.

Equation (4) is identical to the differential equation governing the motion of the associated rigidly supported system when subjected to a base acceleration

$$\ddot{x}_e = \ddot{x} + h\ddot{\theta}. \tag{5}$$

It follows that the deformation of the flexibly supported, interacting structure is the same as that induced by the acceleration $\ddot{x}_e$ in a single-degree-of-freedom (SDF) system. Note that not only is $\ddot{x}_e$ different from the free-field acceleration, $\ddot{y}$, but that it also differs from the acceleration of the foundation, $\ddot{x}$, by the term $h\ddot{\theta}$. The latter term, which represents the contribution of the foundation rotation, may influence significantly the response of the system. The quantity $\ddot{x}_e$ will be referred to as the effective acceleration of the foundation.

The functions $\ddot{x}$ and $\ddot{\theta}$ in Eqs. (5) are evaluated by solving Eq. (4) simultaneously with the two additional differential equations that completely define the motion of the coupled system. This solution also establishes the structural deformation, $u$.

The results of such a solution are presented in Fig. 2 for a short, squatty structure with $h/r = 1$ when subjected to the piecewise linear free-field acceleration diagram shown in dashed lines at the top of the figure. This relatively simple excitation has been used in several previous studies [24,28] which have shown that there is a close relationship between its effects and those of the more complex earthquake motions. The velocity diagram of the free-field motion, which may be obtained by integration of $\ddot{y}(t)$, consists of a sequence of two identical half-cycle pulses of opposite signs, and the associated displacement diagram consists of a single half-cycle pulse. In an effort to accentuate the effects of interaction, the wave parameter is considered to have the low value of $\sigma = 2$, and the frequency parameter is taken as $ft_1 = 0.6$, where $t_1$ is the duration of each velocity half-cycle. The foundation material is considered to be linearly elastic, the damping factor for the structure in its fixed-base condition is taken as $\zeta = 0.02$, and $\gamma = 0.15$. All other parameters are as previously indicated.

The solid curve in the top diagram of Fig. 2 represents the acceleration of the foundation, $\ddot{x}$, and the bottom curve represents the corresponding effective acceleration, $\ddot{x}_e$. The component of $\ddot{x}_e$ contributed by the rotation of the foundation is shown in the middle. The ordinates of all diagrams are normalized with respect to the peak free-field acceleration, $\ddot{y}_o$, and all time scales are normalized with respect to $t_1$.

As would be expected, $\ddot{x}$ is different from $\ddot{y}$. However, the difference is not particularly great, and the two curves have the same general appearance.

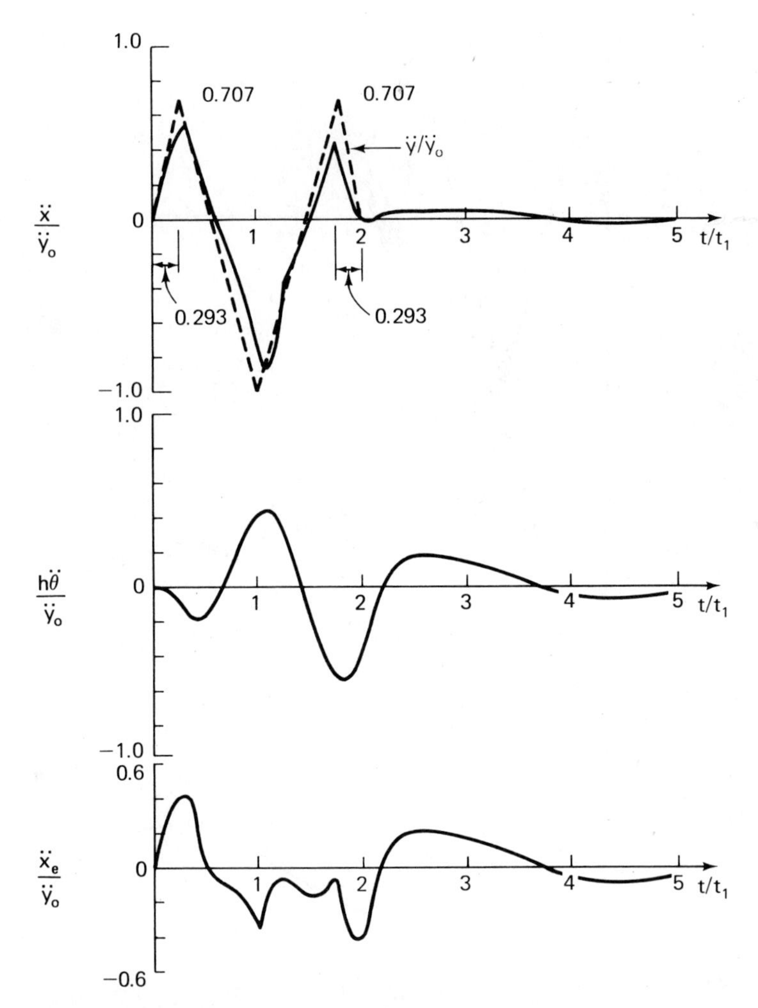


**Fig. 2.** Base accelerations for a squatty structure subjected to a half-cycle displacement input; h/r = 1, $\sigma = 2$, $ft_1 = 0.6$, tan $\delta = 0$, $\zeta = 0.02$, $\gamma = 0.15$

What might be unexpected is that, even for this short structure for which one might have been tempted to assume that the rotation of the foundation would be minimal, the rotation is of such a magnitude that $\ddot{x}_e$ bears almost no resemblance to either $\ddot{y}$ or $\ddot{x}$.

Similar plots are presented in Fig. 3 for a tall, slender structure with $h/r = 5$. In this case, $\ddot{x}$ is almost the same as $\ddot{y}$, but the contribution of the base rotation is of still greater importance than before. A record of the acceleration history obtained at the foundation level would be an excellent approximation in this case to the free-field acceleration history. On the other hand, the deformation of a SDF system to the recorded foundation motion

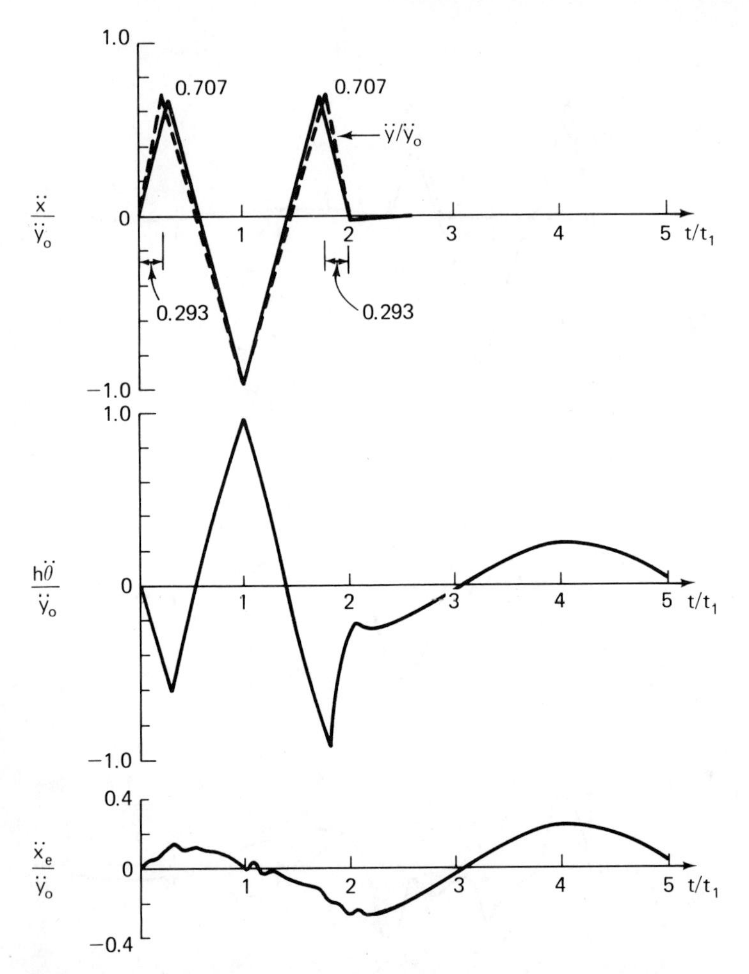


**Fig. 3.** Base accelerations for a slender structure subjected to a half-cycle displacement input; $h/r = 5$, $\sigma = 2$, $ft_1 = 0.6$, $\tan\,\delta = 0$, $\zeta = 0.02$, $\gamma = 0.15$

would again bear no relation to the actual deformation of the interacting structure. To obtain the true deformation, one must evaluate the response of the SDF oscillator to the effective acceleration, $\ddot{x}_e$, represented by the lower-most diagram in the figure.

For the particular value of $ft_1$ used in the development of the results presented in Figs. 2 and 3, the response of the systems is sensitive to the characteristics of the velocity trace of the base motion rather than those of the acceleration trace [28]. It is, therefore, desirable also to examine the relationship between $\dot{x}_e$ and $\dot{y}$. These functions are compared in Fig. 4 for each of the two systems investigated. Also included for the sake of completeness are the corresponding displacement diagrams. In each case, the ordinates are

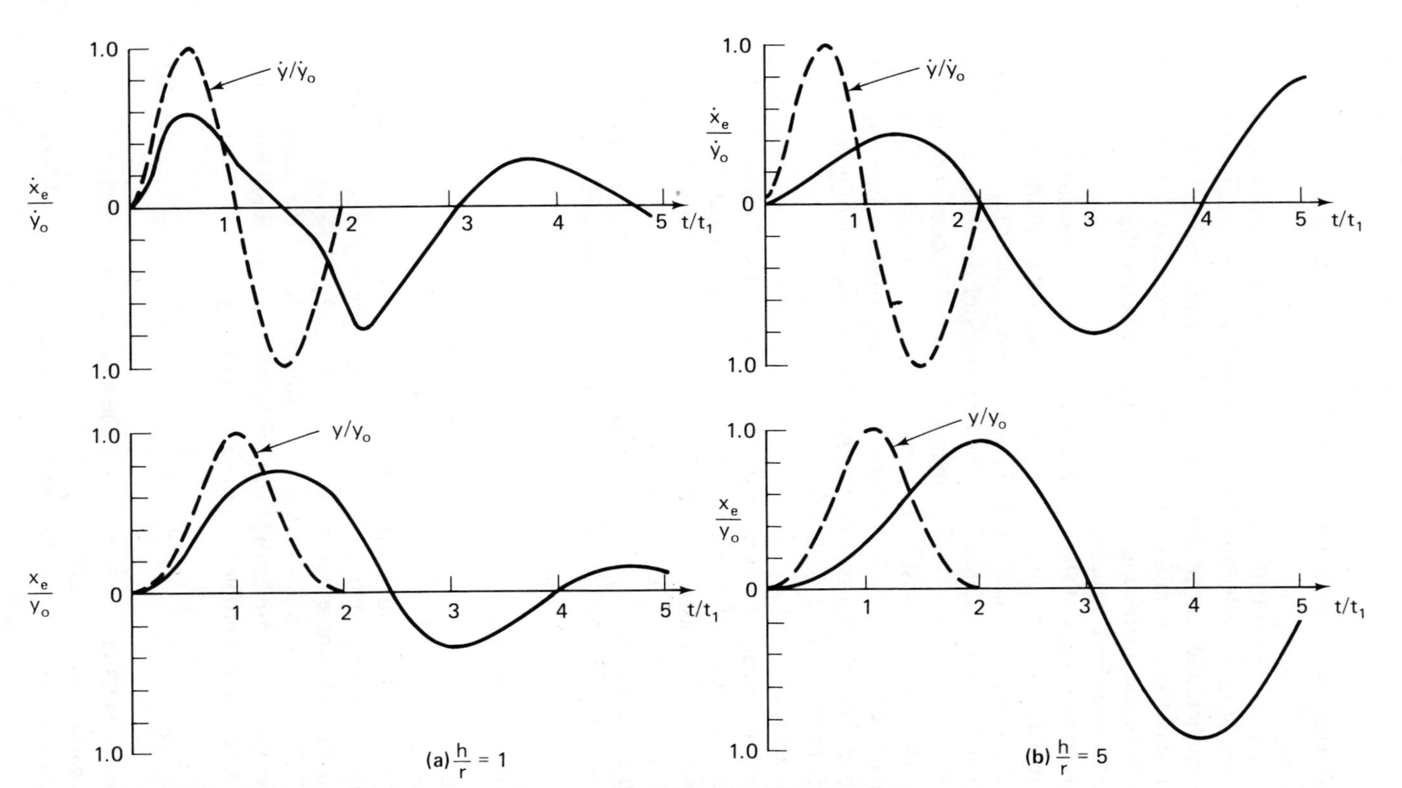


**Fig. 4.** Base velocities and displacements for structures considered in Figs. 2 and 3

normalized with respect to the maximum free-field value of the particular function under consideration.

Compared to the velocity diagram of the free-field ground motion, the velocity traces of the foundation motion are more nearly periodic, their peak values are smaller, and the "period" of the predominant oscillation is longer. It can be shown that the combined effect of these differences is to decrease the deformations of the interacting structures to levels below that applicable to the associated fixed-base structure.

Comparative studies of the type just presented provide valuable insight into the interaction phenomenon. However, the results are extremely difficult to generalize, because the relationship between the motions of the flexibly and rigidly supported systems depends on the properties of the structure and of the foundation medium involved. Changing the natural frequency of the system will change this relationship. In particular, it is not possible to characterize the modified or effective foundation motion of a structure by a response spectrum and then use that spectrum to evaluate the response of other structures to the same free-field excitation.

It appears that the only practical way of assessing the effects of interaction on the response of the superstructure is to examine its response directly. The response quantities of greatest practical interest are the deformation of the structure, $u$, and the associated shearing force, $Q = ku$, particularly their maximum values, $u_o$ and $Q_o$. In the remainder of this chapter, attention will be focused on these quantities, and the results obtained for flexibly supported structures will be compared to those obtained for the associated fixed-base structures.

### *Structural Response*

In Fig. 5 are presented response spectra for the absolute maximum deformation, $u_o$, of fixed-base and interacting systems excited by the first 6.34 sec of the N-S component of the 1940 El Centro, California earthquake record. The acceleration, velocity, and displacement traces of this motion are available in Ref. 24, where it is shown that $\ddot{y}_o = 0.312\,g$, $\dot{y}_o = 14.02$ in./sec, and $y_o = 8.29$ in. Two values of $h/r$ and a single value of the foundation stiffness parameter, $c_s/r$, are considered. The latter parameter is related to the basic parameters of the problem referred to previously by

$$\frac{c_s}{r} = \sigma \frac{h}{r} f. \tag{6}$$

All other parameters are the same as for the solutions presented in Figs. 2 through 4, except that $\zeta = 0.05$.

The results are displayed in the familiar four-way logarithmic form, with the ordinates representing the pseudovelocity of the system, $pu_o$, nondimensionalized with respect to $\dot{y}_o$, where $p = 2\pi f$ is the fixed-base circular natural frequency of the system. The diagonal scales represent the deformation, $u_o$,

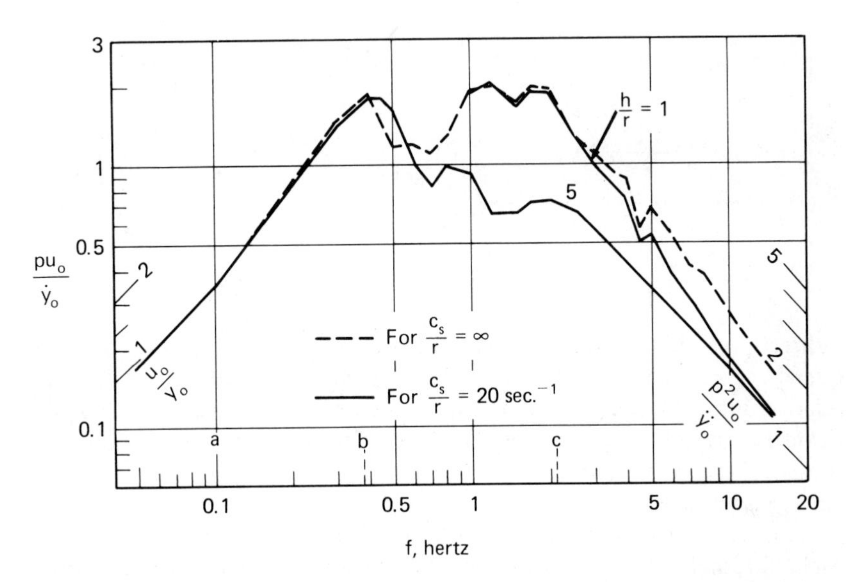


**Fig. 5.** Comparison of deformation spectra for fixed-base and interacting systems subjected to El Centro input; tan $\delta = 0$, $\zeta = 0.05$, $\gamma = 0.15$

and the pseudoacceleration, $p^2u_o$, appropriately normalized. The maximum base shear for the structure, $Q_o$, may then be expressed either in terms of $u_o$ as $Q_o = ku_o$ or in terms of the pseudoacceleration as $Q_o = m(p^2u_o)$.

For the particular combination of parameters considered in Fig. 5, it is clear that foundation-structure interaction reduces the response of the structure. The reduction is generally greater for the taller structures, and for a system of a specified value of $h/r$, it is greater for the stiffer, higher-frequency systems. However, the reader is cautioned against generalizing these observations. Additional spectra illustrating the relationship between the maximum deformations of fixed-base and interacting systems are available in Refs. 24 and 26.

To help define this relationship, it is desirable to relate the maximum deformation of the interacting system to that of a judiciously selected simpler system. The single-degree-of-freedom damped oscillator shown in Fig. 6 provides a valuable standard of comparison and will be used throughout the rest of the chapter.

### *Replacement Oscillator and its Relation to Actual System*

In Fig. 6 the spring connected to the mass represents the elastic resistance of the structure, and its stiffness, $k$, is equal to that of the fixed-base structure. The spring connected to the base accounts for the translational and rotational flexibilities of the foundation, whereas the dashpot accounts for the overall damping of the system, including structural damping, radiation damping, and material soil damping. The characteristics of these elements are defined

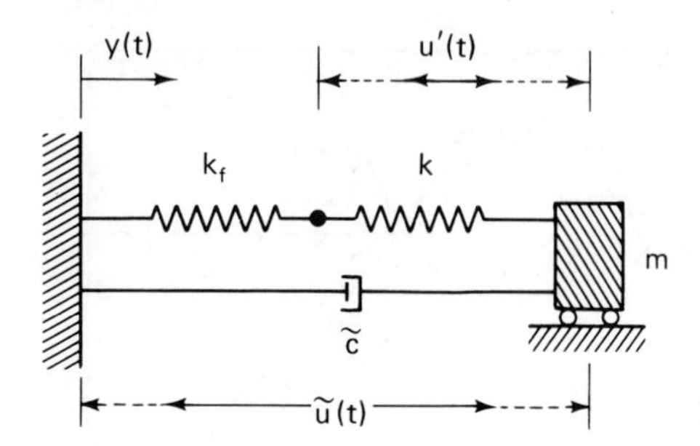


**Fig. 6.** Replacement oscillator

indirectly by the natural period of the oscillator, $\tilde{T}$ (or the associated frequency, $\tilde{f} = \tilde{p}/2\pi = 1/\tilde{T}$) and by the fraction of critical damping, $\tilde{\zeta}$. The relationship of these quantities to those of the fixed-base structure, $T$ and $\zeta$, is defined in the following sections. The mass of the oscillator, $m$, is taken equal to that of the superstructure, and the base motion is taken equal to the free-field ground motion.

Let $\tilde{u}_o$ be the maximum value of the total deformation of the replacement oscillator, and $u'_o$ be the component of $\tilde{u}_o$ developed in the structural spring. The maximum spring force, $\tilde{Q}_o$, may then be expressed either in terms of $u'_o$ as

$$\tilde{Q}_o = ku'_o = m(p^2 u'_o) \tag{7}$$

or in terms of $\tilde{u}_o$ as

$$\tilde{Q}_o = \tilde{k}\tilde{u}_o = m(\tilde{p}^2 \tilde{u}_o) \tag{8}$$

in which $\tilde{k} = m\tilde{p}^2$ is the total stiffness of the two springs in series, and $\tilde{p}^2\tilde{u}_o$ is the pseudoacceleration of the oscillator. From Eqs. (7) and (8) it may be noted in passing that $u'_o$ and $\tilde{u}_o$ are interrelated by the equation

$$u'_o = \left(\frac{\tilde{p}}{p}\right)^2 \tilde{u}_o = \frac{\tilde{u}_o}{(\tilde{T}/T)^2}. \tag{9}$$

The parameters $\tilde{T}$ and $\tilde{\zeta}$ of the replacement oscillator are determined in such a way that the absolute maximum or resonant amplitude of the spring force, $\tilde{Q}_o$, developed by a harmonic excitation of the base, and the period at which this maximum occurs are the same as the corresponding quantities for the actual system when subjected to the same free-field ground motion. This approach amounts to equating the resonant values of $u'_o$ and $u_o$, or, equivalently, the resonant values of $\tilde{p}^2\tilde{u}_o$ and $p^2 u_o$.

With the values of $\tilde{T}$ and $\tilde{\zeta}$ determined in this manner, it can be shown [24] that satisfactory agreement in these two sets of response quantities is also obtained over a wide range of exciting periods on either side of the resonant period.

Now, inasmuch as any transient excitation may be viewed in the context of a Fourier analysis as a linear combination of harmonic motions having different periods and amplitudes, and inasmuch as the components of excitation with periods close to the resonant period are likely to be significant contributors to the response, the peak response of the two systems can be expected to remain in satisfactory agreement for transient ground motions as well.

This expectation is confirmed by the comparison presented in Fig. 7, which refers to systems with $h/r = 5$ subjected to the relatively simple half-cycle displacement pulse investigated previously. Several different values of the dimensionless foundation stiffness parameter, $c_s t_1/r$, are considered, with the damping factor for the structure in its fixed-base condition taken as $\zeta = 0.02$. All other parameters are the same as for the previous solutions.

The spectra for the actual systems were determined by an exact analysis using discrete Fourier transform techniques, whereas those for the replacement oscillators were determined from the spectrum applicable to similarly excited fixed-base systems using the values of $\tilde{T}$ and $\tilde{\zeta}$ determined by the procedure just outlined. It may be seen that the agreement between the two sets of results is indeed excellent.

Based on these results and the results of other comparative studies of this type (see, for example, Refs. 24 and 26), it has been concluded that, within the ranges of parameters that are of interest in studies of the seismic response of building structures, the SDF replacement oscillator may be considered to experience the same maximum spring force as the actual flexibly supported structure. Expressed differently,

$$Q_o = \tilde{Q}_o \tag{10}$$

and

$$u_o = u_o', \tag{11a}$$

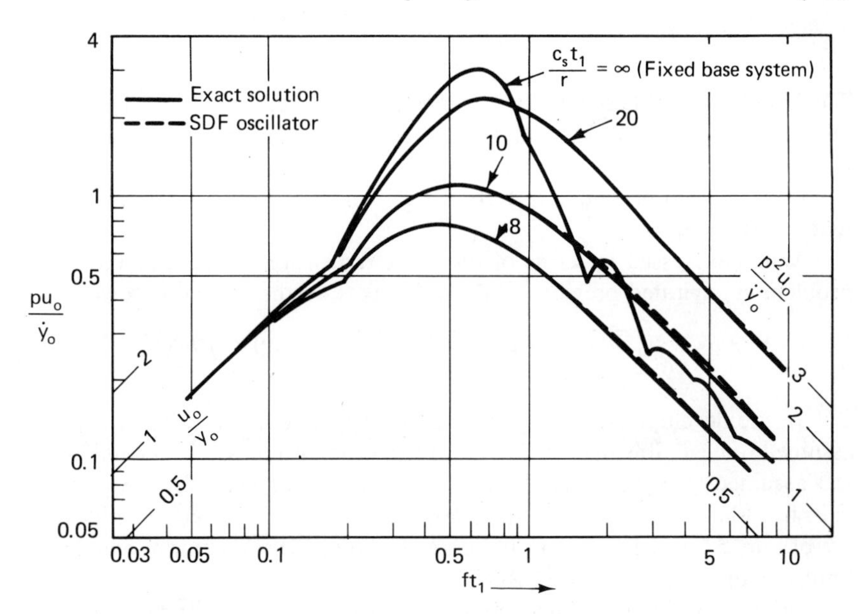


**Fig. 7.** Comparison of exact and approximate deformation spectra for systems subjected to half-cycle displacement input; $h/r = 5$, $\tan \delta = 0$, $\zeta = 0.02$, $\gamma = 0.15$

which, on making use of Eqs. (9), can also be written as

$$u_o = \left(\frac{\tilde{p}}{p}\right)^2 \tilde{u}_o = \frac{\tilde{u}_o}{(\tilde{T}/T)^2}. \tag{11b}$$

To the degree of approximation involved in the use of Eqs. (10) and (11), the effects of interaction may, therefore, be expressed by changes in the values $T$ and $\zeta$ of the fixed-base system. In the remainder of this presentation, the quantities $\tilde{T}$ and $\tilde{\zeta}$ for the replacement oscillator will also be referred to as the effective natural period and effective damping factor of the interacting system. It will be shown that $\tilde{T}$ is always greater than $T$, whereas $\tilde{\zeta}$ may be greater than, equal to, or smaller than $\zeta$.

### *Effective Period of System*

The natural period $\tilde{T}$ is given approximately [7, 24] by the equation

$$\tilde{T} = T\sqrt{1 + \frac{k}{K_x}\left(1 + \frac{K_x h^2}{K_\theta}\right)}, \tag{12}$$

in which $K_x$ is the dynamic translational stiffness of the foundation in harmonic motion, and is defined by

$$K_x = \frac{8\alpha_x}{2 - \nu} Gr, \tag{13}$$

and $K_\theta$ is the associated rocking stiffness, defined by

$$K_\theta = \frac{8\alpha_\theta}{3(1 - \nu)} Gr^3. \tag{14}$$

The quantity $G$ in these equations represents the shear modulus of elasticity of the half-space, and $\alpha_x$ and $\alpha_\theta$ are dimensionless coefficients which are functions of the period of vibration. These coefficients may be determined from information presented in Refs. 10, 29, and 32. For a static condition of loading, $\alpha_x = \alpha_\theta = 1$.

When expressed in terms of the basic dimensionless parameters of the problem enumerated previously, Eq. (12) takes on the following form:

$$\tilde{T} = T\sqrt{1 + \frac{2 - \nu}{2}\frac{\pi^3}{\alpha_x}\frac{\gamma}{\sigma^2(h/r)}\left[1 + \frac{3(1 - \nu)}{2 - \nu}\frac{\alpha_x}{\alpha_\theta}\left(\frac{h}{r}\right)^2\right]}. \tag{15}$$

In the development of Eqs. (12) and (15) the foundation mass, $m_o$, was assumed to negligible in comparison to the structural mass, $m$; the half-space was assumed to be perfectly elastic; and the damping factor for the structure in its fixed-base condition was taken as $\zeta = 0$. Within the ranges of values that are of interest in the design of building structures, these assumptions do not limit the applicability of the results.

Because of the period dependence of the coefficients $\alpha_x$ and $\alpha_\theta$, Eqs. (12) and (15) must be evaluated by iteration. This computation may be materially simplified, however, by use of period-independent stiffnesses, and it is desirable to examine the degree of approximation involved in the use of the static, instead of the actual dynamic, values of $K_x$ and $K_\theta$.

In Fig. 8 the ratio $\tilde{T}/T$ is plotted as a function of the relative flexibility parameter of the half-space, $1/\sigma$, for structures having several different values of $h/r$. The solid lines were determined by the exact procedure, making use of the peak responses of the harmonically excited systems, whereas the dashed lines were computed from Eq. (15) taking $\alpha_x = \alpha_\theta = 1$. Had the relevant dynamic values of $\alpha_x$ and $\alpha_\theta$ been used, the results computed from Eq. (15) would have been practically exact. The agreement achieved even by use of the static stiffness values may be more than adequate for many practical applications, and it improves with increasing value of $h/r$.

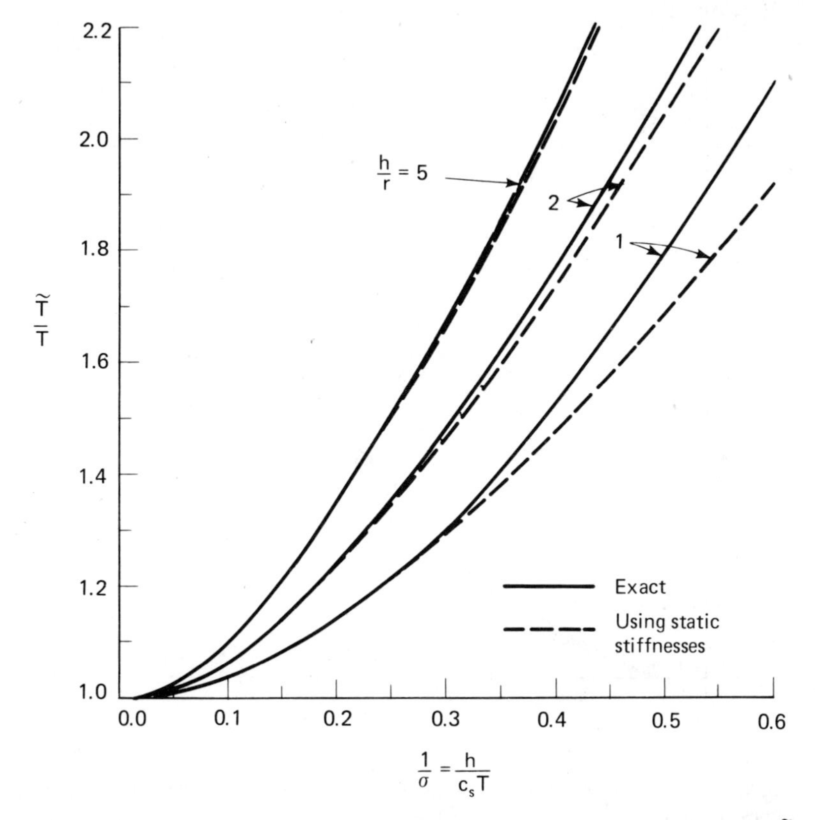


**Fig. 8.** Comparison of exact and approximate values of effective natural period, $\tilde{T}$, for interacting systems; $\gamma = 0.15$, $\tan \delta = 0$, $\zeta = 0$

For the solutions compared in Fig. 8 the mass density factor was taken as $\gamma = 0.15$, and Poisson's ratio was taken as $\nu = 0.45$. Similar comparisons have been made for several values of $h/r$ in the range between 1 and 5, using values of $\gamma = 0.10$ and 0.20 and values of $\nu = 0.30$ and 0.45. In each case, the agreement between the two sets of results was found to be comparable.

The exact solutions for all cases considered are replotted in Fig. 9 as a function of the dimensionless parameter $\sqrt{\gamma}\,\phi$, in which

$$\phi = \frac{1}{\sigma}\left(\frac{h}{r}\right)^{1/4} = \frac{h}{c_s T}\left(\frac{h}{r}\right)^{1/4}. \tag{16}$$

Determined by trial and error so that the results would fall within a relatively narrow band, this parameter is an alternative measure of the relative flexibility of the foundation medium and the overlying structure. The maximum deviation from the mean in this plot is about 5%. The value of $\tilde{T}$ may, therefore, be evaluated readily and with good accuracy from the mean curve presented in this figure.

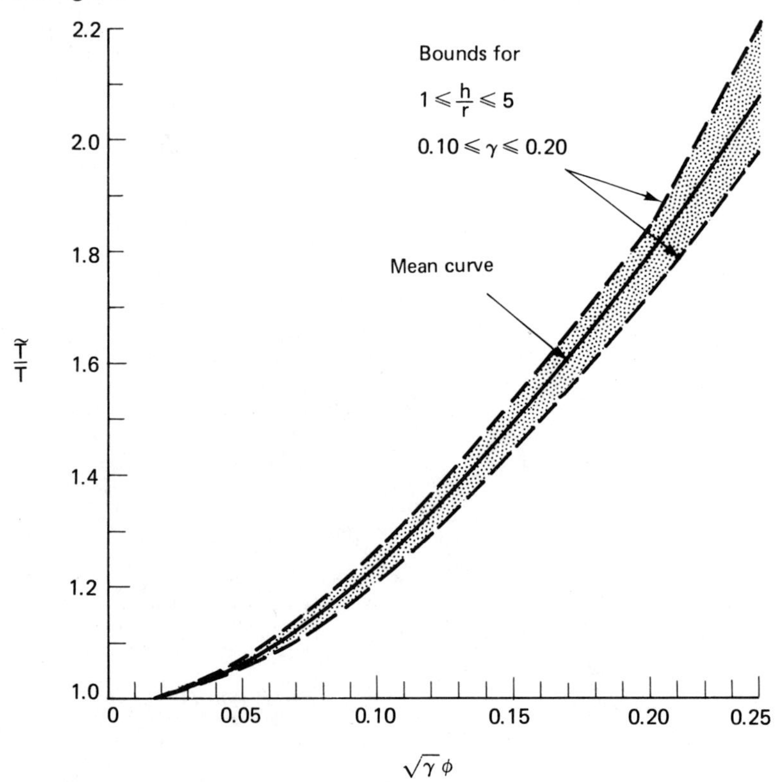


**Fig. 9.** Effective natural period, $\tilde{T}$, of interacting systems for a range of $h/r$ and $\gamma$ values; $\tan\delta = 0$, $\zeta = 0$

### *Effective Damping of System*

The effective damping factor of the interacting system, $\tilde{\zeta}$, is given approximately [26] by

$$\tilde{\zeta} = \tilde{\zeta}_0 + \frac{\zeta}{(\tilde{T}/T)^3} \tag{17}$$

in which the first term on the right represents the contribution of foundation damping, including both radiation and material damping, whereas the second term represents the contribution of structural damping. Note that $\tilde{\zeta}_o$ and $\zeta$ are not directly additive but must be combined in accordance with Eq. (17).

Considering that $\tilde{T}$ is greater than $T$, it follows that foundation-structure interaction reduces the effectiveness of the structural damping and that this reduction may be quite important when $\tilde{T}/T$ is large. In fact, unless this reduction is compensated by the increase due to foundation damping, the overall damping of the interacting system will be less than that of the fixed-base system.

This possibility is demonstrated in Fig. 10, in which the overall damping

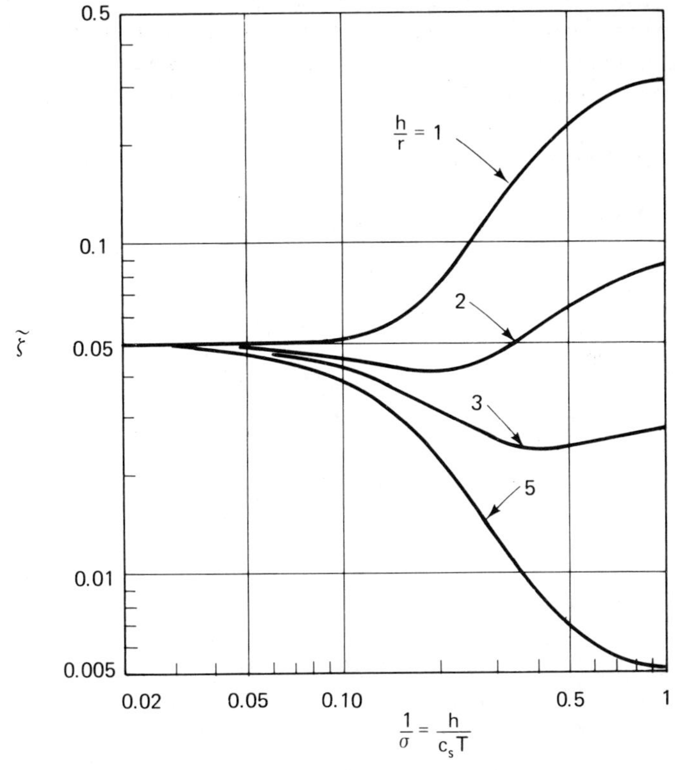


**Fig. 10.** Overall damping factor, $\tilde{\zeta}$, for structures supported on an elastic halfspace; $\gamma = 0.15$, $\zeta = 0.05$

factor, $\tilde{\zeta}$, is plotted as a function $1/\sigma$ for systems involving a purely elastic half-space. Several different values of $h/r$ are considered. The damping factor of the structure in its fixed-base condition is taken as $\zeta = 0.05$. Hence, all curves approach $\tilde{\zeta} = \zeta = 0.05$ as $1/\sigma$ tends toward zero. Note that $\tilde{\zeta}$ may be substantially less than $\zeta$ for the taller structures. As explained in Ref. 24, this reduction is due to the effect of foundation rocking, which tends to increase the inertia force on the structure and the resulting deformation.

The component of $\tilde{\zeta}$ which is contributed by foundation damping is shown in Figs. 11 and 12. The dashed lines, which refer to systems supported on an elastic medium, represent the contribution of radiation damping only, whereas the solid lines, which refer to viscoelastic media with tan $\delta = 0.10$ and 0.20, represent the combined effect of radiation and material damping. Unlike the previous figure in which the results were plotted as a function of the flexibility parameter $1/\sigma$, in these figures they are displayed as a function of the ratio of periods, $\tilde{T}/T$. The latter mode of presentation is believed to be both more instructive and easier to use in design applications. The greater $\tilde{T}/T$, the greater are, of course, the interaction effects.

It is clear from these figures that foundation damping may be a significant contributor to the overall damping of a system and that the component contributed by hysteretic action may be particularly significant for the taller structures for which the contribution of radiation damping is generally quite small.

As a further demonstration of the importance of material soil damping,

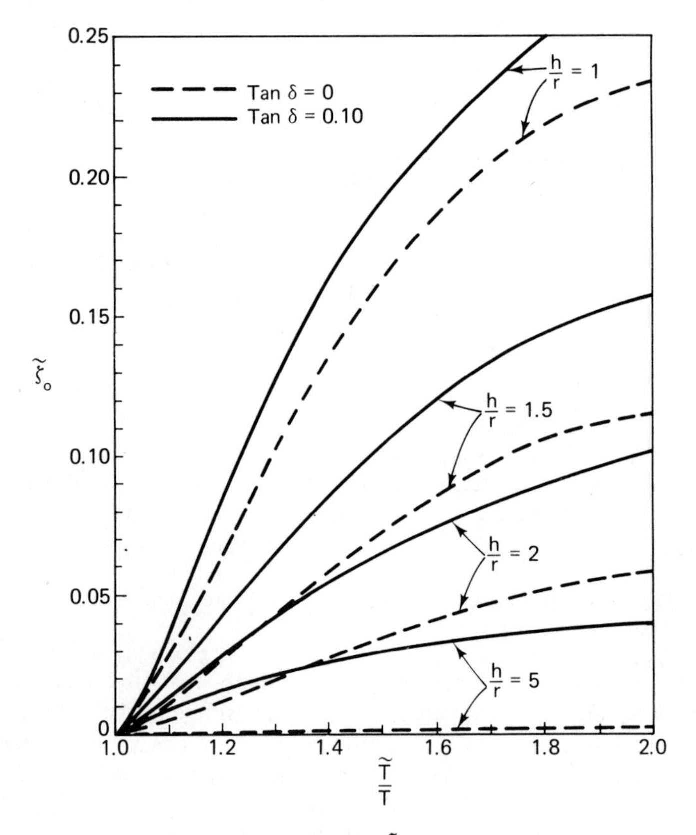


**Fig. 11.** Foundation damping factor, $\tilde{\zeta}_o$, for structures supported on an elastic and viscoelastic halfspace; $\gamma = 0.15$, $\zeta = 0$

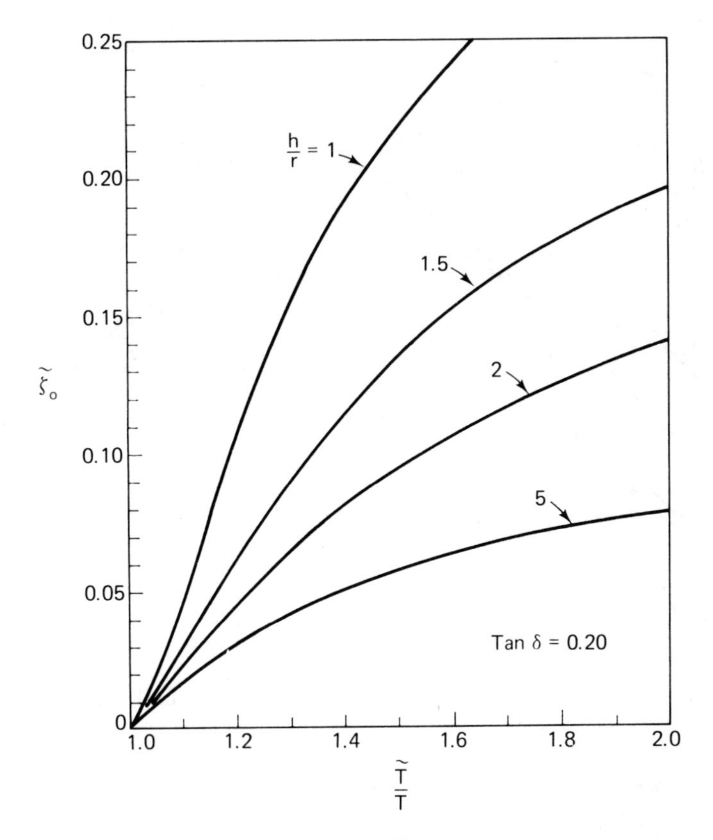


**Fig. 12.** Foundation damping factor, $\tilde{\zeta}_o$, for structures supported on a viscoelastic halfspace with $\tan \delta = 0.20$; $\gamma = 0.15$, $\zeta = 0$

two of the response spectra for systems on an elastic half-space presented previously in Fig. 7 are compared in Fig. 13 with the corresponding spectra obtained for a viscoelastic representation of the half-space using a value of $\tan \delta = 0.30$. It is apparent that the reduction in response is indeed quite significant in the high-frequency region of the spectra. Comparable results have also been obtained for systems subjected to earthquake motions [26].

The data presented in Figs. 11 and 12 are for systems with $\gamma = 0.15$. From additional studies of systems with $\gamma = 0.10$ and 0.20, it has been concluded that the foundation damping factor, $\tilde{\zeta}_o$, of systems having any value of $\gamma$ in the range between 0.10 and 0.20 may be estimated approximately by multiplying the results obtained from Figs. 11 and 12 by the factor

$$C_\gamma = \sqrt{\frac{0.15}{\gamma}}. \tag{18}$$

Note that the smaller the $\gamma$, the larger is this correction factor. The spread in

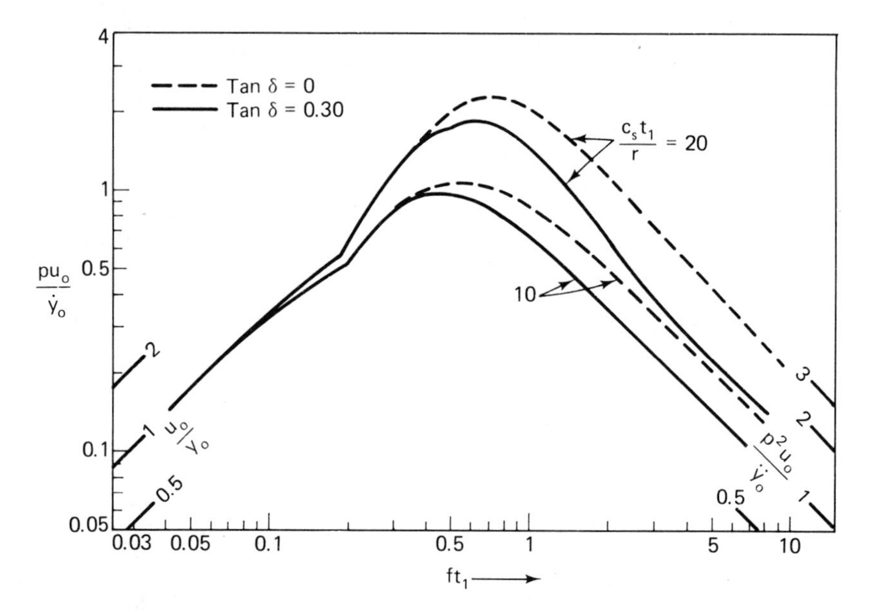


**Fig. 13.** Effect of material soil damping on deformation spectra for systems subjected to half-cycle displacement input; $h/r = 5$, $\zeta = 0.02$, $\gamma = 0.15$

the results obtained in the special case of a viscoelastic half-space with tan $\delta = 0.10$ are shown in Fig. 14.

### *Criterion for Assessing Importance of Interaction*

The ratio $\tilde{T}/T$ may now be used as a means of assessing the importance of interaction. Inasmuch as the fixed-base natural period of an actual structure can hardly be estimated to more than 10 or 20% of its exact value, and inasmuch as the evaluation of the soil parameters is subject to comparable or even greater uncertainty, it might be argued that the interaction effects may be considered to be negligible if $\tilde{T}/T$ is less than about 1.20. However, reference to Figs. 11 and 12 reveals that the foundation damping factor, $\tilde{\zeta}_o$, may be of substantial magnitude for values of $\tilde{T}/T$ of the order of 1.20 and that it would be desirable to use a lower, stricter limit.

From studies of the effects of the various parameters upon the values of both $\tilde{T}/T$ and $\tilde{\zeta}_o$ and the overall damping of the system, $\tilde{\zeta}$, it has been concluded that the interaction effects are generally of insufficient importance to warrant consideration in design when the dimensionless parameter defined by Eq. (16)

$$\phi \leq 0.125. \tag{19}$$

Assuming that $\gamma = 0.15$, a reasonable average value for building structures, this inequality corresponds approximately to values of $\tilde{T}/T \leq 1.08$. When this criterion is satisfied, the structure may be analyzed as if it were fixed at the base.

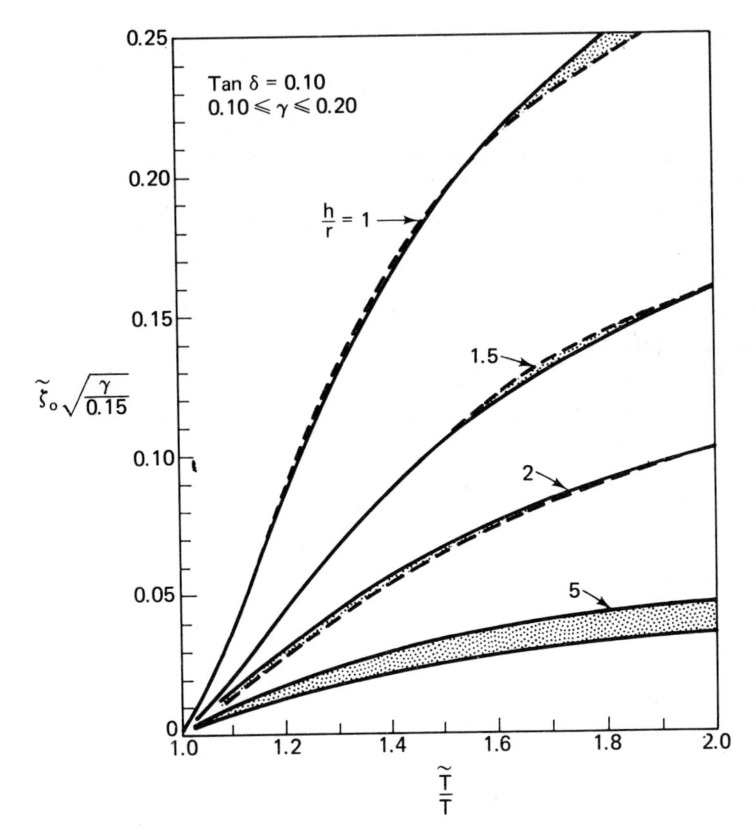


**Fig. 14.** Foundation damping factor, $\tilde{\zeta}_o$, for systems with a range of values of $\gamma$; tan $\delta = 0.10$, $\zeta = 0$

If $\phi > 0.125$, the soil-structure system should be analyzed as a coupled system. However, depending on the interrelationship of the structural characteristics and the characteristics of the excitation, one may still find that the interaction effects are of relatively little practical consequence.

### *Some Practical Considerations*

In the application of the information presented in the preceding sections to actual design problems, provision should be made for the fact that soils are nonlinear materials and that both $c_s$ and tan $\delta$ are in reality strain-dependent quantities. The strain levels induced in a given case are evidently functions of the properties of the soil and of the severity of ground shaking. Other things being equal, the higher the severity of ground shaking, the smaller is the effective value of $c_s$, and the greater is the value of tan $\delta$.

It $(c_s)_o$ denotes the low-amplitude value of the shear wave velocity appropriate to the site under consideration, the effective value of $c_s$ for a high-severity ground shaking may be of the order of about two-thirds of $(c_s)_o$ or less, and the effective value of $\tan\delta$ may well be of the order of 0.25 or 0.30. The choice of these values in a given case must be based on information of the type presented in Refs. 6 and 21, coupled with an estimate of the magnitude of the strains that may be induced in the supporting medium by the stipulated design ground motion.

A few remarks also are in order concerning the minimum value of overall damping factor, $\tilde{\zeta}$, which would be appropriate to use in a practical application. Since the choice of the structural damping factor, $\zeta$, is normally based on the results of tests on full-scale structures, and since such test data reflect the overall damping of the foundation-structure system, not merely the component contributed by the structure itself, it is believed that the value of $\tilde{\zeta}$ should never be taken less than the estimated value of $\zeta$. It is, therefore, recommended that $\tilde{\zeta}$ be taken equal to $\zeta$ if the value computed from Eq. (17) is less than $\zeta$.

## Summary, Generalization, and Limitations of Procedure

### *Summary of Procedure*

With the information that has been presented, the analysis of the interacting system may be implemented as follows:

1. Evaluate the fixed-base natural period of the structure, $T$, and the relative soil flexibility parameter, $\phi$, defined by Eq. (16). Use structural and soil properties which are compatible with the severity of the stipulated ground shaking. If $\phi \leq 0.125$, disregard the effect of interaction, and analyze the structure as if it were fixed at the base. Otherwise, proceed with the following steps.

2. Determine the effective natural period of the system, $\tilde{T}$, from the mean curve presented in Fig. 9. If desired, a more accurate estimate may be obtained by iteration from Eqs. (12) or (15), using the values of $\alpha_x$ and $\alpha_\theta$ which correspond to the desired period, $\tilde{T}$.

3. Estimate the values of $\tan\delta$ and $\zeta$ which would be appropriate for the severity of the stipulated ground shaking, and from Figs. 11 and 12 and by use of Eq. (18), evaluate the foundation damping factor, $\tilde{\zeta}_o$.

4. From Eq. (17), compute the overall damping of the system, $\tilde{\zeta}$. If $\tilde{\zeta}$ turns out to be less than $\zeta$, take $\tilde{\zeta} = \zeta$.

5. From the response spectra for single-degreee-of-freedom systems subjected to the specified free-field ground motion, evaluate the deformation, $\tilde{u}_o$, and the pseudoacceleration, $\tilde{p}^2\tilde{u}_o$, corresponding to $\tilde{T}$ and $\tilde{\zeta}$. The maximum base shear for the actual interacting structure may then be considered to be equal to the product of $m$ and this pseudoacceleration, whereas the maximum

deformation of the structure, $u_o$, may be determined from $\tilde{u}_o$ by application of Eq. (11b).

#### *Generalizations for More Complex Systems*

The procedure summarized in the preceding section can also be applied to more involved, multistory structures which respond essentially as single-degree-of-freedom systems in their fixed-base condition. It is only necessary to interpret $T$ as the *fundamental* natural period of the fixed-base structure, $m$ as the effective mass of the structure when vibrating in its fixed-base *fundamental* natural mode, and $h$ as the distance from the base to the centroid of the corresponding inertia forces. To avoid possible confusion, the last two quantities will be denoted by $m^*$ and $h^*$, respectively. For structures with lumped masses, these quantities are given by the equations

$$m^* = \frac{(\sum m_i x_i)^2}{\sum m_i x_i^2} \tag{20}$$

and

$$h^* = \frac{\sum m_i x_i h_i}{\sum m_i x_i} \tag{21}$$

in which $x_i$ is the modal displacement of the $i$th floor, located at a distance $h_i$ from the base; $m_i$ is the total lumped mass at the $i$th floor level; and the summations extend over all floor levels.

As an indication of the range of applicability of this procedure, in Fig. 15 are presented response spectra for the maximum value of base shear, $Q_1$, for

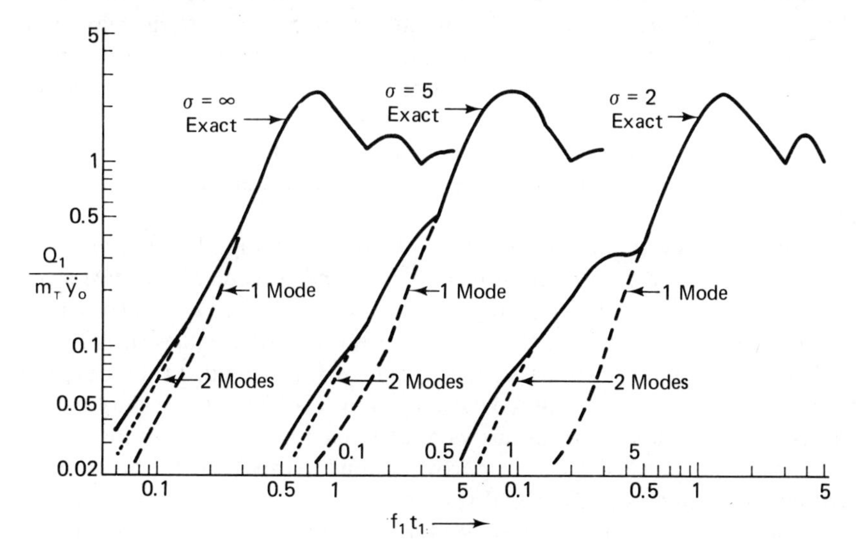


**Fig. 15.** Modal contributions to maximum base shear of five-story structures subjected to half-cycle displacement input; $h/r = 5$, $\tan\delta = 0$, $\zeta_1 = 0.02$, $\gamma_T = 0.15$, $m_o/m_T = 0.2$

five-story, uniform buildings of the shear-beam type excited by the half-cycle displacement pulse referred to previously. Both fixed-base systems and interacting systems having two different values of $\sigma$ and values of $h/r = 5$ and $m_o/m_T = 0.2$ are considered. The symbol $h$ in this case denotes the total height of the structure, and $m_T$ denotes the total mass of the structure, excluding that of the foundation mat. The relative mass density for the structure and the supporting medium was taken as $\gamma_T = 0.15$, where $\gamma_T$ is defined by Eq. (3) with $m$ interpreted as $m_T$. The half-space material was considered to be perfectly elastic, and structural damping was assumed to be stiffness-proportional. The damping factor for the fixed-base fundamental natural mode was taken as $\zeta_1 = 0.02$. The symbol $f_1$ on the abscissa of the figure represents the fixed-base fundamental natural frequency of the system, in hertz.

The response of the system was computed by the "exact" method described in Ref. 13. The method involves the solution of a system of $N + 2$ coupled differential equations, where $N$ is the number of fixed-base natural modes used to approximate the deformation of the superstructure. The analysis was carried out directly in the time domain using the impulse-response functions presented in Ref. 30.

It is apparent from Fig. 15 that, over wide ranges of the frequency parameter, $f_1 t_1$, the results obtained with $N = 1$, i.e., by assuming the structure to respond as a SDF system in its fixed-base fundamental mode, are indeed in excellent agreement with the exact results. Comparable agreement has also been obtained for systems subjected to the El Centro earthquake record.

In the lower-frequency regions of the spectra where the contributions of the higher modes are significant, a reasonable approximation to the maximum response may be obtained by assuming that soil-structure interaction influences only the response component contributed by the fundamental mode of vibration. This component may be evaluated by the procedure just outlined, utilizing the quantities $m^*$ and $h^*$, and the contributions of the higher modes may be determined by standard procedures disregarding the effect of interaction.

The accuracy of this approach is illustrated in Fig. 16, in which are presented response spectra for the maximum base shear of the five-story building frame considered previously when excited by the El Centro earthquake record. The results in this case are given for fixed values of $c_s/r$, and both an elastic and a viscoelastic half-space are considered. In the development of the approximate solutions displayed in this figure, the instantaneous values of the modal contributions were combined exactly. Accordingly, the results are not affected by the approximations involved in the usual procedures of combining peak modal responses.

The agreement in Fig. 16 between the exact and approximate solutions is indeed excellent. Note should also be taken of the very significant effect of material soil damping, indicating that consideration of this factor is in general essential to the accurate evaluation of the response of the system.

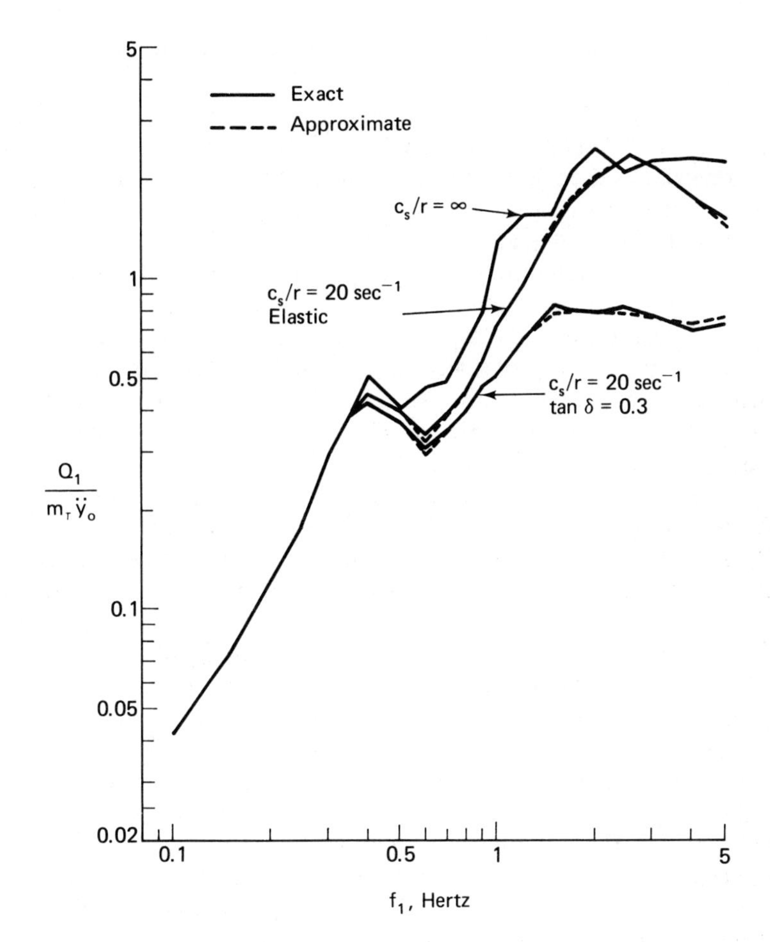


**Fig. 16.** Comparison of exact and approximate spectra for base shear of five-story structures subjected to El Centro input; $h/r = 5$, $\zeta_1 = 0.02$, $\gamma_T = 0.15$, $m_o/m_T = 0.2$

### *Limitations of Procedure and Needed Research*

In the form presented in this chapter, the procedure is applicable only to structures supported at the surface of a homogeneous half-space. However, by appropriate modifications of the effective period and damping of the structure, it can also be applied to systems with embedded foundations and layered media. A study of embedded foundations has been reported recently [2] based on the approximate foundation compliance functions presented in Ref. 1, but only exploratory studies appear to have been made of structures on layered media.

A second limitation of the procedure stems from the assumption of a rigid foundation mat. This assumption may not be realistic for foundations of very large plan dimensions, and additional studies are needed to assess the effects of foundation flexibility, particularly for excitations of high frequency.

Another problem requiring additional research is the response of structures supported on isolated spread footings. Probably the most pressing current need, however, is for studies of the dynamics of structures supported on pile foundations. In spite of its great practical importance, this problem to date has not received the attention it deserves.

An additional limitation of the procedure is the assumption of linear response for the superstructure. Considering that structures are normally designed to deform into the inelastic range during severe earthquakes, it is important that the effects of structural yielding be incorporated in the analysis. The principal effect of such yielding is to increase the relative flexibility of the structure and the supporting medium and thus decrease the effects of interaction. It is also necessary to account for the inelasticity of the supporting soil, but the only practical way of accomplishing this at the present time is by idealizing the soil as a linear viscoelastic material, along the lines used in the investigation reported herein. Some studies have already been made of the response of yielding structures interaction with an elastic half-space [31], but these should be extended to the more realistic situation of a yielding structure interacting with a hysteretic half-space.

While exact analyses of some of these problems do not appear possible in the foreseeable future, it is believed that valuable insight into the effects of the more important parameters may be gained from approximate analyses.

Fundamental to the procedure that has been presented is the assumption that the foundation of the structure remains in continuous contact with the supporting soil, This assumption may not be justified for tall structures, since the overturning moment may temporarily lift off one edge of the foundation. A recent exploratory study of this problem [11] suggests that this tipping tendency may materially reduce the magnitude of the dynamic effects transmitted to the structure. Additional studies are needed to quantify this effect for structures subjected to earthquakes.

Finally, there is a need for judiciously planned and carefully executed programs of laboratory and field tests to check the adequacy of the analytical predictions.

Additional areas of relevant needed research are identified in Ref. 27.

## Acknowledgment

The material presented in this chapter was developed in the course of studies conducted under National Science Foundation Grant GK-25917. This support is gratefully acknowledged. Grateful appreciation is also expressed to the author's former students Drs. J. W. Meek, V. V. D. Nair, B. Verbic and Y. T. Wei and to the author's present student Mr. J. B.

Valdivieso, whose research provided the basis for much of the information presented. The author has also benefitted greatly from discussions during the past year with the following members of the Committee on Soil-Structure Interaction for Project 3 of the Applied Technology Council, California: Drs. M. S. Agbabian, J. Bielak, P. C. Jennings, F. E. Richart, Jr., and J. M. Roesset. It is indeed a pleasure to acknowledge their contributions to the clarification of several of the questions considered herein.

## Notation

$c_s = \sqrt{G/\rho}$ = speed of propagation of shear waves in the half-space

$f$ = natural frequency of fixed-base structure, in hertz

$f_1$ = fundamental natural frequency of fixed-base multistory structure, in hertz

$\tilde{f}$ = effective natural frequency of flexibly supported structure, in hertz; taken equal to natural frequency of replacement SDF oscillator

$G$ = shear modulus of elasticity for half-space material

$h$ = height of structure; for multistory structures which respond as SDF systems in their fixed-base condition, it should be taken equal to $h^*$

$h_i$ = height from base to $i$th floor level of multistory structure

$h^*$ = effective height of multistory structure for motion in its fixed-base fundamental natural mode, defined by Eq. (21)

$K_x, K_\theta$ = translational and rotational stiffnesses of the foundation, defined by Eqs. (13) and (14)

$k$ = lateral stiffness of structure in its fixed-base condition

$m$ = mass of one-story structure, excluding foundation mass; for multistory structures which respond as SDF systems in their fixed-base condition, it should be taken equal to $m^*$

$m_i$ = mass at the $i$th floor level of multistory structure

$m_o$ = mass of foundation

$m_T$ = total mass of multistory structure, excluding $m_o$

$m^*$ = effective mass of multistory structure for motion in its fixed-base fundamental natural mode, defined by Eq. (20)

$p = \sqrt{k/m}$ = circular natural frequency of structure in its fixed-base condition

$\tilde{p} = 2\pi\tilde{f}$ = effective circular natural frequency of flexibly supported structure; also equal to corresponding frequency of replacement SDF oscillator

$Q_o$ = maximum spring force, or base shear, for one-story structure

$\tilde{Q}_o$ = maximum spring force for replacement oscillator; taken equal to $Q_o$

$Q_1$ = maximum base shear for multistory structure

$r$ = radius of foundation

$T = 1/f$ = natural period of fixed-base structure, in seconds

$\tilde{T} = 1/\tilde{f}$ = effective natural period of flexibly supported structure, in seconds

$t$ = time, in seconds

$t_1$ = characteristic time, taken equal to one-half the duration of the half-cycle displacement input

$u_o$ = maximum deformation of superstructure

$\tilde{u}_o$ = total maximum deformation of replacement SDF oscillator; it is generally different from $u_o$

$u_o'$ = component of $\tilde{u}_o$ induced in the spring connected to the mass; taken equal to $u_o$

$y_o, \dot{y}_o, \ddot{y}_o$ = maximum values of the displacement, velocity, and acceleration of the free-field ground motion

$\alpha_x, \alpha_\theta$ = dimensionless, frequency-dependent coefficients in expressions for dynamic stiffnesses of half-space
$\gamma$ = mass density ratio, defined by Eq. (3)
$\delta$ = damping parameter for half-space material, related to $\Delta W/W$ by Eq. (1)
$\Delta W/W$ = specific loss factor for half-space material
$\zeta$ = percentage of critical damping for structure in its fixed-base condition
$\tilde{\zeta}$ = effective overall damping factor for flexibly supported structure
$\tilde{\zeta}_o$ = foundation damping factor, i.e., value of $\tilde{\zeta}$ when $\zeta = 0$
$\nu$ = Poisson's ratio for half-space material
$\rho$ = mass density for half-space material
$\sigma$ = dimensionless parameter defined by Eq. (2)
$\phi$ = dimensionless parameter defined by Eq. (16)

## References


1. Beredugo, Y. O., and M. Novak, "Coupled Horizontal and Rocking Vibration of Embedded Footings," *Can. Geotech. J.*, Vol. 9, No. 4, 1972, pp. 477–497.
2. Bielak, J., "Dynamic Behaviour of Structures with Embedded Foundations," Int. *J. Earthquake Eng. Struct. Dynamics*, Vol. 3, No. 3, 1975, pp. 259–274.
3. Bielak, J., "Modal Analysis for Building-Soil Interaction," *Report E17*, Institute of Engineering, National University of Mexico, Mexico City, 1975.
4. Castellani, A., "Foundation Compliance Effects on Earthquake Response Spectra," *J. Soil Mech. Found. Div. ASCE*, Vol. 96, No. SM4, 1970, pp. 1335–1355.
5. Chopra, A. K., and J. A. Gutierrez, "Earthquake Analysis of Multistory Buildings Including Foundation Interaction," *Int. J. Earthquake Eng. Struct. Dynamics*, Vol. 3, 1974, pp. 65–77.
6. Hardin, B. O., and V. P. Drnevich, "Shear Modulus and Damping in Soils: Measurement and Parameter Effects," *J. Soil Mech. Found. Div. ASCE*, Vol. 98, No. SM6, 1972, pp. 603–624.
7. Jennings, P. C., and J. Bielak, "Dynamics of Building-Soil Interaction," *Bull. Seism. Soc. Am.*, Vol. 63, No. 1, 1973, pp. 9–48.
8. Liu, S. C., and L. W. Fagel, "Earthquake Interaction by Fast Fourier Transform," *J. Eng. Mech. Div. ASCE*, Vol. 97, No. EM4, 1971, pp. 1223–1237.
9. Luco, J. E., "Impedance Founctions for a Rigid Foundation on a Layered Medium," *Nuclear Eng. Des.*, Vol. 31, No. 2, 1974, pp. 204–217.
10. Luco, J. E., and R. A. Westmann, "Dynamic Response of Circular Footings," *J. Eng. Mech. Div. ASCE*, Vol. 97, No. EM5, 1971, pp. 1381–1395.
11. Meek, J. W., "Effects of Foundation Tipping on Dynamic Response," *J. Struct. Div. ASCE*, Vol. 101, No. ST7, 1975, pp. 1297–1311.
12. Meek, J. W., and A. S. Veletsos, "Dynamic Analysis and Behavior of Structure-Foundation Systems," *SRR Report No. 13*, Department of Civil Engineering, Rice University, Houston, 1972.
13. Nair, V. V. D., "Dynamics of Certain Structure-Foundation Systems," Ph. D. Thesis, submitted to Rice University, Houston, 1974.
14. Novak, M., "Dynamic Stiffness and Damping of Piles," *Can. Geotech. J.*, Vol. 11, No. 4, 1974, pp. 574–598.
15. Novak, M., "Effect of Soil on Structural Response to Wind and Earthquake," Int. *J. Earthquake Eng. Struct. Dynamics*, Vol. 3, 1974, pp. 79–96.

16. PARMELEE, R. A., "Building-Foundation Interaction Effects," *J. Eng. Mech. Div. ASCE,* Vol. 93, No. EM2, 1967, pp. 131–162.
17. PARMELEE, R. A., and J. H. WRONKIEWICZ, "Seismic Design of Soil-Structure Interaction Systems," *J. Struct. Div. ASCE,* Vol. 97, No. ST10, 1971, pp. 2503–2517.
18. RAINER, J. H., "Structure-Ground Interaction in Earthquakes," *J. Eng. Mech. Div. ASCE,* Vol. 97, No. EM5, 1971, pp. 1431–1450.
19. ROESSET, J. M., R. V. WHITMAN, and R. DOBRY, "Modal Analysis for Structures with Foundation Interaction," *J. Struct. Div. ASCE,* Vol. 99, No. ST3, 1973, pp. 399–416.
20. SARRAZIN M. A., J. M. ROESSET, and R. V. WHITMAN, "Dynamic Soil Structure Interaction," *J. Struct. Div. ASCE,* Vol. 98, No. ST7, 1972, pp. 1525–1544.
21. SEED, H. B., and I. IDRISS, "Soil Moduli and Damping Factors for Dynamic Response Analysis," *Report No. EERC70–10,* University of California, Berkeley, 1970.
22. SEED, H. B., J. LYSMER, and R. HWANG, "Soil-Structure Interaction Analyses for Seismic Response," *J. Geotech. Eng. Div. ASCE,* Vol. 101, No. GT5, 1975, pp. 439–457.
23. TSAI, N. C., "Modal Damping for Soil-Structure Interaction," *J. Eng. Mech. Div. ASCE,* Vol. 100, No. EM2, 1974, pp. 323–341.
24. VELETSOS, A. S., and J. W. MEEK, "Dynamic Behavior of Building-Foundation Systems," *Int. J. Earthquake Eng. Struct. Dynamics,* Vol. 3, No. 2, 1974, pp. 121–138.
25. VELETSOS, A. S., and V. V. D. NAIR, "Torsional Vibration of Viscoelastic Foundations," *J. Geotech. Eng. Div. ASCE,* Vol. 100, No. GT3, 1974, pp. 225–246.
26. VELETSOS, A. S., and V. V. D. NAIR, "Seismic Interaction of Structures on Hysteretic Foundations," *J. Struct. Div. ASCE,* Vol. 101, No. ST1, 1975, pp. 109–129.
27. VELETSOS, A. S., and F. E. RICHART, JR., "Report of UCEER Panel on Soil Mechanics and Soil-Structure Interaction, "*Proceedings of Third National Meeting Universities Council for Earthquake Engineering Research, UCEER,* California Institute of Technology, Pasadena, 1974, pp. 221–232.
28. VELETSOS, A. S., and W. P. VANN, "Response of Ground-Excited Elastoplastic Systems," *J. Struct. Div. ASCE,* Vol. 97, No. ST4, 1971, pp. 1257–1281.
29. VELETSOS, A. S., and B. VERBIC, "Vibration of Viscoelastic Foundations," *Int. J. Earthquake Eng. Struct. Dynamics,* Vol. 2, No. 1, 1973, pp. 87–102.
30. VELETSOS, A. S., and B. VERBIC, "Basic Response Functions for Elastic Foundations," *J. Eng. Mech. Div. ASCE,* Vol. 100, No. EM2, 1974, pp. 189–202.
31. VELETSOS, A. S., and B. VERBIC, "Dynamics of Elastic and Yielding Structure-Foundation Systems," *Proceedings Fifth World Conference on Earthquake Engineering,* Rome, 1974, pp. 2610–2613.
32. VELETSOS, A. S., and Y. T. WEI, "Lateral and Rocking Vibration of Footings," *J. Soil Mech. Found. Div. ASCE,* Vol. 97, 1971, pp. 1227–1248.
33. VERBIC, B., "Analysis of Certain Structure-Foundation Interaction Systems," Ph.D. Thesis, submitted to Rice University, Houston, 1972.

# The Role of Soil Mechanics in Foundation Structure-Soil Interaction

LEONARDO ZEEVAERT*

## Introduction

Generally foundation structures are constructed of reinforced concrete with sufficient rigidity to take, within tolerable limits, differential vertical displacements between columns. Therefore, the concern of the foundation engineer is to estimate shears, bending moments, and relative deflections in the foundation structure subjected to the action of loads and reactions. The contact stresses are inspected to verify if these are under the allowable soil strength and within the range of the expected deformational behavior. The foundation engineer has to justify the proper placement of the reinforcing steel in the foundation structure. The differential displacements between column loads should not induce high secondary stresses in the building structural frame, and the total settlements must remain under allowable limits. The economy and good behavior of the design should be justified.

To achieve the above-mentioned purpose the foundation engineer has to investigate the compatibility of deformation at the interface of concrete structure and soil mass, that is, at the foundation grade elevation. The stress-strain-time mechanical properties of these two lithological materials, concrete and soil should be investigated to perform a satisfactory analysis. The geometry of the foundation structure and soil mass stratigraphy should be known.

The stiffness of the foundation structure is measured by the product $E_c I_c$, in which $I_c$ is the moment of inertia of a cross section subjected to bending moment and $E_c$ is the so-called modulus of elasticity of concrete, exhibiting

*Professor Civil Engineering, UNAM, Mexico City, Isabel la Catolica 68, Mexico 1, DF, Mexico.

inelastic behavior on long-time static loading. Therefore, it appears more convenient to express the deformational mechanical properties of concrete using the concept of the strain modulus $M_c$ defined by the ratio of unit strain to unit stress $\Delta\epsilon/\Delta\sigma$. The value of $M_c$ is a function of the viscosity of the cement paste, and therefore of the stress level and time, on the aggregate-cement ratio, steel percentage, and age. From a practical point of view the following relation may be considered:

$$M_c = \frac{\Delta\epsilon_e + \Delta\epsilon_p + \Delta\epsilon_v}{\Delta\sigma} \tag{1}$$

in which $\Delta\epsilon_e$ represents the response elastic strain, $\Delta\epsilon_p$ the plastic strain, and $\Delta\epsilon_v$ the viscoplastic strain, which is a function of time (Fig. 1). During fairly rapid load application $\Delta\epsilon_{ep}$ represents the elastoplastic strain for which the corresponding strain modulus $M_{ep}$ may be determined, and thus:

$$M_c = (M_{ep})_c\left(1 + \frac{\Delta\epsilon_v}{\Delta\epsilon_{ep}}\right) \tag{2}$$

The viscous or creep phenomenon is measured by $\Delta\epsilon_v/\Delta\epsilon_{ep} = \kappa_{cv}$:

$$M_c = (M_{ep})_c(1 + \kappa_{cv}). \tag{3}$$

The value of $\kappa_{cv}$ assumes a value on the order of 2 for long-time deformation. The value of $(M_{ep})_c$ has been extensively investigated. The following approxi-

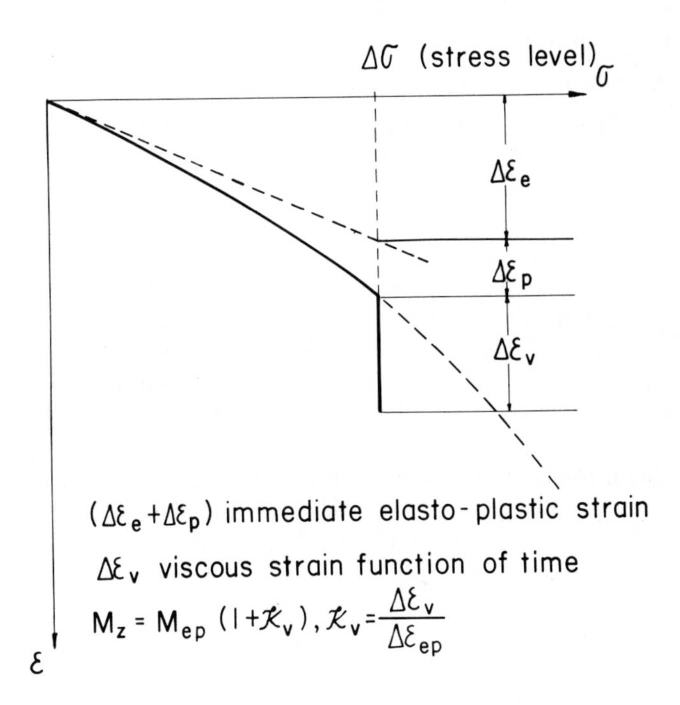


Fig. 1

mate phenomenological law (ACI 435) has been found:

$$(M_{ep})_c = C_0(wf'_c)^{-n} \tag{4}$$

in which $C_0$, $n$ are parameters assumed constant; however, they undoubtedly depend on the aggregate-cement ratio and aggregate quality. The value $w$ represents the concrete weight and $f'_c$ the compressive strength of concrete at 28 days. Here again $f'_c$ increases with age. Therefore, $I_c/M_c$ is a function of $f'_c$, the time, and the geometry of the foundation structure. In case of transient stresses the elastic response strain modulus $M_e$ applies.

The linear strain modulus of soil is investigated in undisturbed soil specimens. This value is a function of the confining stress level at the depth the sample is recovered and of the time the imposed increment of stress on the soil is acting. Hence, it may be expressed for static loading as follows:

$$M_z = f(\sigma_c, t) \tag{5}$$

in which $\sigma_c$ is the equivalent confining stress level and $t$ the time. Using general expression (3) for soil this may be expressed as

$$M_z = M_{ep}(1 + \kappa_v) \tag{6}$$

in which $M_{ep}$ is the elastoplastic strain modulus. The value of $\kappa_v$ measures the intergranular viscosity of the material and becomes an important factor in case of fine saturated soils. The phenomenological laws [12] for the elastoplastic strain modulus may be expressed as

for cohesive soils $$M_{ep} = M_o e^{-n_c \sigma_c} \tag{7}$$

for cohesionless soils $$M_{ep} = C_s \sigma_c^{-n_s} \tag{8}$$

The value of $M_{ep}$ for a specific soil sediment is a function of the confining stress level at which the material is subjected; hence, a change in $\sigma_c$ affects the value of $M_{ep}$. Moreover, the determination of the value $M_{ep}$ is performed in the laboratory on samples representative of the soil stratum in the field. However, when obtaining the soil specimens they are relieved totally from the state of stress they are subjected to in the ground. On the other hand, in the field, during excavations to place the foundation structure the soil mass is not relieved fully of the confined state of stress (Fig. 2), except at the foundation grade elevation; therefore, the values of $M_{ep}$ given in Eqs. (7) and (8) obtained in the laboratory for recompression of the soil are larger than the field values, except close to the foundation grade elevation. To obtain the field value a correction is necessary introducing a recompression factor $\rho_c$ [12,16] (Fig. 3), which is a function of the stress relief induced in the soil mass with respect to the initial state of stress and of the soil intergranular viscosity,

$$\rho_c = f\left(\frac{\sigma_r}{\sigma_0}, \kappa_v\right). \tag{9}$$

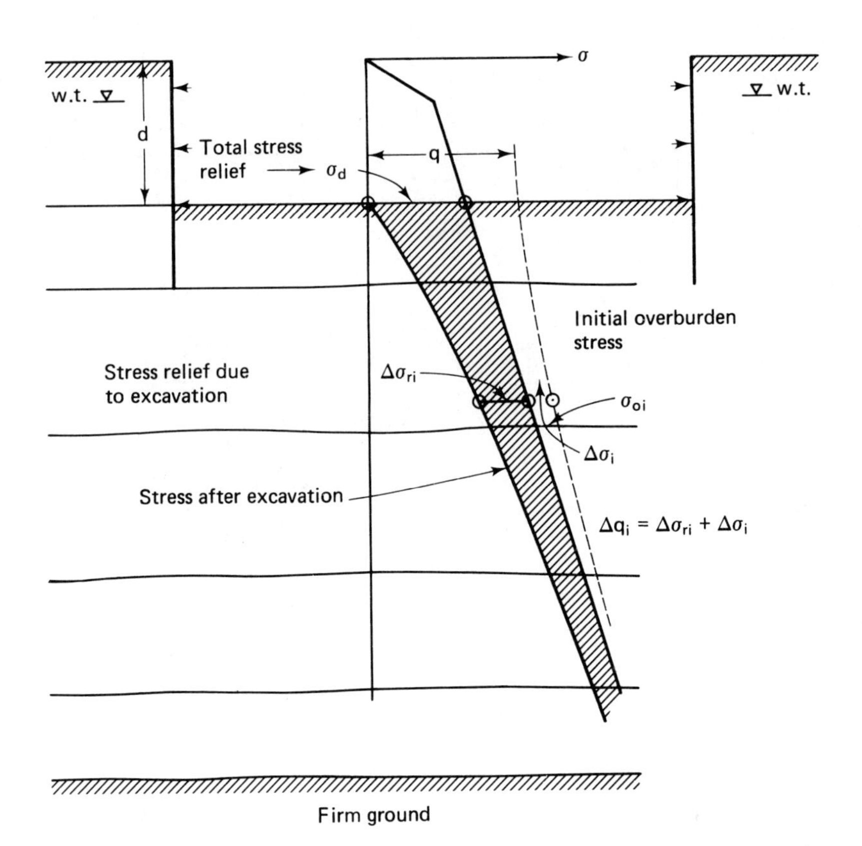


**Fig. 2**

The value of the stress relief $\sigma_r$ is determined at the center of each stratum. Therefore, the corrected linear strain modulus on a long-time term basis is

$$M_z = \rho_c M_{ep}(1 + \kappa_v). \tag{10}$$

The determination of the $M_z$ values are investigated for each stratum with different mechanical properties and up to a depth where the above-mentioned value has an insignificant role in the soil mass deformation.

Two important problems may be encountered, namely, the ones related to a long-applied static state of stress, in which the mechanical stress-strain-time properties of soil are used for calculation, and those related to dynamic forces present in machine foundations or induced by earthquake mass forces. The second group calls for knowledge of the dynamic stress-strain properties of the sediments.

The problems found in the literature dealing with the foundation struc-

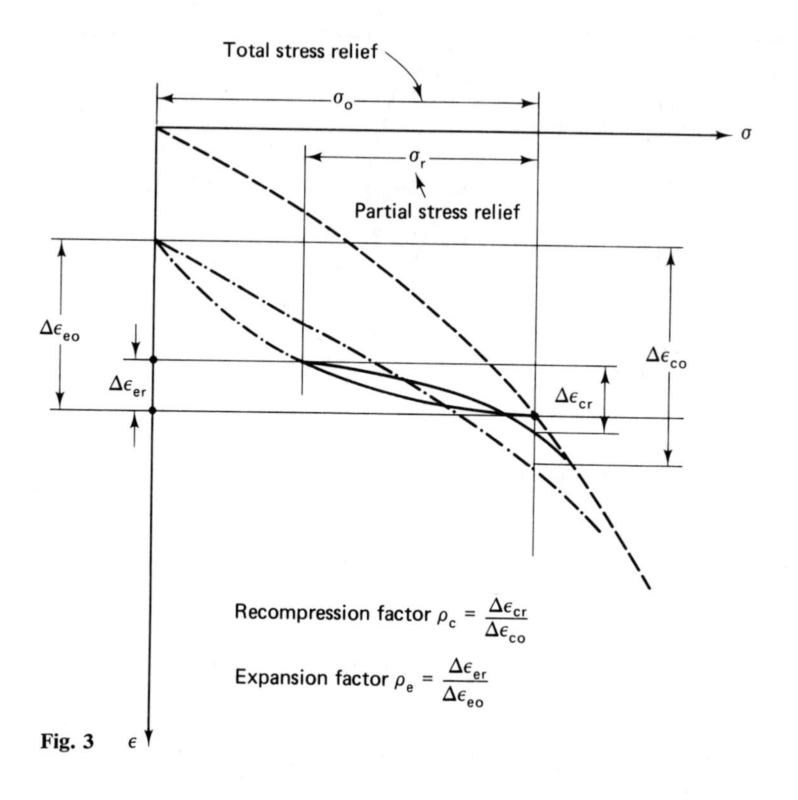


**Fig. 3**

ture-soil interaction are generally recognized as problems of beams on elastic foundations established since Winkler [1] hypothesis the first of the mechanical action of the ground under the foundation structure. Later Hayashi [2] and Hetényi [3] performed extensive work and found solutions for many problems from the mathematical point of view using the Winkler assumption; recently De Beer et al. [8], Kani [13], Chamecki [9], and Heil [10] have proposed different methods of approach. Nevertheless, the solutions of the different variety of problems and the useful tables prepared to facilitate calculations are predominately based on the early Winkler assumption; that is, the soil mass consists of a series of springs independently of each other and therefore no continuity in the soil mass is considered. Under this assumption the foundation moduli have independent values not affected by the contact stress distribution or stress level in the soil mass. These elements, however, may exhibit elastic or elastoplastic behavior. The problems without possible direct mathematical solution have been solved efficiently using numerical methods [4,5,6] and lately using computer programs by the finite element method [11,14].

Nevertheless, it is well recognized that the soil mass cannot be regarded as a system of elements with independent deformational behavior. The deformation of one element affects the neighboring elements and vice versa; hence, the soil mass upon the action of the subgrade reactions should be treated as a continuum [12,15]. The value of the foundation modulus at a point is not a value that may be considered invariant with respect to the deformational behavior of other points; its value depends on the contact stress distribution. Furthermore, in soil mechanics terms, the foundation moduli depend on other factors such as the elastoplastic and viscous properties of soil, time, stratigraphy, and the hydraulic conditions producing changes of stress levels in the ground, and last but not least on the manner in which the stress distribution and lateral restraint to deformation takes place in the soil mass. However, for a specific building load layout, a geometrical form, stiffness characteristics of the foundation structure, and subsoil stratigraphical and mechanical properties, the final foundation moduli have one and only one characteristic value configuration. Therefore, to solve this problem there is a clear need for a method with no more assumptions than those currently made in soil mechanics problems of stress and strain in soil masses and on the continuity of the foundation structure and building.

The role of soil mechanics in analyzing the foundation structure-soil interaction should be used in its full power. The method here proposed is directed toward achieving this goal; it has been applied by the author for a number of years with satisfactory practical results. Today the digital computer has opened new horizons for more accurate solutions of this problem. Notwithstanding, there is a need for theoretical investigations and field research.

## Static Problems

The stress-strain-time properties of soil may be estimated with reasonable accuracy using proper laboratory techniques on undisturbed specimens truly representative of the subsoil strata. The mechanical properties of the subsoil and the hydraulic and stratigraphical conditions are determined to a depth at which the stresses are unimportant in the soil mass behavior because of the load imposed on the soil by the foundation structure, or to a depth where firm ground of very low compressibility is encountered.

In soil mechanics it is customary to determine the compressibility of soil by means of consolidation tests, that is, compression tests subjected to zero lateral deformation, obtaining from these tests the coefficient of unit volume compressibility $m_v$ defined by the increments ratio of volumetric strain $\Delta\epsilon_v$ to stress $\Delta\sigma$; hence,

$$m_v = \frac{\Delta\epsilon_v}{\Delta\sigma}. \tag{11}$$

The value of $m_v$ obtained in the laboratory, for most saturated fine soil sediments, may be represented as a function of the stress level and time:

$$m_v = m_{ep} f(\sigma, t).$$

Here $m_{ep}$ is the coefficient of unit volume compressibility for elastoplastic behavior. Equation (11) may also be expressed as follows:

$$m_v = m_{ep}(T + Z) \tag{12}$$

in which $T$ and $Z$ are time functions; $T$ is the well-known Terzaghi function regarding the volumetric deformation, and $Z$ [12] is a function taking into consideration the intergranular viscosity of soil.

When estimating stresses and strains in the soil mass the theory of elasticity is used based on the well-known solution by Boussinesq. Nevertheless, in nature the subsoil is usually stratified and the mechanical properties change with depth. Limiting solutions as given by Westergaard and Froehlich and other intermediate conditions may be studied by means of stress nets [12] to facilitate the calculations of vertical stresses in the ground. The strains are estimated from the stress change in the ground using the corrected linear strain modulus of the soil and Poisson's ratio.

The coefficient of unit volume compressibility determined in the laboratory for zero lateral deformation is not fully representative of the soil conditions except in the case when the loaded area is very large in comparison with the compressible soil deposit. Furthermore, at the edge of the foundation structure the horizontal strains are not zero; therefore it is better to use the linear strain modulus. The theoretical ratio between the coefficient of unit volume compressibility determined in the laboratory and the linear strain modulus is

$$m_v = \frac{(1 + \nu)(1 - 2\nu)}{1 - \nu} M_z \tag{13}$$

in which $\nu$ is Poisson's ratio: let

$$\nu_c = \frac{(1 + \nu)(1 - 2\nu)}{1 - \nu}. \tag{14}$$

The physical significance of $\nu_c$ is that of a factor determining the volume compressibility. In fact, when $\nu = 0.5$ the material is incompressible. For any other values of $\nu < \frac{1}{2}$ the material shows certain compressibility. In clay the limiting values under fully consolidated conditions may reach values on the order of 0.35 and in coarse granular soils $\nu = 0.25$. Therefore, from consolidation tests the linear strain modulus may be determined theoretically by estimating the value of $\nu_c$,

$$M_z = \frac{m_v}{\nu_c}, \tag{15}$$

and for recompression of a uniform stratum due to partial stress relief,

$$M_z = \rho_c \frac{m_v}{v_c}. \tag{16}$$

With the mechanical properties representative of one stratum $N$ of thickness $d$ the recompression may be estimated due to a change in stress:

$$\Delta\delta_N = \left(\rho_c \frac{m_v}{v_c} d\right)_N \Delta\sigma_N. \tag{17}$$

The value in parentheses will be called the "volumetric compressibility of the stratum," in cm³/kg. Hence, in the case of recompression,

$$\alpha_{rN} = \left(\rho_c \frac{m_v}{v_c} d\right)_N \tag{18}$$

In the case of preconsolidated-type sediments, when the stratum is stressed over the overburden stress $\sigma_{0i}$, $\rho_c = 1$. The total deformation of a stratum due to recompression with average increment of stress of $\Delta\sigma_{ri}$ and average increment of stress $\Delta\sigma_i$ over the overburden stress will be

$$\Delta\delta_i = (\alpha_{rN})\,\Delta\sigma_{ri} + (\alpha_{cN})\,\Delta\sigma_i, \tag{19}$$

from which the change in thickness of the stratum due to the total applied stress $\Delta\sigma_{qi} = \Delta\sigma_{ri} + \Delta\sigma_i$ may be determined from the volume compressibilities of the stratum:

$$\Delta\delta_i = (\alpha_{rN})\,\Delta\sigma_{ri} + (\alpha_{cN})\,\Delta\sigma_{qi} - (\alpha_{cN})\,\Delta\sigma_{ri}.$$

or

$$\Delta\delta_i = \left\{\alpha_{cN} + (\alpha_{rN} - \alpha_{cN})\frac{\Delta\sigma_{ri}}{\Delta\sigma_{qi}}\right\}\Delta\sigma_{qi}. \tag{20}$$

Here $\Delta\sigma_{ri}$ is the relief in overburden stress due to excavation, and $\Delta\sigma_{qi}$ is the total stress applied to the soil at depth $z = i$ because of the foundation reactions $q_n$ at the foundation grade elevation. The value of $\Delta\sigma_{ri}$ may be calculated by determining the relief of effective stress at the foundation grade elevation and using the selected influence factor $I_\chi$ for a definite soil stratigraphical condition and for the average depth $z = i$ of the stratum. Nevertheless, the above-mentioned value of $\Delta\sigma_{ri}$ should be corrected for any change in effective stress that may be induced because of the imposed hydraulic conditions in the soil mass, as for example that due to pumping from the bottom of the excavation in case of deep compensated foundations under the water table. (See reference [16] and [12], Chapter xi.)

The volume compressibility of the stratum is

$$\alpha_N = \alpha_{cN} + (\alpha_{rN} - \alpha_{cN})\frac{\Delta\sigma_{ri}}{\Delta\sigma_{qi}}. \tag{21}$$

The values of $\alpha_r$ and $\alpha_c$ are representative of the volumetric compression of each stratum. In the case of over- or fully compensated foundations when $\Delta\sigma_{ri} \geq \Delta\sigma_{qi}$ only the value $\alpha_r$ is considered. The values of $\alpha_N$ represent the geomechanical compressibility properties of the stratum considered. Their numerical values are determined from laboratory and field information as reported before and for the stress level induced by the foundation structure in the soil and time at which the deformation is required.

When excavations are performed the bottom of the excavation suffers an upward vertical displacement due to the response of the soil elastic elements upon stress relief; not considered is the plastic flow motivated by high shear stresses due to slope stability of the excavation. The plastic flow should be avoided using an ample factor of safety. The elastic response is estimated for several points at the excavation surface. For this purpose the elastic response strain modulus is used corrected for partial stress relief at the required depth by means of the expansion factor $\rho_e$ [12,16], which is a function of the ratio $\Delta\sigma_{ri}/\sigma_{0i}$ (Fig. 3). Here, $\Delta\sigma_{ri}$ is the partial stress relief at average depth $z = i$ of stratum $N$ due to all causes motivated by the excavation, and $\sigma_{0i}$ is the existing overburden effective stress at the same depth. In this case the volumetric expansion of the stratum is represented by

$$\alpha_{eN} = (\rho_e M_e d)_N. \tag{22}$$

## Dynamic Problems

In the case of dynamic effects in building foundations like those induced by earthquakes, one of the problems required is usually to determine the rocking phenomenon of the foundation and building [12,17]. In these cases the dynamic deformations of the strata are estimated from the dynamic shear modulus of elasticity or soil rigidity $\mu$; hence,

$$\alpha_{\mu N} = \left(\frac{d}{2(1+\nu)\mu}\right)_N. \tag{23}$$

The seismic shear stresses in the soil mass are superimposed on to the static shear stresses, investigating the shear stress level and comparing this with the soil shear strength [18]. The soil rigidity is determined in the laboratory on undisturbed samples for a confining volumetric stress level equivalent to the one the material has in the field under the foundation of the building. The value of $\mu$ is a function of the confining volumetric stress $\sigma_c$ according to the following phenomenological laws: (1) cohesive soils:

$$\mu_c = \mu_0 e^{n_c \sigma_c}; \tag{24}$$

(2) sandy soils:

$$\mu_s = C_s \sigma_c^{n_s}. \tag{25}$$

## Volumetric Deformation Matrix

To study the compatibility of deformation at the interface of foundation structure and soil, the contact surface is divided in equal-sized tributary areas $\bar{a}$, as many as required for accuracy. The average stress levels in the strata under each tributary area are estimated, and the stress-strain-time parameters are determined from laboratory information, from which the value of $\alpha_N$ for all the strata are calculated under each tributary area. Hence, the volumetric deformation matrix is formed (Fig. 4):

$$[\alpha_{nN}]. \tag{26}$$

| | λ | λ | λ | λ | λ | λ |
|---|---|---|---|---|---|---|
| stratum | ·a | ·1 | ·2 | ·3 | ·n | ·b |
| A | $\alpha_{aA}$ | $\alpha_{1A}$ | $\alpha_{2A}$ | . . | $\alpha_{nA}$ | $\alpha_{bA}$ |
| B | $\alpha_{aB}$ | $\alpha_{1B}$ | $\alpha_{2B}$ | . . | $\alpha_{nB}$ | $\alpha_{bB}$ |
| C | $\alpha_{aC}$ | $\alpha_{1C}$ | $\alpha_{2C}$ | . . | $\alpha_{nC}$ | $\alpha_{bC}$ |
| N | $\alpha_{aN}$ | $\alpha_{1N}$ | $\alpha_{2N}$ | . . | $\alpha_{nN}$ | $\alpha_{bN}$ |

**Fig. 4** Volume Compressibility of Strata Matrix

## Unit Load Influence Displacements Equation

Selecting the proper stress distribution in the ground compatible with the stratigraphic conditions, one may form the unit influence matrix for each unit loaded tributary area, as shown in Fig. 5. The matrices so obtained are transposed and multiplied by the volumetric compression of the strata matrix to calculate the unit influence vertical displacements in all points at the foundation grade elevation due to the unit load in tributary areas $\bar{a}_n$; hence, for the unit load applied on tributary area point $a$, we can write:

$$\{\bar{\delta}_{ij}\}_a \approx [I_{ij}^N]_a^T[\alpha_{nN}]. \tag{27}$$

In the same manner the unit influence matrices are formed for other unit-

Unit load at tributary area $\bar{a}_a$

| Stratum | a | 1 | 2 | 3 | n | b |
|---|---|---|---|---|---|---|
| A | $1^{A}_{aa}$ | $1^{A}_{1a}$ | $1^{A}_{2a}$ | .. | $1^{A}_{na}$ | $1^{A}_{ba}$ |
| B | $1^{B}_{aa}$ | $1^{B}_{1a}$ | $1^{B}_{2a}$ | .. | $1^{B}_{na}$ | $1^{B}_{ba}$ |
| C | $1^{C}_{aa}$ | $1^{C}_{1a}$ | $1^{C}_{2a}$ | .. | $1^{C}_{na}$ | $1^{C}_{ba}$ |
| N | $1^{N}_{aa}$ | $1^{N}_{1a}$ | $1^{N}_{2a}$ | .. | $1^{N}_{na}$ | $1^{N}_{ba}$ |

Unit stress influence matrix

**Fig. 5**

loaded tributary areas:

$$\begin{aligned}\{\bar{\delta}_{ij}\}_1 &\approx [I^N_{ij}]^T_1[\alpha_{nN}]\\ \{\bar{\delta}_{ij}\}_2 &\approx [I^N_{ij}]^T_2[\alpha_{nN}]\\ &\;\vdots\\ \{\bar{\delta}_{ij}\}_b &\approx [I^N_{ij}]^T_b[\alpha_{nN}].\end{aligned} \tag{28}$$

The column matrices $\{\bar{\delta}_{ij}\}$ shown in the first member of equations (27) and (28) are formed with the numerical values of the diagonal of the full matrix resulting from performing the algebraic operation indicated in the second member of the same equations.

The stress influence matrices $[I_{ij}]$ may be used also to investigate the stress levels in the soil mass because of reactions $q_n$ at the interface of the foundation structure and soil, thus;

$$[\Delta\sigma_{ij}] = \sum_{1}^{n} [I^N_{ij}]_n \cdot q_n \tag{29}$$

## Vertical Displacement Matrix Equation

The settlements or vertical displacements at each tributary area may be calculated by multiplying the influence coefficients of the transposed matrix formed for the $\bar{\delta}_{ij}$ values by the unit reactions columnar matrix for tributary areas $a, 1, 2, \ldots n, b$; hence, the settlements at the center of each tributary area are obtained:

$$\begin{Bmatrix} \delta_a \\ \delta_1 \\ \delta_2 \\ \cdot \\ \cdot \\ \cdot \\ \delta_b \end{Bmatrix} = \begin{bmatrix} \{\bar{\delta}_{ij}\}_a^T \\ \{\bar{\delta}_{ij}\}_1^T \\ \{\bar{\delta}_{ij}\}_2^T \\ \cdot \\ \cdot \\ \cdot \\ \{\bar{\delta}_{ij}\}_b^T \end{bmatrix} \begin{Bmatrix} q_a \\ q_1 \\ q_2 \\ \cdot \\ \cdot \\ \cdot \\ q_b \end{Bmatrix}. \tag{30}$$

Finally,

$$\{\delta_n\} = [\bar{\delta}_{ij}]_{\text{soil}}^T\{q_n\}. \tag{31}$$

The vertical displacement or settlement matrix is necessary to calculate the interaction of the foundation structure with the soil mass.

## Vertical Displacements of the Foundation Structure

The building loads $P$ and reactions $R_n = q_n\bar{a}_n$ for each tributary area of the foundation structure induce displacements that should be compatible [15] with the soil vertical displacements at corresponding points [Fig. 6(a)].

The geometrical condition imposed by the column loads on the foundation structure should be known. The foundation structure is made statically determinate, assuming the unknown reactions to be zero [Fig. 6(b)]. Under these conditions the vertical displacements of the structure are calculated, obtaining, respectively, $\delta_{01}\delta_{02} \ldots \delta_{0i} \ldots \delta_{0n}$ at the center of the chosen tributary areas.

To determine the action of each one of the reactions on the foundation structure and soil one should apply a unit load at the center of each one of the corresponding tributary areas. By this technique one determines the influence vertical displacements $\delta_{ii}$ of the structure at the point of application $i$ and at all other points $j$ in consideration representing the tributary areas of the foundation surface obtaining the unit $\delta_{ji}$ structure vertical displacements coefficients. At point $i$ under consideration the unit load will produce a deformation in the soil $\delta_{ii} = 1/K_{ii}$, that is function of the foundation modulus $K_{ii}$ at that point, Fig. 6(c).

Correspondingly the influence vertical displacements $\delta_{ij}$ may be determined for point $i$ due to unit reactions applied on points $j$. If the reactions considered are $R_aR_1R_2 \ldots R_i \ldots R_nR_b$ in which $R_1$ to $R_n$ are the unknowns, then the total vertical displacements of the foundation structure must be equal to the influence coefficients multiplied by the unknown reactions in order to obtain deformation compatibility at the point in question, that is,

$$\delta_{0i} = \delta_{11}R_1 + \delta_{12}R_2 + \cdots \quad \cdots + \left(\delta_{ii} + \frac{1}{K_{ii}}\right)R_i + \delta_nR_n \tag{32}$$

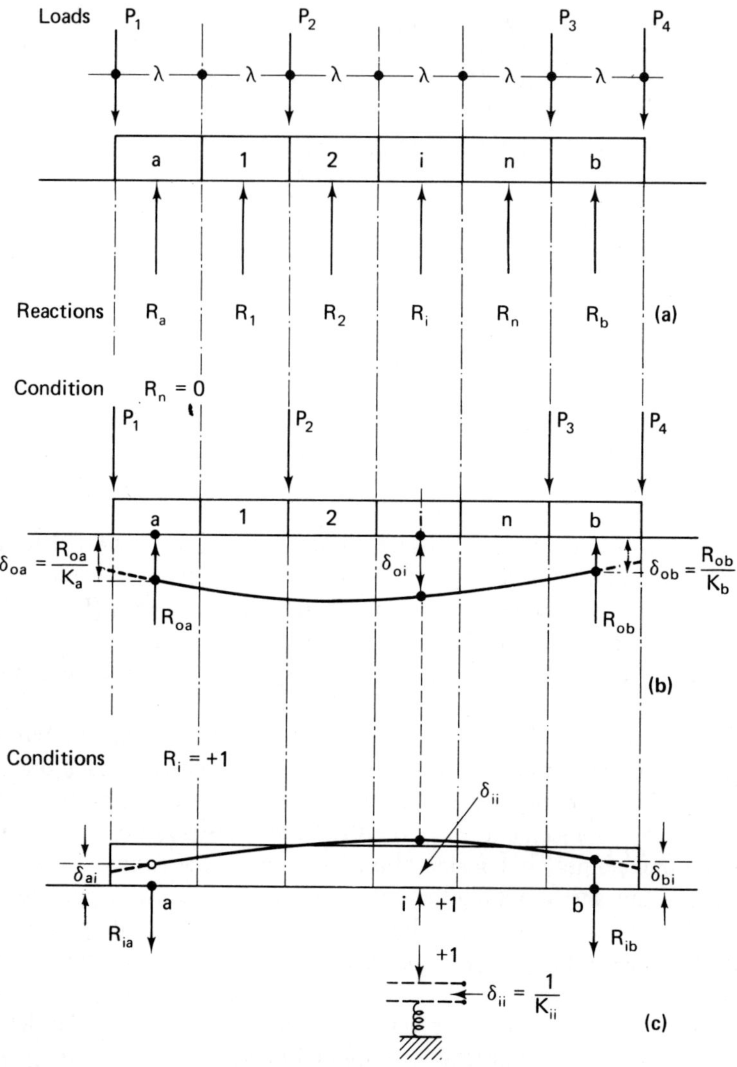


**Fig. 6** Conditions for influence coefficients

in which the $\delta_{ij}$, as stated before, are the influence coefficients on point $i$ due to unit loads placed at points $j$. If $I_c/M_c$ represents the stiffness of the concrete structure, we can write:

$$\frac{I_c}{M_c}\delta_{0i} = \frac{I_c}{M_c}\delta_{11}R_1 + \frac{I_c}{M_c}\delta_{12}R_2 + \cdots + \left(\frac{I_c}{M_c}\delta_{ii} + \frac{I_c}{M_c K_{ii}}\right)R_i + \frac{I_c}{M_c}\delta_n R_n$$

or

$$S_{0i} = S_{11}R_1 + S_{12}R_2 + \cdots + (S_{ii} + \tau_{ii})R_i + S_{1n}R_n \tag{33}$$

in which $\tau_{ii}$ represents the foundation structure soil interaction coefficient at point $i$. A different value of $\tau$ is found under each reaction. For other points similar equations may be formed and as many unknowns as necessary determined. The following matrix equation is formed:

$$\{S_{0n}\} = [S_{ij}]_{str}\{R_n\} \tag{34}$$

from which the unknown reactions may be calculated for certain specific values of $\tau_{11}\tau_{22} \ldots \tau_{ii} \ldots \tau_{nn}$, respectively; hence,

$$\{R_n\} = [S_{ij}]_{str}^{-1}\{S_{0n}\}. \tag{35}$$

## Calculation Method to Obtain the Contact Stress Distribution

Now we have formed two matrix equations to calculate vertical displacements and reactions at the interface of the foundation structure and soil. The first equation, (31), is based on the geomechanical properties of the subsoil mass and gives the vertical displacements or settlements, and the value of the foundation modulus for each tributary area may be determined. The second equation, (35), determines the stiffness of the foundation structure and establishes the interaction between foundation structure and soil by means of the $\tau$ values.

Hence, we have (1) the soil vertical displacements equation:

$$\{\delta_n\} = [\bar{\delta}_{ij}]_{soil}^{T}\{q_n\}. \tag{31}$$

Here, $R_i = \bar{a}_i q_i$, and the values of $K_{ii} = R_i/\delta_i$ may be found, and from $I_c/M_c$ the values of $\tau_{ii} = I_c/M_c K_{ii}$ may be calculated.

(2) The compatibility equation establishing the foundation structure-soil interaction,

$$\{R_n\} = [S_{ij}]_{str}^{-1}\{S_{0n}\}, \tag{35}$$

is used to calculate the corresponding unknown reactions.

Since the values of $\delta_i$, $\tau_{ii}$, and $R_i$ are unknowns, the best procedure is to use an iteration method considering the $\tau_{ii}$ or $K_{ii}$ values as convenient interacting variables. The solution will have one and only one system of $\tau$ values for a particular problem.

For the first approximation a reasonable assumption on the reaction distribution at the interface is made, assuming values $R_i = \bar{a}_i q_i$ for each tributary area. For this initial condition the vertical displacements are calculated by means of Eq. (31), and the values of $K_{ii} = R_i/\delta_i$ are determined—and thus the $\tau_{ii}$ values. These values are entered in Eq. (35) and solved for reactions $R_n$. With newly obtained reactions Eq. (31) is applied again, and improved vertical displacements are determined, and the new $K$ and $\tau$ values found are used as a second cycle in the reactions equation (35). Further cycles are performed until the $\tau$ values do not change significantly and final reactions may be considered sufficiently accurate to calculate shears and bending moments of the foundation structure [12].

Notice that the $K$ values may change some what on approaching the final condition due to the final stress level induced in the soil mass; changing to a certain extent the volume compressibilities of the strata. This condition may be investigated using equation (29). When the change is significant the $\alpha_N$ values should be corrected and used in the last iteration cycles.

Moreover, the analysis is valid only for a certain time for which the $\alpha_N$ values are representative of the compressibility phenomenon. The value for the concrete strain modulus $M_c$ is a time function and should be considered accordingly. A small change in the $\tau$ value, however, will not change the results significantly.

From the discussion presented in this chapter the foundation engineer may realize that in order to obtain more accurate results in designing foundation structures the role of soil mechanics in the calculation of the proper parameters is of a decisive nature. The precision depends on well-determined subsoil mechanical properties and stratigraphical conditions. Therefore, the importance of performing proper subsoil studies and improving laboratory techniques and equipment cannot be overemphasized.

The author, during his professional practice, has observed foundation designs that were unneccessarily costly, because of failure to cover properly the action of the foundation structure-soil interaction. On the other hand, poorly designed foundation structures show improper behavior mainly because the steel reinforcement has been wrongly placed to cover the shears and bending moments at the right place. The economy in foundation design resides in justifying the appropriate stiffness of the foundation structure compatible with the allowable differential and vertical displacements and placing the reinforcing steel in those places where it is more efficient.

## References

1. WINKLER, E., *Die Lehre von der Elästizitat und Festigkeit*, Prague Verlag 1867, p. 182.
2. HAYASHI, K., *Theorie des Trägers auf Elastisher Unterlage and Ihre Anwendung auf den Tiefban*, Springer, Berlin, 1921.
3. HETÉNYI, M., *Beams on Elastic Foundations*, The University of Michigan Press, Ann Arbor, 1937, 1964.
4. NEWMARK, N. M., "Numerical Procedures for Computing Deflections, Moments and Buckling Loads," *Trans. ASCE*, Vol. 108, 1943, pp. 1161–1254.

5. Newmark, N. M., *Numerical Methods of Analysis in Engineering*, Macmillan, New York, 1949, Chap. 9.
6. Salvadori, M. G., and M. L. Baron, *Numerical Methods in Engineering*, Prentice-Hall, Englewood Cliffs, N.J., 1952.
7. Vesic, A. S., "Bending of Beams Resting on Isotropic Elastic Solid," *J. Eng. Mech. Div. ASCE*, Vol. 87, 1961, pp. 35–53.
8. De Beer, E. H., Grasshoff, and M. Kany, *Die Berechnung Elastisher Gründungs balken auf nachgiebigen Untergrund*, West Deutscher Verlag Köln un. Opladen, 1966.
9. Chamecki, S., "Calcul des Tassements Progressifs des Foundations," *Travaux Publics No. 261*, Sept. 1969.
10. Heil, H., "Studies on the Structural Rigidity of Reinforced Concrete Building Frames on Clay," *VII (ICOSOMEF)*, Vol. II, México City, 1969, p. 115.
11. Desai C. S. and J. F. Abel, *Introduction to the Finite Element Method*, Van Nostrand Reinhold, New York 1972.
12. Zeevaert, L., *Foundation Engineering for Difficult Subsoil Conditions*, Van Nostrand Reinhold, New York, 1972, Chaps. II–IV and XI, Appendix E.
13. Kany, M., *Berechnung von Flächengrundungen*, W. Ernst und Sohn, Berlin, 1974.
14. Bowles, J. E., *Analytical and Computer Methods in Foundation Engineering*, McGraw-Hill, New York, 1974, Chaps. 5 and 6.
15. Zeevaert, L., "Interacción de la Estructura de Concreto con la Masa del Suelo," Instituto Mexicano del Cemento y Concreto (IMCYC), Vol. XIII, No. 73, March-April 1975.
16. Zeevaert, L., *Compensated Foundations—Heave and Subsequent Settlement*, Lehigh University, Bethlehem, Pa., Aug. 1975.
17. Zeevaert, L., *Earthquake Effects in Compensated Foundations*, Lehigh University, Bethlehem, Pa., Aug. 1975.
18. Zeevaert, L., *Foundation Problems in Earthquake Regions*, Lehigh University, Bethlehem, Pa., Aug. 1975.

# Earthquake Response Analysis of Concrete Dams

RAY W. CLOUGH AND ANIL K. CHOPRA*

## Introduction

The possible failure of a dam impounding a large body of water upstream of a densely populated area is one of the most critical physical hazards faced by society today. Moreover, seismic damages recently incurred by concrete dams, such as the Hsinfengkiang Dam near Canton, China in 1962 [1] and the Koyna Dam in India in 1967 [2], demonstrate that such failures could be initiated by an earthquake. Consequently, the need for reliable analytical procedures with which the seismic safety of dams may be assessed is apparent.

Traditionally, concrete gravity dams have been designed and analyzed by very simple procedures [3]. The basic assumption in such analyses is that each cross section of the dam is subjected only to a state of plane stress so that no forces are transferred from or to the adjacent sections. The analysis usually is concerned only with the overturning and sliding stability of the plane-stress slice, and seismic forces are treated as static horizontal forces which are combined with the water pressure and gravity loads in the stability analysis.

Arch dams obviously require a much more complicated type of analysis because their primary load-carrying mechanism is three-dimensional in character. The trial load method [4], which has been used extensively for the analysis of arch dams, assumes the structure to behave as an assemblage of arch rings and vertical cantilevers, and the applied load is resisted in part by each type of structural component. As in the case of a gravity dam analysis earthquake loads are treated as static horizontal forces equal to the product

*Professors, Department of Civil Engineering, University of California, Berkeley, California.

of the weights of the system and a seismic coefficient which represents the ground acceleration.

Clearly, these traditional earthquake response analysis procedures introduce gross oversimplifications of the true dynamic behavior. This actually is a complex problem in dynamic three-dimensional solid and fluid mechanics, involving the base excitation of a concrete dam-foundation-reservoir system. However, no more realistic analyses were possible until electronic digital computers became available to carry out the calculations, and concurrently the finite element method was developed [5,6] to make possible the mathematical representation of the complicated physical behavior.

During the past 20 years, the finite element method has become the standard procedure for analysis of all types of complex civil engineering structures. Early in its development it became apparent that this method was uniquely capable of evaluating stresses in dams, and many of its earliest civil engineering applications concerned special problems associated with such structures [7,8]. Pioneering computer programs for the solution of both plane stress and three-dimensional solid elasticity problems were developed under research contracts directed toward the study of dams, and the earliest dynamic finite element analyses of civil engineering structures involved the earthquake response analysis of earth dams [9].

The purpose of this chapter is to summarize the current state of knowledge about earthquake response analysis of concrete dams—both gravity and arch types. First, the standard finite element analysis procedure will be described briefly, and the limitations and deficiencies of the assumptions on which such analyses are based will be discussed. Next will be described recent and current research which is intended to overcome some of these limitations. Finally, the implications to the design profession of these new analytical capabilites will be examined, noting that new performance criteria must be introduced which are consistent with results obtained by the improved methods of analysis.

## Standard Analysis Procedure

The earthquake response analysis of concrete dams generally is carried out by the standard dynamic finite element method. The basic steps in such an analysis are as follows: (1) idealization of the dam and an appropriate segment of the foundation rock as an assemblage of finite elements; (2) evaluation of the stiffness, damping, and mass properties of the elements, as well as the effective earthquake force input, to formulate the equations of motion; (3) evaluation of the vibration mode shapes of the dam-foundation system, and transformation of the equations of motion from the finite element coordinates to these modal coordinates; and (4) calculation of the seismic reponse in each of the uncoupled modal coordinates, using either a response spectrum or a time-history description of the design earthquake, and then appropriately superposing the modal responses to obtain the total response. Each step in this analysis procedure has been described extensively in previous publications [10,11], so only those factors which pertain specifically to the seismic response of concrete dams will be discussed here.

### *Finite Element Idealization*

In the dynamic analysis of a dam, the finite element idealization includes the entire concrete dam plus a portion of the rock on which the dam is founded. A gravity dam usually is idealized as a plane-stress system, and only a unit slice taken normal to the axis is considered. A typical finite element model of a gravity dam and its foundation rock is shown in Fig. 1. Many different types of finite elements have been proposed for analysis of plane sections such as this, but in gravity dam analyses the linear isoparametric element with internal incompatible modes [12] has proven to be very efficient —it provides a good estimate of the stress distribution with a minimum number of degrees of freedom (DOF). The principal decision required in defining the idealization is the extent of the foundation rock to include in the model; typical dimensions to be expressed in terms of the height of the dam are shown in the figure.

An arch dam idealization must be more detailed than a gravity dam model because it must reproduce the three-dimensional structural behavior

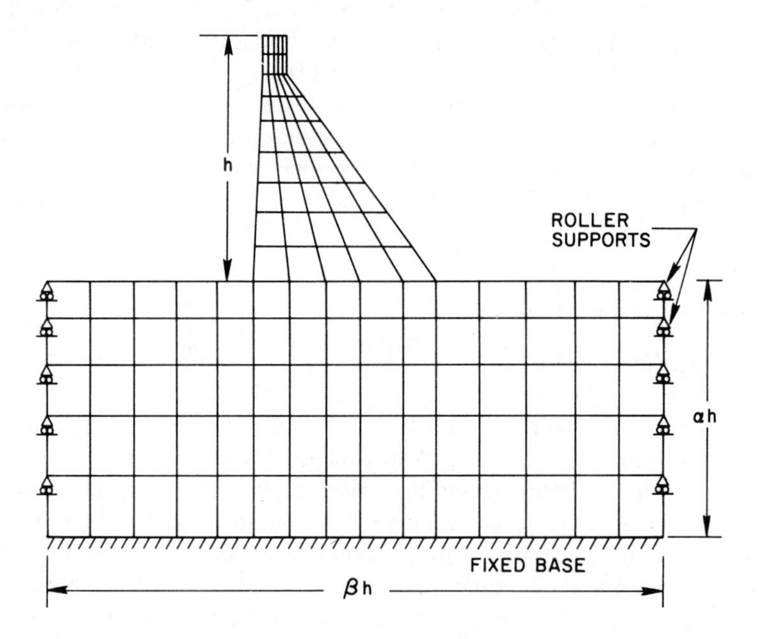


**Fig. 1.** Finite element model of gravity dam and foundation rock

of the dam and foundation rock. A finite element model of a dam in a prismatic canyon is shown in Fig. 2. The three-dimensional counterparts of the finite elements suggested for the plane-stress model (Fig. 1) could be used to model both the dam and the foundation rock; these are eight-node isoparametric bricks with internal incompatible modes [12]. However, for a thin shell dam such as is portrayed here, significantly better performance can be obtained for a given cost of computation by modeling the dam with more refined elements such as 20-node isoparametric bricks or "thick shell" elements derived from these [13]. Again a major decision is required in specifying the size and shape of the foundation block to include with the concrete dam. Typically the block is assumed to extend at least one dam height in all directions from the contact surface at the base of the dam.

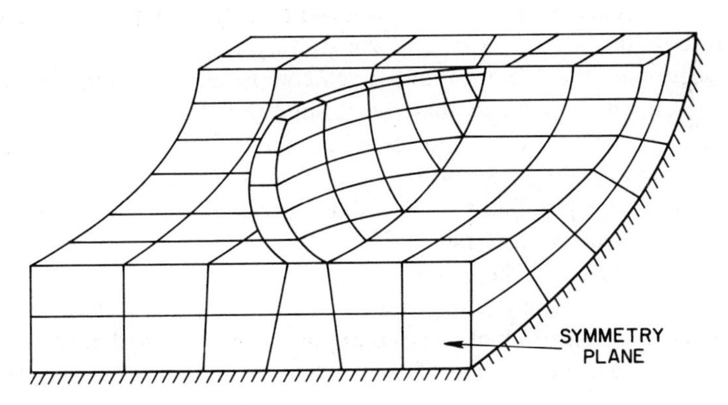


**Fig. 2.** Symmetric half of arch dam and foundation rock

### *Equations of Motion*

The finite element models shown in Figs. 1 and 2 are discretized idealizations of elastic continua in which the dynamic reponse is expressed in terms of displacements of the nodal points. In the plane-stress model there are two displacement components (degrees of freedom) per node, while in the three-dimensional system there are 3 DOF per node.

Representing the complete vector of all nodal displacements by $\mathbf{v}$, the equations of motion of the system may be expressed as

$$\mathbf{m}\ddot{\mathbf{v}} + \mathbf{c}\dot{\mathbf{v}} + \mathbf{k}\mathbf{v} = \mathbf{p}(t), \tag{1}$$

where $\mathbf{m}$, $\mathbf{c}$, and $\mathbf{k}$ are matrices defining the mass, damping, and stiffness properties and $\mathbf{p}(t)$ is the applied load vector. Standard procedures are available to evaluate the mass and stiffness properties of the finite element assemblage [10,11], which need not be described here; moreover, it is customary to express the damping properties in terms of damping ratios, as will be described later, so there is no need to evaluate the damping matrix. The only special problem which arises in evaluation of the property matrices of the dam system results from inertial effects of the water in the reservoir. As the dam responds to the earthquake motions, it causes corresponding motions of the water in contact with the dam face, and the resulting changes of water pressure acting on the dam influence its dynamic response.

In the case of gravity dams, this hydrodynamic effect generally is considered by assuming that the pressure changes at the face of the dam result from the action of a certain volume of water attached to the face. This "added mass" approach was originated by Westergaard [14], who suggested that the required volume of water might be idealized by a parabolic shape, as shown in Fig. 3. In the case of arch dams, the reservoir interaction effect is considerably more complex, but it usually is approximated by an extension of this added mass procedure. The required extension results from the fact that the Westergaard concept applies only when the seismic motion of the dam is normal to its surface. In the case of the arch dam, this condition may be met at one section on the dam face for a given component of earthquake motion; other sections it is assumed that the seismic pressure (i.e., added mass) is reduced in proportion to the cosine of the angle between the input motion and the normal to the face, and this added mass vector is then resolved into components corresponding to the nodal degrees of freedom. The complete mass matrix then includes the mass coefficients of the rock and concrete, plus the added mass of the water.

The effective seismic force input is derived assuming that, during the earthquake, the base to which the foundation rock is attached moves in simple translation as a rigid surface. The effective force vector is then given by

$$\mathbf{p}(t) = -\mathbf{m}\mathbf{r}\ddot{v}_g(t) \tag{2}$$

in which $\ddot{v}_g(t)$ is the acceleration time history of the input earthquake, and $\mathbf{r}$ is the vector of displacement influence coefficients indicating the static displacement of each DOF in $\mathbf{v}$ due to a static displacement of the base ($v_g = 1$). In Eq. (2), it is assumed that each component of the input earthquake is

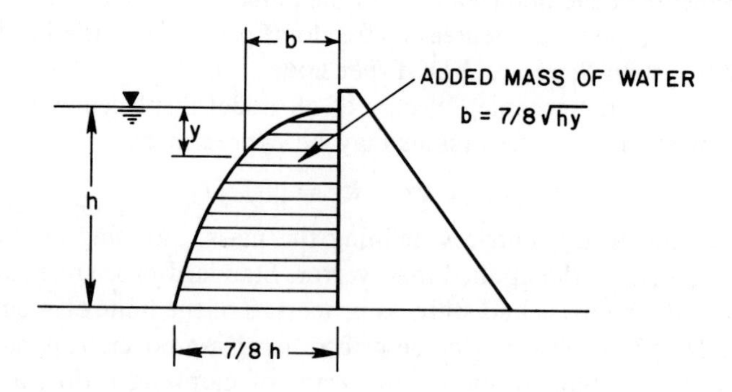


**Fig. 3.** Westergaard's added mass of reservoir water

considered separately; however, an input vector including all base motion components simultaneously could be used if **r** is expanded to include all corresponding influence coefficient vectors.

### *Transformation to Modal Coordinates*

The free vibration mode shapes and frequencies of the undamped finite element idealization are found by solving the eigenproblem

$$[\mathbf{k} - \omega_n^2 \mathbf{m}]\boldsymbol{\phi}_n = \mathbf{0} \tag{3}$$

in which **k** and **m** are the stiffness and mass matrices of Eq. (1) (where **m** includes the added mass of the reservoir water), and $\omega_n$ and $\phi_n$ represent the frequency and shape of mode $n$. Any standard eigenproblem solver can be for this purpose; for a refined idealization which may include many hundreds of degrees of freedom, the subspace iteration method [15] has proven to be most efficient.

In general, only a limited number of the lowest mode shapes are computed, and it is assumed that the dynamic response can be approximated adequately by these relatively few modal coordinates as follows:

$$\mathbf{v}(t) \doteq \boldsymbol{\Phi}\mathbf{Y}(t), \tag{4}$$

where $\boldsymbol{\Phi}$ is the listing of the significant mode shape vectors and **Y** is the generalized coordinate vector defining their respective amplitudes. Introducing the coordinate transformation of Eq. (4) into Eq. (1) results in a set of uncoupled modal response equations of the form

$$M_n\ddot{Y}_n + 2\omega_n\xi_n M_n\dot{Y}_n + \omega_n^2 M_n Y_n = P_n(t) \tag{5}$$

in which $M_n = \boldsymbol{\phi}_n^T\mathbf{m}\boldsymbol{\phi}_n$ (generalized mass of mode $n$),

$$P_n = \boldsymbol{\phi}_n^T\mathbf{p}(t) = -\boldsymbol{\phi}_n^T\mathbf{m}\mathbf{r}\ddot{v}_g(t) \qquad \text{(generalized force)},$$

and $\xi_n$ is the damping ratio assumed for mode $n$. In this formulation, it is assumed that the dam-foundation system (which includes the added mass of the water) is proportionally damped so that no damping coupling is developed between the modes. If nonproportional damping exists, the modal response equations will be coupled; the dynamic response may then be obtained by integrating simultaneously the coupled modal equations [16].

### *Dynamic Response Analysis*

Because of the chaotic nature of the design earthquake excitation, $\ddot{v}_g(t)$, the dynamic response history of the dam can be obtained only by numerical integration of the equations of motion. The step-by-step solution of the uncoupled equations [Eq. (5)] may be performed conveniently by the Newmark $\beta$ method [17], using either the constant average acceleration ($\beta = \frac{1}{4}$) or linear acceleration ($\beta = \frac{1}{6}$) procedure. In this regard it may be noted that an unconditionally stable method is not required because the integration interval is specified separately for each mode, and in each mode the step required for accuracy will ensure stability. The total displacement time-history response is then obtained by superposing the modal contributions as indicated by Eq. (4). In principle the displacement response represents the complete solution of the seismic reponse problem because any other response quantity (stresses or strains, resultant forces, etc.) can be determined from the displacements. In most practical cases it is convenient to extend the analysis to include evaluation of the stress distribution $\boldsymbol{\sigma}(t)$; this is obtained from the displacements by means of stress transformation matrix $\mathbf{T}$, as follows:

$$\boldsymbol{\sigma}(t) = \mathbf{T}\mathbf{v}(t). \tag{6}$$

Alternatively, a good approximation of the maximum seismic response can be obtained, without performing the tedious integration of the response equations, by making use of the response spectrum of the design earthquake. The maximum modal responses derived from the response spectrum are superposed by the root-sum-square method to obtain the total response.

## Free-Field Seismic Excitation

A possibly questionable assumption of the seismic analysis procedure described above is that the earthquake is represented as a rigid body translation of the basement rock on which the finite element model is supported. In this case the specified ground motion is introduced in the geological structure well below the gound surface, where very little is known about the earthquake characteristics. A preferable approach may be to define the earthquake in terms of free-field motions at the ground surface, where typical strong motion accelerograms are recorded.

To rewrite the equations of motion so that the effective seismic input is expressed in terms of these free-field motions, the free-field response to the basement rock excitation first is expressed as follows:

$$\tilde{\mathbf{m}}\ddot{\tilde{\mathbf{v}}} + \tilde{\mathbf{c}}\dot{\tilde{\mathbf{v}}} + \tilde{\mathbf{k}}\tilde{\mathbf{v}} = \mathbf{F}_r \tag{7}$$

in which tildes denote the system property matrices before the dam is constructed as well as the free-field displacements, and $\mathbf{F}_r$ represents the forces exerted by the basement rock on the finite element model (see Fig. 4). The corresponding equation after construction of the dam may be written

$$\bar{\mathbf{m}}\ddot{\bar{\mathbf{v}}} + \bar{\mathbf{c}}\dot{\bar{\mathbf{v}}} + \bar{\mathbf{k}}\bar{\mathbf{v}} = \mathbf{F}_r \tag{8}$$

in which overbars denote the property matrices after construction of the dam (i.e., $\bar{\mathbf{m}} = \mathbf{m} + \tilde{\mathbf{m}}$, where $\mathbf{m}$ is the mass of the added dam structure, etc.) as well as the motion of the combined system after construction, and $\mathbf{F}_r$ again is the input from the basement rock. Expressing the displacements as the sum

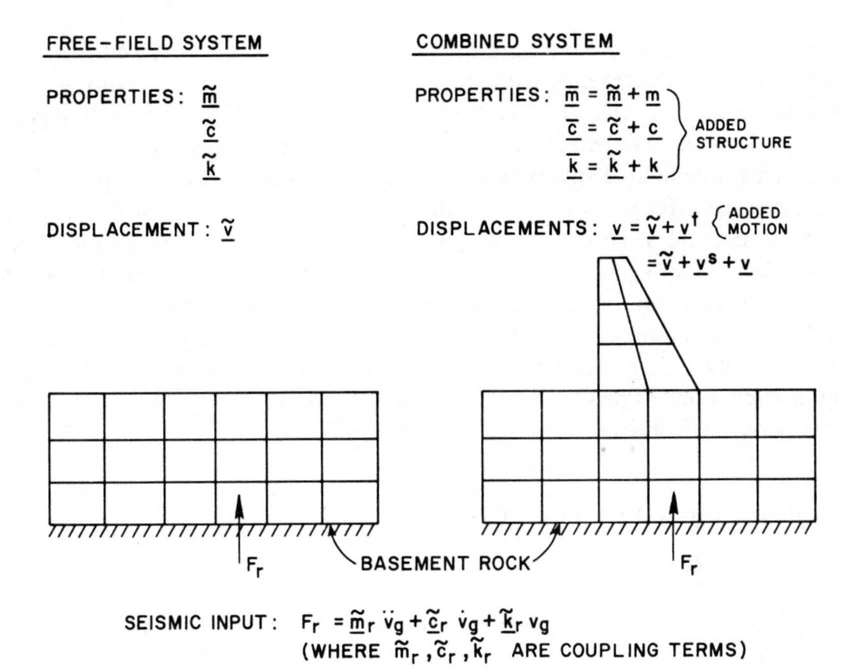


**Fig. 4.** Formulation of free-field seismic excitation

of the free field plus the added motion $\mathbf{v}^t$ (i.e., $\bar{\mathbf{v}} = \mathbf{v}^t + \tilde{\mathbf{v}}$) and substituting Eq. (7), one can reduce Eq. (8) to

$$\bar{\mathbf{m}}\ddot{\mathbf{v}}^t + \bar{\mathbf{c}}\dot{\mathbf{v}}^t + \bar{\mathbf{k}}\mathbf{v}^t = -\mathbf{m}\ddot{\tilde{\mathbf{v}}} - \mathbf{c}\dot{\tilde{\mathbf{v}}} - \mathbf{k}\tilde{\mathbf{v}}. \tag{9}$$

Finally expressing the added displacements as the sum of a dynamic term $\mathbf{v}$, plus a pseudostatic term $\mathbf{v}^s$ (i.e., $\mathbf{v}^t = \mathbf{v} + \mathbf{v}^s$), where the pseudostatic term is given by

$$\mathbf{v}^s = -\bar{\mathbf{k}}^{-1}\mathbf{k}\tilde{\mathbf{v}}, \tag{10}$$

the equations of motion become

$$\bar{\mathbf{m}}\ddot{\mathbf{v}} + \bar{\mathbf{c}}\dot{\mathbf{v}} + \bar{\mathbf{k}}\mathbf{v} = [\bar{\mathbf{m}}\bar{\mathbf{k}}^{-1}\mathbf{k} - \mathbf{m}]\ddot{\tilde{\mathbf{v}}}. \tag{11}$$

This is equivalent to Eq. (1), except that the seismic excitation is given in terms of the free-field accelerations rather than the basement rock accelerations as in Eq. (2). In Eq. (11), the overbars denote the property matrices of the complete dam plus foundation system, while the property matrices without overbars represent only the added structure. Moreover, the pseudostatic displacements of Eq. (10) must be added to the dynamic displacements of Eq. (11) to obtain the total response.

It is important to note that the only important degrees of freedom in the free-field vector $\tilde{\mathbf{v}}$ are those of nodes along the surface which connect with the dam structure, because the seismic input vector is derived from the added structure interacting with the free-field motion. In principle any desired spatial variation of these free-field components could be considered; however, there seldom is sufficient information to specify such a variation, and usually the same free-field displacement is assumed for each contact point. This assumed behavior is reasonable for the contact surface at the base of a gravity dam; hence, the seismic analysis of such structures may be carried out effectively by the free-field approach. On the other hand, the free-field motions cannot be assumed uniform all along the canyon wall contact surface of an arch dam, and no reasonable variation can be hypothesized for this situation. Accordingly, it is preferable to prescribe the seismic input for an arch dam as a rigid body translation of the basement rock even though the actual characteristics of such motions are not well known.

## Hydrodynamic Interaction

### *Gravity Dams*

The above-mentioned Westergaard added mass approach to accounting for hydrodynamic effects of the reservoir is based on two assumptions that are not satisfied in actuality: that the dam is rigid and the water incompressible. Accordingly, even though this concept has long been used in practical dam design throughout the world, the range of conditions for which it is vaild was not well understood, and during recent years extensive research has been devoted to this question. A series of investigations taking into account the water compressibility while retaining the assumption that the dam is rigid [14,18–22] has led to the following conclusions: Neglect of compressibility of water leads to significant errors [19]; hydrodynamic effects during typical strong earthquake motions are appreciable [19]; hydrodynamic effects due to the vertical component of ground motion are comparable to those due to horizontal ground motion for reservoirs of moderate to large depth but much larger for small depths [19]; recognition of deformability of the reservoir bottom leads to reductions in the pressures due to vertical ground motion, which are especially significant for small reservoir depths [22]; hydrodynamic pressures due to the vertical component are strongly influenced by the direction of approach and the velocity of propagation of the earthquake [21].

Although these investigations assumed the dam to be rigid in analyzing the hydrodynamic pressures due to earthquake ground motion, in actuality the earthquake ground motion as well as the hydrodynamic pressures on the upstream face of the dam will cause the dam to deform, which in turn will affect the hydrodynamic pressures. Considering only the fundamental mode of vibration of the dam, analysis of responses to horizontal ground motion including this interaction between the dam and the water in the reservoir [23] revealed that the resonant period as well as earthquake response is significantly influenced by hydrodynamic interaction and compressibility of water [24,25].

A similar investigation [26] of responses to the vertical component of ground motion indicated that flexibility of the dam has a profound effect on the hydrodynamic pressures. It was also shown in this work that, due to the significant hydrodynamic forces generated in the horizontal direction on a vertical upstream face, the contributions of the vertical component of ground motion are of special importance in the response of concrete gravity dams to earthquakes.

The analysis mentioned above [25,26] was later generalized to include any number of modes of vibration of the dam, thus making it possible to obtain results to any desired degree of accuracy [27]. The problem was treated in two dimensions, considering the planar vibration of a linearly elastic monolith of the dam. This simplification appears to be reasonable for practical situations where the length of the dam is many times the cross-sectional dimensions of the monoliths or where the monoliths tend to vibrate independently [2,28].

The fundamental idea behind this method of analysis is to treat the dam and the water in the reservoir as two substructures. With this concept the dam may be idealized by the finite element method, thus taking advantage of its ability to handle systems of arbitrary geometry. At the same time, the reservoir may be treated as a continuum, an approach which is ideally suited to the simplified boundary conditions and great extent of the impounded water and which is computationally more efficient than a finite element idealization [29]. A brief description of the method [27] is presented in the following paragraphs.

A gravity dam of height $H_s$ storing water to depth $H$ is shown in Fig. 5. The equation of motion for a finite element idealization of the dam on rigid base including hydrodynamic effects is

$$\mathbf{m}_d\ddot{\mathbf{v}}_d + \mathbf{c}_d\dot{\mathbf{v}}_d + \mathbf{k}_d\mathbf{v}_d = -\mathbf{m}_d\mathbf{r}\ddot{\mathbf{v}}_g(t) + \mathbf{R}(t), \tag{12}$$

where the subscript $d$ is used to identify the system on a rigid base. $\mathbf{R}(t)$ is the vector of forces at the nodal points of the finite element system associated with the time-varying hydrodynamic pressures; in this formulation no added mass is included in $\mathbf{m}_d$. Because these pressures act only on the upstream face, assumed to be vertical, only the elements of $\mathbf{R}(t)$ corresponding to horizontal displacements of the nodal points on the upstream face are nonzero.

Although classical normal modes do not exist for the dam when hydrodynamic interaction effects are included, expression of its displacements in terms of its modes of vibration with empty reservoir can still be used to advantage. Thus, the truncated modal expansion of Eq. (4) may be used to express

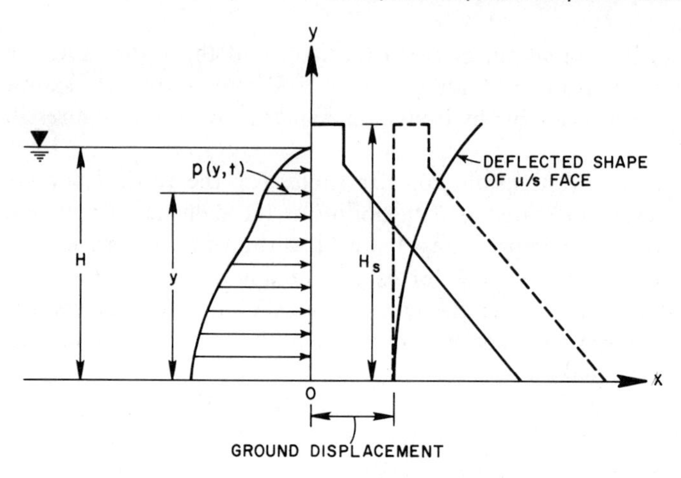


**Fig. 5.** Dam-water system subjected to horizontal ground motion

the displacements of the dam, noting that in this case the mode shapes are those of the system with empty reservoir.

Analysis of the response of structures interacting with fluids by the substructure approach is best carried out in the frequency domain; hence, the responses to harmonic ground acceleration $\ddot{v}_g^x(t) = e^{i\omega t}$ are determined first. The displacement response in the modal coordinates is then of the form $Y_n(t) = \bar{Y}_n(\omega)e^{i\omega t}$, where $\bar{Y}_n(\omega)$ represents the complex frequency response (or transfer) functions. It can be shown that the governing equation is

$$\mathbf{S}(\omega)\bar{\mathbf{Y}}(\omega) = \mathbf{L}(\omega) \tag{13}$$

in which

$$\begin{aligned} S_{nk}(\omega) &= \omega^2 \boldsymbol{\phi}_n^T \bar{\mathbf{R}}_k(\omega), \qquad n \neq k, \\ S_{nn}(\omega) &= \boldsymbol{\phi}_n^T \mathbf{m}_d \boldsymbol{\phi}_n [-\omega^2 + 2i\xi_n \omega\omega_n + \omega_n^2] + \omega^2 \boldsymbol{\phi}_n^T \bar{\mathbf{R}}_n, \\ L_n(\omega) &= -\boldsymbol{\phi}_n^T \mathbf{m}_d \mathbf{l}^x + \boldsymbol{\phi}_n^T \bar{\mathbf{R}}_0(\omega), \end{aligned} \tag{14}$$

where $\omega_n$, $\phi_n$, and $\xi_n$ are the frequency, shape, and damping, respectively, of the $n$th mode of vibration of the dam. The frequency-dependent coefficient matrix $\mathbf{S}(\omega)$ relates the generalized displacement vector $\mathbf{Y}(\omega)$ to the corresponding generalized loads $\mathbf{L}(\omega)$. Unlike the classical mode-superposition analysis outlined earlier, the matrix $\mathbf{S}(\omega)$ is not diagonal because the $\phi_n$ are not the normal modes of the dam-water system.

The nodal force vectors $\mathbf{R}_0(t) = \bar{\mathbf{R}}_0(\omega)e^{i\omega t}$ and $\mathbf{R}_k(t) = \bar{\mathbf{R}}_k(\omega)e^{i\omega t}$ are the static equivalents of the hydrodynamic pressures $p_0(y, t)$ and $p_k(y, t)$ on the upstream face of the dam. Under reasonable assumptions, the small-amplitude irrotational motion of water in the reservoir is governed by the two-dimensional wave equation

$$\frac{\partial^2 p}{\partial x^2} + \frac{\partial^2 p}{\partial y^2} = \frac{1}{C^2}\frac{\partial^2 p}{\partial t^2} \tag{15}$$

in which $p(x, y, t)$ is the hydrodynamic pressure (excluding the hydrostatic pressure) and $C$ is the velocity of sound of water. $p_0(y, t) = \bar{p}_0(y, \omega)e^{i\omega t}$ is the solution at $x = 0$ of the wave equation for the following boundary conditions:

$$\begin{aligned} \frac{\partial p}{\partial y}(x, 0, t) &= 0, \\ p(x, H, t) &= 0, \\ \frac{\partial p}{\partial x}(0, y, t) &= -\frac{w}{g}e^{i\omega t}, \end{aligned} \tag{16}$$

and $p_k(y, t) = \bar{p}_k(y, \omega)e^{i\omega t}$ is the solution at $x = 0$ of the equation for the following boundary conditions:

$$\begin{aligned} \frac{\partial p}{\partial y}(x, 0, t) &= 0, \\ p(x, H, t) &= 0, \\ \frac{\partial p}{\partial x}(0, y, t) &= -\frac{w}{g}f_k(y)e^{i\omega t}, \end{aligned} \tag{17}$$

where $f_k(y)$ is the continuous analogue of the subvector of $\boldsymbol{\phi}_k$ consisting of the $x$ components of displacements of the nodal points on the upstream face of the dam. In Eq. (16) and (17), $w$ is the unit weight of water and $g$ is the acceleration due to gravity. Solutions of the wave equation for the above two sets of boundary conditions, for a reservoir extending to infinity in the upstream direction, are

$$\bar{p}_0(y, \omega) = \frac{4w}{\pi g}\sum_{n=1}^{\infty}\frac{(-1)^n}{(2n-1)\sqrt{\lambda_n^2 - \omega^2/C^2}}\cos\lambda_n y, \tag{18}$$

$$\bar{p}_k(y, \omega) = -\frac{2w}{gH}\sum_{n=1}^{\infty}\frac{I_{kn}}{\sqrt{\lambda_n^2 - \omega^2/C^2}}\cos\lambda_n y \tag{19}$$

in which

$$\lambda_n = (2n-1)\frac{\pi}{2H} \tag{20}$$

and

$$I_{kn} = \int_0^H f_k(y)\cos\lambda_n y\, dy. \tag{21}$$

Once the complex frequency responses $Y_m(\omega)$, $m = 1, 2, \ldots, M$, have been obtained by solving Eq. (13) for a range of values of $\omega$, the responses to arbitrary horizontal ground acceleration $\ddot{v}_g^x(t)$ can be obtained by Fourier synthesis of the responses to individual harmonic components:

$$Y_m(t) = \frac{1}{2\pi}\int_{-\infty}^{\infty}\bar{Y}_m(\omega)A_g^x(\omega)e^{i\omega t}\, d\omega \tag{22}$$

in which $A_g^x(\omega)$ is the Fourier transform of $\ddot{v}_g^x(t)$; i.e.,

$$A_g^x(\omega) = \int_0^d \ddot{v}_g^x(t) e^{-i\omega t}\, dt, \tag{23}$$

where $d$ is the duration of the ground motion. The Fourier integrals can be computed efficiently by the fast Fourier transform algorithm [39]. The nodal point displacements $\mathbf{v}(t)$ are then obtained by the transformation of Eq. (4).

Analysis of response to the vertical component of ground motion involves a parallel sequence of steps [27].

Based on the analytical procedure described, the computer program EADHI [30] has been developed to numerically evaluate the response of gravity dam monoliths, including hydrodynamic interaction effects, to horizontal and vertical components of earthquake ground motion. The output from the program includes the complete time variation of displacements and stresses throughout the dam.

A comprehensive study of the effects of hydrodynamic interaction on earthquake response of concrete gravity dams has been completed [24]. To demonstrate the importance of hydrodynamic effects and the vertical component of ground motion, selected results of this study are presented here. The distribution of critical stresses at selected instants of time, due to the N69W component of the Taft ground motion applied transverse to the axis of the dam, as obtained from two analyses are presented in Fig. 6 and 7. These stresses include the initial stresses due to the weight of the dam and hydrostatic pressures. The hydrodynamic pressures were included in one analysis

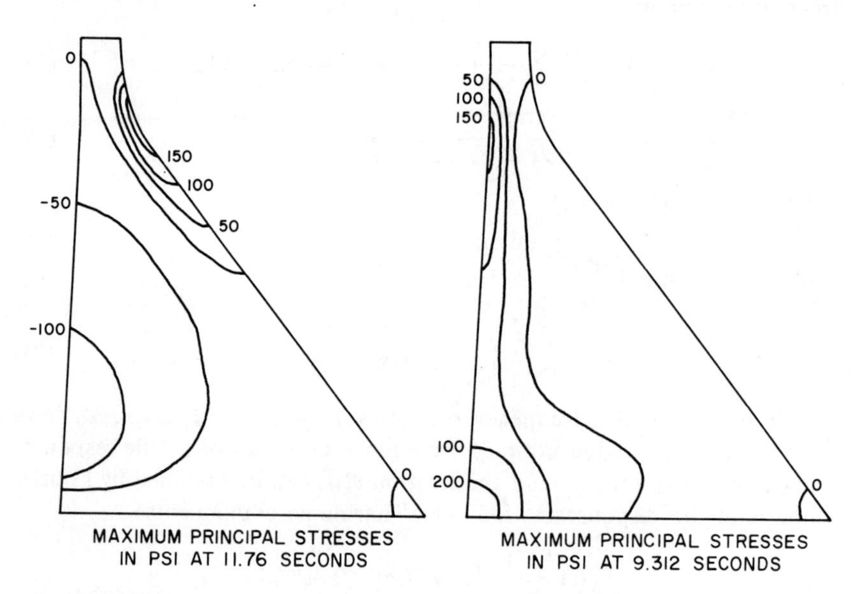


**Fig. 6.** Critical stresses in pine flat dam neglecting hydrodynamic effects due to N69W component of Taft earthquake

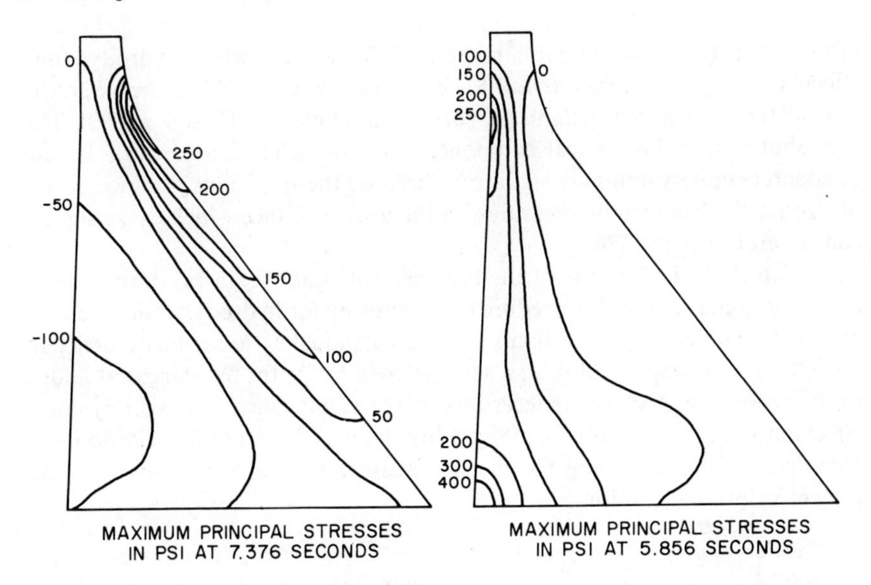


**Fig. 7.** Critical stresses in pine flat dam including hydrodynamic effect due to N69W component of Taft earthquake

and neglected in the other. An examination of these results shows that the critical tensile stresses are approximately 50% larger when hydrodynamic effects are included. When the vertical component of the Taft motion is included, the critical stresses are as shown in Figs. 7 and 8. Vertical ground

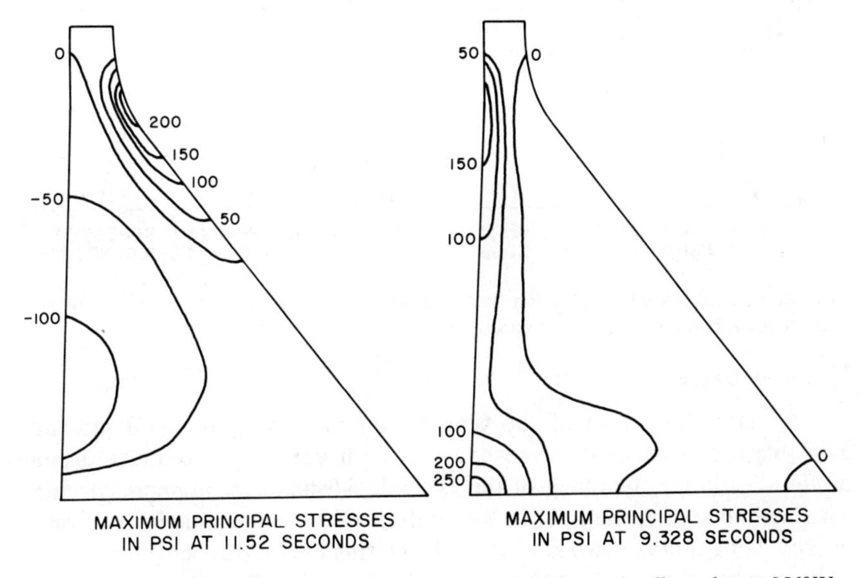


**Fig. 8.** Critical stresses in pine flat dam neglecting hydrodynamic effects due to N69W and vertical components of Taft earthquake

motion has little influence on response of the dam when hydrodynamic effects are neglected (Figs. 6 and 8), but it causes a 40–70% increase in the critical tensile stresses including hydrodynamic effects (Figs. 7 and 9). The contributions of the vertical component of ground motion to the response of concrete gravity dams are significant because these motions produce nearly horizontal hydrodynamic pressures on the upstream face which cause significant lateral response [26].

With the aid of results of the type presented above, it has been demonstrated that the standard procedure of accounting for hydrodynamic reservoir effects on concrete gravity dams during earthquakes is seriously deficient [31]. By use of the typical design seismic coefficient, the Westergaard added mass procedure grossly underestimates the significance of hydrodynamic effects in the response of concrete gravity dams to horizontal excitation and completely fails to account for the significant response to the vertical component of ground motion.

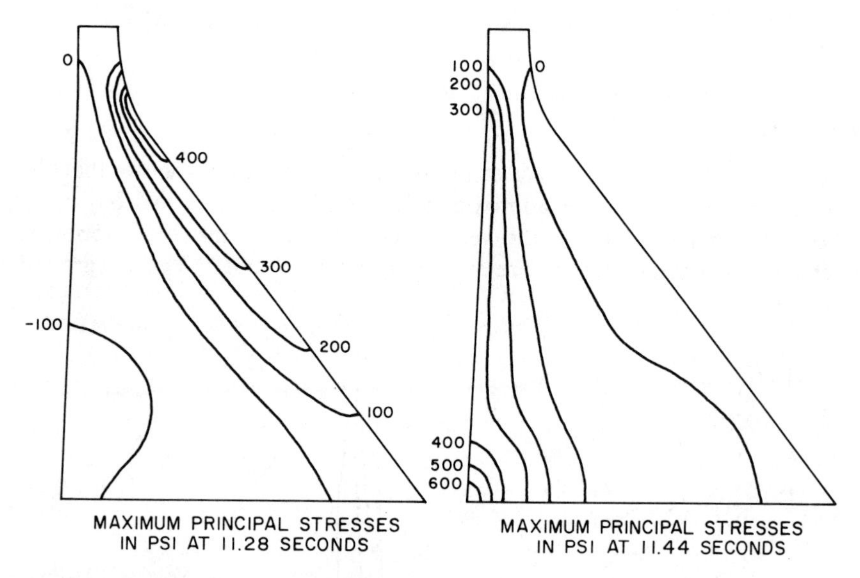


**Fig. 9.** Critical stresses in pine flat dam including hydrodynamic effects due to N69W and vertical components of Taft earthquake

### *Arch Dams*

A major limitation of the general computer programs [13] presently available for analysis of the response of arch dams to earthquake ground motion lies in the treatment of the dynamic effects of the impounded water. The method summarized above for analysis of hydrodynamic interaction of gravity dams contains two key ideas: (1) treating the total system as composed of two substructures, in which the hydrodynamic effects are expressed as frequency-dependent modifications to the equations governing motion of the dam, and (2) transforming these equations in terms of the first few modes of vibration of the dam, thus enabling a drastic reduction in number of unknowns and leading to highly efficient solutions. The modifications to the structural equations due to hydrodynamic interaction are determined as solutions of the wave equation for the fluid domain subjected to appropriate motions of the boundaries. Two-dimensional solutions for the wave equation were obtained for analysis of monoliths of gravity dams. Explicit mathematical solutions were possible under the assumptions that the upstream face is vertical and the reservoir extends to infinity in the upstream direction.

The same two ideas can be employed with similar benefit in analysis of arch dams. The equations of motion for the dam can be formulated by the finite element procedures mentioned earlier; appropriate solutions of the wave equation would be necessary to determine the modifications to the finite element equations due to hydrodynamic interaction. Beyond this point the solution procedure would proceed as in the case of gravity dams, transforming the equations in the frequency domain to modal coordinates and utilizing Fourier transform methods.

The earliest analysis [23, 25] of the response of gravity dams including hydrodynamic interaction was a special case of the general procedure above which considered only the fundamental mode of vibration of the dam. Following identical steps, the corresponding one-mode analysis for arch dams was developed recently [32]. In this analysis, explicit mathematical solutions were obtained for an idealized fluid domain with the dam represented as a segment of a cylinder—thus having a constant radius of the upstream face—and bounded by vertical radial walls of the river valley enclosing a central angle of 90°. Results of this analysis indicated that compressibility of water is important in earthquake response of arch dams and that the response of a dam with full reservoir is much larger—by a factor of 2 to 5—than the response with no water.

Using the above-mentioned hydrodynamic solutions for the idealized fluid domain, a general analysis procedure for arch dams, including as many modes of vibration as necessary, could be developed along the lines of the procedure for gravity dams. However, the accuracy of the results would be open to question because the upstream face of arch dams is far from a segment of a constant radius cyclinder; typically it is a surface of double curvature with variable radius. Also, the walls of the river valley are far from vertical, extending radially with a central angle of 90° in the upstream direction; typically the site is a narrow U- or V-shaped valley. In developing a general analysis procedure and computer program it is necessary to recognize these complications in the geometry, or at least the errors involved in results obtained with the idealized geometry should be evaluated. If the errors can be demonstrated to be insignificant, then the simpler and computationally less demanding mathematical solutions for the hydrodynamic problem with idealized geometry can be employed.

For this purpose, it is necessary to develop the ability to determine the hydrodynamic terms in the structural equations for arbitrary geometry of the impounded water. Departure from the simplified reservoir shape mentioned earlier probably will preclude explicit mathematical solutions of the wave equation, and it will be necessary to employ a finite element type of discretization procedure. Impounded water typically extends to large (equivalent to infinite for purposes of analysis) distances in the upstream direction, whereas the finite element idealization for the fluid domain can extend only to a finite distance. Thus, there is need for a "quiet" boundary of special boundary finite elements which can simulate the conditions of infinite reservoir extent in the upstream direction. Comparison of finite element solutions with explicit mathematical solutions for the idealized geometry should be used as the basis for evaluating the effectiveness of any proposed boundary and for establishing appropriate finite element meshes. Obviously a great deal of research remains to be done on the arch dam-water interaction problem; only the first steps in this direction have been taken to date, but the prospects for success appear good.

## Foundation Interaction

### *Gravity Dams*

The standard approach to accounting for dam-foundation interaction is to directly analyze a finite element idealization of the combined dam-foundation, as was described earlier. In performing a mode superposition analysis of the combined system, it should be noted that a relatively large number of modes generally will have to be considered to obtain adequate definition of the response of the dam because many of the lower modes of vibration may be associated mainly with the foundation elements. Thus, the finite element modeling of the foundation leads to enormous computational requirements, both in the number of degrees of freedom included in the mathematical model and also in the number of modes retained in the transformed equations. An additional drawback of this approach to accounting for foundation interaction is that the boundary hypothesized at some depth in the foundation is usually assumed to be rigid. For sites where materials of similar stiffness extend to large depths and there is no obvious "rigid" boundary such as a soil-rock interface, the location of the rigid boundary introduced in the analysis is often quite arbitrary, and it may introduce significant spurious reflection effects.

The substructure method [33] can be used to overcome this difficulty by permitting representation of the foundation rock as an elastic half-space.

In addition, it provides an alternative formulation of a response analysis making use of a free-field definition of the seismic excitation rather than a basement rock input. In this method, the equations of motion for a monolith idealized as a two-dimensional finite element system including foundation interaction effects but ignoring hydrodynamic interaction are

$$\mathbf{m}_c\ddot{\mathbf{v}}_c + \mathbf{c}_c\dot{\mathbf{v}}_c + \mathbf{k}_c\mathbf{v}_c = -\mathbf{m}_c\mathbf{r}\ddot{v}_g^x(t) + \mathbf{R}_f(t). \tag{24}$$

In Eq. (24), $\mathbf{v}_c$ is the vector of displacements of nodal points, including those at the base of the dam (or dam-foundation interface), relative to the prescribed free-field ground displacements; $\mathbf{m}_c$, $\mathbf{c}_c$, and $\mathbf{k}_c$ are expanded versions of the corresponding matrices in Eq. (12), where the base degrees of freedom had been eliminated because the foundation was taken to be rigid; the $\mathbf{R}_f(t)$ are the interaction forces, which will have nonzero values only at the dam-foundation interface. In Eq. (24), the free-field motion $\ddot{v}_g^x(t)$ is assumed to be identical at all nodal points at the base of the structure; spatially varying ground motion can be treated by procedures discussed elsewhere [34]. Introducing $\ddot{v}_g^x(t) = e^{i\omega t}$, we find that Eq. (24) in terms of complex frequency response function is

$$[-\omega^2\mathbf{m}_c + i\omega\mathbf{c}_c + \mathbf{k}_c]\bar{\mathbf{v}}_c(\omega) = -\mathbf{m}_c\mathbf{r} + \bar{\mathbf{R}}_f(\omega). \tag{25}$$

Partitioning $\mathbf{v}_c$ into $\mathbf{v}$ and $\mathbf{v}_b$ (the displacement vectors for nodal points above and on the dam-foundation interface), writing the interaction forces in corresponding partitioned form $\bar{\mathbf{R}}_f^T = \langle \mathbf{o}\bar{\mathbf{R}}_b^T \rangle$, and relating $\bar{\mathbf{R}}_b$ to $\bar{\mathbf{v}}_b$ as follows:

$$\bar{\mathbf{R}}_b(\omega) = \mathbf{S}_f(\omega)\bar{\mathbf{v}}_b(\omega) \tag{26}$$

[where $\mathbf{S}_f(\omega)$ may be interpreted as a frequency-dependent, complex-valued stiffness matrix for the foundation], we find that Eq. (25) becomes

$$\left(-\omega^2\begin{bmatrix}\mathbf{m} & \mathbf{0}\\ \mathbf{0} & \mathbf{m}_b\end{bmatrix} + i\omega\begin{bmatrix}\mathbf{c} & \mathbf{c}_b\\ \mathbf{c}_b^T & \mathbf{c}_{bb}\end{bmatrix} + \begin{bmatrix}\mathbf{k} & \mathbf{k}_b\\ \mathbf{k}_b^T & \mathbf{k}_{bb} + \mathbf{S}_f(\omega)\end{bmatrix}\right)\begin{Bmatrix}\bar{\mathbf{v}}(\omega)\\ \bar{\mathbf{v}}_b(\omega)\end{Bmatrix} = -\mathbf{m}_c\mathbf{r}, \tag{27}$$

or, more compactly,

$$[-\omega^2\mathbf{m}_c + i\omega\mathbf{c}_c + \mathbf{k}_c + \tilde{\mathbf{S}}_f(\omega)]\bar{\mathbf{v}}_c(\omega) = -\mathbf{m}_c\mathbf{r},$$

where

$$\tilde{\mathbf{S}}_f(\omega) = \begin{bmatrix}\mathbf{0} & \mathbf{0}\\ 0 & \mathbf{S}_f(\omega)\end{bmatrix}.$$

Equation (27) represents a set of linear, simultaneous, algebraic equations with complex-valued coefficients in the unknowns $\bar{\mathbf{v}}_c(\omega)$. $\mathbf{S}_f(\omega)$ is a square matrix of order equal to the number of connection degrees of freedom on the dam-foundation interface. The *m-n* term of this matrix represents the harmonic forces required in degree of freedom *m* if a displacement $e^{i\omega t}$ is imposed in degree of freedom *n*, while all other connection degrees of freedom are kept fixed (Fig. 10). Not all degrees of freedom on the foundation surface

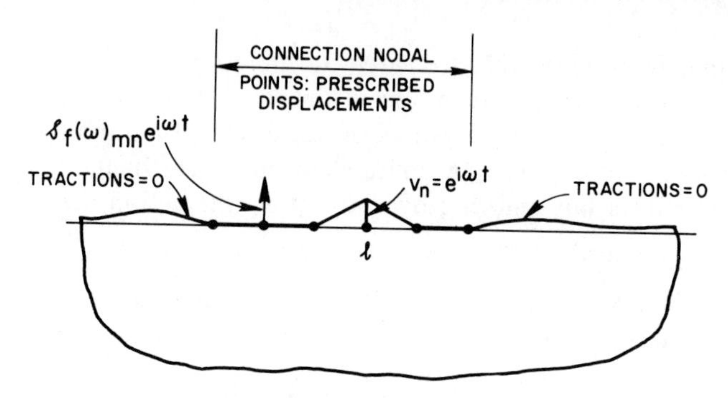


**Fig. 10.** Physical interpretation of $\mathbf{S}_f(\omega)$

are kept fixed, but only those which are associated with nodal points connecting the structure to the foundation, resulting in a mixed boundary value problem where displacements are prescribed over the part corresponding to the dam base and tractions over the remainder of the surface. $\mathbf{S}_f(\omega)$ may be determined by solving for each $\omega$ a mixed boundary value problem associated with each degree of freedom. In determining $\mathbf{S}_f(\omega)$ for a viscoelastic half-plane it was found convenient to first solve the corresponding displacement boundary value problems with displacements also prescribed as zero outside the structure-foundation interface, then to assemble an expanded version of the frequency-dependent foundation stiffness matrix including nodal points outside the interface, and finally to introduce the condition of zero forces and eliminate the outside degrees of freedom [35]. In determining $\mathbf{S}_f(\omega)$ for foundations idealized as finite element systems it was found convenient to analyze stress boundary value problems where loads instead of displacements were prescribed as $e^{i\omega t}$, thus determining $\mathbf{S}_f^{-1}(\omega)$, which is then inverted. For foundations with properties homogeneous in the horizontal direction, the boundary value problems need be solved for prescribed unit displacements or forces at only one nodal point; solutions for the problems associated with other nodal points are given by simple translation of coordinate axes [33,35].

After $\mathbf{S}_f(\omega)$ is determined, a straightforward way to obtain the structural response is to solve Eq. (27) for the complex frequency responses, multiply them by the Fourier transform of the ground acceleration function, and then evaluate the inverse Fourier transform to obtain the nodal point displacements as a function of time. The computational effort required by this approach, however, is prohibitive; instead it is essential to judiciously reduce the number of equations and unknowns in Eq. (27).

Transformation to modal coordinates is the most effective means for reducing the degrees of freedom in the linear analysis of dams with the foundation assumed as rigid. When foundation interaction is considered, the frequency-dependent matrix $\mathbf{S}_f(\omega)$ enters into the structural equations, and the structure does not possess modes of vibration in the classical sense. The number of unknowns and equations can, however, be reduced by introducing into Eq. (27) the transformation

$$\bar{\mathbf{v}}_c(\omega) \simeq \sum_{n=1}^{I} Z_n(\omega)\boldsymbol{\psi}_n, \tag{28}$$

where the $Z_n$ are generalized coordinates and the $\boldsymbol{\psi}_n$ are solutions to the eigenvalue problem

$$[\mathbf{k}_c + \tilde{\mathbf{S}}_f(0)]\boldsymbol{\psi}_n = \lambda_n^2 \mathbf{m}_c \boldsymbol{\psi}_n. \tag{29}$$

While very effective in drastically reducing the number of unknowns and equations, this transformation has the disadvantage that the $\boldsymbol{\psi}_n$ have little physical meaning and depend on the foundation properties.

An approach which is more meaningful—conceptually as well as physically—is to express an appropriate part of the structural displacements in terms of the modes of vibration of the structure on rigid foundation. This has been demonstrated to be effective for a one-dimensional structural system on a rigid footing attached to an elastic half-space [36]. Research in progress has extended this technique to complex structures on a deformable base.

The substructure method along with the use of generalized coordinates outlined above is an approach with considerable promise for earthquake analysis of gravity dams including foundation interaction. Considerable research is needed to efficiently determine $\mathbf{S}_f(\omega)$ for various models for the foundation. Further work related to finite element models is in progress. It would be desirable to relax the assumption of material homogeneity in the viscoelastic half-plane and develop techniques for determining $\mathbf{S}_f(\omega)$ for layered half-plane models.

With the use of the substructure method, a systematic series of analyses should be carried out to evaluate the significance of effects of foundation interaction on the dynamic behavior and earthquake response of gravity dams; also the influence of the choice of foundation model—half-plane of finite element—on dam response should be studied.

### *Arch Dams*

The basic concept of the substructure method is applicable also to arch dams, but considerable research in evaluation of the foundation matrix $\mathbf{S}_f(\omega)$ is needed before the method can be implemented. Furthermore, as noted earlier, it is not presently possible to define the free-field motions at the canyon wall contact surface for an arch dam. Clearly, it is not reasonable to assume that the entire free-field surface would move in rigid body translation, but no measurements have been obtained of actual ground motion variations in arch dam locations. To refine the foundation interaction analysis of arch dams, it will be necessary to deploy arrays of strong motion accelerographs at typical arch dam sites in regions of high seismicity. With suitable records from such arrays, supplemented by analytical research concerning the effects of canyon topography on free-field surface motions, it will be possible to make more realistic evaluations of this type of interaction. Meanwhile, the only feasible treatment of the problem is the combined dam-foundation block analysis described earlier, assuming that the seismic input is a rigid body translation of the basement rock boundary of the finite element mesh, although it may be noted that this assumption is also unreasonable for the same reason mentioned earlier.

## Hydrodynamic and Foundation Interaction

The preceding discussion was concerned separately with the dam-water system and the dam-foundation system. In each of these two cases, the impounded water and the foundation, respectively, modify the dynamic properties of the dam and may significantly affect the response. However, the two problems actually are coupled, and the results obtained by separate analyses in general will be invalid. There is need, therefore, for developing techniques for analysis of complete dam-water-foundation system, studying the dynamic response, and assessing the significance of effects of hydrodynamic interaction and of foundation interaction considered simultaneously.

This general problem has been examined in a recent paper [37], but the work is only exploratory. The substructure methods developed for dynamic analysis of the dam-water system and the dam-foundation system are ideally suited for and extendable to analysis of the complete system. Such an extension for gravity dams is nearing completion, but a similar type of combined interaction analysis for arch dams clearly is not possible in the immediate future.

## Application to Engineering Practice

Analytical procedures for predicting the earthquake response of concrete dams are important not only for the obvious function of designing new structures to be built in seismic regions; more important at the present time is evaluation of the safety of the hundreds of such structures already standing in areas of frequent earthquake activity. Most of these dams were designed using oversimplified concepts with respect both to the mathematical model of the structure and to the dynamic response mechanisms, and current analysis capabilities make possible a much more reliable estimate of their expected earthquake behavior.

The three basic steps in an analytical assessment of the seismic safety of either an existing or a proposed dam are as follows:

1. Estimation of the maximum expected earthquake excitation.
2. Analysis of the response to this dynamic input.

3. Comparisons of predicted response with the strength and deformation capacity of the structure.

The selection of the design earthquake may well be the most important part of the total process, but that step is beyond the scope of this chapter. The principal concern here has been with the methods now available for analysis of the dynamic structural response to any specified earthquake input, and it will be convenient to summarize the status of these methods in present practice.

Dynamic response analysis of a gravity dam section, including a segment of the foundation rock for interaction purposes and representing hydrodynamic effects by the added mass approach, may be considered the current state-of-the-art in engineering design offices. The corresponding three-dimensional analysis of an arch dam system also is a current capability but is less likely to be employed. Techniques that are presently available to treat the water-dam or foundation-dam interaction problem for gravity dams have been described in this chapter, but these are only now being put into practical use. Further research is needed to develop corresponding improvements for arch dam analysis and also to treat the combined foundation-water-dam interaction of gravity dams; however, the direction that these research efforts should follow has been indicated.

An important limitation of all these analytical methods is that they assume the structure to be linearly elastic. In general it seems reasonable to require a concrete dam to resist the maximum expected earthquake without exceeding the strength of the materials, and for such designs a linear analysis generally would be appropriate. However, this requirement may not ensure that the system will behave linearly; for example, opening of the joints between monoliths of an arch dam would introduce a nonlinear mechanism. Moreover, in the safety evaluation of an existing dam, stresses may be indicated which exceed the strength of the materials, and this also would imply nonlinear performance. In principle, nonlinear analyses can be performed [38] to determine the response in such cases, but nonlinear analyses are beyond the present state-of-the-art in engineering practice, and it is very difficult to provide an adequate description of the nonlinearity mechanisms in any case.

Another aspect of the analytical investigation which must be kept in mind is that the stress analysis results are no more important than the performance criteria which are used to assess the safety of the structure. Criteria which were used for evaluating gravity dam analyses in the past were concerned mainly with sliding and overturning stability, but such considerations have little meaning in the context of a finite element stress analysis. The trial load arch dam analysis technique was considerably more refined than the gravity dam analyses, and it provided quite accurate estimates of the static load stress distributions. However, the equivalent static load procedure for representing seismic effects was not reliable, because it totally disregarded the dynamic nature of the earthquake input. Dynamic amplification effects as well as the oscillatory (positive-negative) aspects of the earthquake were ignored; thus, the stress criteria which formerly were considered suitable for evaluating performance cannot be applied to the more precise results obtained by a dynamic finite element analysis.

It is important to note that the more refined analysis procedures invariably predict higher peak stress levels than are indicated by the former methods of analysis, because the refined methods are able to define stress concentration effects which previously were ignored and also because the dynamic loads introduced by a major earthquake greatly exceed the equivalent static seismic loads that were prescribed by design specifications. To make proper use of the more precise analytical methods, it is necessary to adopt correspondingly improved design criteria, i.e., criteria which express the true allowable stress state. At present few data are available on the dynamic combined stress capacity of mass concrete, especially where one or more stress components are in tension. Consequently, the benefits which may be derived from further refinement of analytical techniques will be somewhat limited until further research is done on failure mechanisms and ultimate deformation capabilities of mass concrete.

## References


1. Shen, C. K., H. C. Chen, L. S. Huang, C. J. Yang, C. H. Chang, T. C. Li, and T. C. Wang, *Earthquakes Induced by Reservoir Impounding and Their Effect on the Hsinfengkiang Dam*, Ministry of Water Conservancy and Electric Power, Peking, April 1973.
2. "Koyna Earthquake of December 11, 1967", *Report of the UNESCO Committee of Experts*, New Delhi, April 1968.
3. U.S. Army Corps of Engineers, "Gravity Dam Design," *Engineering Manual EM 1110–2–2200*, Washington, D.C., Sept. 1958.
4. U.S. Bureau of Reclamation, "Concrete Dams, Chapter 1, Arch Dams," *Design Standards No. 2*, Denver, March 1965.
5. Turner, M. J., R. W. Clough, H. C. Martin, and L. J. Topp, "Stiffness and Deflection Analysis of Complex Structures," *J. Aero. Sci*, Vol. 23, No. 9, Sept. 1956, pp. 805–824.
6. Clough, R. W., "The Finite Element Method in Plane Stress Analysis," *Proceedings, 2nd ASCE Conference on Electronic Computation, Pittsburgh*, Sept. 1960, pp. 345–378.
7. Clough, R. W., F. W. Sims, and J. A. Rhodes, "Cracking in Norfork Dam," *Proc. ACI*, Vol. 61, No. 3, March 1964, pp. 265–286.
8. Clough, R. W., and J. M. Raphael, "Construction Stresses in Dworshak Dam," *Structural Engineering Laboratory Report No. 65–3*, University of California, Berkeley, April 1965.
9. Clough, R. W., and A. K. Chopra, "Earthquake Stress Analysis in Earth Dams," *Proc. ASCE*, Vol. 92, No. EM-2, April 1966, pp. 197–211.

10. Clough, R. W., "Analysis of Structural Vibrations and Dynamic Response," *Recent Advances in Matrix Methods of Structural Analysis and Design*, U.S.-Japan Seminar, Tokyo, 1969. University of Alabama Press, University, ALA., pp. 441–486.
11. Clough, R. W., and K. J. Bathe, "Finite Element Analysis of Dynamic Response," *Advances in Computational Methods in Structural Mechanics and Design*, 2nd U.S.-Japan Seminar, Berkeley, 1972. University of Alabama Huntsville Press, Huntsville, ALA., pp. 153–180.
12. Bathe, K. J., E. L. Wilson, and F. E. Peterson, "SAP IV—A Structural Analysis Program for Static and Dynamic Response of Linear Systems," *Earthquake Engineering Research Center Report No. EERC 73–11*, University of California, Berkeley, June 1973.
13. Clough, R. W., J. M. Raphael, and S. Mojtahedi, "ADAP—A Computer Program for Static and Dynamic Analysis of Arch Dams," *Earthquake Engineering Research Center Report No. EERC 73–14*, University of California, Berkeley, June 1973.
14. Westergaard, H. M., "Water Pressure on Dams During Earthquakes," *Trans. ASCE*, Vol. 98, 1933, pp. 418–472.
15. Bathe, K. J., and E. L. Wilson, "Solution Methods for Eigenvalue Problems in Structural Mechanics," *Int. J. Num. Meth. Eng.*, Vol. 6, No. 2, 1973, pp. 213–266.
16. Clough, R. W., and S. Mojtahedi, "Earthquake Response Analysis Considering Nonproportional Damping," accepted for publication, *Int. J. Earthquake Eng. Struct. Dynamics*, Vol. 4, No. 5, 1976, pp. 489–496.
17. Newmark, N. M., "A Method of Computation for Structural Dynamics," *Proc. ASCE*, Vol. 85, No. EM3, 1959, pp. 67–94.
18. Kotsubo, S., "Dynamic Water Pressures on Dam due to Irregular Earthquakes," *Memoirs, Faculty of Engineering*, Vol. 18, No. 4, Kyushu University, Fukuoka, Japan, 1959.
19. Chopra, A. K., "Hydrodynamic Pressures on Dams during Earthquakes," *J. Eng. Mech. Div. ASCE*, Vol. 93, No. EM6, Proc. Paper 5695, Dec. 1967, pp. 205–223.
20. Bustamante, J. I., E. Rosenblueth, I. Herrera, and A. Flores, "Presion Hidrodinamica en Presas y Depositos," *Bol. Soc. Mexicana Ing. Sismica*, Vol. 1, No. 2, Oct. 1963, pp. 37–54.
21. Flores, A., I. Herrera, and C. Lozano, "Hydrodynamic Pressure Generated by Vertical Earthquake Component," *Proceedings, Fourth World Conference on Earthquake Engineering, Santiago*, 1969, B-4, pp. 25–36.
22. Rosenblueth, E., "Presion Hidrodinamica en presas Debida a Acceleracion Vertical con Refraccion en el Fondo," *II Congreso Nacional de Ingenieria Sismica, Veracruz*, 1968.
23. Chopra, A. K., "Earthquake Behavior of Reservoir-Dam Systems," *J. Eng. Mech. Div. ASCE*, Vol. 94, No. EM6, Dec. 1968, pp. 1475–1500.
24. Chakrabarti, P., and A. K. Chopra, "Hydrodynamic Effects in Earthquake Response of Gravity Dams," *J. Struct. Div. ASCE*, Vol. 100, No. ST6, June 1974, pp. 1211–1224.
25. Chopra, A. K., "Earthquake Response of Concrete Gravity Dams," *J. Eng. Mech. Div. ASCE*, Vol. 96, No. EM4, Aug. 1970, pp. 443–454.

26. Chakrabarti, P., and A. K. Chopra, "Hydrodynamic Pressures and Response of Gravity Dams to Vertical Earthquake Component," *Int. J. Earthquake Eng. Struct. Dynamics*, Vol. 1, No. 4, April–June 1973, pp. 315–335.
27. Chakrabarti, P., and A. K. Chopra, "Earthquake Analysis of Gravity Dams Including Hydrodynamic Interaction," *Int. J. Earthquake Eng. Struct. Dynamics*, Vol. 2, 1973. pp. 143–160.
28. Rea, D., C.-Y. Liaw, and A. K. Chopra, "Mathematical Models for the Dynamic Analysis of Concrete Gravity Dams," *Int. J. Earthquake Eng. Struct. Dynamics*, Vol. 3, 1975. pp. 249–258.
29. Zienkiewicz, O. C., and R. E. Newton, "Coupled Vibrations of a Structure Submerged in a Compressible Fluid," *International Symposium on Finite Element Techniques, Stuttgart*, May 1969.
30. Chakrabarti, P., and A. K. Chopra, "A Computer Program for Earthquake Analysis of Gravity Dams Including Hydrodynamic Interaction," *Report No. EERC 73–7*, Earthquake Engineering Research Center, University of California, Berkeley, May 1973.
31. Chopra, A. K., "An Examination of Standard Earthquake Design Forces for Concrete Gravity Dams," *Proceedings International Symposium on Criteria and Assumptions for Numerical Analysis of Dams, Swansea, U.K.*, Sept. 1975, pp. 589–602.
32. Perumalswami, P. R., and L. Kar, "Earthquake Behavior of Arch Dam-Reservoir Systems," *Proceedings, Fifth World Conference on Earthquake Engineering, Rome*, June 1973.
33. Vaish, A. K., and A. K. Chopra, "Earthquake Finite Element Analysis of Structure-Foundation Systems," *J. Engineering Mech. Div. ASCE*, Vol. 100, No. EM6, Dec. 1974, pp. 1101–1116.
34. Chopra, A. K., M. Dibaj, R. W. Clough, J. Penzien, and H. B. Seed, "Earthquake Analysis of Earth Dams," *Proceedings Fourth World Conference on Earthquake Engineering, Santiago*, 1969, A-5, pp. 55–72.
35. Chopra, A. K., P. Chakrabarti, and G. Dasgupta, "Dynamic Stiffness Matrices for Viscoelastic Half Plane Foundations," *Journal of the Engineering Mechanics Division, ASCE,* Vol. 102, No. EM3, June 1976, pp. 497–514.
36. Chopra, A. K., and J. A. Gutierrez, "Earthquake Response Analysis of Multistory Buildings Including Foundation Interaction," *Int. J. Earthquake Eng. Struct. Dynamics*, Vol. 3, 1974, pp. 65–67.
37. Finn, W. D. L., and E. Varoglu, "Dynamics of a Concrete Dam-Reservoir System on a Flexible Layer Foundation," *Proceedings, McGill-EIC Conference on the Finite Element Method in Civil Engineering*, McGill University, Montreal, 1972.
38. Pal, N., "Nonlinear Earthquake Response of Concrete Gravity Dams," *Report No. EERC 74–14*, Earthquake Engineering Research Center, University of California, Berkeley, Dec. 1974.
39. Cooley, J. W., and J. W. Tukey, "An Algorithm for the Machine Calculation of Complex Fourier Series," *Math. Comput.*, Vol. 19, April 1965, pp. 297–301.

# Optimum Seismic Design and Research of Single-Degree Systems

EMILIO ROSENBLUETH*

## Introduction

Uncertainties in earthquake engineering make a probabilistic treatment of design inescapable. Earthquake prediction is in its infancy; its influence on design seems remote. Even if accurate long-term predictions were feasible, uncertainties about microregionalization and structural behavior would demand the use of probabilities.

There is at present no possibility of establishing a sufficiently low upper limit to earthquake effects, at least in strongly seismic regions. Therefore, optimizing the resistance of a structure to earthquakes amounts to optimizing its expected time to failure. The earthquake engineer's task is thus the optimization of some parameters of the structural reliability function.

General expressions are available [2] for the sum of expected present values of losses due to a structure's entrances into a limit state when the disturbances constitute a stationary renewal process. Using this result, Rosenblueth [7] derives the optimum resistance of a structure having limit states in cascade (the $n$th state can only be entered after limit state $n - 1$), whose resistances are completely correlated, for disturbances constituting a generalized Poisson process.

Here we shall present the application of Ref. 7 to disturbances that constitute generalized Poisson processes, and we shall summarize the preposterior analysis in Ref. 6 to establish earthquake engineering research priorities. A close parallel is found between optimization in design and in resource allocation to research and development. Most uncertainties are dealt with using second-moment treatments contained in Appendix A, specialized to the present problem in Appendix B.

*Professor of Engineering, Universidad Nacional Autónoma de México, México 20, D.F.

## Formulation of the Problem

When we design a structure we control some quantities, ordinarily called *design parameters*, which determine (or constitute) some parameters of the probability distributions of structural properties and of some disturbances that will act on the structure. Other random variables (environmental) escape our control. Let $\mathbf{x}$ denote the vector of design parameters, $\mathbf{y}$ the vector of uncertain environmental variables, $\mathbf{c}$ that of initial costs, and $\mathbf{a}$ that of losses incurred in case the structure enters its potential limit states. Say that we discount future losses multiplying them by $\exp(-\gamma t)$, where $\gamma$ = discount rate and $t$ = time. Then $\gamma$ is a random variable that enters as a term in vector $\mathbf{a}$ as well as in $\mathbf{c}$. We can write the present value of initial cost as $C(\mathbf{c}, \mathbf{x})$ and the sum of present values (of losses due to entrances into limit states) as $D(\mathbf{a}, \mathbf{x}, \mathbf{y})$. We shall take $Z = \bar{C} + \bar{D}$ as the objective function, in the sense that $\mathbf{x}$ is optimum, say equal to $\mathbf{x}_o$, when it minimizes $Z$. Here the overbar signifies expectation.

Choice of $Z$ as the objective function implies additivity of utilities and, hence, linear relation between money and utility. The assumption is tenable except for very heavy losses, such as those due to collapse, and we can compensate therefore by magnifying certain terms in vector $\mathbf{a}$.

Our first problem is to compute $\mathbf{x}_o$, which is that vector $\mathbf{x}$ which makes $Z$ equal to $Z_o = \min Z$. After a structure enters a limit state it can be rebuilt (if it collapsed) or repaired if need be. Presumably this is also done in an optimal way but with improved knowledge about some variables, for use of Bayesian statistics allows incorporating information about disturbances and about performance of the structure in question as well as of other structures and improvements in the theory of seismicity and in the theory of structures. Given a set of these variables, we would design in the future for the optimum $\mathbf{x}'_o$. The present value of losses is a function of $\mathbf{x}'_o$. Hence, so is $Z$. We must thus compute its expectation with respect to these variables on the basis of our present information. The structure will again suffer damage or collapse and the process will be repeated, with improved, optimal design parameters $\mathbf{x}''_o, \mathbf{x}'''_o, \ldots$.

$Z$ is not very sensitive to the precise values of $\mathbf{x}'_o, \mathbf{x}''_o, \ldots$, so that ordinarily there is little error in assuming these vectors equal to $\mathbf{x}_o$. If the disturbances constitute a stationary process, this assumption furnishes an upper bound on $Z$ and (if $\bar{C}$ is an increasing function of every term of $\mathbf{x}_o$) on all terms of $\mathbf{x}_o$, for the better information we have, the smaller will be our objective function. If we wish to have lower bounds, we can assume $\mathbf{x}'_o = \mathbf{x}''_o = \cdots$ $\hat{\mathbf{x}}_{o'}$, where the circumflex accent means that we have perfect information about the variables the are amenable to Bayesian updating.

During the fail-rebuild-fail sequence a cost-benefit analysis based on the updated probability distributions may show that it is uneconomical to rebuild or repair. The structure should then be abandoned. The effect of the possibility that this decision will be made is to lower $\bar{D}$ and hence $Z$. Under practical conditions the effect is insignificant [7] and will be disregarded.

While a structure survives it usually produces benefits (rent or social benefits, depending on whom we optimize for). If the structure has entered a serviceability limit state, those benefits are smaller than when the system was intact. Variations in the present value of these benefits should be incorporated into $C$ and $D$. There may be need to modify $C$ to take into account reductions in rentable area due to increase in column sizes stemming from adoption of a more conservative design. This will also affect the cost of reconstruction and hence increase $D$ slightly. $D$ will also be affected by benefit reductions due to the possibility of the system's entering potential limit states.

There is a close parallel between the design problem as formulated and that of resource allocation to research projects. We now take as the objective function $Z = \sum(\bar{C} + \bar{D})$, where the sum extends to all future structures potentially affected by results of research. The value $Z_o$ of $Z$ associated with $\mathbf{x}_o$ gives us the value of the objective function in the present state of affairs under the assumption that structures are designed optimally in terms of the information we now possess. $\mathbf{x}_o$ is functionally related to $\sum(\bar{C} + \bar{D})$. Now suppose that we had perfect information about a group of variables. If we knew their actual values, we could write $Z_o = \min \sum[C(\mathbf{c}, \hat{\mathbf{x}}, \mathbf{y}) + D(\mathbf{a}, \hat{\mathbf{x}}, \mathbf{y})]$ and find the value of $\hat{\mathbf{x}}$ that minimizes $\sum(C + D)$, say $\hat{\mathbf{x}}_o$. Our present uncertainty about these variables made us replace this unknown $\mathbf{x}_o$ with its expectation, $\hat{\hat{\mathbf{x}}}_o$, with respect to the variables whose dispersion we can potentially dispel. Hence, $Z_o$ should in reality be replaced with $\hat{\hat{Z}}_o = \sum[\bar{C}(\mathbf{c}, \hat{\mathbf{x}}_o) + \bar{D}(\mathbf{a}, \hat{\mathbf{x}}_o, \mathbf{y})]$. The difference $\Delta = Z_o - \hat{\hat{Z}}_o$ is the value of perfect information. It marks an upper limit to the amount worth spending on research.

At the end of a proposed research project we shall have some value $Z'$ of the objective function. Again we should use $\bar{Z}'_o = \sum[\bar{C}(\mathbf{c}, \bar{\mathbf{x}}'_o) + \bar{D}(\mathbf{a}, \bar{\mathbf{x}}'_o, \mathbf{y})]$, where $\mathbf{x}'_o$ is the value of $\mathbf{x}$ that minimizes the objective function under the assumption that we have reduced our uncertainty about the variables to be studied in the project under consideration, and $\bar{\mathbf{x}}'_o$ is the expectation of $\mathbf{x}'_o$ computed on the basis of our present information about these variables. By comparing the reductions from $Z_o$ to $\bar{Z}'_o$ and research costs for different proposed projects we can select to most profitable one.

The approach allows gauging the advisability of running pilot research projects to improve our estimates of the outcome of the full projects. We then deal with future uncertainties as our random variable. The outcome will sometimes be that certain full projects, which at the outset seemed profitable, should not be launched because the improved probability distributions have reduced their initially expected net benefits. The possibility of reaching this conclusion and of concluding that the order of priority of full projects should be changed determines the expected benefit of the pilot projects. It is formally the same as the computation of the reduction in $\bar{D}$ in the design of an individual structure due to the possibility that it will be found uneconomical to rebuild or repair after one or more failures or entrances into other limit states.

In both kinds of problems—design and resource allocation—we should also consider activities (research and development) leading to innovation. As a consequence of these activities there may be changes in expectations (and occasionally in other parameters of probability distributions, say through the improvement of quality-control methods) contained in vectors **a**, **c**, **x**, and **y** producing reductions in $\bar{C}$ and $\bar{D}$. Again through comparison of $Z_o$ and $\bar{Z}'_o$ we can judge whether a proposed research and development project deserves priority. Effects on $\bar{\mathbf{x}}'_o$ for design optimization are minor; they can be incorporated into the framework described.

In principle, side benefits, "intangibles," and hidden costs [4] can be treated quantitatively and incorporated into $C$ and $D$. Even when this is not formally done, the present formulation in terms of direct material costs and benefits can serve as a guide for rational decision making.

## Expected Losses

We shall idealize earthquake occurrences as generalized Poisson processes. Suppose first that the mean exceedance rate $\lambda(U)$ of a given structural response $U$ (say base shear coefficient) were known deterministically. If the failure criterion were $U > X$, where $X =$ resistance, the probability that failure occurs in the interval $t$, $t + dt$ would be $\lambda \exp(-\lambda t)$ dt, where $\lambda = \lambda(X)$ and $t =$ time. Hence, the expected present value of the loss due to the first collapse would be

$$D_1 = A\lambda \int_0^\infty e^{-\lambda t} e^{-\gamma t}\, dt, \tag{1}$$

$$\frac{A\lambda}{\gamma + \lambda} = \frac{A\Lambda}{1 + \Lambda}, \tag{2}$$

where $A =$ loss in case of collapse, $\gamma =$ discount rate, $\Lambda = \lambda/\gamma$, and $t =$ time [2]. For the $n$th failure,

$$D_n = A\left(\frac{\Lambda}{1 + \Lambda}\right)^n. \tag{3}$$

There are actually, though, several sources of uncertainty, which result in a number of stochastic variables. These will be classified into three groups depending on their time correlations [7]:

1. Disturbance variables: Fluctuations in structural effects relative to computed values due to uncertainty about disturbance characteristics. We assume that the fluctuations vary uncorrelated from one disturbance to another. Variables in this group include the ratio of spectral ordinates

to their mean values for given intensity and effects of uncertainty about the causative mechanism.

2. Structural variables: Discrepancies between actual and computed structural properties. We assume that the discrepancies remain constant as long as a structure is not rebuilt even if it is repaired following damage but that upon rebuilding they can change without correlation. Cumulative damage and live load fluctuations are ignored in the present model.

3. Variables of analysis: Systematic, uncertain deviations from computed structural effects of the disturbances, due to ignorance about the nature of the phenomena at play, and systematic discrepancies between actual and computed structural properties. This group includes, as well, errors in computed seismicity, microregionalization, initial costs, costs of failure, and discount rate. These deviations are taken as time independent.

We assume that only the probability distributions of third-group variables are amenable to updating through Bayesian statistics in the light of experience and research. Accordingly, only changes in the statistics of these variables will affect $\mathbf{x}_o'$ and $Z_o'$. In addition, research and development may affect other parameters.

We shall use symbols $E_i(\cdot)$ and $V_i(\cdot)$, respectively, to denote expectation and coefficient of variation with respect to variables in the $i$th group and an overbar to denote expectation with respect to all the random variables. Also, $V_Y = V_3(Y)$, where $Y$ is any random variable.

Uncertainty makes us write Eq. (3) in the form

$$D_n = AE_2(\mu^n), \tag{4}$$

where

$$\mu = \frac{E_1(\Lambda)}{1 + E_1(\Lambda)}. \tag{5}$$

The total expected present value of losses is the sum of $D_n$ from $n = 1$ to infinity. Thus, if the structure is rebuilt systematically after each failure,

$$\bar{D} = \overline{A\delta}, \tag{6}$$

where $\bar{A} = E_3(A)$, $\bar{\delta} = E_3(\delta)$, and

$$\delta = \frac{E_2(\mu)}{1 - E_2(\mu)} \tag{7}$$

If the structure has a series of potential limit states in cascade, so that it can enter them only in a fixed order, and it is known that it experienced a response smaller than $X$, the expected loss will be $\int_0^x (\lambda_U/\lambda)a'(U)\,dU$, where $\lambda_U = \lambda(U)$, $a(U)$ is the loss associated with response $U$, and the prime denotes derivative with respect to $U$. If the limit states are strictly correlated, so that $a$ is a function only of $\xi = U/X$, under some circumstances there is little error in treating these losses and $\delta$ as statistically independent [7], so that Eq. (6) remains valid, with

$$A = A_c + A_d + C, \tag{8}$$

where $A_c$ = direct loss in case of collapse,

$$A_d = \int_0^1 \frac{\lambda(\xi X)}{\lambda(X)} a'(\xi)\, d\xi, \tag{9}$$

and $C$ = present value of initial cost. Under more general conditions we must write

$$\bar{D} = E_3(A\delta). \tag{10}$$

Because of the assumption that after each entrance to a limit state the system is taken to its original state, Eqs. (6) and (9) overestimate $\bar{D}$. We obtain a lower bound by assuming that the structure is redesigned optimally as though there were perfect information about variables in the third group. The exercise is ordinarily not justified, as both limits lie very close to each other. It will be described, though, as it indicates a solution to the problem of resource allocation to research.

Let $x = E_{23}(X)$ denote the original design value, $\hat{x}$ the redesign value of $X$, and $\hat{c} = d\hat{C}/d\hat{x}$. Then $\hat{x}_o$ is found by solving

$$\hat{c} + A\frac{d\hat{\delta}}{d\hat{x}} = 0. \tag{11}$$

Beginning with $n = 2$, $D_n$ is no longer given by Eq. (4) but by

$$\hat{D}_n = AE_2(\hat{\mu}^n), \tag{12}$$

and we must replace $\Lambda(x)$ with $\Lambda(\hat{x})$ in Eq. (5) to get $\hat{\mu}$. Also, $C$ must be replaced with $\hat{C}$ in Eq. (8). Summing with respect to $n$ and taking the expectation with respect to the third-group variables, we get

$$\bar{D} = E_3[(A_c + A_d + \hat{C})(1 + \delta)E_2(\hat{\mu})]. \tag{13}$$

Precise evaluation of $\delta$ and $\hat{\delta}$ is cumbersome and unjustified. Methods in Appendix A suffice for most practical purposes. When $\bar{\Lambda}V_2^2(\Lambda) \ll 1$, which is the usual case, they give

$$\bar{\delta} = \bar{\Lambda}(1 - \ldots), \tag{14}$$

$$\hat{\delta} = E_{12}(\hat{\Lambda})(1 - \ldots), \tag{15}$$

$$E_2(\mu) = \frac{E_{12}(\Lambda)}{1 + E_{12}(\Lambda)}(1 - \ldots), \tag{16}$$

where the ellipsis stands for positive terms of order $\bar{\Lambda}V_2^2(\Lambda)$, $E_{12}(\hat{\Lambda})V_2^2(\Lambda)$, and $E_{12}(\Lambda)V_2^2(\Lambda)$, respectively (Appendix B). When $\bar{\Lambda}V_2^2(\Lambda)$ is not small compared with 1 we can resort to graphs and formulas [6].

We can also assign probabilities to various possible reductions in $C + D$ due to future innovations to take this possibility into into account.

Suppose, for example, that

$$\lambda = \alpha X^{-r}, \tag{17}$$

where $\alpha$ and $r$ are constants and the latter usually lies between 2 and 4. This expression is satisfactory provided $X$ is not excessively large [3]. Its upper limit of applicability depends on the definition of $X$, on site seismicity, and on local geology. For $\alpha$ and $\beta$ to be independent, $X$ must be expressed in units of some value $x_m$. According to Appendix A,

$$\bar{\Lambda} = \frac{\bar{\alpha}}{\bar{\gamma}} x^{-\bar{r}}(1 + \ldots), \tag{18}$$

where the terms omitted are of order $V_\gamma^2$, $V_r^2$, and $V_i^2(X)$, $i = 1, 2, 3$. $V_i^2(\Lambda)$ is of this same order. If

$$C = C_1 + cx, \tag{19}$$

where $C_1$ and $c$ are constants, replacing in Eqs. (6) and (14) and solving $dZ/dx = 0$ for $x_o$ gives

$$x_o = \left\{\frac{\overline{\alpha r}}{\bar{\gamma}\bar{c}}\left[A_c + A_d + \left(1 - \frac{1}{\bar{r}}\right)\bar{c}x_o\right]\right\}^{1/(\bar{r}+1)}(1 + \ldots), \tag{20}$$

which can be solved iteratively. Terms omitted are again of order $V_\gamma^2$, $V_r^2$, and $V_i^2(X)$, and the factor $1 + \ldots$ always exceeds 1 and can well exceed 2. This expression gives us the upper limit to the optimal resistance. The term in $x_o$ inside the brackets stems from the cost of reconstruction after failure. It can be neglected in first approximation if $x_o \ll \bar{A}/\bar{c}$. Indeed, by so doing we find a lower bound to $x_o$ which is lower than we would obtain assuming that the structure would be redesigned optimally after accomplishing all improvements imaginable. The latter lower bound results from replacing $x_o$ with $\hat{x}_o$ in the appropriate terms $D_n$. In turn the expression for $\hat{x}_o$ is similar to Eq. (20), but its corrective factor $1 + \ldots$ is smaller than for $x_o$.

When Eq. (17) holds, Eq. (9) gives us

$$A_d = \int_0^1 \xi^{-r} \frac{da}{d\xi}\, d\xi \tag{21}$$

provided $a$ and $da/d\xi$ are zero as $\xi$ tends toward zero. (When this condition is not fulfilled it is uneconomical to repair every time that the structure enters a serviceability limit state.) The assumption $E_3(A\delta) = \overline{A\delta}$ holds provided $r$ is known deterministically. Otherwise it requires corrective terms of order $V_r^2$.

The expression we adopted for $\lambda$ [Eq. (17)] implies that the probability distribution of the maximum response in a fixed time interval is extreme type 2. Assuming, on empirical and qualitative theoretical grounds [3], that this distribution is extreme type 1, we have

$$\lambda = \alpha_1 e^{-\alpha_2(X - X_m)}, \tag{22}$$

where $\alpha_1$ and $\alpha_2$ are constants. We must then replace Eq. (20) with

$$x_o = X_m + \frac{1 + \cdots}{\bar{\alpha}_2} \ln \frac{\bar{\alpha}_1 \bar{\alpha}_2 \bar{A}}{\gamma c}, \tag{23}$$

which can also be solved iteratively and in which the ellipsis stands for terms of order $V_{\alpha_2}^2$, $V_\gamma^2$, $V_r^2$, and $V_i^2(X)$. In this case,

$$A_d = \int_0^1 e^{-\bar{\alpha}_2(x\xi - X_m)} \frac{da}{d\xi} d\xi. \tag{24}$$

A Bayesian analysis of the effect of not rebuilding a structure that has failed, when it is uneconomical to rebuild, gives under typical conditions a reduction in $\bar{D}$ of less than 2% for fixed $x$ [7]. The effect on $x_o$ is consequently smaller than 0.5% when $\bar{r} = 3$ and not worth considering.

## Optimum Resource Allocation to Research and Development

Because of the objective function that we have chosen for this problem, we can use the same expressions as for design optimization, merely inserting a summation sign to include all structures potentially affected by the projects under consideration. For evaluating the benefits of research we must now fix our attention on the terms of order $V_3^2$ of the various variables, and these we had left implied as ellipses in each of those expressions.

Consider, for example, our uncertainty about $X/x$. Let $\lambda$ be given by Eq. (17). Neglect terms of order $\bar{\Lambda} V_2^2(\Lambda)$ in comparison with 1. If we assign $X/x$ a log normal distribution, we find $Z_o$ proportional to $W_3^{\bar{r}/2}$, where $W_3 = 1 + V_3^2(X)$. On the other hand, $\hat{Z}_o$ does not contain $V_3(X)$. The value of perfect information about $X$ is therefore $(W_3^{\bar{r}/2} - 1)\hat{Z}_o$. Now consider $c$. $Z_o$ does not contain $V_c$, but if we assign $c$ a log normal distribution, $Z_o$ is proportional to $(1 + V_c^2)^{-\bar{r}/2(\bar{r}+1)^2}$. The value of perfect information about $c$ is hence 1 minus this quantity and times $Z_o$.

Proceeding in this manner, Ref. 6 solves the hypothetical example of a small country where the expected present value of investments in future structures of the type of interest corresponds to $\bar{c} = \$2 \times 10^9$, $x$ is the design base shear coefficient, $\bar{\gamma} = 0.1$ year$^{-1}$, $X_m = 0.01724$, and $\bar{r} = 3$; if all coefficients of variation were nil, we would get $x_o = 0.1$. With the coefficients of variation in Table 1 we find $\hat{x}_o = 0.0982$, $x_o = 0.1313$, and the values of perfect information contained in the table. The combined value of reducing $V_\alpha$ and $V_r$ to zero is $\$44.0 \times 10^6$. It is also found that reducing $\bar{c}$ to $0.9\bar{c}$ brings an expected benefit of $\$26.6 \times 10^6$, while reducing $\bar{A}$ to $0.9\bar{A}$ results in an expected benefit of $\$7.8 \times 10^6$.

Appendix B shows that the expected value of the information gained from

**Table 1**
**Assumed Dispersions of Pertinent Variables and Ensuing Benefits (after Ref. 6)**

| *Variable* | *V* | *Value of Perfect Information* $\$10^6$ |
|---|---|---|
| $\alpha$ | 0.4 | 4.9 |
| $\gamma$ | 0.2 | 0.3 |
| $c$ | 0.4 | 4.8 |
| $A$ | 0.4 | 4.9 |
| $X$ | 0.2 | 22.5 |
| $r$ | 0.2 | 39.1 |
| Sum | | 76.5* |

*Value of perfect information about all the variables.

a project that reduces the coefficient of variation $V$ of a variable to an expected value $\bar{V}'$ with coefficient of variation $V'_V$ is approximately equal to $1 - (1 - V^2_{V'})\bar{V}'^2/V^2$ times the original value of perfect information for that variable. Accordingly, the net expected benefit of a project with expected cost $\bar{R}$ is that quantity minus $\bar{R}$. For example, if reducing $V_3(X)$ from 0.2 to 0.1 with a coefficient of variation of 0.5 requires a research project expected to cost $\$2.0 \times 10^6$, the expected net benefit is $(1 - 1.25 \times 0.1^2/0.2^2)22.5 \times 10^6 - 2.0 \times 10^6 = \$13.5 \times 10^6$.

The expected net benefit of a research and development project that, if successful, would reduce $Z_o$ to say $Z_o - \Delta$ is $(Z_o - \Delta)P - \bar{R}$, where $P$ is the probability of success and $\bar{R}$ and expected cost.

Once we have analyzed a set of proposed projects we can list them in a decreasing order of expected net benefits and decide that all those having positive net benefits are worth sponsoring down to the limits of available human and material resources.

The benefit of running a pilot research project is to reduce uncertainty on coefficients of variation, success probabilities, and costs of research and development. At the end of a pilot project we may have changed the order of priority of the full proposals or discovered that the signs of the expected net benefits of some proposals have changed.

## Numerical Example of Optimum Design

The following example is taken from Ref. 7. Adopt the parameters in Table 2. Suppose besides that $X_m = 0.025$, that $\bar{a} = 0$ when $\xi \leq 0.5$, and that $\bar{a} = (\xi - 0.5)A_c$ when $\xi \geq 0.5$ (Fig. 1). Results appear in Fig. 2. The central curve for the case when $\lambda$ is defined by Eq. (17) was computed using Eq. (20)

**Table 2**
**Parameters of the Probability Distributions in Example of Optimization (after Ref. 7)**

| *Variable* | *Expectation* | *Coef. of Variation* |
|---|---|---|
| $\alpha$ | $10^{-6}$ yr$^{-1}$ | 0.1 |
| $\gamma$ | $10^{-1}$ yr$^{-1}$ | 0.1 |
| $A$ | — | 0.2 |
| $c$ | — | 0.2 |
| $r$ | 3 | 0.1 |
| $X$ | — | $V_1(X) = 0.3$ |
| | | $V_2(X) = 0.2$ |
| | | $V_3(X) = 0.4$ |

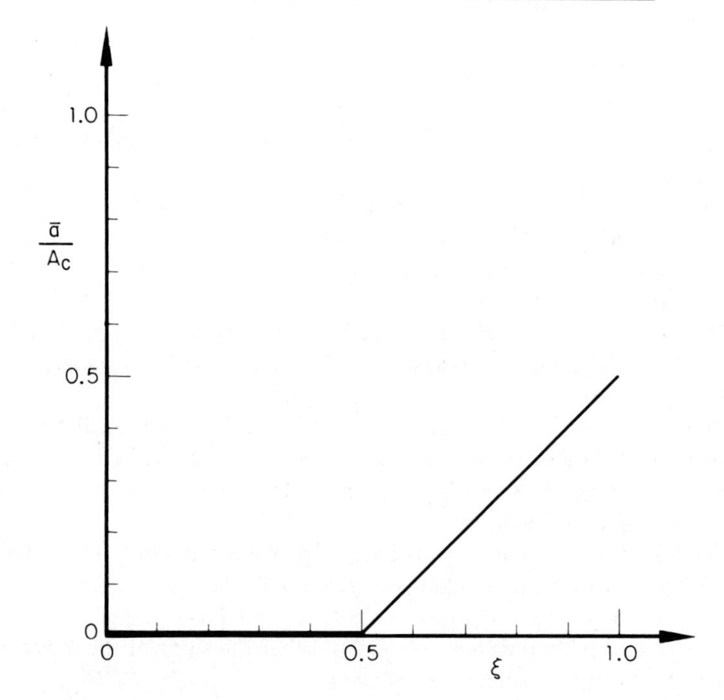


**Fig. 1.** Loss due to entrance into serviceability limit states, after Ref. 7

with $1 + \ldots = W^{\bar{r}/2}$, which neglects the influence of $V_\gamma$ and $V_r$ on design. The one for the case when $\lambda$ is defined by Eq. (22) was found from Eq. (23) and corresponds to the conservative assumption that the structure is always rebuilt as originally designed.

Differences of 20% in $x_o$ in the range of high $\bar{A}_c/\bar{c}$ have an influence of about 5% in $\bar{c}x_o + \bar{D}$.

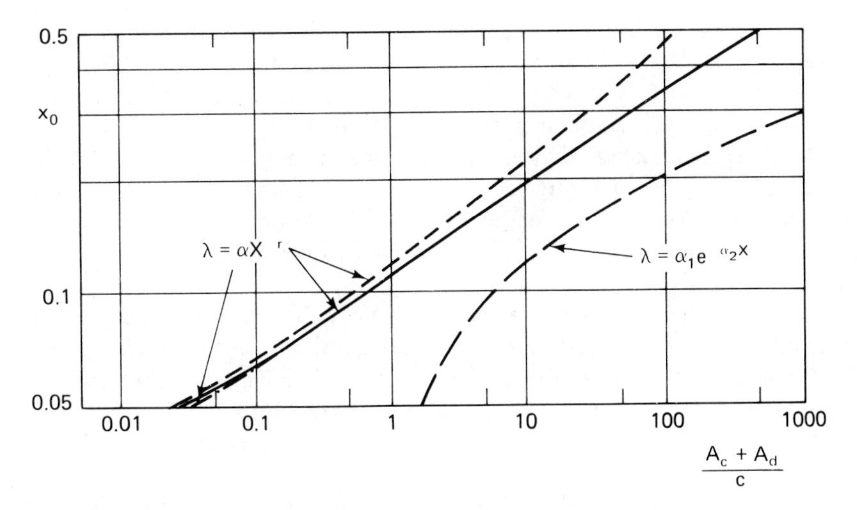


**Fig. 2.** Optimum base shear coefficient, after Ref. 7

## Research Needed

The following order of priority is guided by results in Table 1 and based on considerations in Ref. 4 and on an intuitive interpretation of experience.

*First priority* should go to seismicity, structural behavior, special phenomena in special structures, tending to reduce initial costs, and design optimization.

In seismicity we need better descriptions of earthquake occurrence, improved microregionalization, and means for predicting the various translational and rotational components of earthquakes. Such goals require the deployment of a vast number of instruments, simultaneous recording through telemetry, and automated processing. Instrumental records should be supplemented with information about historical and geological motions. Interpretation should be based on conceptual models of tectonic processes. Microregionalization requires determination of dynamic properties of soil at various strain levels and numerical solutions of effects of site conditions.

There is sore need for simple methods leading to trustworthy prediction of the responses of nonlinear multidegree-of-freedom structures, especially those exhibiting stiffness degradation.

Special phenomena about which our uncertainty is still extremely large include hydrodynamic pressures on dams, particularly as influenced by nonlinear behavior of structures; pressures exerted by tsunamis; and forces acting on retaining walls.

Development of new materials and structural solutions requires ingenuity well founded in mechanics, chemistry, and architecture.

We have delved into design optimization for single-degree systems. That of more complicated structures is still a forbidding task.

*Second priority* is reserved for improved knowledge about material behavior under earthquake-like excitation, definition of initial costs as a function of earthquake resistance, information and analysis of losses associated with a structure's entering its various potential limit states, means for reducing these losses, and methods for deciding optimally on resource allocation to research and development, based on simplified, yet realistic preposterior analysis.

*Third priority* is assigned to an endless list of subjects. One we detected in our analysis is financial studies to improve our estimate of the discount rate. More generally, we could study the discount and inflationary processes, which will not necessarily proceed at constant rates in the future.

For rhetorical reasons we have postponed the most urgent project until the end.

There will be little benefit stemming from research unless we improve our record for implementing our conclusions in building codes and design and (particularly) construction practice. All this requires that we find out more about how human beings process information and make decisions.

## Acknowledgment

The writer expresses his gratitude to Luis Esteva for his conscientious revision of the manuscript and for his many and useful critical comments.

## Appendix A. Second-Moment Approximations

Given a well-behaved function $Y(X)$, the mean $\bar{X}$, and the standard deviation $\sigma$ or coefficient of variation $V$ of $X$, we are interested in the mean and standard deviation or coefficient of variation of $Y$. The following expressions are based on a Taylor expansion of $Y$ about $\bar{X}$ [1]:

$$\bar{Y} \doteq y + \frac{\sigma^2 y''}{2}, \tag{A1}$$

$$\sigma_Y \doteq |\sigma y'|, \tag{A2}$$

whence

$$V_Y \doteq \left|\frac{\bar{X} y' V}{\bar{Y}}\right|. \tag{A3}$$

Here $\doteq$ means "equal to, save for higher-order terms," $y = y(\bar{X})$, and primes denote derivatives with respect to $X$ at $X = \bar{X}$. Equation (A1) uses the first two nonzero terms in the expansion and hence is a second-order approximation. The other two expressions are first-order approximations.

The following approximations [5] are of the same respective orders:

$$\bar{Y} \doteq \frac{y_+ + y_-}{2}, \tag{A4}$$

$$V_Y \doteq \left| \frac{y_+ - y_-}{2} \right|, \tag{A5}$$

$$V_Y \doteq \left| \frac{y_+ - y_-}{y_+ + y_-} \right|, \tag{A6}$$

where $y_+ = y(\bar{X} + \sigma)$, $y_- = y(\bar{X} - \sigma)$. They are derived by assuming the probability density function of $X$ concentrated equally at $\bar{X} \pm \sigma$.

When $Y(X)$ is irregular (say that it has no first or second derivative at $\bar{X}$ or in its neighborhood), Eqs. (A1)–(A3) are not applicable, while Eqs. (A4)–(A6) may given excessively large errors. For mild irregularities we may use

$$\bar{Y} = \frac{y_{++} + 2y_+ + 6y + 2y_- + y_{--}}{2}, \tag{A7}$$

where $y_{++} = y(\bar{X} + 2\sigma)$ and $y_{--} = y(\bar{X} - 2\sigma)$ and whose coefficients are such that $Y$ is exact when $Y = X^n$, $n = 0, 1, 2, 3$, and 4, and $X$ is normally distributed [6]. It is a second-order approximation for other distributions. With this expression we can also get $\bar{Y}^2$, $E(Y^2)$, and hence $\sigma_Y^2$ and $V_Y$ to first order.

The foregoing approximations are satisfactory if $V_Y \ll 1$. Otherwise results are quite sensitive to the actual probability distribution of $X$. A case deserving special interest in earthquake engineering is that in which $X$ has log normal distribution and $Y$ is proportional to $X^k$, where $k$ is a constant. Then the following expressions are exact:

$$\bar{Y} = (1 + V^2)^{k(k-1)2} y, \tag{A8}$$

$$1 + V_Y^2 = (1 + V^2)^{k^2}. \tag{A9}$$

When $Y$ is a function of several random variables $X_1, X_2, \ldots, X_n$, Eq. (A1) becomes

$$\bar{Y} \doteq y + \frac{1}{2} \sum_i \sum_j \operatorname{Cov}(X_i, X_j) \frac{\partial^2 Y}{\partial X_i \, \partial X_j}, \tag{A10}$$

where the sums extend from 1 to $n$ and the derivatives are evaluated at $\bar{X}_1, \bar{X}_2, \ldots, \bar{X}_n$ [1].

Under these conditions the joint probability density function of $X_1, X_2, \ldots, X_n$ must be assumed concentrated at points in the hyperspace of these variables outside their axes [5]. For example, if $n = 2$, the coordinates and values of the concentrations are as shown in Fig. A1. The scheme can be generalized to $n$ dimensions. It allows computing $\bar{Y}$, $\bar{Y}^2$, $E(Y^2)$, and hence $\sigma_Y^2$.

If the dispersion of $X_2$, say, is a function of $X_1$, the points in the figure no longer form a rectangle. An example of this sort is considered in Ref. 6.

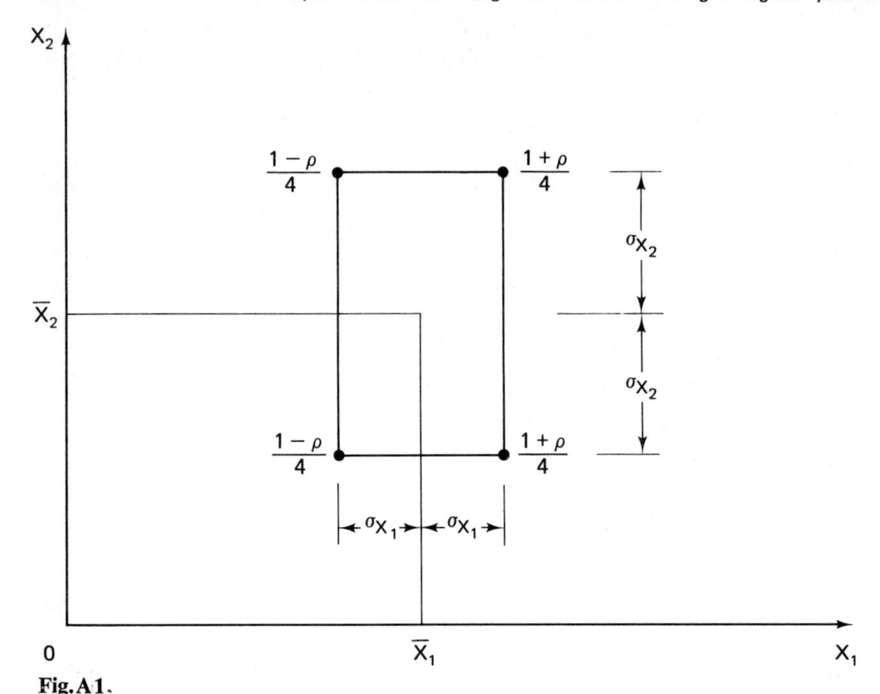


**Fig. A1.**

When the $X$'s are statistically independent it may be more convenient to compute $\bar{Y}$ and $V_Y$ from

$$\frac{\bar{Y}}{y} \doteq \frac{Y_1}{y}\frac{Y_2}{y}\cdots\frac{Y_n}{y}, \tag{A11}$$

$$1 + V_Y^2 = (1 + V_1^2)(1 + V_3^2)\ldots(1 + V_n^2), \tag{A12}$$

where $Y_i$ and $V_i$ are computed as $Y$ and $V$, respectively, but assuming that $X_i$ is the only random variable and the other $X$'s are equal to their expectations. In particular, if $Y = X_1^{k_1}X_2^{k_2}\ldots X_n^{k_n}$, Eqs. (A11) and (A12) are exact.

## Appendix B. Application to Optimum Design

With basis on the foregoing results the following expressions are obtained almost immediately.

If $\bar{\Lambda}V_2^2(\Lambda) \ll 1$,

$$\bar{\delta} \doteq \bar{\Lambda}\left\{1 - \frac{\bar{\Lambda}V_2^2(\Lambda)}{1+\bar{\Lambda}}\left[1 + \frac{V_3^2(\Lambda)}{(1+\bar{\Lambda})^2}\right]\right\}, \tag{B1}$$

$$\hat{\delta} \doteq E_{12}(\hat{\Lambda})\left[1 - \frac{E_{12}(\hat{\Lambda})V_2^2(\Lambda)}{1+\hat{\Lambda}}\right], \tag{B2}$$

$$E_2(\mu) \doteq \frac{E_{12}(\Lambda)}{1+E_{12}(\Lambda)}\left[1 - \frac{E_{12}(\Lambda)V_2^2(\Lambda)}{[1+E_{12}(\Lambda)]^2}\right], \tag{B3}$$

which stand, respectively, for Eqs. (14), (15), and (16) (see Refs. 6 and 7). It may seem superfluous to include a term proportional to $V_2^2(\Lambda)V_3^2(\Lambda)$ in Eq. (B1), as it is of fourth order. However, $V_3^2(\Lambda)$ can easily exceed 2, so it may be quite significant.

When $\lambda'$ is given by Eq. (17) and $X$ has log normal distributions with respect to all the random variables and $\bar{X} = x$,

$$E_{12}(\Lambda) \doteq \frac{\alpha}{\gamma} x^{-r}(W_1 W_2)^{r(r+1)/2}, \tag{B4}$$

$$\bar{\Lambda} \doteq \frac{\bar{\alpha}}{\gamma} x^{-\bar{r}} W^{\bar{r}(\bar{r}+1)/2}\left\{1 + V_\gamma^2 + \frac{[rV_r \ln(x - X_m)]^2}{2}\right\}, \tag{B5}$$

$$1 + V_i^2(\Lambda) \doteq W_i^{r^2}, \qquad i = 1, 2, \tag{B6}$$

$$1 + V_3^2(\Lambda) \doteq W_3^{\bar{r}^2}[1 + V_\gamma^2 + (\bar{r}V_r \ln(x - X_m)^2], \tag{B7}$$

where $W = W_1 W_2 W_3$ and $W_i = 1 + V_i^2(X)$; Eq. (B5) stands for Eq. (18). Hence, in Eq. (20), if $\bar{\Lambda}V_2^2(\Lambda) \ll 1$, so that $\bar{\delta} \doteq \bar{\Lambda}$,

$$1 + \ldots \doteq W^{\bar{r}/2}\left\{1 + \frac{V_\gamma^2 + [\bar{r}V_r \ln(x_o - X_m)]^2/2}{\bar{r} + 1}\right\}. \tag{B8}$$

Here we have chosen to write the term in brackets in this form rather than as the more obvious $\{1 + V_\gamma^2 + [\bar{r}V_r \ln(x_o - X_m)/2]\}^{1/(\bar{r}+1)}$ because, for the usual ranges of the variables, Eq. (B5) tends to overestimate the effect of uncertainty about $r$, and our choice partly counters this error. If $\bar{\Lambda}V_2^2(\Lambda)$ is not very small, we resort to Eq. (B1), from which

$$\frac{d\bar{\delta}}{d\bar{\Lambda}} \doteq 1 - \frac{\bar{\Lambda}V_2^2(\Lambda)}{(1 - \bar{\Lambda})^2}\left[2 + \bar{\Lambda} + \frac{(2 - \bar{\Lambda})V_3^2(\Lambda)}{(1 - \bar{\Lambda})^2}\right], \tag{B9}$$

and we multiply the factor in Eq. (B8) by $(d\bar{\delta}/d\bar{\Lambda})^{1/(\bar{r}+1)}$. If $d\bar{\delta}/d\bar{\Lambda} > \frac{1}{2}$, say, this approach is not likely to give sufficiently accurate results. We may go then to the graphs and formulas in Ref. 7.

We must also evaluate $\bar{A}_d$. This is done perhaps most easily by using Eq. (4): computing $A_d$ for $r = \bar{r}(1 \pm V_r)$ and averaging the results.

Consider now the problem of optimum resource allocation to research projects. Before we undertake the research project we find $x_o$ by minimizing $\bar{C} + \bar{D}$. If we replace $x_o$ in the expression for $Z_o$, we find

$$Z_o = C_1 + \left\{\frac{\overline{ac^r r}}{\bar{\gamma}}\left[\bar{A} + \left(1 - \frac{1}{\bar{r}}\right)\bar{c}x_o\right]\right\}^{1/(\bar{r}+1)}(1 + \ldots), \tag{B10}$$

where the factor $1 + \ldots$ is the same as in Eq. (20) and is given by Eqs. (B8) and (B9). On the other hand,

$$\hat{Z}_o = C_1 + \left\{\frac{ac^r r}{\gamma}\left[A + \left(1 - \frac{1}{r}\right)c\hat{x}_o\right]\right\}^{1/(r+1)}(1 + \ldots), \tag{B11}$$

and the factor $1 + \ldots$ does not contain terms in the coefficients of variation with respect to variables in the third group, as these variables are assumed known. When we compute $\hat{\bar{Z}}_o$ we notice that the second term in brackets is usually quite small compared with the first. Hence, we can obtain the new corrective factor from $E_3[(\alpha A c^r r/\gamma)^{1/(r+1)}]$.

We find that a project that would reduce $V_3(X)$ to $V_3'(X)$ would leave a remaining value of perfect information equal to $(W_3'/W_3)^{\bar{r}/2} - 1$ times its original value for $X$. If it reduced $V_\alpha$ to $V_\alpha'$, it would leave a remaining value of perfect information equal to $1 - (1 + V_\alpha^2)/(1 + V_\alpha^2)^{\bar{r}/2(\bar{r}+1)^2}$ times the original value for $\alpha$, and so on. These quantities are of order $V_3'^2$, etc. Hence, the remaining value of perfect information for each variable is approximately proportional to the square of the corresponding coefficient of variation. For example, with $\bar{r} = 3$, if $V_3(X) = 0.4$ and $V_3'(X) = 0.2$, we find that the remaining value of perfect information is 24.3 rather than 25% of the original value. If $V_\alpha$ is reduced from 0.4 to 0.2, the reduction in value is to 26.6% of the original.

We can hardly predict the values that the coefficients of variation will have at the end of a proposed research project unless the project is designed to stop when that value is reached. Treating a coefficient of variation, say $V$, as a random variable we must replace $V^2$ with $E(V^2)$ to take into account our uncertainty. But $E(V^2)$ equals $\bar{V}^2$ plus the variance of $V$. Hence, $V^2$ should be replaced with $(1 + V_V^2)\bar{V}^2$.

## Notation

- $A$ = loss in case of failure
- $A_c$ = direct loss in case of collapse
- $A_d$ = loss in case of entrance to all serviceability limit states
- $a$ = loss associated with given structural response not causing collapse
- $\mathbf{a}$ = vector of parameters defining the probability distributions of losses due to entrances into limit states
- $C$ = present value of initial cost
- $C_1$ = part of $C$ independent of $x$
- $c$ = $dc/dX$ at $X = x_0$
- $\mathbf{c}$ = vector of parameters defining the probability distributions of initial costs
- $D$ = sum of present values of losses due to entrances into limit states
- $E_i(\cdot)$ = expectation with respect to variables in $i$th group
- $o$ = subscript denoting optimal
- $P$ = success probability of a research and development project
- $R$ = cost of research project or of research and development project
- $r$ = exponent in expression for $\lambda$
- $t$ = time
- $U$ = structural response
- $V_i(\cdot)$ = coefficient of variation with respect to variables in $i$th group
- $V_Y$ = $V_3(Y)$, where $Y$ = any random variable
- $W$ = $W_1 W_2 W_3$
- $W_i$ = $1 + V_i^2(X)$

$X$ = (random) structural resistance to earthquakes; in Appendix A, any random variable
$X_m$ = value of $x$ for which $\alpha$ and $r$ are uncorrelated
$x$ = realization of $X$; in design, $x = \bar{X}$
$\mathbf{x}$ = vector of design parameters
$Y$ = function of random variables
$y = y(\bar{X})$
$y_+ = y(\bar{X} + \sigma)$
$y_{++} = y(\bar{X} + 2\sigma)$
$y_- = y(\bar{X} - \sigma)$
$y_{--} = y(\bar{X} - 2\sigma)$
$y' = dY/dX$ at $X = \bar{X}$
$y'' = d^2Y/dX^2$ at $X = \bar{X}$
$\mathbf{y}$ = vector of parameters defining probability distributions of environmental variables
$Z = \bar{C} + \bar{D}$
$\alpha$ = coefficient in expression for $\lambda$
$\gamma$ = discount rate
$\Delta$ = value of perfect information
$\delta = E_2(\mu)/[1 - E_2(\mu)]$
$\Lambda = \lambda/\gamma$
$\lambda$ = mean exceedance rate
$\mu = E_1(\Lambda)/[1 + E_1(\Lambda)]$
$\xi = U/X$
$\rho$ = correlation coefficient
$\sigma$ = standard deviation of $X$
$\sigma_Y$ = standard deviation of $Y$

An overbar signifies expectation with respect to all the variables.
A circumflex accent refers to the state of perfect information about a set of variables.
$\doteq$ means "equal to, save for higher-order terms."

## References


1. BENJAMIN, J. R., and C. A. CORNELL, *Probability, Statistics, and Decision for Civil Engineers*, McGraw-Hill, New York, 1970.
2. HASOFER, A. M., "Design for Infrequent Overloads," *Int. J. Earthquake Eng. Struct. Dynamics*, Vol. 2, No. 4, April–June 1974, pp. 387–88.
3. NEWMARK, N. M., and E. ROSENBLUETH, *Fundamentals of Earthquake Engineering*, Prentice-Hall, Englewood Cliffs, N. J., 1971.
4. ROSENBLUETH, E., "La Investigación más Deseable en Ingeniería Sísmica," *Ingeniería Sísmica*, Mexico, No. 12, Jan.–Apr. 1974, pp. 1–24.
5. ROSENBLUETH, E., "Point Estimates for Probability Moments," *Proc. Natl. Acad. of Sciences*, U.S.A., Vol. 72, No. 10, Oct. 1975, pp. 3812–14.
6. ROSENBLUETH, E., "Optimum Resource Allocation in Earthquake Engineering," Proceedings Fifth European Symposium on Earthquake Engineering, Istanbul, Turkey, Sept. 1975, Vol. 2, Paper No. 153, pp. 1–28.
7. ROSENBLUETH, E., "Optimum Design for Infrequent Disturbances" Accepted for publication in *Proc. Am. Soc. Civil Engr*, Engineering Mechanics Division. In press.

# Seismic Water Pressures Against Concrete Dams

W. D. L. FINN,* EROL VAROĞLU,† AND S. CHERRY‡

## Introduction

Our present understanding of the seismic response of concrete dam-reservoir systems has its origin in the classic paper by Westergaard [21]. He derived an expression for the hydrodynamic pressure exerted on a dam by the reservoir as a result of harmonic ground motion. In his analysis, Westergaard assumed the dam to be rigid. In effect, this settled a priori the boundary conditions on the interface between the dam and reservoir and uncoupled the solid and fluid phases. He was led to the assumption of rigidity by his belief that the predominant periods of earthquake accelerations were much longer than those of concrete gravity dams. Westergaard took into account the compressibility of the water, which he assumed was contained in an infinitely long reservoir. He showed the possibility of resonance in the hydrodynamic force response when the excitation frequencies were close to the fundamental frequency of the reservoir.

Since 1959 the seismic response of rigid dam-reservoir systems has been analyzed for a wide variety of boundary conditions and input motions and for both compressible and incompressible water. Kotsubo [16,17] obtained a more general solution for the hydrodynamic pressure which contains both steady-state and transient terms and includes radiation damping. Bustamante et al. [2], using Kotsubo's equations, investigated the effect of reservoir dimen-

*Dean and Professor, Faculty of Applied Science, The University of British Columbia, Vancouver, British Columbia, Canada.

†Assistant Professor, Department of Mathematics, Middle East Technical University, Ankara, Turkey.

‡Professor, Department of Civil Engineering, The University of British Columbia, Vancouver, British Columbia, Canada.

sions and surface waves. Chopra [5] developed an expression for the hydrodynamic force on a vertical dam due to vertical accelerations. His formulations are in terms of harmonic functions rather than the Bessel functions associated with horizontal excitation and result in undamped reservoir response. Chopra [5] also considered both compressible and incompressible water and showed the hydrodynamic responses to be entirely different; one interesting result is that when the water is considered incompressible resonance does not occur at the natural frequencies of the reservoir. Nath [18] also developed solutions for vertical excitation for both vertical and inclined dam faces and for finite reservoir lengths.

All the studies discussed above did not account for the flexibility of the dam. Subsequent analyses which include the flexibility show that the hydrodynamic response may be substantially different from that determined using the assumption of a rigid dam.

The first attempt to account for the flexibility of the dam was made by Brahtz and Heilbron [1] in their discussion of Westergaard's paper. They assumed that the sum of the first mode deformations in shear and bending gave approximately a straight line. Using a linear deflected shape and an iterative procedure of analysis, they calculated the response of the coupled system. Bustamante et al. [2] prescribed a parabolic deformation of the dam, and their solution provided a clear indication of the decisive effect of flexibility on the hydrodynamic pressure. Chopra [6–8] also used a parabolic deformation pattern; the parabola was fitted by a least-squares method to the first mode shape of the dam vibrating freely, i.e., with an empty reservoir. Later this approach was expanded by Chakrabarti and Chopra [3,4] to include additional mode shapes. The deformation of the interface of the coupled dam-reservoir system was expressed as a linear combination of the first $K$ mode shapes of the dam itself. This assumption has been questioned by Nath [20] on the grounds that these are not the modes of the system. It seems likely, however, that the approach yields reasonable practical results. In the same paper, Nath presented an approximate method for determining the fundamental frequency of the coupled system.

Finn and Varoḡlu [10,13] provided an analytical solution to the problem for the case when the cross section of the dam is rectangular. No restrictions were placed on the deformations of the dam. A finite element formulation based on the approach used in the analytical solution was presented in 1972 for dams on rigid and elastic layer foundations [11,12] and was extended in 1973 to dams on an elastic half-space [14]. In these solutions the finite element formulation was used only for the dam; the reservoir and foundations were treated analytically.

When the reservoir and foundations are of irregular configuration, a complete finite element formulation for both dam and reservoir becomes necessary. Chopra et al. [9] investigated the potential of this approach. They noted difficulties in selecting a suitable time step for a stable integration scheme. Recently, Wylie [22] has suggested analyzing the fluid motion by a two-dimensional lattice network consisting of line elements in a square grid. The complete one-dimensional flow equations are treated in each element. The method assumes that motion in the liquid continuum can be modeled by solving one-dimensional transient flow equations in line elements that are free to interact at interconnection nodes.

## Scope of Chapter

In this chapter a general formulation of the problem of dynamic response of the coupled system of dam, reservoir, and foundation is presented. The formulation consists of five stages: (1) a closed form solution for the pressures in the reservoir is obtained for general displacements of the dam-reservoir interface; (2) the equations of motion of the dam represented by a system of finite elements are formulated, taking into account the general hydrodynamic nodal forces in stage 1; (3) using the equations of motion general expressions are derived for the base shear and overturning moment of the dam in terms of displacement amplitude functions; (4) alternative expressions are derived for the base shear and overturning moment by considering the motion of the foundation; and (5) the displacement amplitude functions may be obtained by solving the equations in stages 3 and 4. The complete dynamic response is determined once the displacement amplitude functions are known.

Earthquakes generate both vertical and horizontal accelerations, and a full analysis of the problem should take both into account. Chakrabarti and Chopra [3,4] have shown that the effect of vertical accelerations can be significant for flexible dams. The equations governing the coupled system are linear, and superpositions of the solutions for vertical and horizontal accelerations are possible. The general procedure developed by Finn and Varoǧlu [12] applies to either acceleration provided appropriate changes in boundary conditions are made. The procedure is outlined in what follows for horizontal accelerations only.

Dynamic responses are evaluated only for input motions with complex frequency. The hydrodynamic force or any other dynamic response to arbitrary input motions can be readily found by superposition in the frequency domain.

The finite element formulation is checked by application to a dam of rectangular section for which an analytical solution is available.

## Motion of the Reservoir

It is assumed that the base of the dam is subjected to a lateral translation $u_g(t)$ and to a rotation $\theta_g(t)$ as shown in Fig. 1 and that the reservoir is infinitely long. The lateral displacement $U(y, t)$ of points on the dam-reservoir

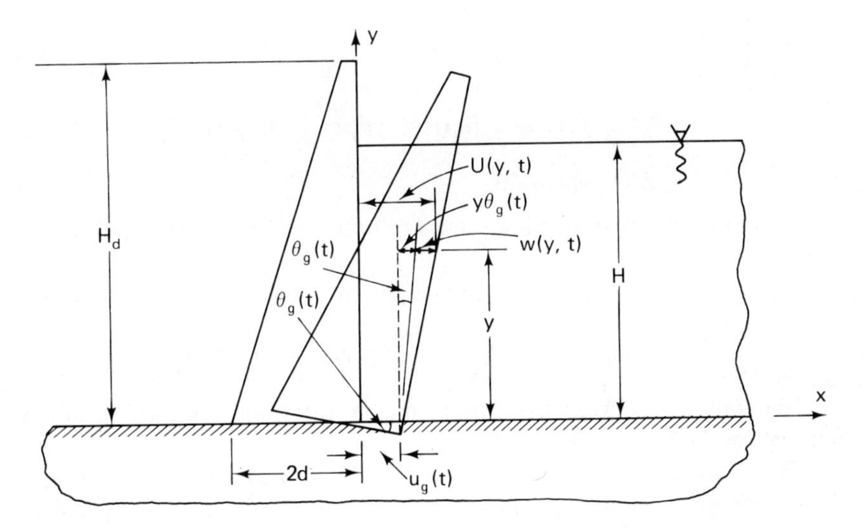


**Fig. 1.** Geometry of the dam-reservoir-foundation showing base rotation and translation of the dam

interface can then be written as

$$U(y, t) = U_g(t) + y\theta_g(t) + w(y, t). \tag{1}$$

Here, $w(y, t)$ denotes the lateral deflections of points on the interface due to distortions of the dam cross section.

Assuming that water in the reservoir is inviscid and compressible and that the motion of the water is limited to small amplitudes, one finds that the motion of the water is governed by

$$\frac{\partial^2\phi}{\partial x^2} + \frac{\partial^2\phi}{\partial y^2} = \frac{1}{c^2}\frac{\partial^2\phi}{\partial t^2}, \tag{2}$$

where $\phi$ is the velocity potential and $c$ denotes the velocity of sound in water (4720 ft/sec). The hydrodynamic pressure $p$ can be expressed as

$$p = \rho\frac{\partial\phi}{\partial t}, \tag{3}$$

where $\rho$ denotes the mass density of water.

The boundary conditions are formulated by noting that (1) on the free surface of the reservoir the hydrodynamic water pressure vanishes if the effect of surface waves is neglected, (2) the velocity component of water normal to the reservoir base vanishes at the reservoir base, (3) at the reservoir-dam interface the velocity components of the water and dam normal to the interface are the same, and (4) at infinity the velocity potential vanishes. The boundary conditions are then expressed by the equations

$$\frac{\partial\phi}{\partial t}(x, H, t) = 0, \tag{4}$$

$$\frac{\partial \phi}{\partial y}(x, 0, t) = 0, \tag{5}$$

$$-\frac{\partial \phi}{\partial x}(0, y, t) = \frac{\partial}{\partial t}[u_g(t) + y\theta_g(t) + w(y, t)], \tag{6}$$

$$\phi(\infty, y, t) = 0. \tag{7}$$

Assuming that reservoir and dam are initially at rest, the initial conditions are

$$u_g(0) = \theta_g(0) = w(y, 0) = 0, \tag{8}$$

$$\phi(x, y, 0) = 0, \qquad \frac{\partial \phi}{\partial t}(x, y, 0) = 0. \tag{9}$$

The coupling between the motion of the water and the motion of the dam appears in Eq. (6).

The solution of this initial boundary value problem for $\phi$ has been presented previously employing a Laplace transform technique [11]. The hydrodynamic pressure is found to be

$$p(x, y, t) = \begin{cases} \dfrac{2\rho c}{H} \displaystyle\sum_{k=1}^{\infty} \cos \sigma_k y \int_{x/c}^{t} \frac{d^2 B_k}{dt^2}(t - \tau) J_0[\sigma_k \sqrt{(\tau c)^2 - x^2}]\, d\tau, & t > \dfrac{x}{c} \\ 0, & t < \dfrac{x}{c} \end{cases} \tag{10}$$

where
$$\frac{d^2 B_k}{dt^2}(t) = \int_0^H [\ddot{u}_g(t) - y\ddot{\theta}_g(t) + \ddot{w}(y, t)] \cos \sigma_k y\, dy, \tag{11}$$

$$\sigma_k = \frac{2k - 1}{2H}\pi, \qquad k = 1, 2, \ldots, \tag{12}$$

and $J_0$ is the Bessel function of order zero.

For the following harmonic accelerations of the base of the dam,

$$\ddot{u}_g(t) = X_1(\Omega) \exp(i\Omega t), \tag{13}$$

$$\ddot{\theta}_g(t) = X_2(\Omega) \exp(i\Omega t), \tag{14}$$

the steady-state lateral acceleration of the dam-reservoir interface is in the form

$$\ddot{U}(y, t) = [X_1(\Omega) + yX_2(\Omega) + u(y, \Omega)] \exp(i\Omega t), \tag{15}$$

where

$$\ddot{w}(y, t) = u(y, \Omega) \exp(i\Omega t). \tag{16}$$

In view of Eqs. (13), (14), and (15), Eq. (11) reduces to

$$\frac{d^2 B_k}{dt^2} = [-\frac{(-1)^k}{\sigma_k} X_1 - \frac{1 + (-1)^k \sigma_k H}{\sigma_k^2} X_2 + \int_0^H u(y, \Omega) \cos \sigma_k y\, dy] \exp(i\Omega t). \tag{17}$$

Setting $x = 0$, substituting the right-hand side of Eq. (17) for the second derivative of $B_k$ into Eq. (10), and noting that

$$\int_0^t \exp(-i\Omega\tau)J_0(\sigma_k c\tau)\,d\tau = \frac{1}{\sqrt{(\sigma_k c)^2 - \Omega^2}} + \int_t^\infty \exp(-i\Omega\tau)J_0(\sigma_k c\tau)\,d\tau, \tag{18}$$

we find that the steady-state pressure distribution at the dam-reservoir interface becomes

$$\begin{aligned} p(0, y, t) = \frac{2\rho c}{H}\Bigg\{ & -X_1 \sum_{k=1}^{\infty} \frac{(-1)^k \gamma_k \cos \sigma_k y}{\sigma_k \sqrt{|\Omega^2 - (\sigma_k c)^2|}} \\ & - X_2 \sum_{k=1}^{\infty} \frac{[1 + (-1)^k \sigma_k H]\gamma_k \cos \sigma_k y}{\sigma_k^2 \sqrt{|\Omega^2 - (\sigma_k c)^2|}} \\ & + \sum_{k=1}^{\infty} \frac{\gamma_k \cos \sigma_k y}{\sqrt{|\Omega^2 - (\sigma_k c)^2|}} \int_0^H u(y, \Omega) \cos \sigma_k y\, dy \Bigg\} \exp(i\Omega t), \end{aligned} \tag{19}$$

where

$$\gamma_k = \begin{cases} 1, & \sigma_k c > \Omega, \\ -i, & \sigma_k c < \Omega, \end{cases} \qquad k = 1, 2, \ldots. \tag{20}$$

This analysis of the hydrodynamic pressures differs from the analyses given by Kotsubo [16] and Chopra [7,8] due to the inclusion of the effects of the general flexibility of the dam cross section.

## Motion of the Dam

Employing finite element discretization, the equations of motion for the dam can be written as

$$[M]\{\ddot{q}\} + [C]\{\dot{q}\} + [K]\{q\} = \{F\} - \ddot{u}_g[M]\{a'\} - \ddot{\theta}_g[M]\{e'\} \tag{21}$$

in which $\{q\}$ denotes the displacements of various nodes, $[K]$ and $[M]$ are the assembled stiffness and mass matrices, and $[C]$ is the damping matrix. The over dots denote differentiation with respect to time. The vector $\{a'\}$ contains one and zero elements so that $-\ddot{u}_g[M]\{a'\}$ represents the effective loading resulting from the horizontal acceleration $\ddot{u}_g(t)$ of the base of the dam; the elements of $\{e'\}$ are defined so that $-\ddot{\theta}_g[M]\{e'\}$ is the effective loading resulting from a clockwise rotation $\theta_g(t)$ of the base of the dam; the vector $\{F\}$ denotes the external forces applied to nodes. Since only the interface nodes are subject to hydrodynamic forces, the elements of $\{F\}$ corresponding to all but the interface nodes are zero. For clarity, we denote the number of nodes at the dam-reservoir interface by $N$ and the ordinate of the $n$th node from the bottom of the reservoir by $y_n$. By evaluating the integral $\int_0^H u(y) \cos \sigma_k y\, dy$ in Eq. (19) employing the trapezoidal rule, we find that the pressure at the $n$th node becomes

$$p(0, y_n, t) = \frac{2\rho c}{H}\Bigg\{-X_1 \sum_{k=1}^{\infty} \frac{(-1)^k \gamma_k \cos \sigma_k y_n}{\sigma_k \sqrt{|\Omega^2 - (\sigma_k c)^2|}} - X_2 \sum_{k=1}^{\infty} \frac{[1 + (-1)^k \sigma_k H]\gamma_k \cos \sigma_k y_n}{\sigma_k^2 \sqrt{|\Omega^2 - (\sigma_k c)^2|}} + \frac{1}{2} \sum_{k=1}^{\infty} \sum_{m=1}^{N} \frac{u_m \, \Delta y_m \gamma_k \cos \sigma_k y_n \cos \sigma_k y_m}{\sqrt{|\Omega^2 - (\sigma_k c)^2|}}\Bigg\} \exp(i\Omega t), \qquad (22)$$

where

$$\begin{aligned} \Delta y_1 &= y_2 - y_1, \\ \Delta y_i &= y_{i+1} - y_{i-1}, \qquad i = 2, 3, \ldots, N-1, \\ \Delta y_N &= H - y_{N-1}. \end{aligned} \qquad (23)$$

Here, $u_m \exp(i\Omega t)$ denotes the horizontal component of the acceleration at the $m$th interface node resulting from the deflections of the interface. From Eq. (22), the lumped hydrodynamic forces $\{f\}$ at the interface nodes can be written in matrix notation as

$$\{f\} = \frac{2\rho c}{H}(X_1\{b\} + X_2\{s\} - [D]\{u\}) \exp(i\Omega t), \qquad (24)$$

where the elements of $\{b\}$, $\{s\}$, and $[D]$ are given by

$$b_i = \frac{1}{2} \Delta y_i \sum_{k=1}^{K} \frac{(-1)^k \gamma_k \cos \sigma_k y_i}{\sigma_k \sqrt{|\Omega^2 - (\sigma_k c)^2|}}, \qquad i = 1, 2, \ldots, N, \qquad (25)$$

$$s_i = \frac{1}{2} \Delta y_i \sum_{k=1}^{K} \frac{[1 + (-1)^k \sigma_k H]\gamma_k \cos \sigma_k y_i}{\sigma_k^2 \sqrt{|\Omega^2 - (\sigma_k c)^2|}} \qquad i = 1, 2, \ldots, N, \qquad (26)$$

$$d_{ij} = \frac{1}{4} \Delta y_i \, \Delta y_j \sum_{k=1}^{K} \frac{\gamma_k \cos \sigma_k y_i \cos \sigma_k y_j}{\sqrt{|\Omega^2 - (\sigma_k c)^2|}} \qquad \begin{aligned} i &= 1, 2, \ldots, N, \\ j &= 1, 2, \ldots, N. \end{aligned} \qquad (27)$$

Here, the infinite series occurring in Eq. (22) are truncated by taking the first $K$ terms in each. The elements of $\{u\}$ are the horizontal components of acceleration at the interface nodes resulting from the deflections of the interface. The elements of $\{b\}$, $\{s\}$, and $[D]$ are real for $\Omega < \pi c/(2H)$ and complex otherwise.

Now we take the steady-state accelerations of the nodes in the form

$$\{\ddot{q}\} = \{\delta\} \exp(i\Omega t).$$

Then, for the base motion of the dam,

$$\begin{aligned} \ddot{u}_g(t) &= X_1 \exp(i\Omega t), \\ \ddot{\theta}_g(t) &= X_2 \exp(i\Omega t). \end{aligned}$$

By partitioning $\{F\}$ in Eq. (21) and substituting the right-hand side of Eq. (24) for the nonzero subvector of $\{F\}$, Eq. (21) becomes

$$\left([K] + i\Omega[C] - \Omega^2[M] - \frac{2\rho c}{H}\Omega^2[D']\right)\{\delta\} = X_1\Omega^2\left(-\frac{2\rho c}{H}\{b'\} + [M]\{a'\}\right)$$
$$+ X_2\Omega^2\left(-\frac{2\rho c}{H}\{s'\} + [M]\{e'\}\right). \tag{28}$$

Here, the nonzero elements of $\{b'\}$, $\{s'\}$, and $[D']$ can be taken directly from $\{b\}$, $\{s\}$, and $[D]$, respectively. In Eq. (28), the term $(2\rho c/H)\Omega^2[D']\{\delta\}$ represents the coupling between the reservoir and the nonrigid dam. If this term is neglected in Eq. (28), then Eq. (28) gives the steady-state response of the reservoir-dam system for which the hydrodynamic pressures are evaluated assuming that the dam is rigid.

The solution $\{\delta\}$ of Eq. (28) can be written as

$$\{\delta\} = X_1\{\delta_1\} + X_2\{\delta_2\}, \tag{29}$$

where $\{\delta_1\}$ and $\{\delta_2\}$ can be determined by solving the following systems of linear equations:

$$\left([K] + i\Omega[C] - \Omega^2[M] - \frac{2\rho c}{H}\Omega^2[D']\right)\{\delta_1\} = \Omega^2\left(-\frac{2\rho c}{H}\{b'\} + [M]\{a'\}\right), \tag{30}$$

$$\left([K] + i\Omega[C] - \Omega^2[M] - \frac{2\rho c}{H}\Omega^2[D']\right)\{\delta_2\} = \Omega^2\left(-\frac{2\rho c}{H}\{s'\} + [M]\{e'\}\right). \tag{31}$$

The dynamic horizontal force $F_0 \exp(i\Omega t)$ and the overturning moment $M_0 \exp(i\Omega t)$ exerted on the unit length of the foundation by the base of the dam can be expressed as

$$F_0 \exp(i\Omega t) = -\{a'\}^T[M](\{\delta\} + X_1\{a'\} + X_2\{e'\}) \exp(i\Omega t) + \{a\}^T\{f\}, \tag{32}$$

$$M_0 \exp(i\Omega t) = -\{e'\}^T[M](\{\delta\} + X_1\{a'\} + X_2\{e'\}) \exp(i\Omega t) + \{e\}^T\{f\}. \tag{33}$$

All the elements of $\{a\}$ are equal to one, so the second term on the right-hand side of Eq. (32) represents the total hydrodynamic force acting on the dam; the elements of $\{e\}$ consist of the $y$ ordinates of the interface nodes, so that $\{e\}^T\{f\}$ in Eq. (33) gives the hydrodynamic moment. In view of Eqs. (29) and (24), Eqs. (32) and (33) can be rewritten as

$$F_0 = \left\{-\{a'\}^T[M](\{\delta_1\} + \{a'\}) + \frac{2\rho c}{H}\{a\}^T(\{b\} - [D]\{u_1\})\right\}X_1$$
$$+ \left\{-\{a'\}^T[M](\{\delta_2\} + \{e'\}) + \frac{2\rho c}{H}\{a\}^T(\{s\} - [D]\{u_2\})\right\}X_2, \tag{34}$$

$$M_0 = \left\{-\{e'\}^T[M](\{\delta_1\} + \{a'\}) + \frac{2\rho c}{H}\{e\}^T(\{b\} - [D]\{u_1\})\right\}X_1$$
$$+ \left\{-\{e'\}^T[M](\{\delta_2\} + \{e'\}) + \frac{2\rho c}{H}\{e\}^T(\{s\} - [D]\{u_2\})\right\}X_2. \tag{35}$$

Here, $\{u_1\}$ and $\{u_2\}$ are the subvectors of $\{\delta_1\}$ and $\{\delta_2\}$, respectively. The vectors $\{u_1\}$ and $\{u_2\}$ contain the elements of $\{\delta_1\}$ and $\{\delta_2\}$ which correspond to the dam-reservoir interface nodes.

A computer program has been developed to construct stiffness and mass matrices using triangular constant strain elements and to evaluate the displacements $\{\delta_1\}$ and $\{\delta_2\}$ from Eqs. (30) and (31), respectively.

The amplitude $X_1$ of the lateral acceleration and the amplitude $X_2$ of the rotational acceleration of the dam-foundation interface are found by analyzing the coupled motion of the foundation and dam. This analysis yields two other equations for $F_0$ and $M_0$ in terms of $X_1$ and $X_2$ which when combined with Eqs. (34) and (35) allows us to solve directly for $X_1$ and $X_2$.

## Response of Dam-Reservoir-Foundation Systems

The most important parameters of the dynamic response of a dam are the hydrodynamic pressure, $p$; the displacements, $\{\delta\}$ (or the stresses); the base shear, $F_0$; and the overturning moment, $M_0$. All these quantities have been determined in terms of the frequency-dependent amplitudes $X_1$ and $X_2$. The particular forms of these amplitudes depend on the type of foundation underlying the dam. We shall consider three particular kinds of foundations: (1) a rigid foundation, (2) an elastic layer, and (3) a semiinfinite half-space. In each case unit harmonic motion, $\exp(i\Omega t)$, is used as input motion. Response to more complex motions such as earthquake accelerations can be obtained by integration in the frequency domain.

### *Rigid Base Foundation*

If the dam is founded on a rigid layer and a ground acceleration $\ddot{u}_g(t) = \exp(i\Omega t)$ is used as input, then clearly $X_1 = 1$ and $X_2 = 0$. All the equations defining dynamic response parameters have a greatly simplified form in this case.

For this particular case, Finn and Varoğlu [10,13] obtained an analytical solution. They assumed the dam to have a rectangular section, to be in effect a plate. This solution is useful in providing a standard against which various approximate methods of solution may be judged. For this reason, the solution is presented here in some detail.

### *Analytical Solution for a Plate Dam*

The motion of the plate is governed by

$$\frac{\partial^2}{\partial y^2}\left[K\frac{\partial^2}{\partial y^2}w(y, t)\right] + \mu\frac{\partial^2}{\partial t^2}[w(y, t) + u_g(t)] = -p(0, y, t) \qquad (36)$$

in which $w$ denotes the deflections of the plate. The rigidity $K$ of the plate is given by

$$K = \frac{Ed^3}{12(1 - \nu^2)}. \qquad (37)$$

The symbols $E$, $\nu$, $\mu$, and $d$, denote Young's modulus, Poisson's ratio, mass per unit area of the plate, and the thickness of the plate, respectively. By considering a plate with constant thickness $d$, the equation of motion becomes

$$\frac{\partial^4 w}{\partial y^4} + \frac{\mu}{K}\ddot{w} = -\frac{\mu}{K}\ddot{u}_g - \frac{1}{K}p(0, y, t). \tag{38}$$

Substituting $\ddot{w}(y, t)$ and steady-state pressure distribution $p(0, y, t)$ from Eqs. (16) and (19) into Eq. (38), the differential equation becomes

$$\frac{d^4u(y)}{dy^4} - \frac{\mu}{K}\Omega^2 u(y) = \frac{\mu}{K}\Omega^2 - \frac{2\rho c\Omega^2}{KH}\left\{\sum_{n=1}^{\infty} \frac{\gamma_n(-1)^n \cos\sigma_n y}{\sigma_n\sqrt{|\Omega^2 - (\sigma_n c)^2|}}\right.$$
$$\left. - \sum_{n=1}^{\infty} \gamma_n \cos\sigma_n y \int_0^H u(y)\cos\sigma_n y\, dy \Big/ \sqrt{|\Omega^2 - (\sigma_n c)^2|}\right\}. \tag{39}$$

In view of the form of $\ddot{w}(y, t)$ given in Eq. (16), the boundary conditions are

$$u(0) = 0, \qquad \frac{du(0)}{dy} = 0, \qquad \frac{d^2u(H)}{dy^2} = 0, \qquad \frac{d^3u(H)}{dy^3} = 0. \tag{40}$$

Now the solution of the boundary value problem given by Eqs. (39) and (40) will be obtained. For brevity, writing

$$z = \left|\left(\frac{\Omega^2\mu}{K}\right)\right|^{1/4}, \qquad \beta_n = \frac{\gamma_n\rho c z^4}{\mu(\sigma_n^4 - z^4)\sqrt{|\Omega^2 - (\sigma_n c)^2|}}, \tag{41}$$

$$m_n = \int_0^H \cosh zy \cos\sigma_n y\, dy, \qquad q_n = \int_0^H \sinh zy \cos\sigma_n y\, dy,$$
$$r_n = \int_0^H \cos zy \cos\sigma_n y\, dy, \qquad s_n = \int_0^H \sin zy \cos\sigma_n y\, dy, \tag{42}$$

we obtain the general solution of Eq. (39) as follows:

CASE 1:

For $\sigma_i \neq z$, and $\beta_j \neq 1$, $i, j = 1, 2, \ldots,$

$$u(y) = C_1 \cosh zy + C_2 \sinh zy + C_3 \cos zy + C_4 \sin zy$$
$$+ \frac{2}{H}\sum_{n=1}^{\infty} \{(C_1 m_n + C_2 q_n + C_3 r_n + C_4 s_n)\frac{\beta_n}{1 - \beta_n}\cos\sigma_n y\} - 1. \tag{43}$$

CASE 2:

For $\sigma_i = z$,

$$u(y) = C_1 \cosh zy + C_2 \sinh zy + C_3 \cos zy + C_4 \sin zy$$
$$- \frac{4}{H}\frac{z(C_1 m_i + C_2 q_i + C_3 r_i + C_4 s_i)}{1 + (8\mu/\rho c\gamma_i)\sqrt{|\Omega^2 - (zc)^2|}} y \sin zy$$
$$+ \frac{2}{H}\sum_{\substack{n=1 \\ n\neq i}}^{\infty} \{(C_1 m_n + C_2 q_n + C_3 r_n + C_4 s_n)\frac{\beta_n}{1 - \beta_n}\cos\sigma_n y\} - 1. \tag{44}$$

CASE 3:

For $\beta_i = 1$,

$$u(y) = C_1 \cosh zy + C_2 \sinh zy + C_3 \cos zy + C_4 \sin zy$$
$$+ \frac{2}{H} \sum_{\substack{n=1 \\ n \neq i}}^{\infty} \{(C_1 m_n + C_2 q_n + C_3 r_n + C_4 s_n) \frac{\beta_n}{1 - \beta_n} \cos \sigma_n y\}$$
$$+ C_5 \cos \sigma_i y - 1, \tag{45}$$

and

$$C_1 m_i + C_2 q_i + C_3 r_i + C_4 s_i = 0. \tag{46}$$

These solutions can be verified by direct substitution into the differential equation (39). In cases 1 and 2, the general solution contains four arbitrary constants. In case 3, there are five constants. In view of Eq. (46), it is clear that only four of these constants can be chosen arbitrarily.

Employing the four boundary conditions given in Eq. (40), four arbitrary constants in the general solution are evaluated.

Once the amplitude of the horizontal steady-state acceleration of the plate $u(y)$ is determined, pressure distribution on the plate can be evaluated from Eq. (19). By integrating Eq. (19) over $(0, H)$, the total hydrodynamic lateral force on the plate for a base acceleration $\ddot{u}_g(t) = \exp(i\Omega t)$ can be expressed as

$$P_{\text{hyd}} = \frac{2\rho c}{H} e^{i\Omega t} \sum_{n=1}^{\infty} \frac{\gamma_n}{\sigma_n^2 \sqrt{|\Omega^2 - (\sigma_n c)^2|}} + \frac{2\rho c}{H} e^{i\Omega t} \sum_{n=1}^{\infty} \frac{\lambda_n \gamma_n (-1)^{n+1}}{\sigma_n \sqrt{|\Omega^2 - (\sigma_n c)^2|}} \tag{47}$$

where

$$\lambda_n = \int_0^H u(y) \cos \sigma_n y \, dy. \tag{48}$$

The case

$$\lambda_n \equiv 0, \qquad n = 1, 2, \ldots,$$

corresponds to the problem of a rigid dam retaining a reservoir. Therefore, the first term on the right-hand side of Eq. (47) gives the total hydrodynamic lateral force on a rigid plate.

Once the total hydrodynamic lateral force response to a harmonic base acceleration is evaluated from Eq. (47), the total hydrodynamic force response $F_{\text{hyd}}$ to an arbitrary known base acceleration $\ddot{u}_g(t)$ can be obtained by

$$F_{\text{hyd}}(t) = \frac{1}{2\pi} \int_{-\infty}^{\infty} U_g(\Omega) P_{\text{hyd}}(\Omega, t) \, d\Omega \tag{49}$$

in which

$$U_g(\Omega) = \int_0^T \ddot{u}_g(t) e^{i\Omega t} \, dt$$

with $T =$ duration of base motion $\ddot{u}_g(t)$.

Analytical results for various plate rigidities are given by Finn and Varoḡlu [10,13]. Results for a plate 100 ft high and 10 ft thick retaining a

100-ft-deep reservoir are given here. The natural frequencies of the plate, which is fixed at the bottom and free at the top, are obtained by evaluating the roots of the frequency equation

$$\cosh zH \cos zh + 1 = 0 \tag{50}$$

as given by Young [23]. The natural frequencies of the reservoir $\Omega_n^r$ are found from Eq. (19) as

$$\Omega_n^r = \frac{2n-1}{2H}\pi c. \tag{51}$$

The weight of concrete is taken as 155 lb/ft³, the velocity of sound in water as $c = 4720$ ft/sec, and the rigidity of the plate as $7.23 \times 10^8$ lb-ft. The normalized complex frequency response for total hydrodynamic force, $P(\Omega)$, on the plate for unit amplitude of input is given by

$$P(\Omega) = \frac{|P_{\text{hyd}}|}{\rho g H^2/2}. \tag{52}$$

A plot of $P(\Omega)$ versus normalized excitation frequency $\Omega/(\pi c/2H)$ is shown in Fig. 2.

Resonance effects occur at natural frequencies of the coupled system. For the plate considered, two of these frequencies have values less than that of the fundamental frequency of the reservoir. Normalized natural frequencies of the plate alone are shown in Fig. 2 by open circles. It may be seen that each natural frequency of the coupled system is less than the corresponding natural frequency of the plate alone. At higher excitation frequencies, the amplitude of the total hydrodynamic force is sharply reduced because of radiation damping in the long reservoir even though damping is ignored in analyzing the motion of the plate.

A solution of the plate problem was also obtained using the finite element formulation described above [11], and the results are indicated by

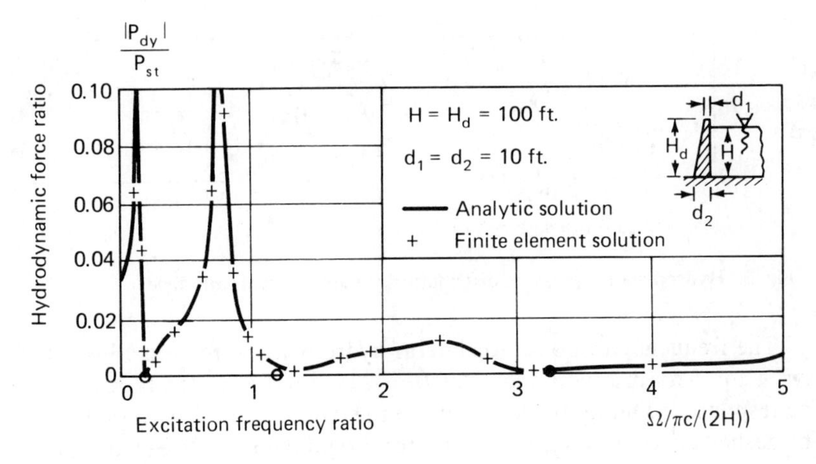


**Fig. 2.** Concrete plate-reservoir interaction

crosses in Fig. 2. The agreement between the analytical solution and the finite element solution is extremely good.

Solutions for a concrete gravity dam having a conventional roughly trapezoidal section and resting on a rigid base have been developed by Finn and Varoḡlu [11] using the finite element formulation outlined above. The dam is 300 ft high, 30 ft wide at the top, and 240 ft wide at the base. The Young's modulus, Poisson's ratio, and the mass density of the concrete are taken as $0.72 \times 10^9$ lb/ft², 0.17, and 155 lb/ft³, respectively. The cross section of the dam is approximated by 335 triangular finite elements. There are 202 nodal points, 36 of which are on the dam-reservoir interface.

For zero structural damping and two values of reservoir depth, $H = 275$ ft and $H = 155$ ft, the response of the dam-reservoir system has been investigated for the range 0–5 of the nondimensional excitation frequency $\Omega/(\pi c/2H)$. The first three resonant frequencies of the dam itself are 32.98 73.96, and 89.04 rad/sec.

The distribution of hydrodynamic pressures on the dam-reservoir interface is given in Fig. 3 in normalized dimensionless form for three widely separated frequencies of excitation. Normalization is achieved by dividing the pressure distribution by the hydrodynamic pressure at the base. The results indicate that the shape of the hydrodynamic pressure distribution is not very sensitive to the frequency of excitation.

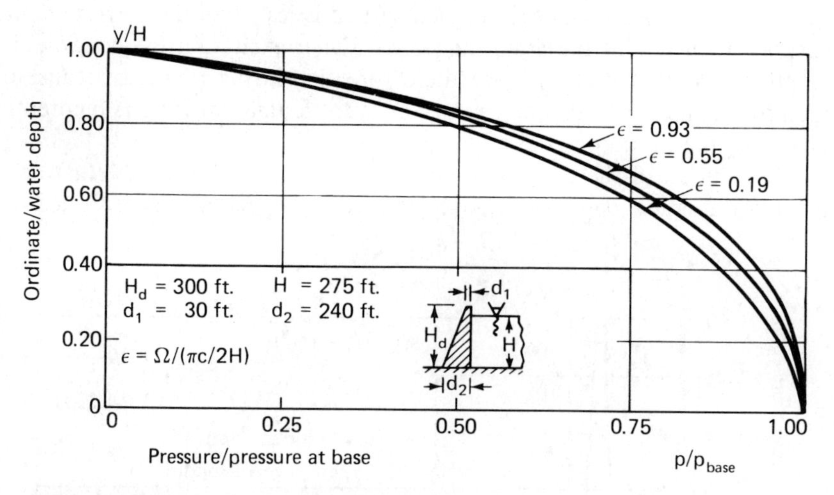


**Fig. 3.** Hydrodynamic pressure distribution at dam-reservoir interface

The frequency response for lateral hydrodynamic force is illustrated in Figs. 4 and 5 for reservoir depths of $H = 275$ ft and $H = 155$ ft, respectively. The response including the flexibility of the dam is shown by the solid curve. The dashed curve shows the response for a rigid dam. It is clear that even for

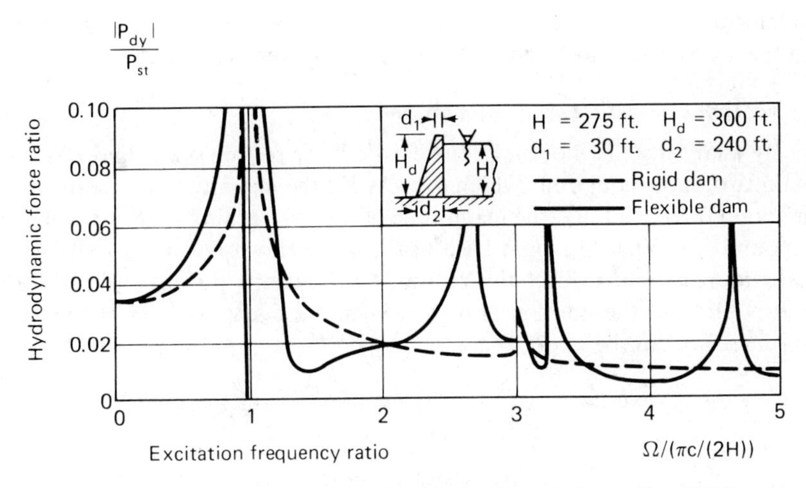


**Fig. 4.** Frequency response for normalized hydrodynamic force, $H = 275$ ft.

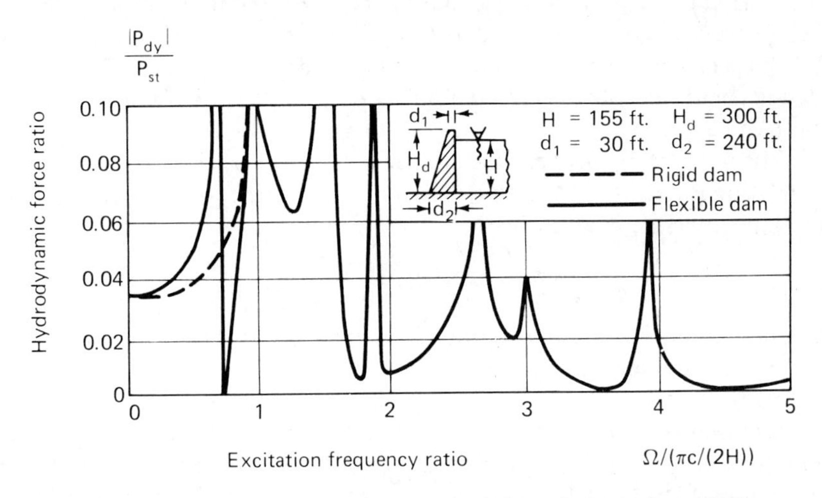


**Fig. 5.** Frequency response for normalized hydrodynamic force, $H = 155$ ft.

a quite stiff dam section the hydrodynamic force on the dam can be underestimated under the assumption that the dam is rigid.

When the dam is assumed to be rigid, resonance occurs at the first fundamental frequency of the reservoir. Amplification at the higher reservoir frequencies is controlled by radiation damping. As already noted in the analytical solution for a flexible plate, resonance tends to occur at dimensionless excitation frequencies corresponding to the natural frequencies of the flexible coupled system. In the case where the depth of water is 275 ft, the first natural frequency of the coupled system happens to be rather close to the fundamental frequency of the reservoir. When the water depth is 155 ft, the fundamental frequency of the coupled system is less than that of the reservoir, and the second natural frequency is close to the reservoir frequency.

***Motion of Elastic Layer Foundation***

By analyzing the motion of the elastic layer resting on a rigid base, we obtain two linear equations which express $F_0$, the magnitude of the dynamic horizontal force, and $M_0$, the magnitude of the overturning moment, in terms of $X_1$ and $X_2$. When the rigid base of the elastic layer is subject to a lateral acceleration $\ddot{u}_B = \exp(i\Omega t)$, the relationship between the total shear force $\ell F_0 \exp(i\Omega t)$ and the horizontal displacement $-X_1 \exp(i\Omega t)/\Omega^2$ of the dam-layer interface can be expressed as

$$-\frac{u_0}{\Omega^2}\exp(i\Omega t) + \frac{1}{G_f d} k_H \ell F_0 \exp(i\Omega t) = -\frac{X_1}{\Omega^2}\exp(i\Omega t), \tag{53}$$

where

$$u_0 = \sec(\Omega H_f / c_f). \tag{54}$$

The constants $H_f$, $c_f$ and $G_f$ denote the depth of the foundation layer, the shear wave velocity in the foundation and the shear modulus of the foundation, respectively. The lateral ground compliance of the layer is denoted by $k_H$, and $d$ and $\ell$ denote the half-width and length of the dam-foundation layer interface.

The relationship between the moment $\ell M_0 \exp(i\Omega t)$ exerted on the dam-foundation layer interface by the dam and the rotation $-X_2 \exp(i\Omega t)/\Omega^2$ of the same interface is given by

$$\frac{3}{G_f d^3} k_R \ell M_0 \exp(i\Omega t) = -\frac{X_2}{\Omega^2}\exp(i\Omega t) \tag{55}$$

in which $k_R$ is the rotational ground compliance of the soil layer. In the original formulation of this problem Finn and Varoḡlu [12], the multiplier $\ell$ was inadvertently omitted from the interaction Eqs. (53) and (55). The lateral and rotational compliances of an elastic layer which is loaded over a rectangular area on the surface have been investigated by Kobori et al. [15]. In the evaluation of the lateral compliance $k_H$, the shear stress distribution over a rectangular area is assumed to be uniform, and $k_H$ relates the total shear force to the lateral displacement at the center of the rectangular area; the rotational ground compliance $k_R$ is evaluated assuming that the normal stress distribution over the rectangular area is triangular, that is, proportional to the distance from the axis of rotation.

The compliances $k_H$ and $k_R$ are functions of dimensionless excitation frequency $a_0 = \Omega d / c_f$, the Poisson's ratio, and the ratio $H_f/d$ for each value of the aspect ratio (length/width) of the rectangular dam-foundation layer interface.

The real and imaginary parts of the compliance functions $k_H(a_0)$ and $k_R(a_0)$ are illustrated in the paper by Finn and Varoḡlu [12] for $H_f/d = 2$, Poisson's ratio $= 0.25$, and an aspect ratio of $\ell/2d = 2$.

By substituting $F_0$ and $M_0$ from Eqs. (53) and (55) into Eqs. (34) and (35), respectively, we obtain two linear equations in two unknowns $X_1$ and $X_2$:

$$\frac{u_0 G_f d}{l k_H \Omega^2} = \left\{-\{a'\}^T[M](\{\delta_1\} + \{a'\}) + \frac{2\rho c}{H}\{a\}^T(\{b\} - [D]\{u_1\}) + \frac{G_f d}{\ell \Omega^2 k_H}\right\} X_1$$
$$+ \left\{-\{a'\}^T[M](\{\delta_2\} + \{e'\}) + \frac{2\rho c}{H}\{a\}^T(\{s\} - [D]\{u_2\})\right\} X_2, \qquad (56)$$

$$0 = \left\{-\{e'\}^T[M](\{\delta_1\} + \{a'\}) + \frac{2\rho c}{H}\{e\}^T(\{b\} - [D]\{u_1\})\right\} X_1$$
$$+ \left\{-\{e'\}^T[M](\{\delta_2\} + \{e'\}) + \frac{2\rho c}{H}\{e\}^T(\{s\} - [D]\{u_2\}) + \frac{G_f d^3}{3\ell \Omega^2 k_R}\right\} X_2. \qquad (57)$$

For a particular value of $\Omega$ once Eqs. (56) and (57) are solved for $X_1$ and $X_2$, the hydrodynamic force on the dam and the dam base shear and overturning moment are found from Eqs. (24), (32), and (33), respectively, and the displacements from Eq. (29).

Once the response of the dam-reservoir and elastic layer system to each of a series of harmonic ground excitations (the complex frequency response) is determined, the response of the system to an arbitrary excitation can be evaluated by using the Fourier integral of the excitation.

As an example, the response of the concrete dam described above, resting on an elastic layer 240 ft thick, will be studied.

The response of this dam on the elastic layer assuming no damping in the dam and a full reservoir ($H = 275$ ft) was numerically evaluated for dimensionless excitation frequencies $\epsilon = \Omega/[\pi c/(2H)]$ less than 3. Analyses were performed for two different types of soil (elastic layer). The physical properties of these soils are as follows:

| | *Soft Soil* | *Stiff Soil* |
|---|---|---|
| Shear modulus of soil ($G_f$) | $0.33 G_{\text{dam}}$ | $1.00 G_{\text{dam}}$ |
| Mass density of soil ($\rho_f$) | $0.90 \rho_{\text{dam}}$ | $1.00 \rho_{\text{dam}}$ |
| Poisson's ratio ($\nu_f$) | 0.25 | 0.25 |

The translational and rotational ground compliances of the elastic layer were computed assuming that the length of the dam is 480 ft.

The first three natural frequencies of the soil layer are 31.42, 94.25, and 157.08 rad/sec for the soft soil and 52.36, 157.08, 261.80 rad/sec for the stiff soil.

Frequency response curves for the normalized hydrodynamic force and the normalized hydrodynamic moment are shown in Fig, 6 and 7. The forces and moments are normalized by dividing their magnitudes by the hydrostatic force ($\rho g H^2/2$) and the hydrostatic moment ($\rho g H^3/6$), respectively. In Fig. 8 and 9,

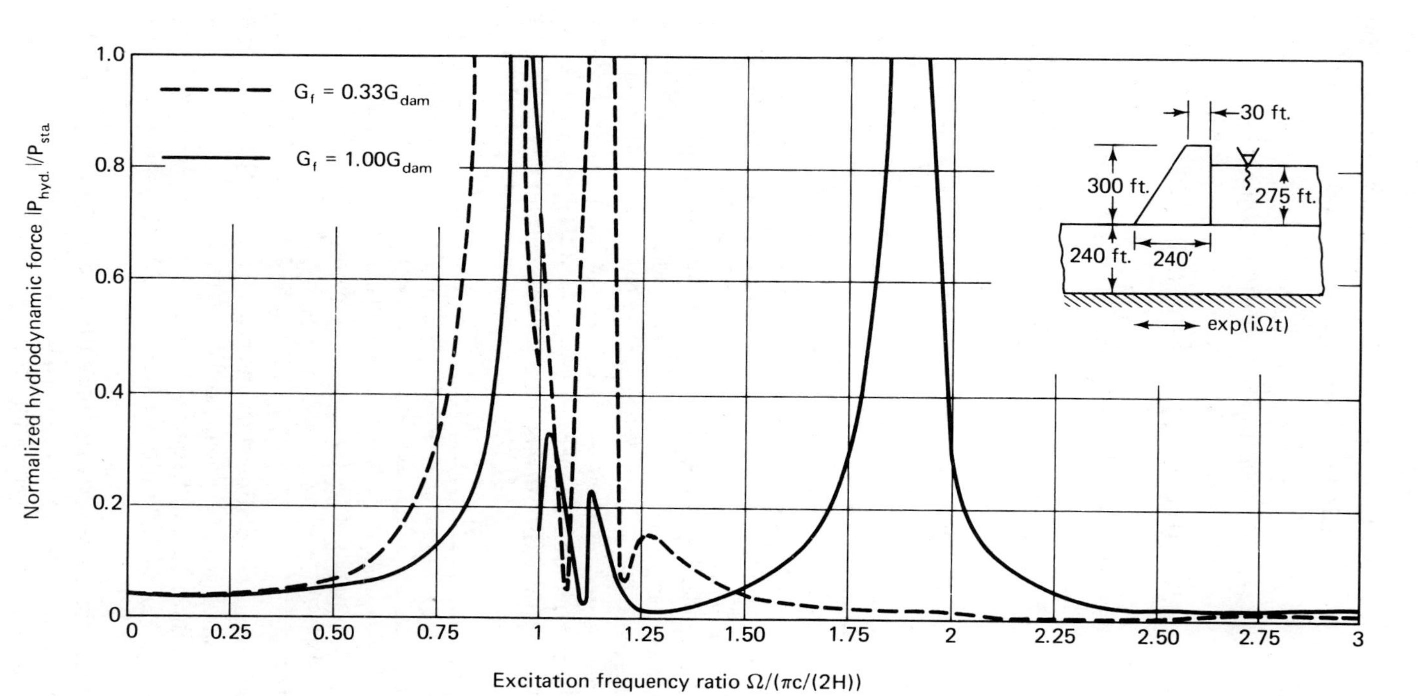


**Fig. 6.** Frequency response for normalized hydrodynamic force

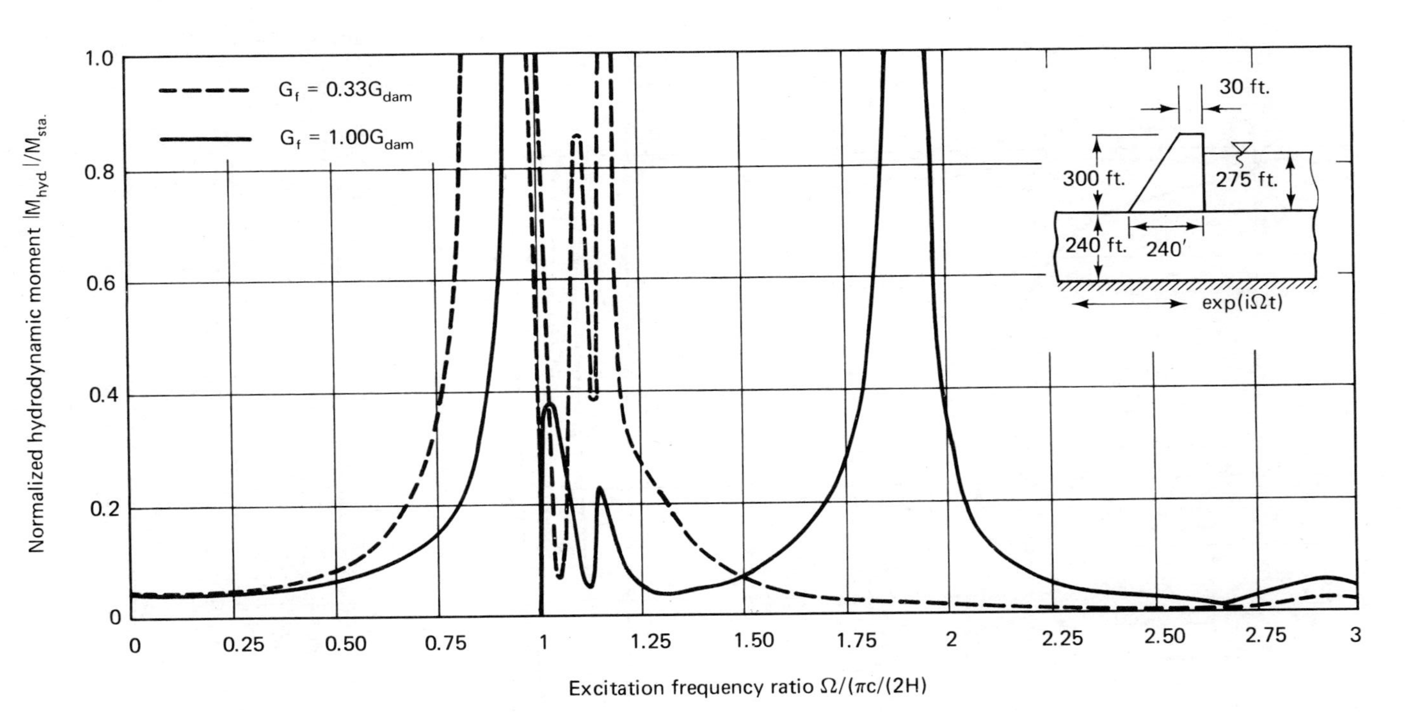


**Fig. 7.** Frequency response for normalized hydrodynamic moment

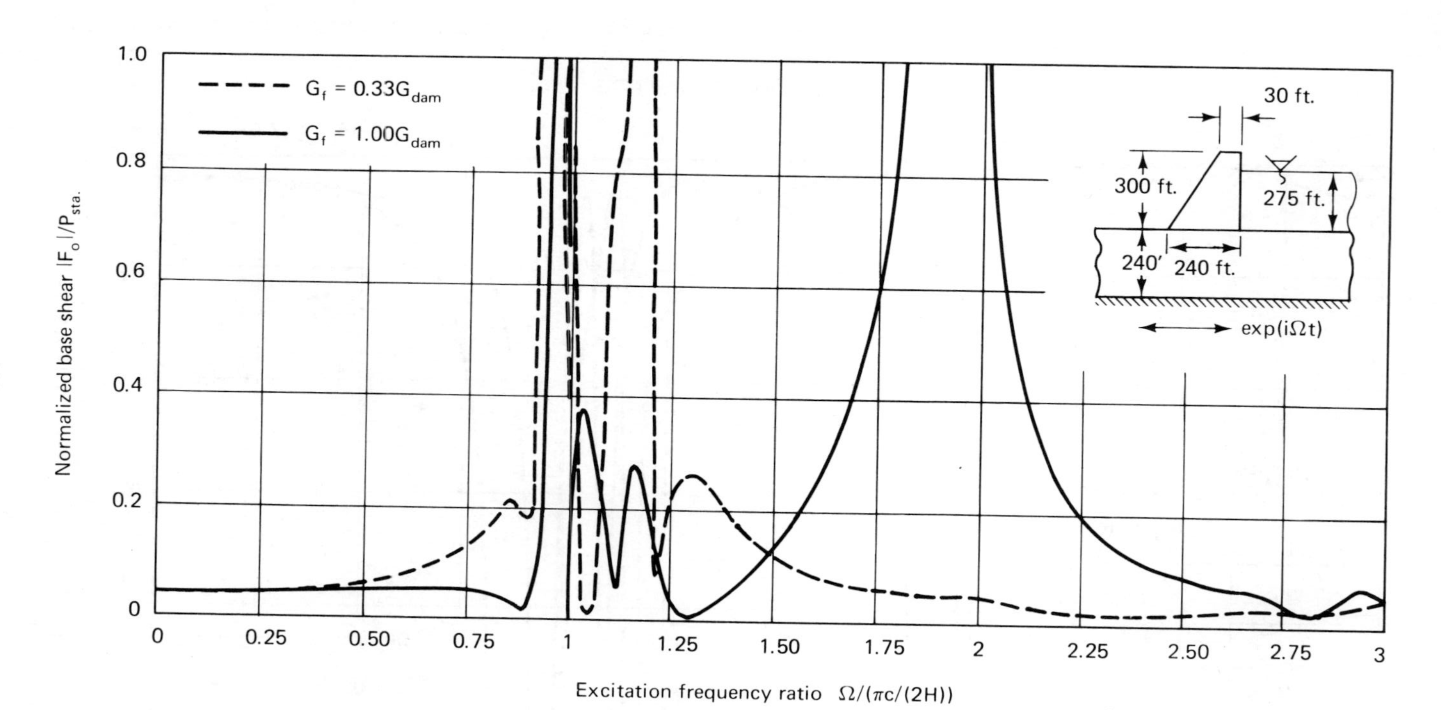


**Fig. 8.** Frequency response for normalized base shear force

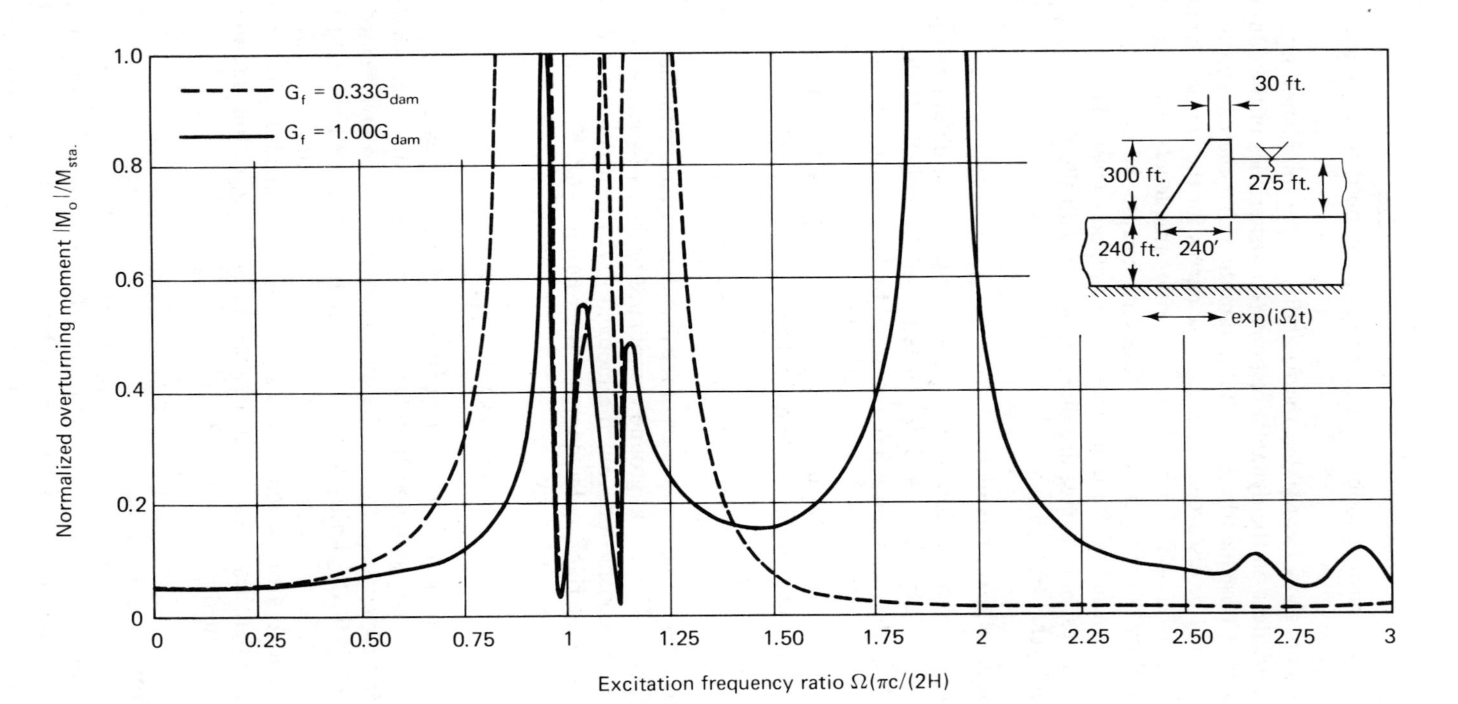


**Fig. 9.** Frequency response for normalized overturning moment

frequency response curves are shown for the normalized base shear and the normalized overturning moment, respectively, for both the soft and stiff foundation layers.

The results show clearly that the flexibility of the foundation layer has an important effect on the dynamic response characteristics of the dam reservoir system. Consequently, the usual assumption that the dam rests on a rigid base should be discarded. The response curves for the various dynamic parameters show amplification effects at various frequencies which depend on the flexibility of the layer. These frequencies correspond to various characteristic frequencies of the dam and the foundation layer. Therefore the shapes of the response curves are directly tied in with the flexibility of the foundation layer.

### *Elastic Half-Space Foundation*

By analyzing the motion of the elastic half-space, we obtain two linear equations which express $F_0$ and $M_0$ in terms of $X_1$ and $X_2$. If the lateral acceleration of the free surface (not disturbed by the existence of the dam) is given by $\ddot{u}_B = \exp(i\Omega t)$, the relationship between the total shear force $\ell F_0 \exp(i\Omega t)$ and the horizontal displacement $-(X_1/\Omega^2)\exp(i\Omega t)$ of the dam-layer interface in the coupled system can be expressed as

$$\frac{k_H \ell}{G_F d} F_0 \exp(i\Omega t) = \frac{1}{\Omega^2}(1 - X_1)\exp(i\Omega t). \tag{58}$$

Here, $G_F$ denotes the shear modulus of the foundation, and $d$ is the half-width of the dam base. The lateral ground compliance of the half-space is denoted by $k_H$. The relationship between the moment $\ell M_0 \exp(i\Omega t)$ exerted on the half-space-dam interface by the dam and the rotation $-(X_2/\Omega^2)\exp(i\Omega t)$ of the same interface is given by

$$\frac{3\ell}{G_F d^3} k_R M_0 \exp(i\Omega t) = -\frac{X_2}{\Omega^2}\exp(i\Omega t). \tag{59}$$

Here, $k_R$ is the rotational ground compliance of the half-space.

The lateral and rotational compliances of an elastic half-space which is loaded over a rectangular area on the surface have also been investigated by Kobori et al. [15]. By substituting $F_0$ and $M_0$ from Eqs. (58) and (59) into Eqs. (34) and (35), respectively, we obtain two linear equations in two unknowns $X_1$ and $X_2$ from which $X_1$ and $X_2$ may be determined. The procedure is identical to that described for the case of the elastic layer foundation and will not be repeated here.

## Conclusions

The history of the dynamic response analysis of concrete gravity dams including reservoir effects has been traced since its formal beginnings in the work of Westergaard in 1933. The growth in our capacity to solve the response problem is marked by the adoption of increasingly more realistic boundary conditions and assumptions. Today, the general flexibility of the dam and its foundation can be taken into account as well as both vertical and horizontal components of earthquake acceleration.

Current methods use a combination of closed form solutions for the reservoir, in combination with finite element solutions for the dam and either analytical or finite element solutions for the foundation. Closed form solutions for the reservoir are particularly advantageous as they include radiation damping and lead to greater stability in the integration schemes for the equations of motion of the system. They can be used, however, only when the reservoir is of regular shape. For irregular reservoirs discrete formulations for the reservoir are necessary using either finite elements of latticeworks of line elements. There are few published data as yet on solutions derived by these methods for flexible dams on flexible foundations, but we are confident that the early difficulties will be successfully overcome.

The large number of parametric studies available for dams with reservoirs of rectangular cross section provide a deep insight into the response characteristics of gravity dam-reservoir systems during earthquakes and provide useful guidance for the safe design of such structures.

## Acknowledgments

The work described in this chapter was supported by the National Research Council of Canada under Grant No. 1498. This support is gratefully acknowledged.

## References

1. Brahtz, H. A., and C. H. Heilbron, "Discussion of Water Pressures on Dams During Earthquakes, by H. M. Westergaard," *Trans. ASCE*, Vol. 98, 1933, p. 452.
2. Bustamante, J. I., E. Rosenblueth, I. Herrera, and A. Flores, "Presion hidrodinámica en presas y depósitos," *Bol. Soc. Mex. de Ing. Sismica*, Vol. 1, No. 2, 1963, p. 37.
3. Chakrabarti, P., and A. K. Chopra, "Hydrodynamic Pressures and Response of Gravity Dams to Vertical Earthquake Component," *Int. J. Earthquate Eng. Struct. Dynamics* Vol. 1, No. 4, 1973, p. 325.
4. Chakrabarti, P., and A. K. Chopra, "Earthquake Analysis of Gravity Dams Including Hydrodynamic Interaction," *Int. J. Earthquake Eng. Struct. Dynamics*, Vol. 2, No. 2, 1973, p. 143.
5. Chopra, A. K., "Hydrodynamic Pressures on Dams During Earthquakes," *J. Eng. Mech. Div. ASCE*, Vol. 93, EM6, Proc. Paper 5695, 1967, p. 205.
6. Chopra, A. K., "Reservoir-Dam Inteıaction During Earthquakes," *Bull. Seism. Soc. Am.*, Vol. 57, No. 4, 1967, p. 675.

7. Chopra, A. K., "Earthquake Behaviour of Reservoir-Dam Systems," *J. Eng. Mech. Div., ASCE*, Vol. 94, No. EM6, Paper 6297, 1968, p. 1475.
8. Chopra, A. K., "Earthquake Response of Concrete Gravity Dams," *J. Eng. Mech. Div., ASCE*, Vol. 96, EM4, Paper No. 7485, 1970, p. 443.
9. Chopra, A. K., E. L. Wilson, and I. Farhoomand, "Earthquake Analysis of Reservoir-Dam Systems," *Proceedings, 4th World Conference on Earthquake Engineering, Santiago*, B-4, 1969, p. 1.
10. Finn, W. D. L., and E. Varoḡlu, "Forced Vibrations of a Plate-Reservoir System," *Civil Engineering Soil Mechanics Series No. 22*, University of British Columbia, Vancouver, Canada, 1971.
11. Finn, W. D. L., and E. Varoḡlu, "Dynamics of Gravity Dam-Reservoir Systems," *Computers Struct.*, Vol. 3, 1972, p. 913.
12. Finn, W. D. L., and E. Varoḡlu, "Dynamics of a Concrete Dam-Reservoir System on a Flexible Layer Foundation," *Proceedings, Specialty Conference on Finite Elements in Civil Engineering, Montreal, Canada*, 1972, p. 619.
13. Finn, W. D. L., and E. Varoḡlu, "A Study of Dynamic Interaction in a Plate-Reservoir System," Paper presented at the 5th European Conference on Earthquake Engineering, Istabul, Turkey, 1975.
14. Finn, W. D. L., E. Varoḡlu, and I. S. R. Miller, "Dynamics of a Concrete Dam-Reservoir System on a Flexible Half-space," *Proceedings, Iranian Congres, of Civil Engineering and Engineering Mechanics, Shiraz, Iran*, 1973, p. 764.
15. Kobori, T., R. Minai, and T. Suzuki, "Dynamic Ground Compliance of Rectangular Foundation on an Elastic Stratum over a Semi-infinite Rigid Medium," *Annual Report, Research Institute of Prevention of Natural Disaster*, Vol. 11, Parts 2 and 3, Kyoto University, Kyoto, 1968.
16. Kotsubo, S., "Dynamic Water Pressure on Dams due to Irregular Earthquakes," *Memoirs of Faculty of Engineering*, Vol. 18, No. 4, Kyushu University, Kyushu, 1959, p. 119.
17. Kotsubo, S., "External Forces on Arch Dams During Earthquakes," *Memoirs of Faculty Engineering*, Vol. 20, No. 4, Kyushu University, Kyushu. 1961, p. 327.
18. Nath, B., "Hydrodynamic Pressures on High Gravity Dams During Vertical Earthquake Motions," Paper 7171, *Proceedings, Institute of Civil Engineers, London*, 1969, p. 413.
19. Nath, B., "Structural and Hydrodynamic Coupling for a Gravity Dam During Vertical Earthquake Motions," *Proceedings, Conference on Dynamic Waves*, Wiley, New York, 1970, p. 487.
20. Nath, B., "Coupled Hydrodynamic Response of a Gravity Dam," Paper 7308, *Proceedings, Institution Civil Engineers., London*, 1971, p. 245.
21. Westergaard, H. M., "Water Pressures on Dams During Earthquakes," *Trans. ASCE*, Vol. 98, 1933, p. 418.
22. Wylie, E. B., "Seismic Response of Reservoir-Dam Systems," *J. Hyd. Div. ASCE*, Vol. 101, No. Hy. 3, Paper 11184, 1975, 403.
23. Young, D., "Continuous Systems," in *Handbook of Engineering Mechanics*, W. Flugge, ed., McGraw-Hill, New York, 1962, Chap. 61.